11.30

MANUFACTURING PROCESSES
METALS AND PLASTICS

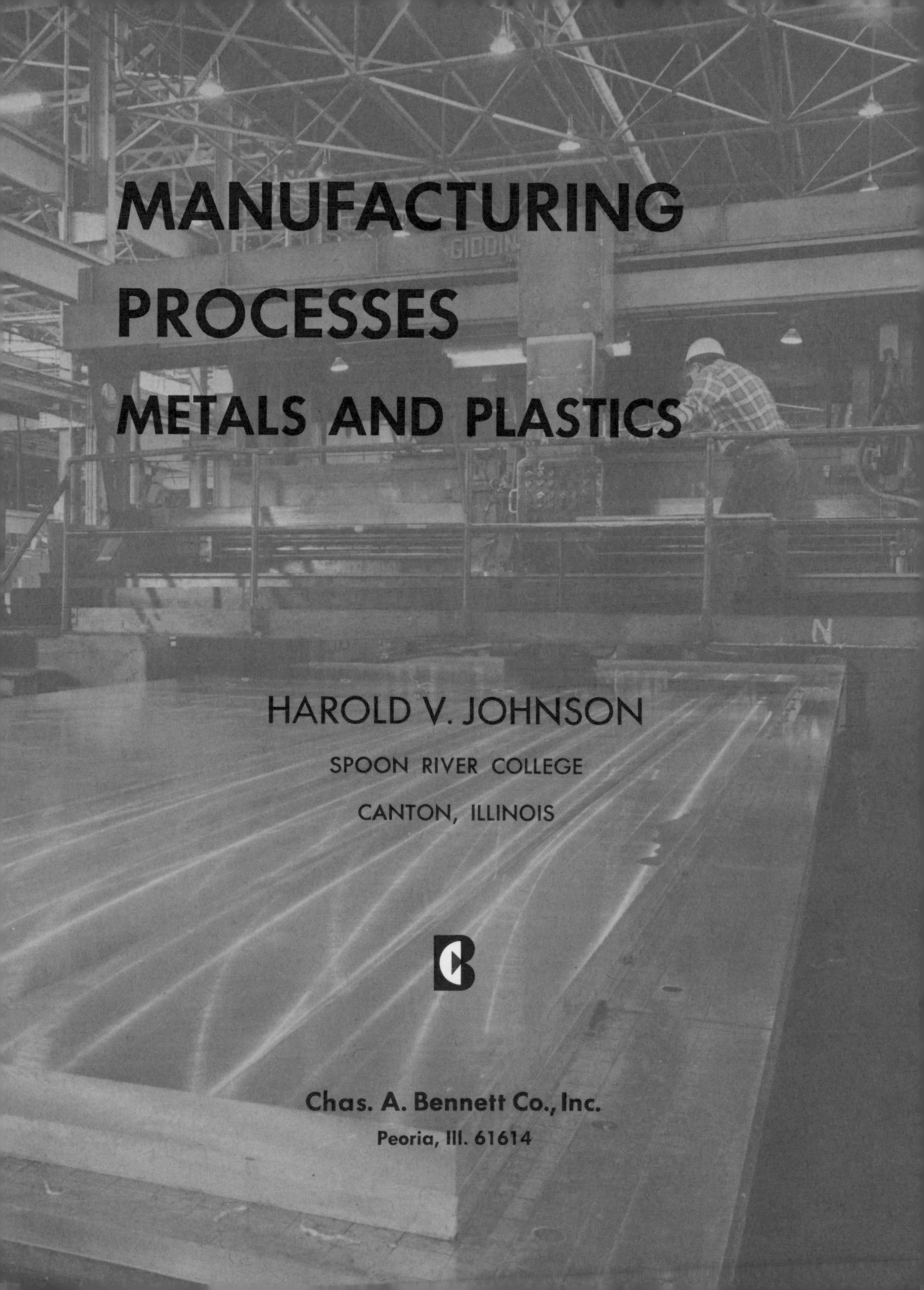

MANUFACTURING PROCESSES
METALS AND PLASTICS

HAROLD V. JOHNSON

SPOON RIVER COLLEGE

CANTON, ILLINOIS

B

Chas. A. Bennett Co., Inc.

Peoria, Ill. 61614

73 74 75 76 77 RM 8 7 6 5 4 3 2 1

ISBN 87002-141-9

Library of Congress Catalog Number: 72-94735
Printed in the United States of America

ACKNOWLEDGMENTS

Without the assistance of the many companies that supplied illustrations, data, and suggestions, production of this text would not have been possible. I wish to thank all of the companies involved for their contributions.

Appreciation is also expressed to my family for their encouragement and to Carol and Sarah Harkless for their assistance in reading the proof.

A great part of the work on a text is always represented by the work of the editorial staff as they take the manuscript and bring it to life. My thanks to Paul Van Winkle, head of the editorial department, William C. Yates, late assistant editor, and the many other people of the Bennett Company for their part in making this book possible.

Harold V. Johnson

PREFACE

This book has been written to serve as a text to be used in vocational schools, technical institutes, junior colleges, and similar institutions and is intended to supply information on modern manufacturing processes and materials in the metalworking industries.

The processes of manufacturing are becoming increasingly complex due to the rapid development of automation/mechanization/electronics, and new materials.

Students must be trained in the new and advanced methods by which modern materials are processed. Also, it is important that they have an understanding of modern industrial machines and their operations to enable them to design component parts properly.

This text on industrial manufacturing processes in the metalworking/plastics fields presents the course as simply as possible. Basic principles are emphasized. Most companies are equipped to further train the individuals they employ for the more specific requirements of the job.

It is the author's opinion that it is advantageous to the student to spend some time in the operation of machine tools in order to obtain a better understanding of the processes involved. Reading from a text about how a machine functions does not qualify the student to become a machine designer or operator. Since a student can ordinarily learn more by doing, time should be spent in practice as well as theory. Even a few days in a metalworking shop, with the instructor pointing out the various operations that can be performed on the machines, can be highly beneficial to each student and make his understanding of the material in the text more meaningful.

Contents

Acknowledgments 5

Preface 6

Section One: HUMAN NEEDS 13

1. **Occupations in the Metalworking Industries** 14
   Draftsmen, Machining Occupations, All-Round Machinists, 14; *Tool and Die Makers, Experimental Machinists, Layout Men,* 15; *Setup Men, Machine Tool Operators, Forge Shop Operations,* Hammersmiths, Press Operators, 16; *Upsetter Operators, Foundry Occupations,* 17; Patternmakers, Molders, 18; Coremakers, Melters, 19; Cleaning Castings, Inspectors, Welders and Oxygen and Arc Cutters, 20.

2. **Safety** 21
   General Safety Instruction, 21; *Safety on the Bench, Tool Material Safety, Machine Safety,* The Lathe, 22; Shaper, Planer, Slotter, Broach, and Power Saw, Milling Machine, 23; Drilling Machine, Grinding Machine, *Casting Safety,* 24; *Forging Safety, Rolling Safety, Punch Press and Blanking Safety, Welding Safety,* 25; *Heat-Treatment Safety,* Check Your Knowledge, References, 26.

Section Two: PRODUCING AND PROCESSING FERROUS AND NONFERROUS METALS 27

3. **Classification of Metals** 28
   Alloys, Understanding Alloys, 28; *Solutions, Alloy Characteristics,* 29.

4. **Properties of Metals** 30
   Chemical Properties, Mechanical Properties, Hardness, *Brittleness,* Plasticity and Ductility, 30; Toughness and Malleability, Strength, 31; Elongation, Yield Point, Stress, Fatigue, Fusibility, Strain, 32.

5. **Production of Iron and Its Uses** 33
   Iron Ore, Materials Used in Extracting Iron, 33; *Production of Pig Iron,* Preheating Air for the Blast Furnace, Operation of the Blast Furnace, 34; *Characteristics and Uses of Pig Iron, Cast Iron,* 35.

6. **The Manufacture of Steel** 35
   Open-Hearth Process, 35; *Electric Furnace Process,* 36; *Basic Oxygen Process,* 37; *Bessemer Process,* 38.

7. **Plain Carbon and Alloy Steels** 39
   Low-Carbon Steel, Medium-Carbon Steel, High-Carbon Steel, Alloy Steel, 39; Alloying Elements and Their Effects, 40.

8. **Classification and Identification of Steels** 42

9. **Nonferrous Metals** 44
   Furnaces for Nonferrous Melting, 44; *Aluminum,* 45; *Magnesium,* 47; *Copper-Base Alloys, Zinc-Base Alloys, Nickel-Base Alloys, Tin-Base Alloys,* 48; Check Your Knowledge, 49; References, 50.

Section Three: METALLURGY AND HEAT TREATMENT OF STEEL 51

10. **Introduction to Heat Treatment** 52
    Furnaces and Temperature Control, 52; Temperature Indicating and Control Equipment, 53.

11. **Grain Structure of Steel** 54
    Allotropy, 55; *Grain Formation,* 56; Grain Size, 57.

12. **Heat Treatment of Steel** 59
    Effects of Carbon, 59; *Iron-Carbide Phase Diagram,* 60; *Hardening, Martensite,* 62; *Quenching,* 63; *Hardenability,* 64; *Isothermal Transformation Diagram,* 65.

13. **Tempering, Annealing, and Normalizing; Surface Hardening** 66
    Martempering, Austempering, Annealing, 68; Full Annealing, Process Annealing, Spheroidizing, *Normalizing, Surface Hardening,* Carburizing, 69; Nitriding, Cyaniding, Carbonitriding, 71; Flame Hardening, 72; Induction Hardening, 73.

14. **Testing** 76
    Hardness Testing, Rockwell Hardness Test, 76; Brinell Hardness Test, Vickers Scale, 78; Shore Scleroscope Hardness Test, Microhardness Testers and the Knoop Hardness Scale, 79; *Tensile Testing,* 80; *Impact Testing,* 81; *Fatigue Testing, Spark Testing,* 82; Check Your Knowledge, References, 83.

Section Four: FOUNDRY PROCESSES 85

15. **Patternmaking** 86
    Pattern Construction, Procedure for Making a Split Pattern, Fillets, 87; *Types of Common Patterns,* One-Piece Flat Back Pattern, Split Pattern, Multi-Piece Pattern, 88; Loose-Piece Pattern, Cored Pattern, 89; Sweep Pattern, Match Plate, 90.

16. **Foundry Sands** 91
    Types of Sand, Albany No. 1, Oil Binder Synthetic Sand, Sand Grain, 92; Core Sands, Facing Sand, Core Binders, Parting Compounds, Core Paste, 93.

17. **Sand Testing** 93
Permeability Test, Surface Hardness of Green Sand Molds and Cores, 94; *Testing for Sand Strength, Testing for Moisture Content,* 95; *The Fineness Test,* 96.

18. **Cores and Core Making** 96

19. **Foundry Tools and Equipment** 98
Flasks, 100; *Other Tools and Devices,* 101; *Gating,* Types of Gates, 103; *Risers, Chills,* 104.

20. **Fundamental Processes of Molding** . . . 105
Making a Mold of a One-Piece Pattern on the Bench, 105; *Molding a Split Pattern,* 107.

21. **Machine Molding** 108
Jolt-Squeeze Molding Machine, Jolt-Rollover Molding Machine, The Sand Slinger, 109; *Modern Molding Machine Operations,* 110.

22. **Melting and Casting Metals** 111
Cupola Furnace, 111; *Casting Nonferrous Metals,* Crucibles, 112; *Ladles, Tongs,* 113; *Shanks, Tips on Using a Crucible, Metal Temperature and Pouring,* 114; *Cleaning Casting,* 115; *Cast Iron,* Gray Cast Iron, 116; White Cast Iron, Malleable Cast Iron, 118; Black-Heart Malleable Iron, 119; White-Heart Malleable Iron, Nodular or Ductile Cast Iron, *Wrought Iron,* 120; Check Your Knowledge, 121; References, 122.

Section Five: SPECIAL CASTING PROCESSES 123

23. **Permanent Mold Casting** 124

24. **Die Casting** 125
Hot-Chamber Process, Process Details, 125; *Cold-Chamber Process,* 126; *Die-Casting Dies,* 127; *Advantages of Die Casting, Die-Casting Metals and Their Alloys,* Zinc-Base Alloys, Aluminum-Base Alloys, 128; Copper-Base Alloys, Magnesium-Base Alloys, 129.

25. **Centrifugal Casting** 132

26. **Investment Casting** 134

27. **Investment Casting by the Solid or Mono-Shell Process** 136
Automation in Mono-Shell Molding, 137; *Advantages of the Mono-Shell Process,* 139.

28. **Shell Molding** 140

29. **Plaster Mold Casting** 141
Check Your Knowledge, References, 143.

Section Six: HOT-WORKING METAL 145

30. **Rolling** 146
Rolling Temperature, 146; *Two-High and Four-High Design,* 147; *Continuous Design,* 148; *Plates, Sheets and Strip,* 149.

31. **Forging** 151
Hammer or Smith Forging, Drop Forging, Equipment, 151; *Upset Forging, Press Forging,* 155; *Roll Forging,* 156.

32. **Special Forging Techniques** 157
Bending, Piercing, Ring Rolling, 157; *Swaging,* How Swaging Machines Function, *Finishing Operations, Trimming,* 158; *Punching,* Coining, Sizing, and Ironing, 159.

33. **Pipe and Tube Manufacture** 159
Roll Piercing, 159; *Plug Rolling, Reeling,* 160; *Sizing, Welding Steel Tubing or Pipes,* Butt-Welding Pipe, Lap-Welding Pipe, Electric Resistance-Welding, 161; Electric-Fusion Welding, 162.

34. **Hot Extrusion and Spinning** 162
Hot Spinning, Check Your Knowledge, 163; References, 164.

Section Seven: COLD-WORKING METAL . . . 165

35. **Cold-Rolling** 166
Tube Drawing, 166; *Cold-Drawing Wire from Rod,* 167.

36. **Cold-Heading** 168
Dies, Solid Die, Open Die, 168; *Cold-Heading Process,* 169; Advantages, 170.

37. **Metal Spinning** 171
Power Spinning, Floturn Process, 173; How Floturning is Done, 175.

38. **Thread and Form Rolling** 178
Physical Characteristics of Rolled Threads, 178.

39. **Stretch Forming** 179

40. **Riveting, Staking; Sizing, Coining, and Hobbing** 181

41. **Cold Roll-Forming; Plate Bending: Shot Peening** 181
Cold Roll-Forming, 181; *Plate Bending,* 182; *Shot Peening,* 183.

42. **Cold Extrusion** 183
Methods of Extrusion, Forward Extrusion, Backward Extrusion, Combined Extrusion, 183.

43. **High-Energy-Rate Forming Methods** . . 184

44. **Flo-Peeling** 185
Check Your Knowledge, References, 186.

Section Eight: FORMING METAL ON PRESSES 187

45. **Press Types** 188
Frame and Bed Design, 188; *O.B.I. Press, Gap Press,* 189; *Horning Press, Knuckle-Joint Press, Straight-Side Mechanical Press,* 190; *Hydraulic*

Contents

Press, 191; *Turret Press, High-Production Transfer Press and Others*, 192; *Press Brake*, 193; *Shears*, 194.

46. Press Drives and Feed Mechanisms ... 194
Press Drives, Feed Mechanisms, 195.

47. Press Operations 196
Shearing, 196; *Blanking, Bending and Forming*, 197; *Drawing, Rubber Forming*, 198; *Marforming, Hydroforming, Hydrodynamic Process*, 199.

48. Dies and Die Sets 200
Progressive Dies, 201; *Combination Dies, Urethane (Adiprene) Die Pads*, 202; Check Your Knowledge, 203; References, 204.

**Section Nine: MEASUREMENT AND
                  INSPECTION** 205

**49. Nonprecision Linear Measuring
        Tools** 206
Rules, Combination Set, Calipers and Dividers, 206; Telescoping Gage, *Angular Measuring Instruments*, Protractors, 208; Universal Bevel Protractor, Sine Bar, Sine Plate, 209; Direct Measure—Taper Micrometer, 210.

50. Precision Measuring Instruments 210
Micrometer Caliper, 210; *Micrometer Depth Gage, Vernier Depth Gage, Vernier Caliper*, 212; *Micro-Height Gage, Vernier Height Gage*, 213, *Toolmaker's Microscope, Optical Comparator*, 214.

51. Gage Blocks and Gages 215

52. Surface Measurements 216
Surface Plate, 216; *Surface Gage, Optical Flat*, 217; *Surface Texture*, 220; Selecting a Finish, 221; Checking Surface Texture, 222; *Go and No-Go Gages*, Snap Gages, Ring Gages, 223; Plug Gages, 224; Thread Snap Gages, Thread Ring and Plug Gages, *Dial Indicator*, 225.

53. Air and Electronic Gaging 226
Air or Pneumatic Gaging, 226; *Air Plug*, 227; Contact Gaging, Advantages of Air Gaging, *Electronic Gaging*, 228.

54. Inspection and Quality Control 230
Nondestructive Inspection, Magnetic Particle Testing, Fluorescent Penetrant Testing, 230; *Ultrasonic Testing*, 231; *Pulse Ultrasonics, X-Ray and Gamma-Ray Testing, Fundamentals of Quality Control*, 232; Methods of Controlling Quality, 233; *Tolerance and Allowance*, 234.

55. The Metric System of Measure 235
Adoption of the Metric System, Advantages of the Metric System, 235; *Metric Units, Dual Dimensioning*, Dual Dimensioning Explained, 236;

Industrial Conversion to the Metric System, 241; Using Conversion Scales, 242; Check Your Knowledge, References, 243.

**Section Ten: CHANGING THE SHAPE OF
                  METALS WITH MACHINE
                  TOOLS** 245

**56. Metal Cutting Tools and Cutting
        Fluids** 247
Chip Formation and Cutting Action, 247; *Obtaining a Desired Surface Finish*, 248; *Tool Shapes*, 249; *Chip Breakers, Tool Materials*, Carbon Steels, 250; *Medium-Alloy Steels*, High-Speed Steels, Cast Alloys, Cemented Carbides, 251; *Machinability*, 252; *Tool Failure*, Temperature Failure, Fracture of Tool Point, Tool Wear, *Cutting Speeds and Feeds*, Speeds, 254; Feed, *Cutting Fluids, Classification of Cutting Fluids*, 255; Transparent-Type Cutting Oil, Classification of Water-Soluble Oils, Selection of the Correct Cutting Fluid, 256; Check Your Knowledge, 257; References, 258.

**Section Eleven: MACHINING METAL WITH
                  TURNING MACHINES** 259

57. The Engine Lathe 260
Holding and Controlling Devices, The Headstock, 260; *The Spindle, Workpiece Holders*, Faceplate, Live Center, and Dog, Universal and Independent Chucks, 262; Collet Chucks, The Tailstock, Quick Change Gear Box, 263; The Carriage, Steady Rest and Follow Rest, Taper Attachment, *Sizes and Types of Lathes*, 264; *Lathe Cutting Tools*, 265.

58. Lathe Operations 265
Factors in Basic Turning Operations, Cutting Speed, Feed, Depth of Cut, *Operations*, Facing, 268; Plain Turning, Taper Turning, 269; Thread Chasing, 271; Boring, Drilling on the Lathe, Reaming, 273.

59. Turret Lathes 274
Vertical Turret Lathes, Bar and Chucking Machines, 274, *Ram and Saddle Types*, Turret Lathe Construction, 275; *Tooling*, 276; Tools and Attachments, 278.

60. Automatic Cycle Lathes 279
Two Automatic Lathe Types, Automatic Screw Machines, Single-Spindle Automatic, 280; *Swiss-Type Automatic*, 282; *Multiple-Spindle Automatic*, 283; Numerical Control Turning Center, *Vertical Boring Mill*, 284; *Tracer Control Lathe*, 285; *Special Lathes*, 286; Check Your Knowledge, 287; Problems, References, 288.

**Section Twelve: PRODUCING CYLINDRICAL
                  HOLES** 289

61. Drills **290**
Drill Parts, 290; Lip Clearance, Lip Angle and Length, Drill Shanks, 291; *Drill Sizes, Types of Drills*, 292; Spiral-Point Drills, 294; Split-Point Drills, *Boring Tools and Boring*, 295; *Counterboring, Spotfacing, and Countersinking*, 297; Grinding the Drill, Point Angle, Web Thinning, 298; Chip Formation in Drilling, 299; *Speeds and Feeds for Drills, Drill Jigs and Fixtures*, Jigs, Vises, 301; Drill Chucks and Holders, 302; *Multiple-Spindle Drill Heads*, 303; *Cutting Fluids*, 304.

62. Reaming **305**
Stock Removal Allowance for Reaming, Alignment, Reaming Speeds and Feeds, 308.

63. Drilling Machines **308**
Portable Drills, The Drill Press, 308; Sensitive Drilling Machine, Upright Drilling Machine, Gang Drilling Machine, 309; Multiple-Spindle Drilling Machine, Turret Drilling Machine, Radial Drilling Machine, Gun Drilling Machines, 311; Transfer-Type Drilling Machines, 313; *Boring Machines*, Horizontal Boring Machine, Jig Boring Machines, 314; Double-End Boring Machine, Check Your Knowledge, Problems, References, 316.

Section Thirteen: MACHINING METAL WITH SHAPERS AND PLANERS .. 317

64. The Shaper **318**
Horizontal Shapers, Crank Shapers, 318; The Hydraulic Shaper, *Vertical Shaper, Draw-Cut Shaper*, 319.

65. Shaper Tools **321**
Types, Using Shaper Tools, Shaper Toolholders, 321; Holding the Workpiece, 323; *Shaper Operations*, 324; *Shaper Speeds and Feeds*, Cutting Speed, 326; Feed, 327.

66. Planers **327**
Planer Drives, 327; *Planer Sizes and Capacities, Planer Tools and Accessories, Types of Planers*, Double-Housing Planer, 328; Open-Side Planer, Pit-Type Planer, Plate or Edge Planer, 329; Check Your Knowledge, Problems, References, 330.

Section Fourteen: MACHINING METAL WITH MILLING MACHINES **331**

67. Classification of Milling Machines **332**
General Types, Plain Horizontal Milling Machine, Universal Milling Machine, 332; *Ram-Type Milling Machine*, 333; *Vertical Milling Machine*, 334; *Fixed-Bed Milling Machine*, 335; *Planer-Type Milling Machine*, 336.

68. Special Milling Machines **336**
Rotary Table Milling Machine, Profiling Machine, 336; *Pantograph Engraving Machine*, 338; *Auto-Scan Milling Machine*, 339.

69. Milling Machine Attachments and Holding Devices **339**
Vises, The Indexing or Dividing Head, Direct Indexing, 339; Simple Indexing, 340; Differential Indexing, Spiral Milling, 341; *Rotary Attachments, Vertical Milling Attachments*, 342.

70. Milling Cutters **343**
Arbor Cutters, Plain Milling Cutters, Side Milling Cutters, Staggered Tooth Milling Cutter, Metal-Slitting Saws, Angular Milling Cutters, Inserted Tooth Milling Cutters, Form-Relieved Cutters, *Shank Cutters*, End Mills, 343; Shell End Mills, T-Slot Cutters, Woodruff Key Seat Cutters, 346; Fly Cutters, *Arbors, Collets, and Adapters*, 347; *Cutter Teeth*, 348; *Speeds and Feeds, Feed*, 349.

71. Milling Operations **350**
Methods of Milling, Up Milling, 351; Down Milling, Plain or Slab Milling, 353; *Side Milling and Straddle Milling*, 354; Slotting and Cutting Off, Form Milling, Gang Milling, Vertical Milling, Check Your Knowledge, Problems, 357; References, 358.

Section Fifteen: SAWING AND FILING **359**

72. Sawing **360**
Hand Sawing, Power Saw Blades, Sawing Machine Types, Reciprocating Sawing Machines—Hacksaws, 360; Power Hacksaw Blades, Feed Selection, 361; *Circular Sawing Machines*, Circular Saw Blades, 363; *Friction Sawing with Steel Discs, Abrasive Sawing*, 364; *Band Sawing Machines*, 365; Vertical Band Sawing Machines, 366; Vertical Band Machining Operations, 367.

73. Filing **370**
File Classification, 370; *Die-Filing Machines, Band Filing Machines, Disc-Filing Machines*, Check Your Knowledge, 371; Problems, References, 372.

Section Sixteen: BROACHING **373**

74. Classification **374**
Broaching Tools, 374; *Types of Broaches*, 375; *Broach Design*, Length of Cut, 378; The Face Angle, Land and Clearance Angle, Cutting Action of a Broach-Chip Area, 379; Pilots, 380; Broach Puller, *Sharpening Broach Tools*, 381.

75. Broaching Machines **382**
Vertical Pull-Down Machines, 382; *Vertical Pull-Up Machines*, 383; *Vertical Surface Broaching, Horizontal Pull Broaching Machine, Horizontal*

Contents

Surface Broaching Machines, 384; *Continuous Broaching Machines, Rotary Broaching Machines*, 385; *Pot Type Broaching Machines*, 386; Check Your Knowledge, Problems, 387; References, 388.

Section Seventeen: GRINDING AND GRINDING MACHINES 389

76. Abrasives 390
Manufactured Abrasives, 390; Silicon Carbide, Aluminum Oxide Abrasive, 391; Grain Sizes, Structure, Grinding Wheels, 392; *Grinding Wheel Shapes*, 393; *Grinding Wheel Functions*, 395; *Grinding Wheel Markings*, 396; *Grinding Wheel Selection, Coated Abrasives, Production of Coated Abrasives*, 397.

77. Grinding Machines 399
Surface Grinding, Reciprocating Table Surface Grinders, 399; Rotary Table Surface Grinders, *Face Grinders, Cylindrical Grinders*, 401; *Universal Grinders*, 403; *Centerless Grinding*, 404; *Internal Grinders*, 405; Types of Internal Grinders, *Tool and Cutter Grinders*, 406; *Jig Grinders*, 407.

78. Electrochemical Grinding 407

79. Abrasive Machining 410

80. Honing and Lapping 411
Honing, 411; *Lapping, Superfinishing*, 412; Check Your Knowledge, References, 414.

Section Eighteen: SCREW THREADS 415

81. Screw Thread Terms and Forms 416
Terms, Forms, 416.

82. The Manufacture of Screw Threads ... 418
Thread Designation, Cutting Screw Threads with Taps and Dies, 418; *Styles of Taps*, 419; *Hand Tapping*, 421; *Thread Cutting Dies*, 422; Self-Opening Die Heads, 423.

83. Tapping and Threading Machines 424
Special Tapping Machines, 424; *Thread Milling, Tapping Speeds*, 425; *Cutting Fluids for Machine Tapping*, 426; *Thread Grinding, Thread Measurement*, 427; Check Your Knowledge, Problems, References, 429.

Section Nineteen: GEARING 431

84. Gear Terminology 432

85. Types of Gears 434
Spur Gears, Helical Gears, 434; *Bevel Gears*, 435; *Hypoid Gears*, 436; *Internal Gears, Herringbone Gears, Worm Gears, "Spiroid" and "Helicon" Gears*, 437.

86. Gear Manufacturing Processes 438
Form Cutting, Cutting a Spur Gear, 439; *Speed, Feed, and Depth of Cut, Generating Gears by Hobbing*, 440; The Hobbing Process, 441; *Generating with a Reciprocating Tool*, 442; *Bevel Gear Generators*, 445; *Gear Broaching, Shear Cutting of Gears, Gear Finishing, Gear Shaving*, 446; *Gear Grinding, Gear Lapping, Gear Honing*, 448; *Gear Inspection*, 449; Check Your Knowledge, Problems, References, 450.

Section Twenty: POWDER METALLURGY .. 451

87. Powders 453
Production Methods of Powders, 454; *Aluminum Powder*, 455.

88. Producing the Part 456
Blending, Compacting, 456; *Sintering*, 457; Spark Sintering, 459.

89. Compacting Presses 460
Repressing, Sizing, Coining, 461; *Machining, Infiltration*, 462; *New Techniques*, Slip Casting, Isostatic Pressing, Check Your Knowledge, References, 463.

Section Twenty-One: POLISHING AND FINISHING METALS .. 465

90. Cleaning and Smoothing Methods 466
Abrasive Cleaning, Tumbling, 466; *Barrel Rolling*, 468.

91. Machine Polishing and Buffing 468
Polishing, Buffing, 468; *Polishing and Buffing Wheels*, 470; *Polishing and Buffing Compounds, Polishing Metals with Abrasive Belts*, 471; *Power Brush Finishing*, 472.

92. Decorative and Protective Metal Finishes 474
Chemical Cleaning, Vapor Degreasing, Emulsified Solvent Cleaning, *Pickling, Electroplating*, Preparation for Plating, 474; Copper Plating, 475; Silver Plating, Chrome Plating, *Color Anodizing*, 476; *Protective Metal Finishes*, Primers, Metal Fillers, Metal Enamels, Lacquers, *Manufacturing Painting Systems*, 477; *Galvanizing*, 478; *Tin Coating, Parkerizing*, Check Your Knowledge, References, 479.

Section Twenty-Two: RECENT TECHNIQUES IN METAL WORKING 481

93. Chemical Milling 482
The Process, 482; *Advantages of Chemical Milling*, 484.

94. Flame Spraying 486
Metallizing Process, Powder, or Thermospray, Process, 486; *Plasma Flame Process*, 487.

11

95. Laser Machining **488**
Types of Lasers, 489.

96. Ultrasonic Machining **490**
Tooling for Ultrasonics, 490; *Machining Rates, Machining Capacity, Finish and Accuracy*, 491.

97. Electron Beam Machining **491**

98. Electrical Discharge Machining **492**
EDM Terms, Rate and Frequency, 492; Electronic Envelope (Overcut), 493; Coolant, Electrode Material, Workpiece Material, 494; *The Process*, 495.

99. Electrochemical Machining **495**
Advantages of ECM Process, 497.

100. Chemical Machining **497**
Processing Steps, Artwork and Negative Preparation, Metal Preparation, 497; Image Printing and Developing, Etching and Resist Removal, 498; *Abrasive Jet Machining*, Check Your Knowledge, References, 499.

Section Twenty-Three: NUMERICAL CONTROL MACHINING 501

101. What is "Numerical Control" and How Does it Work? **502**
Basic Components of an N/C System, 503; *How Numerical Control Works*, 505; *Types of Numerical Control*, 506; *Measuring Basis for N/C Control Systems*, 507.

102. Programming and Tape Preparation **508**
Language Codes, 509; Code on Tape Formats, 510; *Programming a Point-to-Point Drilling Operation*, 512; Sample Milling Program, 513; Tape Controlled Continuous Path Milling, 514; *Advantages of Numerical Control, Disadvantages of Numerical Control*, 516.

103. Modern Numerically Controlled Machines **516**
N/C Turning Center, A 3-Axis Milling Center, 516; *Omnimill 5-Axis N/C Machining Center*, 517; *N/C Machining Center*, 518; Check Your Knowledge, References, 520.

Section Twenty-Four: WELDING PROCESSES 521

104. Forge Welding **522**
Types of Joints and Welds, 522.

105. Gas Welding **524**

Oxyacetylene Welding, 524; Welding Equipment, 525; *Air-Acetylene Welding, Pressure Gas Welding, Oxyhydrogen Welding, Flame Cutting*, 527.

106. Arc Welding **528**
Arc Welding Equipment, 528; *Carbon-Electrode Welding, Metal-Electrode Welding*, 529; Electrodes for Metal-Electrode Welding, 530; Gas Tungsten-Arc Welding—Inert Shielding (TIG), 531; Gas Metal-Arc Welding—Inert Shielding (MIG), Submerged-Arc Welding, 532; Open-Arc Welding Process, Gas Metal-Arc CO_2 Shielding, Micro-Wire Welding, 533; Stud Welding, Electroslag Welding, 534.

107. Other Welding Processes **535**
Resistance Welding, Spot Welding, 535; Machines for Spot Welding, Seam Welding, 536; Flash-Butt Welding, Projection Welding, 537; Percussion Welding, Inertia Welding, 538; Advantages of the Process, *Ultrasonic Welding, Thermit Welding*, 540; *Electron Beam Welding*, 541.

108. Soldering and Brazing **543**
Fluxes, Soldering Devices, Resistance Soldering, 544; *Brazing*, 545; *Types of Joints for Brazing*, 546; Check Your Knowledge, References, 547.

Section Twenty-Five: PLASTICS 549

109. Types of Plastics **550**

110. Thermosetting Compounds **551**
Epoxides, Phenolics, Furane Resins, 551; *Silicones, Amino Resins*, 552.

111. Thermoplastic Compounds **553**
Nylons (Polymides), Polyethylene Resins, Polystyrene, Polypropylene, 553; *Polycarbonate, Acrylic Resin*, 554; *Cellulose Acetate, Cellulose Nitrate, Cellulose Acetate Butyrate*, 555; *Cellulose Propionate, Synthetic Rubber*, 556.

112. Production Processes **556**
Compression Molding, 556; *Transfer Molding, Injection Molding*, 557; *Extrusion, Blow Molding*, 560; *Rotational Molding*, 561; *Forming Sheet and Film, Thermoforming*, 562; Thermoforming Processes, 563; *Laminates and Laminating*, The Process, *Reinforced Plastic Molding*, 564; *Casting*, 565.

113. Machining and Finishing Plastics . . . **565**
Machining, 565; *Finishing, Coloring*, Check Your Knowledge, 566; References, 567.

Section One

Human Needs

1–2. An all-around machinist.

Unit 1. Occupations in the Metalworking Industries

Never before in the history of our country has the individual American devoted so much time and thought to the selection of a work career. One of the most significant factors responsible is that today's youth can anticipate changing jobs three or four times over the course of a career, while individuals in the past spent a lifetime at one task.

Modern technology and new skill demands have introduced to the American worker an unprecedented era of change. This change has been so sweeping that it requires the continuing attention of students, workers, and parents.

This unit will give the individual some idea of the requirements of various types of jobs and the opportunities that are available in the modern metalworking industries today.

DRAFTSMEN

Although draftsmen do not work on metalworking machines, they are an important part of the metalworking industry. 1–1.

Draftsmen translate ideas, sketches, specifications, and calculations of engineers into working plans which are necessary at all stages of development in producing the finished product.

To prepare drawings, draftsmen use such instruments as compasses, dividers, triangles, and protractors, as well as drafting machines that combine the functions of several devices.

Young people interested in becoming draftsmen can acquire the necessary training in vocational and technical high schools, and in junior colleges. On-the-job training can also be obtained.

MACHINING OCCUPATIONS

Almost any product of the American factory contains metal parts or is manufactured by machines made of metal parts. Machining workers make up the largest occupational group in the metalworking trades. About a million workers are employed in these trades.

All-Round Machinists

The all-round machinist is a skilled metalworker who can both set up and operate machine tools. 1–2. He is skilled in using hand tools. He has to have the ability to read working drawings and to plan and carry through all operations needed in turning out the machined product. Generally, he is required to make standard shop computations relating to dimensions, tooling, feeds, and speeds. He also has to be able to read precision measuring instruments with accuracy.

A four-year apprenticeship is the standard requirement for this

1–1. Draftsmen.

Eugene Dietzgen Co.

trade. A high school vocational training course in machine shop is of great help in preparation. Some companies require their machinists to take courses (at company expense) in electronics and mathematics so that these employees can operate numerically controlled machine tools.

Tool and Die Makers

Mass production in industry requires workers who are highly skilled in the construction of tools, dies, and special fixtures. These skilled workers also make gages and other measuring devices that are used in the mass production of metal products.

Because they make highly specialized items, tool and die makers are required to have more knowledge of machining operations, mathematics, bench work, layout, and blueprint reading than regular machinists. 1–3.

Also, the increasing complexity of modern metalworking equipment is raising technical re-

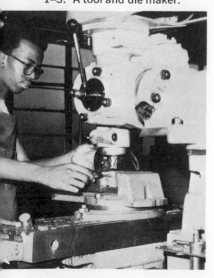

1–3. A tool and die maker.

quirements for tool and die making. A better understanding of mathematics, basic sciences, electronics, and hydraulics will provide greater opportunities for the worker.

This trade can be learned through the four- or five-year apprenticeship programs.

Experimental Machinists

Though not always called experimental machinists, they work closely with engineers and scientists in translating designs and ideas into custom (one-of-a-kind) instruments, special laboratory equipment, and experimental models. 1–4.

Experimental devices made by these craftsmen also are used to measure distance, regulate heat, and record earthquakes. They make many instruments used in the space program.

Of course, experimental machinists are required to have a knowledge of the operation of all types of machine tools as well as skill with hand tools.

Because accuracy is important in their work, they use a wide variety of precision measuring equipment including micrometer calipers, vernier tools, dial indicators, profilometers, and standard optical measuring instruments.

An experimental machinist may be called upon to construct products from start to finish. This requires an even broader knowledge of all types of machine tools as well as a high degree of skill.

Some experimental machinists advance from the ranks of regular production machinists as well as from machine tool operators of broader background.

1–4. Experimental machinist.

Layout Men

The layout man is a highly skilled worker who must follow plans in order to mark castings, forgings, or metal stock to indicate where machining (metal removal) is necessary. 1–5. He has to be able to use various types of layout and measuring tools such

1–5. Layout man.
North American Aviation, Inc.

Heald Machine Co.

1–6. A setup man is a skilled machinist who readies machine tools for operation.

1–7. Machine tool operator.

chine for the proper feeds and speeds and runs the first few pieces while checking the speeds, feeds, tooling, and operating sequence.

He must instruct the operator on how to operate the machine and check the work.

The setup man must work from blueprints and must have a broad knowledge of different types of metals and their machining properties. He is generally an all-round machinist but may be a highly qualified specialist on one of the basic types of machine tools used in production work.

Machine Tool Operators

These men machine metal to dimensions by the use of various types of machine tools. Some operate only one or two machine tools while others operate several types. An operator often performs repetitive work, making identical parts. Others are skilled workers who can set up or vary the operations.

Most machine tool operators learn their trade by on-the-job training. 1–7. Operators must have the ability to use various types of measuring instruments to check the machined product. General machine shop courses in school are advantageous.

FORGE SHOP OPERATIONS

Forging is one of the principal methods of shaping and working metal. In this process, metal is heated to the proper temperature in furnaces and shaped by pounding or squeezing in presses. Examples of forged products include wrenches, gears, parts for farm machinery, crankshafts, and many other similar products.

as rules, dividers, squares, height gages, fixed calipers, micrometer calipers, and electronic measuring instruments. He not only must work with extreme care and accuracy, but also must be familiar with the operation of all types of machine tools.

From six to ten years of training is needed to learn this trade. A good knowledge of mathematics and blueprint reading is essential.

Setup Men (Machine Tools)

The setup man is a skilled specialist who works in industries that do a large volume of machining on a production basis. 1–6. He "sets up" machine tools which are then operated by semiskilled or, in some cases, unskilled operators. He frequently is a specialist on one type of production machine, such as an automatic screw machine. He installs the proper cutting tools, fixtures, and gages necessary for the production of a particular part. He sets the ma-

The following are some of the classifications of forge production workers:

Hammersmiths

Hammersmiths are skilled workers who operate open-die power hammers which pound metal into desired shapes. The hammersmith must be able to interpret blueprints, know how to work the metal under the hammer, and know how to use various forming tools to produce angles and curves.

He supervises a *hammer driver* who operates the controls of the machine, a *craneman* who transfers the hot metal blanks from the furnace to the hammer, and a *heater* who heats the metal to the correct forging temperature.

Most forge shop workers learn their trade through on-the-job training.

Press Operators

These workers—also called *press-smiths*—operate presses of various types equipped with either open or impression (cavity) dies. 1–8. The metal is squeezed rather than pounded into shape. Metal blanks are manipulated between two open dies. 1–9. Ability to read blueprints is essential.

Aluminum Co. of America

1–8. Operators of a 50,000-ton hydraulic closed-die forging press.

1–9. Press operation.

International Silver Co.

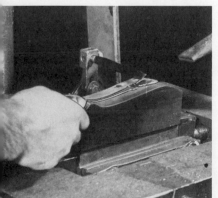

makers, as well as many others, in less specialized work.

FOUNDRY OCCUPATIONS

The foundry industry offers a good livelihood in a broad range of work for men—and women —with special interests, experience, or education. Foundry work ranges from simple materials handling to actual casting production and includes highly technical research. A great many foundry jobs require a considerable amount of dexterity and skill. Some call for imagination and the ability to develop the completed pattern and castings from blueprints. Many positions require special talents in the supervision of others.

Included among the many production workers employed in the foundry industry are molders, patternmakers, machine operators, furnace tenders, and coremakers. In addition, special jobs are classified primarily according to the type of metal produced and foundry work involved. Connected with the work are chemists, metallurgists, designers, engineers, and maintenance men.

Foundries consist fundamentally of five departments: molding, coremaking, melting, cleaning, and control. (Some departments may be combined, depending upon the size of the foundry.) *Patternmaking* is also keyed to foundry production.

An estimated 300,000 workers are employed in ferrous foundries and about 100,000 are employed in nonferrous foundries. Nonferrous foundries produce castings made from aluminum, brass, bronze, magnesium, and zinc. The estimated number of workers in the principal occupations unique

Upsetter Operators

These workers operate machines that shape the metal by applying pressure through the horizontal movement of one impression die against another. Upsetter operators supervise a crew of several helpers. Products such as bolts, valves, and deep socket wrenches are made by this method.

Forge shops also employ inspectors, die sinkers (men who make dies), machinists, and tool-

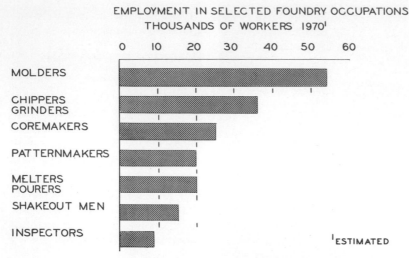

EMPLOYMENT IN SELECTED FOUNDRY OCCUPATIONS
THOUSANDS OF WORKERS 1970[1]

1–10. Types of employment in foundry occupations.

many shops operate independently, making patterns for anyone needing them.

Trade school courses in patternmaking provide the necessary preparation for the apprentice.

Molders

Every casting must have a mold. 1–12.

Sand molds may be made by hand (floor and bench molding) or by machine (machine molding), depending upon the kind of casting wanted, its size, and the quantity to be produced. In the modern mechanized foundry, molds are made almost entirely by machine, and conveyor systems are used for delivering the sand. 1–13. Large castings are produced in pit molds.

Each type of molding job calls for varying skills, according to the use and design of the product.

A four-year apprentice training program is needed to become a journeyman molder.

to foundries and foundry departments are shown on the graph. 1–10.

The most common process is sand casting. However, there are foundries engaged in die casting, plaster mold casting, shell molding, and investment casting which employ a great number of skilled workers. 1–11.

Patternmakers

In the development of any product there must be a beginning point. Such is the case of patternmaking. The first step in the production of any casting is the construction of a pattern. There are two main types of patternmakers—wood and metal. Some also work with plaster, plastics and clay.

Master patterns are first made of wood, from which a permanent metal pattern is cast.

A high degree of accuracy and skill is required in this trade. The final casting can only be as good as the pattern from which it is made. The patternmaker uses various types of hand tools and machines that are adaptable to shaping wood and metal. Working from engineering drawings, patternmakers must construct their forms in accordance with the principles of good foundry practice—for good, practical results. This takes experience.

Although pattern shops are frequently affiliated with foundries,

1–11. Die-casting machines are operated by skilled workers.

Reed-Prentice Div., Package Machinery Corp.

18

American Foundryman

1–12. These foundry workers are skin drying a large floor mold.

Link Belt Co.

1–13. Worker in a modern auto-mated foundry. Programming of the molds is done from the console.

Coremakers

Cores are portions of foundry molds. Making cores may involve hand operations, but mechanical equipment is very often employed in larger foundries. Coremaking consists essentially of packing pre-pared sand mixtures in boxes so as to give the desired form to the mold. Cores are then dried on flat plates in an oven, till they have sufficient hardness and strength to resist the flow and erosion of molten metal. These cores are placed on core seats in the mold cavity. Upon solidification of the metal around them, the core forms a hollow or void in a casting.

Coremakers, like molders, take their names from the type of work performed or the kind of core machine operated. There are bench coremakers, floor core-makers (when the cores are too large to be made on the bench), and operators for core blowing machines, jolt-rollover machines, and stock core machines.

This trade is usually learned in a four-year apprentice program, although less skilled coremaking jobs require only a brief on-the-job training.

Melters

Melters operate furnaces. 1–14. They must know how to make the necessary adjustments to produce the desired melting conditions. Melters are designated by the type of furnace that they operate, such as cupola tenders, crucible tend-ers, electric furnace tenders, open-hearth tenders, and others.

The melter's job is to decide when the molten metal is ready to

1–14. Melter operating a furnace.

Howmet Corp., Misco Div.

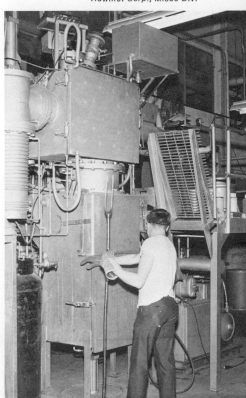

19

1–15. Blast cleaning small castings.

be poured, by tests which are performed at the furnace or in the control laboratory.

After pouring the metal into the molds and solidification has taken place, the molds are broken open in an operation known as "shaking out," and the castings are transferred to the cleaning department.

Cleaning Castings

In the cleaning department the gates, sprues and risers are removed with band saws, hammers, or cutting torches. 1–15. Sand that has adhered to the casting is removed by shot blasting, tumbling, or salt baths. Areas where the sprues and risers were removed are smoothed by grinding or by means of chisels operated by compressed air.

Cleaning operators are designated by job classifications, such as grinders, chippers, and blasters.

Inspectors

All large-scale manufacturing concerns employ inspectors to cneck their products. 1–16. In the foundry, inspectors use a variety of gages and similar aids in checking casting dimensions. Surface defects in products are often recognized by visual inspection, while smaller sub-surface defects require the use of X-ray machines and magnetic equipment. Mass-produced items must be inspected systematically to be sure that they will function properly.

Inspectors are required to have the ability to read blueprints and do arithmetic involving decimals. Being able to read all types of measuring instruments is a necessity.

Inspectors generally learn the requirements of their work through on-the-job training.

Welders and Oxygen and Arc Cutters

Welding has become one of the most common ways of joining metal parts, by using heat, pressure, or both, with or without filler metal, to produce a permanent bond.

Most manual welding is done by arc welders, gas welders, and workers who can combine both processes. 1–17.

The principal duty of the manual welder is to control the melting of the metal edges by directing heat either from an electric arc or gas-welding torch.

In production processes, where work is repetitive, the work is done by operators of welding machines.

Oxygen cutters and arc cutters —called *flame* and *thermal* cutters—use hand-guided torches to trim or cut metals.

It takes several years to become a broadly skilled arc or gas welder; however, manual jobs can be learned in the school or after a few months of on-the-job training.

1–16. A trichlorothylene degreasing unit gets an operational inspection.

Hooker Chemical Corp.

1–17. Welders working on microwave parabolic antennas.

Spincraft

Columbian Vise and Mfg. Co.

2–1. The worker *should* wear safety glasses at all times and sleeves *should* fit tightly or be rolled up to the elbow. Files *should* be equipped with suitable handles.

Unit 2.   Safety

It is the author's opinion that the subject, safety, makes this the most important unit in the book.

Besides protecting you now, the major objective of teaching safety in school is to provide accident-free and accident-conscious workers for life in industrial occupations. Recent records point out that 17,000 workers are killed every year; over 2,000,000 workers receive injuries of some type, and 300,000 workers are permanently injured.

Most companies stress safety in their plants. One example of such emphasis is the International Harvester Company, where personnel are regularly trained and drilled in all phases of safety. The wearing of safety glasses by all production workers is mandatory.

GENERAL SAFETY INSTRUCTION

1. Avoid wearing clothing that might catch in moving or rotating parts. Long sleeves on shirts, long hair, neckties, and jewelry are a definite hazard in the shop. 2–1.

2. Remove all burrs from workpieces to avoid cuts.

3. Always wear safety glasses while in the shop. 2–2.

4. Industrial workers should wear safety shoes. Don't wear canvas shoes; they give no resistance to hard objects dropped on the feet. 2–3 (See page 22).

5. Keep away from moving belts.

6. Be sure all guards are in place.

2–2. An approved type of safety glasses should be worn at all times.

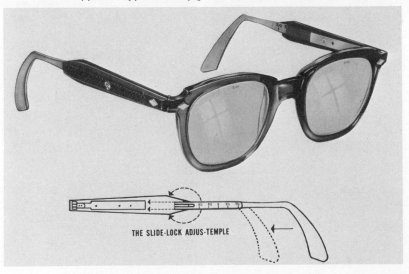

THE SLIDE-LOCK ADJUS-TEMPLE

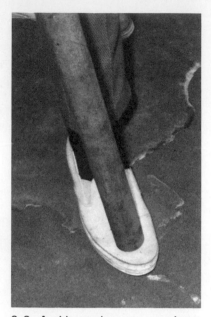

2–3. Avoid wearing canvas shoes. A heavy object dropped on the foot can cause serious injury.

7. Protect against inhaling noxious fumes.

8. Protect against inhaling dust of any kind, especially from grinding wheels.

9. There is a correct method for lifting heavy workpieces to the machine. Learn the proper method.

10. Gloves should be worn when handling sheet metal or large pieces of stock. 2–4.

11. Be careful of other workers when carrying long pieces of bar stock.

SAFETY ON THE BENCH

1. Thoughtless use of bench tools includes using the tool incorrectly or carelessly.

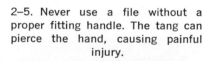

2–5. Never use a file without a proper fitting handle. The tang can pierce the hand, causing painful injury.

Columbian Vise and Mfg. Co.

2–4. Good safety rules are being observed by this worker.

3M Co.

2–6. Always check the fit of a hammer handle in the head of the hammer.

2. Sharp-edged or pointed tools should not be carried in pockets of your clothes.

3. Never use a file without a handle. 2–5.

4. Do not use a file as a hammer. Flying broken pieces can cause injury, besides ruining the file.

5. Always check the fit of the handle in the hammer head. 2–6.

6. Be sure a wrench fits the nut snugly. The wrong wrench can slip and injure the hand against other metal.

TOOL MATERIAL SAFETY

1. When no chip breaker is ground into a tool for turning metal, the turnings come off the workpiece in long, hot bands that wind around the workpiece or the controls of the machine. Such ribbons are dangerous. They can be prevented by a well designed chip breaker.

2. Again, safety glasses or goggles should be worn at all times. 2–7. Broken chips or fine particles of metal can fly from the machine. They are usually hot and

2–7. Safety glasses are a necessity for eye protection. There are different types for the many metalworking tasks.

2–8. Ties should be removed when working at machines. They can catch in revolving parts. This couldn't happen to the sleeves.

2–9. Never leave a chuck key in the chuck. It will fly from the chuck if the lathe is started.

sharp, capable of causing a serious eye injury.

MACHINE SAFETY

The Lathe

In lathe work the most common injuries result from hands or clothing being caught or entangled in rotating parts such as the workpiece, exposed gears, and lathe dog. 2–8. Flying chips are also a hazard. Proper guards should always be in place. State labor laws are very explicit in the provisions for use of guards in industry. If such laws are needed to insure safe working conditions for adult workers, you should place even greater emphasis on your own safe working habits as you learn.

Again, clothing should not be worn that will create a hazard. Cotton waste and rags must be kept clear of the machine and must not hang out of the pockets of clothing. *Rings* or *wristwatches* should not be worn, as they can also be caught in the machine.

Lathes should always be stopped before making any adjustment on the tool holder.

Again, a chuck key should never be left in the chuck. 2–9. Starting the lathe with the key in the chuck can cause serious injury.

Shaper, Planer, Slotter, Broach, and Power Saw

Although some of these machines will not be found in every school, they will be found in industry.

Most of the machines employ the reciprocating technique of cutting. A great deal of the potential danger in operating a shaper or planer is in injuries to the hands from the moving tool. 2–10. Fly-

ing chips are a constant source of eye danger if safety glasses are not worn. Lifting heavy workpieces without means of a mechanical hoist can also cause a serious injury.

The slotter is not a dangerous tool provided the hands are kept from the moving tool. The main potential danger from the broaching machine is the moving slide containing the moving broaching teeth.

Power saws, even though guarded, can be dangerous for the careless operator. Fingers can be lost through carelessness. A pusher device should always be used when there is danger of the fingers slipping from the workpiece into the revolving blade.

Milling Machine

The basic danger of milling machine operation is that the hands

2–10. In operating a shaper keep the hands away from the moving tool. Note that the operator wears safety glasses and his shop coat has close-fitting sleeves.

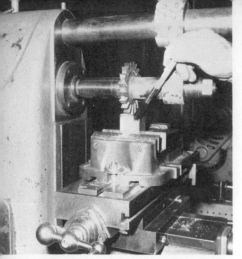

2–11. Remove chips when doing a milling operation. Use a brush instead of the fingers to prevent injury.

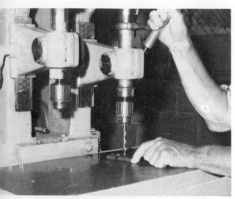

2–12. The operator is not using a vise drill, jig, or fixture to hold the workpiece while drilling. This workpiece can become caught in the drill and injure the hand.

2–13. Massive valve core ground on the lathe with .0001″ accuracy. Lack of safety glasses can be extremely hazardous to this operator.

Dumore Co.

may be caught in the revolving cutter. To remove chips from around the cutter or table, stop the machine and use a brush. 2–11.

Clamp the workpiece securely to the table to prevent slippage. Be sure the "start" and "stop" switches are within easy reach at all times in case of an emergency.

Because milling cutters have sharp edges, they should be handled with care.

Drilling Machine

Because drilling machines usually operate at high speeds, the operator must be alert. Gloves should never be worn when operating this machine as they can be caught in the revolving drill. The wearing of loose clothing that can become entangled in the revolving drill should be avoided. Long hair that is not protected is also a source of danger.

A loose workpiece can become caught in the revolving drill and cause serious injury to the hands. 2–12. The workpiece should be held securely in a vise, a jig, or fixture, or bolted to the table. Many drilling accidents are caused by the workpiece not being securely fastened.

Grinding Machine

Whenever a grinding wheel or machine accident occurs, the cause may be traced to one of four sources: (1) wheel, (2) machine, (3) mounting, or (4) operation.

The greatest care should be taken in the mounting of the wheel. The hole in the wheel should be slightly larger than the spindle or arbor, so that the wheel need not be forced on. Wheels

should always be mounted with flanges made in accordance to specifications adopted by abrasive wheel manufacturers.

When starting a new wheel, the operator should stand to one side until it has reached its full speed for at least one minute. When grinding offhand, the operator should see that the work-rests are as close to the wheel as possible. In any grinding operation, the operator should always wear close-fitting (yet comfortable) safety goggles or a face shield at all times even though the wheel is shielded. 2–13.

Most accidents occur through the personal (human) factor in operating.

CASTING SAFETY

The major danger from casting is that of being burned by molten

2–14(A). The danger from casting operations results from not observing the proper safety rules. Burns can occur from molten metal while it is being poured.

Inductotherm—Induction Heating and Melting Co.

McEnglevan Heat Treating and Mfg. Co.

2–14(B). This foundry worker is properly dressed for handling molten metal.

Dempsey Industrial Furnace Corp.

2–15(A). Care should be taken in handling hot metal from a forging furnace. A severe burn can occur unless safety precautions are observed. This worker should be wearing safety glasses.

2–15(B). This stamping press operator's hand is protected by a safety device that does not permit the hand to be under the press.

International Silver Co.

metal, both while pouring into molds and while the metal is being moved by overhead cranes. Dress safely and wear protective goggles at all times. 2–14(A). In industry the foundry foremen will insist on all protective devices being worn at all times to protect the worker. 2–14(B).

Never pick up hot castings, as a serious burn can result.

Putting *wet metal* into a crucible in the school foundry is a very dangerous practice. An explosion can result from this practice.

FORGING SAFETY

Forging operations are highly dangerous. Extreme care must be exercised at all times around the equipment. Hot sparks fly freely during hammer forging, making the wearing of goggles a necessity. 2–15(A). Keep hands and fingers away from all stamping processes. 2–15(B).

Danger can exist from overhead cranes which move hot steel from one place to another. A hot forging can slip from its holding device. Most industries require that steel-toed shoes be worn by all forging workers.

ROLLING SAFETY

This type of work is done on a large scale, yet steel mills have set up excellent safety devices to protect the workers. 2–16. Workers are given safety training in relation to their area of work.

PUNCH PRESS AND BLANKING SAFETY

The greatest danger in this area is to fingers and hands, which may be caught in presses. Most machines are equipped with adequate safety devices that require the op-

International Silver Co.

2–16. Care must be taken in this rolling operation that the hands are not drawn into the rolls.

erator to have both hands on the controls that operate the machine. General safety rules also apply to this operation. 2–17.

WELDING SAFETY

There can be many hazards when operating welding equipment if the worker is not familiar with the equipment.

When welding, a hood, shield, or goggles should be worn at all times. Proper filter glass, gloves, and sensible work clothing should also be worn at all times.

2–17. A blanking operation producing a blank of the required size and shape to manufacture a piece of flatware. Extreme care must be used to protect the operator from a serious hand injury.

Republic Steel

2–18. Working with intense heat demands extra care at all times.

HEAT-TREATMENT SAFETY

Heat treatment involves either direct exposure or handling metal that has been heated, which is hazardous at any time. 2–18. Cyanides are included in some proportion in the salt baths used in liquid carburizing. Cyanide salts are highly poisonous. They are fatal if taken internally. The fumes which are developd when cyanide is brought into contact with acids are dangerous when inhaled.

In summary, dangers can exist in all metalworking operations, but proper safeguards can protect the worker from an accident that might be serious.

Check Your Knowledge

1. What future does the metalworking industry hold for the youth of today?

2. Why are draftsmen an important part of the metalworking industry?

3. What is an all-round machinist?

4. Compare the work of the all-round machinist with that of the tool and die maker.

5. Is a four-year apprenticeship necessary to learn most machining occupations?

6. Why are experimental machinists so important to some industries?

7. What is the work of the layout man?

8. Explain the work done by a setup man?

9. Name five products made by forging operations.

10. Why is forging important to many industries today?

11. Compare the work of the old-time blacksmith with that of the modern forge shop worker.

12. What is the most common casting process?

13. What part does wood patternmaking play in the metal patternmaking trade?

14. Why is coremaking an important part of foundry work?

15. Is welding a skilled occupation? Explain your answer.

16. State several reasons why modern industry stresses safe working conditions.

17. Give as many safety rules as you can.

18. What is your philosophy regarding safety?

19. Name every safety precaution you can think of regarding the operations performed on grinding machines.

20. List three main precautions which should be taken when working with hand tools.

21. What factors cause most accidents?

22. What types of clothing are considered safe in the school shop?

23. When should safety goggles or face shields be worn?

24. Why should you make it a practice to see that the work and cutting tools are mounted securely before starting the machine?

25. Why should extreme caution be taken while grinding?

26. Compare the dangers of working on an engine lathe with other types of machine tools.

27. Is a new, unused grinding wheel safe to use before making a test of the wheel?

28. What are the main safety precautions that should be taken in working with molten metal?

29. What is the danger of inhaling grinding wheel dust?

30. If you were teaching trainees to weld, what would you tell them in regard to safety precautions in welding?

31. Why are strict safety rules so important in school as well as in industry?

References

America's Industries, Bloomington, Ill., McKnight & McKnight Publishing Co., 1971.

Lasher, Williard K., *How You Can Get a Better Job,* Chicago, American Technical Society, 1962.

Robertson, Von H., *Career Counseling Yearbook,* T & I Div., American Vocational Association, Chicago, American Technical Society.

Section Two

Producing and Processing Ferrous and Nonferrous Metals

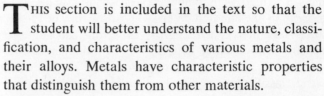

THIS section is included in the text so that the student will better understand the nature, classification, and characteristics of various metals and their alloys. Metals have characteristic properties that distinguish them from other materials.

The study of both ferrous and nonferrous metals is important because our civilization, as we know it, depends upon metals in one form or another.

The gradual discovery of new metals, or metals and alloys with new properties, was responsible for most of the development of mankind. Economists measure the importance of countries by their use of metals.

The first important use of metals was known as the Bronze Age when metal first replaced the stone weapons and implements that had been used during the earlier period of man's history. The Bronze Age was succeeded by the Iron Age, then the Steel Age, and now we regard the age in which we live as the Alloy Steel Age, because of the development of alloy and special steels.

Ferrous and nonferrous metals are both important in the present era. However, greater emphasis is placed on ferrous metals in this text due to the fact that they have had a greater impact upon the development of our civilization.

Units in this section concerning the producton of iron and steel are included because the properties of metal depend largely upon how they are produced and processed.

Bethlehem Steel Corp.

Unit 3. Classification of Metals

In industry today there are more than a thousand different metals being used to manufacture products. The modern automobile has more than one hundred different metals used in its construction. An attempt will be made in this unit to give an understanding of the basic classification of metals.

Metals were formerly considered to be those elements which had a metallic luster and were good conductors of heat and electricity. This is still the standard accepted by the average individual, who thinks of iron, copper, aluminum, etc., and their alloys —steel, brass, cast iron, bronze, etc. Actually, metals are generally defined as those elements whose hydroxides form bases (such as sodium or potassium), while the nonmetals' hydroxides form acids (such as sulphur). Metals may exist as pure elements, or, as noted, when two or more metallic elements are combined, they form a mixture called an alloy.

ALLOYS

The term alloy is used to identify any metallic system. In metallurgy it is a substance, with metallic properties, which is composed of two or more elements, intimately mixed. Of these elements one must be a metal and the others are usually metallic or nonmetallic. Plain carbon steel, in this sense, is basically an alloy of iron and carbon, with other elements present in the form of impurities. However, for commercial purposes, plain carbon steel is not classified as an alloy steel.

Alloys may be further classified as ferrous and nonferrous.

All commercial varieties of iron and steel are alloys. The ordinary steels are thought of as iron-carbon alloys, yet practically all contain silicon and manganese as well. In addition, there are thousands of recognized alloy steels, such as special tool steels, steels for castings, forgings, and rolled shapes. The base metal for all these is iron.

Steels are often called by the principal alloying element present, such as silicon steel, manganese steel, nickel steel, and tungsten steel.

Even nonferrous alloys may contain iron in a small amount, as impurities. Some of the nonferrous alloys are bronze, copper, brass, and Monel.

UNDERSTANDING ALLOYS

Most of the metals with which we come in contact are alloys that are formed by a mixture. For instance, pure gold, which is too soft for jewelry, is generally alloyed or mixed with copper.

Not all alloys form the same mixtures. Some take the form of *heterogeneous* (having unlike qualities) mixtures, while other mixtures form as *homogeneous* (consisting of similar parts or elements).

Homogeneous mixtures generally are known as solutions. When two or more ingredients are mixed together without regard for any specific proportion, you obtain a mixture. In a compound the ingredients unite chemically, but in a mixture none of the components has lost its identity. The individual ingredients in a mixture can be in the form of elements, compounds, or other mixtures.

Pearlite, a mixture composed of alternate lamellae of ferrite and iron carbide, is found in most irons and carbon steels. 3–1. This constituent adds strength and wear resistance to the metal. It is so called because of its "mother of pearl" appearance. Pearlite, a heterogeneous mixture in the form of a solid, is fre-

3–1. Microscopic structure of fine pearlite (normalized).

U.S. Steel Corp.

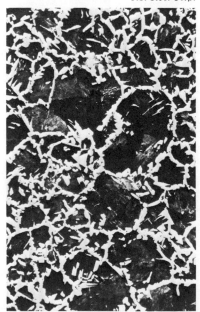

quently called a mechanical mixture.

Metals are not usually found existing in nature in a pure state. They are more often found in a form of mixtures or compounds. Iron occurs in nature in the form of iron oxide, compounded with rock and other materials of an earthy nature.

Most metals are not used in the pure state because they do not possess the required properties for most practical applications. In order to improve their properties, they are mixed with other substances which are either metallic or nonmetallic, thus forming alloys.

SOLUTIONS

Ordinarily we think of a solution as a liquid form. However, there are solid solutions and gaseous solutions. There are solutions of one molten metal in another. When such solutions cool and solidify, we have an alloy.

A substance which is dissolved is called a *solute* and the substance which does the dissolving is a *solvent*. The result is a mixture.

A solid solution is formed in the same manner in which salt and water form a liquid solution. Solid solutions are comparatively ductile, soft, and malleable. They have a tendency to confer these properties on alloys in which they are present. Many brasses and bronzes are examples of nonferrous alloys containing solid solutions.

Even commercially pure iron (ferrite) contains such elements as carbon, silicon, manganese,

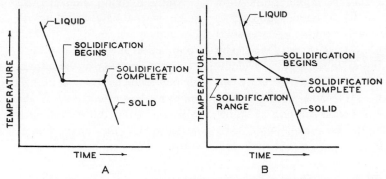

3–2. (A) Time-temperature curve for pure metal; (B) Time-temperature curve for an alloy.

sulphur, and phosphorous in small proportions. This form of iron is in solid solution.

Ferrite is capable of holding in solution the elements mentioned above. The solubility of these elements varies according to the temperature. At temperatures below 1330°F. ferrite exists within the grain structures of plain unhardened steels, gray iron, wrought iron, and in many alloy steels.

ALLOY CHARACTERISTICS

Although pure metals solidify at a constant temperature, alloys do not. 3–2(A). The first nuclei have a tendency to form at a higher temperature than that at which complete solidification occurs. 3–2(B). Since each element in an alloy has its own peculiarities relative to temperature, the change in temperature as solidification progresses causes the solid being formed to change in chemical composition.

The accompanying equilibrium diagram for copper-nickel alloys illustrates the way an alloy forms a solid solution of two or more materials. 3–3.

A metal consisting of 67% nickel and 33% copper is known as *Monel*. It has qualities that are highly resistant to saltwater corrosion. As signified by the heavy dotted line in the illustration, the metal begins to solidify when cooled to the temperature of L_1. At this point the first metal to solidify as indicated by the diagram will be 23% copper and 77% nickel as shown by S_1. L_1 being a liquid, will have a composition of 67% nickel and 33% copper when freezing begins. With a temperature drop to the

3–3. Equilibrium diagram for copper-nickel alloys.

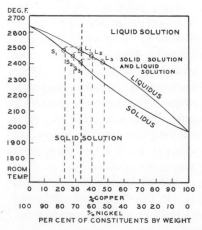

L_2-S_2 line, the liquid composition will be 41% copper and 59% nickel as shown by L_2. The solid composition is shown by S_2. The last liquid to solidify is of composition L_3 at a temperature between 2400 and 2500°F. The result is a solid solution of Monel metal, 67% nickel and 33% copper.

Many alloying elements dissolve in the base metal in different proportions in liquified and solidified steels.

The proportion of the alloying element which remains in solid solutions has a tendency to vary with the temperature and grain structure of the alloy that e is formed.

indented easily. Others, like tungsten carbide, approach diamond hardness and are of great value as dies for drawing wire and cutting tools of various types. Heat treatment causes changes in the hardness. Annealed tool steel can readily be machined, but often with difficulty after it has been hardened and tempered. Annealed brass is comparatively soft but, when cold-worked the hardness is increased to a great degree.

Unit 4. Properties of Metals

Metals have characteristic properties distinguishing them from other materials. Most important of these properties is their strength, or ability to support weight without bending or breaking. This property combined with toughness, or ability to bend without breaking, is important. The ability to resist corrosion in some metals, responsiveness to heat treatment and plasticity, and the ability to be formed into desired shapes also compare favorably with other materials.

Metals can be cast into shapes and sizes ranging from a few ounces to many tons, if weight is needed. They can be welded, hardened, softened, etc. Metals also possess another important property: When a particular product is discarded it can be cut into convenient sections, put into a furnace, remelted, and used in another product.

The properties of metal may be classified in three categories: (1) chemical properties, (2) mechanical properties, and (3) physical properties.

CHEMICAL PROPERTIES

It is not within the scope of this book to go into detail regarding the chemical properties of metals. This information can be obtained from machinists' handbooks, the ASME handbook —*Metal Properties,* and manufacturers' catalogs. The chemical properties of metals have to do with chemical composition, melting temperatures, corrosion resistance, etc. By consulting Table 4, some of the most important chemical properties of metals can be ascertained.

MECHANICAL PROPERTIES

In understanding the related areas of metalworking and methods used today, the mechanical properties of metals are of the utmost importance.

Hardness

The hardness of metals varies greatly. Some, like lead, can be

BRITTLENESS

This is the opposite of plasticity. Brittleness is related to the hardness in metals, as hardened tool steel, which may exhibit very little plasticity. Gray cast iron is brittle in comparison with unhardened steel. A brittle metal usually has little strength to resist tensile loading and it has very little shock or impact strength. A brittle metal can fail without warning of impending failure.

Plasticity and Ductility

Due to its plasticity sheet metal can be shaped by spinning, forming, and other processes. Any metal that can be bent, drawn out, twisted or changed in shape without breaking easily is ductile. Copper, silver, aluminum, soft steel, and wrought iron are classified as ductile metals. As said, brittle metals break abruptly under increasing loads while ductile metals have a tendency to break gradually with increased stress or load. Ductility may be measured by the amount a material can be elongated. This characteristic permits the metal to be drawn down from a larger diameter to a

Table 4. Properties of Principal Metals

Metal	Chemical symbol	Specific gravity	Weight per cu. in. (pounds)	Weight per cu. ft. (pounds)	Average melting point (deg. F.)
Aluminum	AL	2.70	0.0975	168.5	1220
Antimony	Sb	6.618	0.2390	413.0	1167
Bismuth	Bi	9.781	0.3532	610.3	520
Boron	B	2.535	0.0916	158.2	4172
Brass*	—	8.60	0.3105	536.6	1560–1900
Bronze*	—	8.78	0.3171	547.9	1300–1800
Cadmium	Cd	8.648	0.3123	539.6	610
Chromium	Cr	6.93	0.2502	432.4	2939
Cobalt	Co	8.71	0.3145	543.5	2696
Copper	Cu	8.89	0.3210	554.7	1981
Gold	Au	19.3	0.6969	1204.3	1945
Iron	Fe	7.86	0.285	491.0	2802
Iron, cast*	—	7.03–7.73	0.254–0.279	438.7–482.4	1990–2300
Iron, wrought*	—	7.80–7.90	0.282–0.285	486.7–493.0	2750
Lead	Pb	11.342	0.4096	707.7	621
Magnesium	Mg	1.741	0.0628	108.6	1204
Manganese	Mn	7.3	0.2636	455.5	2300
Molybdenum	Mo	10.2	0.3683	636.5	4748
Nickel	Ni	8.8	0.3178	549.1	2651
Platinum	Pt	21.37	0.7717	1333.5	3224
Silver	Ag	10.42–10.53	0.376–0.380	650.2–657.1	1761
Steel, carbon*	—	—	0.283–0.284	489.0–490.8	2500
Tantalum	Ta	16.6	0.5998	1035.8	5162
Tellurium	Te	6.25	0.2257	390.0	846
Tin	Sn	7.29	0.2633	454.9	499
Titanium	Ti	4.5	0.1621	280.1	3272
Tungsten	W	1.86–19.1	0.672–0.690	1161–1192	6098
Uranium	U	18.7	0.6753	1166.9	3362
Vanadium	V	5.6	0.2022	394.4	3110
Zinc	Zn	7.04–7.16	0.254–0.259	439.3–446.8	788

* Properties may vary according to kind and amount of alloying elements or impurities.

smaller one without breaking, as with wire.

Toughness and Malleability

A tough metal is one possessing high strength and the ability to deform permanently and resist rupture. Toughness enables the metal to survive shock or impact forces without fracture. Testing devices are used to determine the toughness of metals. *These tests will be explained in a later unit.*

The ability of a metal to deform permanently under compression without rupture is known as malleability. In order to be rolled and hammered into thin sheets, metals have to have this property. The great majority of metals that come under the classification of ductile metals are malleable. Note: One of the exceptions to the malleability of ductile metal is lead which does not have the property of tensional strength.

Strength

Strength of a metal is its ability to resist deformation or rupture. A combination of strength and plasticity in certain structures, such as machine tools that are subjected to being overloaded in use, is desirable. The most common tests of strength are tensile strength, shear strength, torsion strength, and compression strength.

Tensile Strength

Tensile strength may be defined as the property of a material which resists forces tending to pull it apart. In a specimen, tensile strength is the maximum resistance that the material will offer before rupture occurs.

Tests are usually conducted on standard symmetrical specimens less than a square inch and are expressed in unit terms of psi. The American Society for Testing Materials has standardized the shapes of test specimens. These are quite generally ac-

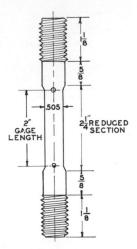

4–1(A). Standard 0.505″ tensile test bar for steel. The 0.505″ diameter is chosen because its area is 0.2 sq. in., an easy factor to divide into the results read.

cepted. However, of course, it is possible to test the tensile strength of specimens of various shapes and sizes. 4–1(A).

Elongation

Elongation may be defined as the amount of permanent extension of metal in the vicinity of a rupture. When measured it is expressed as a percentage of the original gage length of the piece.

Yield Point

Some materials, notably low-carbon steel, are tested for their yield point. It is usually expressed in thousands of psi. In making the test, a specimen is tested for tensile strength with a steady increase in load. The specimen will continue to elongate a certain amount until the yield point is reached. Further application of the load will cause a rupture.

All metals do not behave in this manner. Ductile metals such as copper and aluminum lack the

elasticity of some metals and deform steadily under load until failure occurs.

Stress

There are four types of stress: (A) tension, which acts to pull materials apart; (B) compression, the force that tends to squeeze material; (C) shear, the tendency to cause one part to slide by another part; and (D) bolt under shear stress. 4–1(B).

Stress may be defined as the internal resistance to an external force or load; it is equal to the load or force applied, specified in terms of load per unit of cross-sectional area.

Fatigue

A material can fail due to a single load well above its strength, or due to repeated stress, well below the strength of the material. An axle may break after months of use, even though

4–1(B). Types of stress: (A) tension, (B) compression, (C) shear, and (D) bolt under shear stress holds material.

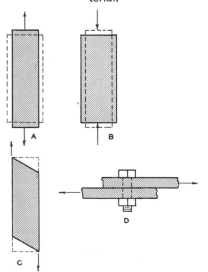

the loading has not been changed. After breaking the axle shows no deformation. Parts of machines subjected to repeated vibrations may fail due to fatigue.

Slots, holes, tool marks, and sharp reentrant angles have a tendency to increase fatigue failures. By using fillets and rounding off corners and shoulders, fatigue failures can be controlled.

Fusibility

Fusibility is important when welding metals. Melting points of the same degree enable metals to join readily when heated to a liquid state.

Strain

When an external force is applied to a structure or material, a certain amount of deformation takes place. In the illustration, "A" is under strain from the load force, creating a bend in the material. After the strain is removed, the elasticity of the material permits it to return to its original shape and size. Some materials lack this elasticity and, therefore,

4–2. Effects of load force on a structural member: (A) strain, (B) elasticity; member returns to original shape, and (C) a permanent deformation; the member does not return to original shape.

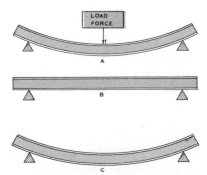

do not have the ability to regain their original shape but remain in a state of permanent deformation. 4–2(A–C).

Various types of deformation can take place when products are under strain: (1) shear, (2) torsion, (3) elongation, (4) bending, and (5) compression. 4–3.

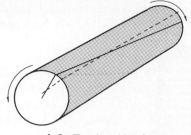

4–3. Torsional load.

Another important source of iron is a flinty rock called taconite. However, taconite is too low in iron content to be used in blast furnaces. Steel companies have solved this problem by working out a method to extract iron oxide from taconite and concentrate it in marble-sized pellets with an iron content of about 65%. There is sufficient taconite in the Lake Superior region to last the United States for hundreds of years.

The leading iron-ore producing region in this country is still the Lake Superior region of Minnesota, Michigan, and Wisconsin, which includes the Mesabi Range. In the past, the Mesabi Range supplied about 80% of this country's iron. The ore averages about 50% iron content. Other producing areas are located in Pennsylvania, New York, New Jersey, and Alabama. Ores are also imported from Chile, Venezuela, Brazil, Peru, and Canada.

Unit 5. — Production of Iron and Its Uses

"The term iron has such a variety of applications in referring to the many alloys of which iron is a base that it is difficult for the average person to use the term correctly." *Encyclopedia Americana.* Iron has been known from prehistoric times. No one has found out how man first discovered the utility of iron, or how he first learned the process of extracting iron from its ores.

The beginnings of iron, as far as can be determined, go back as far as 4000 B.C. There is evidence that the Egyptians used iron tools when they built the pyramids as early as 3000 B.C. Early Egyptian artisans became remarkably skillful in the art of forging iron. From bars they produced numerous weapons, cooking utensils, locks, and richly ornamented suits of armor.

In the Middle East the ancient Persians, Medes, Hittites, and Phoenicians carried on trade in iron long before the Christian era. The Phoenicians probably introduced iron to the western world.

The first ironworks in the New World was built at Falling Creek, Virginia. Another ironworks was completed in Saugus, Massachusetts, about 1650. One of the first articles produced was a simple cooking pot which is still in existence.

IRON ORE

The basic source of all iron and steel is iron ore, which is an oxide of iron mixed with alumina, silica, phosphorous, manganese, sulphur, and other material. Traces of iron are found everywhere, but profitable mining areas with heavy iron content are rare.

Most of the iron ores mined in America are of two types, hematite and magnetite. These ores contain about 52% iron. The remaining contents are considered largely impurities. Hematite is a brick-red oxide and magnetite is a black oxide. The ore is taken from open-pit and shaft mines.

MATERIALS USED IN EXTRACTING IRON

There are three basic materials used in extracting iron from iron ore: *coal* (from which coke is made), *limestone,* and *air.*

Coking coal, a special type of bituminous coal, is mined principally in western Pennsylvania, West Virginia, Kentucky, and Alabama.

Coke—produced by cooking coal at high temperatures—is the ideal combustion material for blast furnaces. It burns at a rapid rate with intense heat and supplies the carbon needed to make carbon monoxide gas, which is important in the blast furnace process.

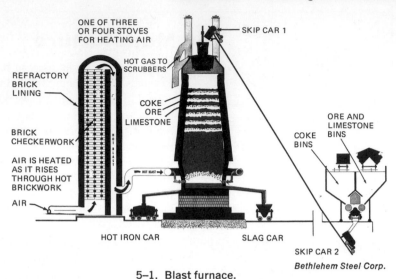

ONE OF THREE
OR FOUR STOVES
FOR HEATING AIR

SKIP CAR 1

HOT GAS TO
SCRUBBERS

REFRACTORY
BRICK
LINING

COKE
ORE
LIMESTONE

ORE AND
LIMESTONE
BINS

COKE
BINS

BRICK
CHECKERWORK

AIR IS HEATED
AS IT RISES
THROUGH HOT
BRICKWORK

AIR

HOT BLAST

HOT IRON CAR

SLAG CAR

SKIP CAR 2

Bethlehem Steel Corp.

5–1. Blast furnace.

Limestone is used as a flux, soaking up the impurities and forming a scumlike slag. Limestone is a gray rock consisting mainly of calcium carbonate.

From 4 to 4½ tons of air must be supplied to a blast furnace in order to make one ton of pig iron.

PRODUCTION OF PIG IRON

Pig iron, the principal base material for all steel furnaces, is the product of the blast furnace. Pig iron is obtained by smelting iron ore with coke and limestone. The final analysis depends primarily upon the quality of the ore used. Pig iron contains about 4% carbon, 1% silicon, 1% manganese, and smaller percentages of phosphorous and sulphur.

The blast furnace, together with its stoves and other equipment, is a huge, complicated structure, yet its design is comparatively simple. 5–1. The typical blast furnace is a tall, brick-lined steel shell over 200′ high,

with a hearth diameter of 20 to 30′, and with a daily production of between 800 to 3,000 tons of iron.

As shown in the illustration, skip cars, running up and down an inclined track, carry the charge—which consists of iron ore, coke, and limestone—from bins in the stock house to the top of the blast furnace through a hopper.

Very large pipes bring preheated air to furnace and also carry away the gases that are produced.

Preheating Air for the Blast Furnace

Three or four cylindrical structures, over 100′ tall, are located close to the blast furnace. These are stoves that heat the air before it is blown into the furnace. It will be noted from the illustration that they contain thousands of heat-resisting bricks arranged in a checkerboard pattern, which permits gas and air to pass through. Gas from the blast fur-

nace is burned in the stoves, heating the bricks. The gas is then diverted to another stove, and air to be blown into the furnace is forced through the first stove. As the air passes through the hot brickwork, it absorbs heat from the bricks, raising the temperature to the range of 1000° to 1800°F.

Operation of the Blast Furnace

The blast furnace is charged with alternate layers of iron ore, coke, and limestone. The hot air from the stoves is blown through the nozzles, called *tuyeres,* which are located near the base. The carbon in the coke and the oxygen in the air combine to form carbon monoxide gas at a temperature of about 3000°F., which reduces the ore to metallic iron. On some modern furnaces, the blast of air is enriched with oxygen, which serves to speed up the process. The molten iron forms droplets which trickle down through the charge and collect in a pool on the hearth.

The intense heat converts the limestone into lime. The lime acts as a flux and reacts with the impurities, forming a slag which drips down to the hearth. The slag is lighter than the iron, so it floats to top.

Every five or six hours the molten iron is tapped through a hole at the bottom. Approximately 150 to 350 tons of iron is drawn off at a time. Slag is drawn off more often through a hole located above the level of the iron.

The blast furnace produces about 6 tons of gas and ½ ton of

slag for every ton of pig iron. Note: The slag is used as aggregate in concrete and some is processed into mineral wool.

Blast furnaces are operated continuously except when they are shut down for repairs.

CHARACTERISTICS AND USES OF PIG IRON

Pig iron is hard and brittle. It lacks the great strength, ductility, and resistance to shock that steel is noted for. Pig iron is sold to foundries to make various types of iron castings.

CAST IRON

Iron castings are so called because they are shaped by pouring or "casting" into molds. These castings have a great compressive strength but are brittle and lack ductility. Cast iron has many direct uses, such as for engine blocks and parts for machine tools.

Unit 6. The Manufacture of Steel

It might be said of steel that it is refined pig iron. Technically speaking, steel is iron combined with carbon ranging from a few 100ths of 1% up to about 1.40%. Steel also contains certain amounts of manganese and silicon, and, when desired, other elements.

Over 90% of all steel made is classified as carbon, which means that it contains a regulated amount of carbon, small amounts of manganese, and traces of other elements. The remaining 10% of steel produced consists of alloy steels.

The two most widely used steel-making processes are the open-hearth and the electric furnace processes. Another process is the basic oxygen process, which is rapidly increasing in importance.

The Bessemer process of making steel has declined in the United States, with about only 3% of the steel in this country being produced by this method.

All of these processes will be described in the following paragraphs.

OPEN-HEARTH PROCESS

This process of producing steel derives its name from the type of furnace used. The open-hearth furnace is so named because the pool of slag-topped molten metal lies on the open hearth of the furnace, exposed to the sweep of the flames. 6–1. Excess carbon is oxidized by oxygen from the

6–1. Simplified cutaway of a typical open-hearth furnace.

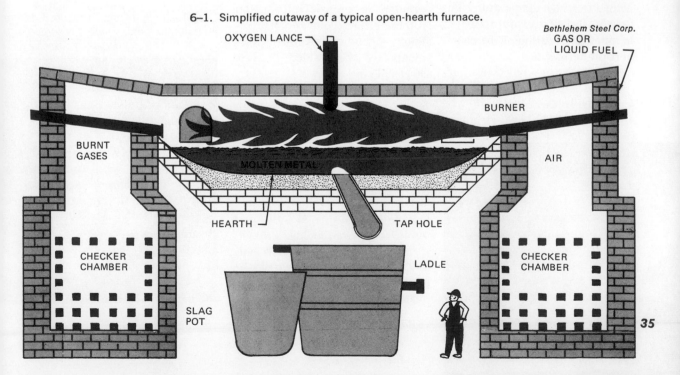

Bethlehem Steel Corp.

OXYGEN LANCE — GAS OR LIQUID FUEL — BURNER — BURNT GASES — MOLTEN METAL — AIR — HEARTH — TAP HOLE — CHECKER CHAMBER — LADLE — CHECKER CHAMBER — SLAG POT

iron oxide and the slag absorbs most impurities.

A modern open-hearth furnace is rectangular in shape, about 26′ wide and 100′ long. As shown in the illustration, there are doors on the charging side (front). The back or tapping side has a tap hole through which the molten steel is drawn. This hole is kept sealed with a plug of special clay until the molten metal is ready for tapping.

Beneath the furnace are checker chambers, which contain bricks in a checkerboard pattern through which air and exhaust gases pass alternately.

Preheated air from one checker chamber flows in at one end of the furnace, where it mixes with gas or other fuel. This mixture is blown into the furnace, burning as it sweeps across the molten metal in the hearth. The exhaust gases pass out the other end of the furnace and enter the opposite checker chamber. The brickwork in this chamber is heated to a high temperature. The flow is reversed every 10 or 15 minutes and heating of the chambers is alternated.

6–2. Steel being jet-tapped from an open-hearth furnace.

U.S. Steel Corp.

Limestone is put into the furnace to remove the impurities and build up the slag. Iron ore (or some other source of oxide) which supplies oxygen needed to oxidize the excess carbon is placed in the furnace. Steel scrap is added to the charge in amounts of 30 to 40%. Of course, this is almost pure iron.

After the scrap metal has been partially melted, the molten pig iron—60 to 70% of the total load—is poured into the furnace.

The refining and purification period then takes place as the excess carbon is oxidized and other impurities in gas form are absorbed by the slag. A temperature of about 2900°F. is created by the flames sweeping across the molten metal. Some furnaces are equipped with oxygen "lances" so that a rich stream of oxygen can be introduced into the bath. This speeds up the oxidation process.

Test samples are taken from the furnace from time to time and checked in the metallurgical laboratory, to provide information for the proper control of the refining operation. Alloying elements are then added if alloy steel is being made.

It takes approximately 8 to 10 hours to make a heat of steel. The heat is tapped and the steel poured out into a huge ladle. 6–2. The slag leaves the furnace after the steel. It is deposited in a slag pot and transferred to a storage area.

The steel is poured into ingot molds and the molds stripped from the ingots while still hot. 6–3. The ingots are then placed in soaking pits, where they are held at high temperature until

ready to be rolled in the rolling mill. 6–4.

ELECTRIC FURNACE PROCESS

The electric furnace is ideal for meeting exacting specifications, such as for stainless or other high-alloy steels, or special steels requiring very close metallurgical control of grain or other structural quality. 6–5.

In this type furnace the metal is heated by an electric arc. Both the temperature and the atmosphere can be closely controlled.

Because the electric furnace uses no fuel (which tends to build up sulphur), it is the only known process by which all sulphur can be removed.

Electric furnaces resemble tea kettles in shape. They are tilted to pour out the molten steel through a spout. 6–6. They vary in capacities from 5 to 100 tons. The electric furnace is lined with refractory brick and the metallic charge is inserted through a door, on the side or through the top,

6–3. Teeming ingots. The steel is poured into molds where it solidifies.

Bethlehem Steel Corp

Bethlehem Steel Corp.

6–4. Open-hearth charging floor at the Saucon division of the Bethlehem plant, where steel is made for rolling into structural shapes.

which can be swung to one side. Three large carbon or graphite electrodes, 10″ to 14″ in diameter, are located in the top of the furnace to conduct the current for the electric arc that melts the charge.

The furnace is charged with carefully selected steel scrap; the electrodes are lowered and the current turned on. The intensely hot arcs between the electrodes and scrap metal quickly melt the charge directly under the electrodes and form a pool of molten metal. The electrodes are then adjusted to a determined distance from the molten metal. After the charge is 70% melted, iron ore and burnt lime are added and melting is completed. Samples of the melt are then taken to be analyzed in the laboratory.

The kind of steel to be made determines the next step of operation. If it is to be carbon steel, the operation is rather similar to the open-hearth method. If an alloy steel is to be produced, the initial slag is removed and a second slag is made so that close control of the final analysis is possible. The materials added to form the second slag, as well as the alloying elements, are in the form of carefully dried material of known composition. The steel is then "teemed" or poured into molds that form ingots. From 4 to 12 hours is required for the entire process, depending upon the type of steel to be made.

BASIC OXYGEN PROCESS

It has been known for a century that the use of oxygen would speed up the steel refining process and make it more efficient. How-

6–5. Cross section of an electric furnace.

Bethlehem Steel Corp.

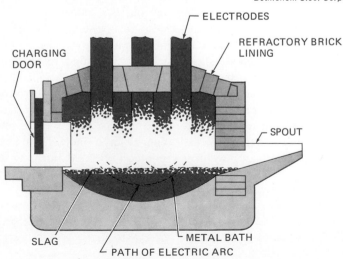

ELECTRODES

REFRACTORY BRICK LINING

CHARGING DOOR

SPOUT

SLAG

METAL BATH

PATH OF ELECTRIC ARC

6–6. An electric furnace is tilted to pour its steel into the huge ladle below. Both temperature and atmosphere can be closely controlled.

Bethlehem Steel Corp.

ever, oxygen was extremely costly and not available in large quantities until recent years.

Today large steel companies have installed oxygen-making equipment at their plants, providing the necessary amounts of steel at a reasonable cost.

Several new oxygen steel-making processes have been developed, some of which are still in the experimental stages. The most widely used has been the "basic oxygen process," known as BOP. 6–7. The furnace used in this process resembles the old Bessemer converter in general appearance. However, the furnace is much larger and the process is entirely revised, designed expressly to get the best results with oxygen in steel-making.

Whereas in the converter, air bubbled up through the bath, in the BOP furnace, a lance blows oxygen down from the top. By this method, steel of excellent quality can be made at an amazingly high rate of speed—roughly one heat an hour.

The furnace is charged with molten iron by tilting it to its side and pouring the metal in through the mouth. It is then turned to an upright position and oxygen is blown through the lance as shown in the illustration. Burned lime is added to the bath. Upon purification of the steel, the necessary elements are added to meet the required specifications for the type being made. Upon completion of the melt, the furnace is tilted and the metal poured into a large ladle.

It has been stated that in the 1970's a third of the steel produced in the United States may be processed this way.

BESSEMER PROCESS

The Bessemer converter is used for making only about 3% of the steel produced in the United States today. 6–8. It is difficult to control the heat as well as the alloying elements.

Bessemer steel is made by charging the converter with molten metal direct from the blast furnace. A number of holes are located in the bottom of the converter through which air is blown. The air pressure is usually 20 to 30 psi. The air ·first oxidizes the silicon and manganese, which, together with the iron oxide, rise to the top to form a slag.

The carbon then begins to burn, and the blowing continues until most of the carbon is eliminated. Sparks appear first, followed by flames. The progress of the "blow" can be determined from the flame coming from the converter; change in color and length indicates which impurities are being burned out first. It ordinarily takes about 20 minutes for the burn-out of the impurities. When the blow is finished, the amount of carbon necessary to bring the carbon content to the desired percentage, plus manganese to counteract the influence of sulphur and silicon to de-gassify, is added to the molten mass.

The finished steel is poured from the converter into a ladle. The floating slag is removed and caught in a ladle. The steel is poured into molds forming ingots which are then ready for various processing methods.

Bessemer steels are used in low-grade sheets, wire, pipe, and screw stock.

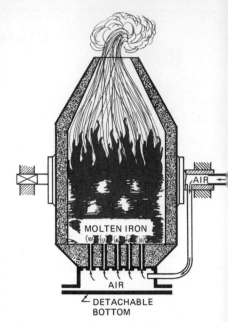

6–8. Section of round body Bessemer converter.

6–7. Basic oxygen process. Oxygen blown into the furnace through a lance speeds production by 30%.

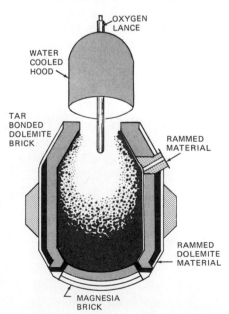

Unit 7. Plain Carbon and Alloy Steels

All steels contain carbon. However, the term carbon steel is used to distinguish a steel to which no alloying elements, such as tungsten, nickel, or chromium, have been added in appreciable amounts. By adding carbon or other elements the properties of steel can be changed significantly.

Iron and carbon are the essential elements of plain carbon steels. However, plain carbon steel, in addition, includes small amounts of silicon, sulphur, manganese, and phosphorous in the form of impurities.

The carbon content in plain carbon steels varies from 0.05% to 1.7% but seldom exceeds 1.5%. The following table represents an analysis of the range of elements.

Table 7. Range of Plain Carbon Steels	
Carbon	0.05 to 1.5%
Manganese	0.025 to 1.65%
Phosphorus	0.040% maximum
Sulphur	0.050% maximum
Iron	97%

The most important factor in determining the properties of plain carbon steels is the carbon content. The properties are influenced by significant increases in carbon content with a result that: (1) tensile strength is increased, (2) greater hardness is obtained, (3) ductility decreases, and (4) weldability decreases.

There are three classes of plain carbon steels—low, medium, and high. They are classified according to the relative amount of carbon content.

LOW-CARBON STEEL

This is frequently known as "soft" or mild steel, used where ductility and softness are important and a high tensile strength is not required. This steel has a carbon content under 0.25%.

Low-carbon steels are used for such operations as spinning, cold bending, riveting, swagging, and many similar operations. They are used in their natural condition and are only slightly responsive to heat treatment. Note: These steels may be case hardened, a description of which will be given in a later unit.

Products such as screws, nails, nuts, bolts, washers, wire fence, machine parts, and forged parts can be made from this type of steel.

Low-carbon steels are available in sheets, squares, rounds, plates, and wire.

MEDIUM-CARBON STEEL

Medium-carbon steels, with a carbon content of 0.30% to 0.60% are less ductile, harder, and have a greater tensile strength than the low-carbon steels. They also have better machining qualities. These steels are quite responsive to heat treatment.

Some of their uses are: for shafts, connecting rods, spindles, gears, and other machine parts requiring medium-strength and wear-resisting surfaces.

HIGH-CARBON STEEL

This type of steel has a carbon content that ranges from 0.60% to 1.70%. Most high-carbon steels have less than 1.30% carbon content. They have a higher tensile strength and hardness than those in the lower carbon range. They respond readily to heat treatment. High-carbon steel is used for cutting tools, especially with alloys.

ALLOY STEEL

The requirements of an alloy steel, as defined by the American Iron and Steel Institute (AISI), are as follows: "Steel is considered an alloy steel when the maximum of range given for the content of alloying elements exceeds one or more of the following limits: manganese 1.65%; silicon 0.060%; copper 0.60%; or in which a definite maximum quantity of any of the following elements is specified or required within limits of the recognized field of constructional alloy steels: aluminum, boron, chromium up to 3.99%, cobalt, columbium, molybdenum, nickel, titanium, vanadium, zirconium, or any other element added to obtain a desired alloy effect."

Alloy steels can be classified as (1) constructional alloy steels, (2) alloy tool steels, and (3) special alloy steels.

Constructional alloy steels are used in machine parts such as levers, shafts, gears, bolts, pistons, springs, and connecting rods. They are also used for structural members in ships, automobile frames, bridges, and railroad construction.

In the standard constructional alloy steels, carbon, manganese, and silicon are elements which occur normally. The alloy content is usually lower than that of alloy tool steels. Total alloy content ranges from 0.25% to 6%.

Alloy tool steel may be defined as any steel that is used for the working parts of tools.

Tool steel is almost always hardened and contains some elements which, when alloyed with iron, will give it the ability to harden. Carbon is most important. In general, tool steels seldom contain less than 0.50% or more than 1.30% carbon. Other alloying elements are frequently used to supplement the carbon in order to give the steel the properties required for its particular use.

Alloy tool steels are used in the manufacture of cutting and forming tools, taps, dies, reamers, drills, milling cutters, punches, and similar items.

The alloy content of tool steel is higher than the constructional grades, ranging from 0.25% to more than 38%.

Alloying elements, which are added to the steel during the process of melting, are thoroughly mixed throughout the bath.

There are many variations in the composition of tool steels. These may be classified as follows: (1) water-hardening, (2) oil-hardening, (3) high-speed, (4) hot-working, (5) cold-working, and (6) special-purpose.

The analysis of various grades of tool steels can be secured from manufacturers' catalogs. The basic types of tool and die steel are listed according to the AISI numbering system in machinists' handbooks, which also give data regarding the basic properties and heat-treatment methods.

Special alloy steels are designed for specific purposes when high heat or corrosion-resistant steel is required. Also included in this group are the steels used on equipment where extreme toughness is required. Tractors, rock crushers, and power shovels use these steels.

Alloying Elements and Their Effects

Alloying elements are incorporated in steel for one or more of the following reasons:

1. To improve mechanical properties through the control of the factors which affect hardenability. Also to permit higher tempering temperature while, at the same time, maintaining high strength and improving ductility.

2. To improve mechanical properties at low or elevated temperatures.

3. To increase resistance to chemical changes.

4. To increase strength and toughness.

5. To increase resistance to high temperatures.

6. To secure greater hardness for wear resistance or cutting.

7. To provide high impact resistance.

8. To secure better machinability.

Of the above properties the first two are probably required the most often.

Microstructure of steel is generally considered as being composed of two phases: (1) ferrite, the magnetic alpha (low-temperature) modification of iron, with minimal carbon, possessing high ductility but poor tensile strength and (2) cementite, the iron-carbide phase, a hard, brittle constituent. The carbide phase in alloy steel is not generally pure iron carbide, but rather a complex combination of iron and alloy carbides.

The ferrite and carbide phases present are affected by the alloying elements present and improve the mechanical properties in the following manner: (1) by changing the state of dispersion of the carbide in the ferrite and (2) by changing the properties of the ferrite and carbide phases.

Alloying elements can be classified according to their specific effect on either the ferrite or carbide phase. Elements such as manganese, vanadium, and molybdenum will dissolve in the ferrite phase and form carbides, while elements such as copper, nickel, and silicon do not form carbides in steel, but usually dissolve and strengthen the carbide.

There are many elements used either singly or in combination in the production of alloy steels. Not all of them will be described in this unit; however, the most important ones with their influence on the properties of alloy steel will be described.

Carbon

The function of carbon is to make the steel harder and more wear resistant. The lowest carbon ratio to be found in plain carbon tool steel would be about

0.50% to 0.60%. As more carbon is added (until 0.80% is reached), tensile strength and response to heat treatment are increased.

Carbon content in greater amounts does not cause the steel to harden significantly more; however, it does increase the wear resistance of the steel.

Manganese

Manganese is normally present in all commercial steels. It is essential to steel production, not only in the melting process but also in rolling and other processing methods. In hot forging, the action of manganese on sulphur improves both the hot-working characteristics and seems to produce a better surface on the forging.

Manganese steels have a greater impact and yield strength than plain carbon steels. Manganese steels used in constructional parts have from 0.90% to 1.50% manganese present.

The addition of manganese has a tendency to lower the critical temperature point and hence the temperature to which the steel must be heated for hardening.

As the manganese content of the steel is increased, the steel undergoes a change from pearlitic (pearlite is a structural constituent in steel that has been cooled slowly from above its critical temperature range) to martensitic, to an austenitic steel. An important steel is one containing 1.5% manganese. This is an oil-hardening steel and is used in many types of tools and dies that are fully hardened.

Increasing the manganese content from 0.30% to 1.0%, changes the steel from water to oil hardening.

Martensitic (structure obtained when steel is treated to obtain maximum hardness) manganese steels are not used because of great hardness and brittleness.

Austenitic (a solid solution structure with gama iron acting as a solvent) manganese steels contain up to 15% manganese and 1% to 1.5% carbon and are sometimes called Hadfield steels. This steel in the cast condition is weak and brittle because it contains free carbides. However, heat treatment can give this steel great wearing power with much ductility, making it useful in steel crusher jaws.

Silicon

One of the most important applications of silicon is its use as a deoxidizer in molten steel. Silicon increases hardenability and strengthens low-alloy steel. Silicon is usually present in fully deoxidized constructional steels in amounts up to 0.35%. In larger amounts it increases resistance to scaling at elevated temperatures.

Silicon decreases the solubility of carbon in iron, so for this reason, a stronger type of steel can be obtained with less carbon than would otherwise be needed.

Usually a deep hardening element such as manganese, chromium, or molybdenum is added along with the silicon to give strength and toughness to tool steel.

Nickel

Nickel has very little effect on the hardenability of steel but adds to the toughness and wear resistance when used in conjunction with an alloy such as chromium. The usual alloying quantity is 3% to 3.70%.

Nickel steels are used for machine parts subject to repeated shock and stress. They are easily heat-treated because nickel lowers the critical cooling rate that is necessary to produce hardening by quenching.

Nickel-chrome steels have higher elastic ratios, greater hardenability, and higher impact and fatigue resistance than carbon steels. These steels are used for parts such as axles, crankshafts, spined shafts, and parts for earth-moving equipment.

Chromium

Chromium is essentially a hardening agent. Like manganese, chromium causes the hardness to penetrate deeper and, when present in sufficient quantity, will confer oil-hardening properties. It is frequently used with nickel as a toughening element to produce superior mechanical properties. Steels containing chromium are noted for wear-resistance.

Chromium is a strong carbide former, similar in this respect to molybdenum and tungsten. It raises the Ac_3 critical point, especially when large amounts of chromium are present.

The chromium content in constructional steels amounts to about 0.30% to 1.60% and the carbon content from 0.20% to 1.30%.

Low- and medium-chromium steels do not hold size as accurately as manganese steels, and those which are water-hardening will change size more than even plain carbon tool steel.

Chrome steels are used in machine parts, races for bearings, ball bearings, gears, shafts, coil springs, and flat springs.

Molybdenum

This element added to steel improves the heat-treatment properties. Molybdenum shares somewhat the properties of both chromium and tungsten. It increases the hardness penetration and inclines the steel toward oil-hardening.

Molybdenum as an alloying element in steel can form a solid solution with the ferrite phase and also, depending upon the molybdenum and carbon content, can form a complex carbide. Molybdenum slightly increases the electrical resistance of low-carbon steel, indicating that it is largely in solid solution in ferrite.

When used in conjunction with silicon, manganese, or chromium (between 0.25% and 1.50%), this element increases the strength and toughness of tool steel. Machine parts such as propeller shafts, transmission shafts, bolts, differential gears, coil springs, and leaf springs are made from this type of steel.

Tungsten

One of the principal alloying elements found in many alloy tool steels is tungsten. It must be added in fairly large amounts to be effective. If tungsten is added (about 4% with about 1.30% carbon), the steel acquires a high wear resistance and, upon being hardened, is very difficult to grind on an ordinary grinding wheel.

This element is used in cemented-carbide tools. By cementing grains of tungsten-carbide with cobalt, a very hard and wear-resistant material is obtained.

High-speed tool steel containing 18% tungsten and 4% chromium is the most important tool steel in use today.

Vanadium

Vanadium is one of the strong carbide-forming elements. It dissolves to some degree in ferrite, imparting strength and toughness. The complex carbides formed by vanadium additions are quite stable.

Vanadium has a more powerful effect upon the properties of steel than any other element. Comparatively small amounts are necessary. The best results are obtained from 0.1% to 0.2% of vanadium alloy. If more than 0.3% is used, the strength of the steel is decreased. The tensile strength of steel, with approximately 0.2% vanadium and 0.8% carbon, is not changed by the vanadium, but the elastic limit and ductility are increased.

Vanadium gives other important alloying effects, namely: increased hardenability; secondary hardening effect upon tempering; and increased hardness at elevated temperatures.

In alloy tool steels, vanadium is usually alloyed in combination with other elements such as chromium, tungsten, molybdenum, and cobalt.

Cobalt

Cobalt is used extensively in cutting tool materials. Included are high-speed steels, cast alloys, and cemented carbides. Cobalt improves the red-hardness and hot-hardness of cutting tool materials, which is important in machining the type of metals in use today. A high cobalt content serves to give materials the ability to retain their hardness at lower heat temperatures. Wear resistance is also increased. Cobalt is similar to nickel in nearly all its properties. High-speed steels have a cobalt content of 5% to 12%.

Other elements such as aluminum, copper, titanium, columbium, zirconium are also added to steel for definite purposes.

Unit 8. Classification and Identification of Steels

For many years the Society of Automotive Engineers (SAE) classified steel by a four-digit number. This system designates the first digit as the principal alloying element present. The second digit represents the amount of principal alloying element present. The last two digits indicate the points of carbon in the steel, where one point is 0.01%. This system has been known as the SAE numbering system.

Eventually the number of alloy steels increased to such an extent that the system could not give clear identification of a type. A new identification was developed through the joint efforts of the Society of Automotive Engineers and the American Iron and Steel Institute (AISI). The numbers used in both systems are now essentially the same; however, the AISI code uses a letter before the number to indicate the method by which a particular steel is produced:

B—Acid Bessemer carbon steel.

C—Basic open-hearth or basic electric furnace carbon steel.

E—Electric furnace alloy steel.

CB—Either Bessemer or open-hearth process at the option of the steel mill.

In the SAE and AISI systems, the first number frequently, but not always, indicates the basic type of steel as follows:

1—Carbon
2—Nickel
3—Nickel-chromium
4—Molybdenum
5—Chromium
6—Chromium-vanadium
7—Tungsten
8—Nickel-chromium-molybdenum
9—Silicon-manganese

The first two digits represent the alloy or alloys present. The last two digits of the four-numeral series are intended to indicate the approximate middle of the carbon range. In some cases five digits are given and the last three represent the carbon content as

in the high carbon-chromium bearing steels.

As an example, consider AISI-SAE E 51100. The steel is made in the electric furnace. It is of the chromium type as indicated by the digit 5, about 1% of the alloying element is chromium and, in this case, the last three digits mean that the steel has 1% (1.00) carbon.

Table 8–A, which is shown below, summarizes some of the series designations and also the types of steel which they designate. More complete listings can be obtained from the engineering materials handbooks of AISI-SAE steels.

Table 8–B on page 44 gives the classification of carbon and alloy steels.

Table 8-A. AISI and SAE Numerical Designations of Alloy Steels
(Elements are expressed in percents)

Series	Types			
10XX	Nonsulphurized carbon steels			
11XX	Resulphurized carbon steels (free machining)			
12XX	Rephosphorized and resulphurized carbon steels (free machining)			
13XX	*Mn 1.75			
23XX†	Ni 3.50			
25XX†	Ni 5.00			
31XX	Ni 1.25	Cr 0.65		
33XX	Ni 3.50	Cr 1.55		
40XX	Mo 0.20 or 0.25			
41XX	Cr 0.50 or 0.95	Mo 0.12 or 0.20		
43XX	Ni 1.80	Cr 0.50 or 0.80	Mo 0.25	
44XX	Mo 0.40			
45XX	Mo 0.52			
46XX	Ni 1.80	Mo 0.25		
47XX	Ni 1.05	Cr 0.45	Mo 0.20 or 0.35	
48XX	Ni 3.50	Mo 0.25		
50XX	Cr 0.25, 0.40 or 0.50			
50XXX	C 1.00	Cr 0.50		
51XX	Cr 0.80, 0.90, 0.95 or 1.00			
51XXX	C 1.00	Cr 1.05		
52XXX	Cr 1.00	Cr 1.45		
61XX	Cr 0.60, 0.80 or 0.95			
	V 0.12, 0.10 min., or 0.15			
81XX	Ni 0.30	Cr 0.40	Mo 0.12	
86XX	Ni 0.55	Cr 0.50	Mo 0.20	
87XX	Ni 0.55	Cr 0.05	Mo 0.25	
88XX	Ni 0.55	Cr 0.50	Mo 0.35	
92XX	Mn 0.85	Si 2.00	Cr 0 or 0.35	
93XX	Ni 3.25	Cr 1.20	Mo 0.12	
94XX	Ni 0.45	Cr 0.40	Mo 0.12	
98XX	Ni 1.00	Cr 0.80	Mo 0.25	

Consult current AISI and SAE publications for latest revisions.

† Nonstandard steel
* Abbreviations

C—Carbon	Mo—Molybdenum	V—Vanadium
Cr—Chromium	Ni—Nickel	
Mn—Manganese	Si—Silicon	

Table 8-B. Classification of Carbon and Alloy Steels

Type of steel	AISI No. (1942)	SAE No. (1942)	Characteristics	Common Uses
	C 1010	1010	Low tensile strength	Welding steel, nails
	C 1020	1020	Very tough	Pipe, structural steel, sheet steel
	C 1030	1030	Heat treats well	Shafting, gears
	C 1040	1040	Average heat treating	Crankshafts, bolts, connecting rods
	C 1045	1045	Careful quenching required of thin sections	Screw drivers, auger bits
Carbon	C 1060	1060	Soft tool steel	Lock washers, valve springs, upholstery springs
	C 1070	1070	Very tough and hard	Wrenches, dies, knives, anvils
	C 1080	1080	Holds keen edges	Chisels, hammers, shear blades
	C 1085	1085	Tool steel—hard	Taps, dies, music wire, auto bumpers, knives
	C 1090	1090	Tool steel—very hard	Milling cutters, springs, taps, hacksaw blades
	B 1112	1112	Good machining	Screw machine parts, bolts, screws
	C 1115	1115	Strong and tough	Screw machine stock
	C 1117	X 1314	Case hardens well	Surface hardening products
	C 1132	X 1330	Good machinability	Used where hardness is desired
Manganese	A 1330	1330	Hard wear and shock characteristics	Safes, curved rails
Nickel	A 2317		Shock resisting	Steel rails, armor plate, wire cables
Nickel-chromium	A 3115	3115	Very hard and strong	Gears, springs, axles, armor plate
Molybdenum	A 4130	4130	Withstands high heat and hard blows	Ball and roller bearings, high grade machine and auto parts
Chromium	A 5120	5120	Hard and tough	Safes, cutting tools, bearing rollers
Chromium-vanadium	E 6150		Resists corrosion	Axles, frames, tools, chisels
Stainless-chromium	414	51310	Can be heat treated	Sinks, cooking utensils

Unit 9. Nonferrous Metals

Nonferrous metals are seldom found in the pure state, but since they must be separated from the gangue (foreign materials) before the ore can be reduced, a process known as ore dressing is performed. Metals and metal compounds, being heavier than the gangue, settle to the bottom if such a mixture has been agitated in water. This process is similar to the method used by the early gold miners panning gold. However, refinements have been developed to speed up the accumulation of metal compounds by using this principle.

FURNACES FOR NONFERROUS MELTING

The reverberatory furnace is the type most often used in the smelting of nonferrous metals. 9–1. This furnace is constructed of refractory brick with a steel

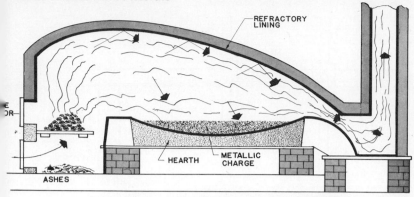

9–1. Reverberatory furnace for smelting copper.

structure on the outside. The charge is placed in the furnace and heated indirectly by the flame. Slag inducers or fluxes are added to the charge to reduce oxidation.

The fuel may be gas, oil, or powdered coal. This furnace has a capacity of 100 to 1,000 tons per day.

ALUMINUM

Aluminum is the most abundant metallic element found in the earth's crust. Never occurring in the native state, its compounds are principally silicates and oxides. Thus far only bauxite has proved economical as a commercial source of the metal. Because of the locations in which bauxite is found, both open-pit and underground methods are used in mining it.

The Bayer process, named for the German chemist Karl Josef Bayer, is the most widely used.

First the bauxite, as it comes from the mines, is broken into small pieces, washed, screened, and dried. It is then shipped to a refining plant where it is reduced to aluminum oxide or alumina.

In the Bayer process, the finely ground bauxite is charged into a digester where it is treated with hot sodium hydroxide solution, under pressure, at a temperature well above the boiling point. The caustic soda reacts on the bauxite to form sodium aluminate, which remains in solution in the liquid. Not being dissolved, the oxides of titanium, iron, silicon, and other impurities settle out and are removed in large filter presses. The filtrate is pumped into precipitating tanks.

In the precipitating tanks, fine crystals of aluminum hydroxide from a previous cycle are added to the bath. These crystals, continuously circulated through the solution, grow in size as the aluminum hydroxide separates. The aluminum hydroxide is then removed to tanks and any caustic remaining is washed out. Next, it is heated in kilns to more than 1000°F. to drive off all chemically combined water. This changes the alumina to a crystalline form.

Approximately 2 pounds of alumina are required to make 1 pound of aluminum.

Aluminum works are built near an ample source of electrical power. In each reduction works, steel pots lined with carbon are connected electrically to form a pot line. These pots contain carbon blocks which serve as anodes, while the carbon linings act as cathodes. 9–2. Synthetic cryolite and alumina are introduced into pots. An electric current is passed through the anode to the cathode, generating a heat of around 1800°F. which melts the cryolite and forms a cryolite bath. The alumina is added and dissolved in the bath. The molten aluminum is deposited on the carbon bottom of the pot. 9–3. About every two days it is tapped into a large mixing ladle from which it is cast into pigs or ingots. (Figs. 9–2 and 9–3 shown on page 46.)

The pure metal as it comes from the cells contains some dross and electrolyte. These impurities are removed by remelting the aluminum and casting again into ingots. Alloys are often added at this time.

In its pure state aluminum is lightweight, cuts very easily, yet it is relatively strong and has many applications. Aluminum is usually alloyed with copper, manganese, or nickel.

Aluminum and its alloys are abrasive to all forms of cutting tools and have a tendency to form built-up edges on the tools. The harder grades of straight tungsten carbide tools are recommended for cutting aluminum. Aluminum alloys containing over 10% silicon are the most difficult to machine. Machining this type of aluminum requires tools with greater rake angles, in combination with reduced speeds.

There are various designations for aluminum. The Aluminum Association has established symbols which can be found by

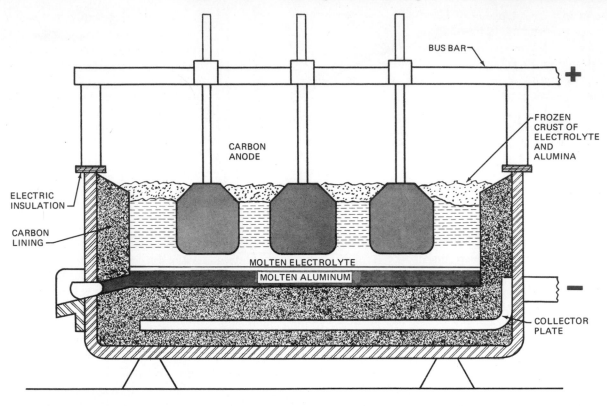

BUS BAR

+

FROZEN CRUST OF ELECTROLYTE AND ALUMINA

CARBON ANODE

ELECTRIC INSULATION

CARBON LINING

MOLTEN ELECTROLYTE

MOLTEN ALUMINUM

−

COLLECTOR PLATE

9–2. Purified aluminum oxide dissolved in molten cryolite is electrolyzed. Metallic aluminum is deposited on the carbon lining which forms the cathode. The heat produced is sufficient to keep the aluminum in a melted condition.

9–3. Aluminum is reduced from alumina (aluminum oxide) in electrolytic cells, or pots, lining each side of the central aisle.

Kaiser Aluminum and Chemical Corp.

referring to *Machinery Handbook,* the Aluminum Company of America, Reynolds Metals Company, or an SAE Handbook.

Aluminum can be turned, forged, cast, spun, welded, and extruded. It can also be machined on all types of conventional machine tools.

Aluminum has a wide range of applications. It is widely used in the aircraft industry as well as in the space programs. It is used as structural material for office buildings. Windows, doors, siding for homes, furniture, boats, home appliances, and marine applications are among its other uses. In many instances it is competitive with steel.

MAGNESIUM

Within the past 25 years, magnesium has gained an important commercial position among metals. Its most striking characteristic is its lightness (specific gravity 1.74), the weight of a given volume being only 23% that of iron and 64% that of aluminum. It has excellent machinability characteristics. However, the strength of pure magnesium is relatively low. For this reason it is almost always used in the alloyed form for fabricated parts and structural applications. The common alloys are aluminum, zinc, and manganese.

The selection of an alloy for a particular application depends upon the form in which the metal is used—in sheet or extrusions— the method to be used in its fabrication, and the characteristics and properties required in the final product.

Most of the magnesium in this country is extracted from seawa-

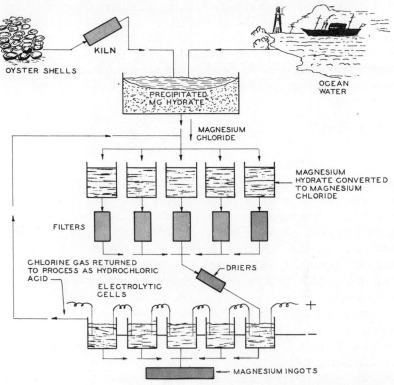

Based on sketch by Dow Chemical Co.

9–4. Extracting magnesium from ocean water.

ter. 9-4. The illustration shows the important steps. In this process seawater consisting of approximately 1,300 parts per million of magnesium is treated with milk of lime. The lime is produced from oyster shells which have been treated in a kiln at 2400° F. Magnesium hydrate is formed by the reaction between the seawater and oyster shells. The magnesium hydrate settles to the bottom of a tank, forming about 12% magnesium hydrate. The precipitated magnesium hydrate is filtered to provide a more concentrated hydrate, which is converted to magnesium chloride by the addition of hydrochloric acid. The water is removed from this solution by evaporation. By means of special drying and filtration, magnesium chloride of 68% concentration is produced.

After the magnesium chloride has been converted to a granular form, it is transferred to electrolytic cells which hold about 25,000 gallons and operate at 1,300° F. The pots themselves are the cathodes and the anodes are graphite electrodes. Decomposition of the magnesium chloride is created by a direct current of 60,000 amperes. The magnesium metal floats to the top of the liquid. Approximately 1,200 pounds of magnesium is produced per day in each pot. The magnesium is then cast into ingots which weigh from 18 to 19 pounds each.

Magnesium alloys have a low modulus (measure) of elasticity.

47

Shaping the metal, such as drawing or bending, must be done at a temperature of 400° to 600° F.

Magnesium alloys may be fabricated by welding if the weld metal and filler are protected by an inert gas.

COPPER-BASE ALLOYS

Copper is seldom employed industrially in its pure state except for electrical conductors and similar uses. It has more strength and value commercially when alloyed with other elements, as in brass and bronze. Additions of lead, tin, aluminum, and manganese are made to improve its properties.

Brass is essentially an alloy of copper and zinc. Zinc percentages range from 10% to 40%. By increasing the percentage of zinc, hardness, strength, and ductility of the alloy are improved. Beyond 40% the zinc has a tendency to volatilize (evaporate) in melting. The addition of a small percentage of lead improves machinability of the alloy. Much of brass is used in industrial applications because of its strength, appearance, ductility, and resistance to corrosion.

There are many names for brasses. Among these are red brass, cartridge brass, yellow brass, and Muntz metal.

Bronze has (in addition to copper) tin, manganese, and sometimes several other elements, depending upon its uses. By adding tin up to 20%, the tensile strength is increased but beyond this point the metal tends to become brittle. Because tin bronzes are primarily used in engineering applications, where machinability is an important factor, they frequently contain some lead. Usually the quantity is very small, not exceeding 0.05%. Little or no improvement in machinability may be expected beyond 2% lead.

Bronze is used in bearings because of the toughness, wear and corrosion resistance, and strength of the metal.

The making and working of bronze has been known since 5000 B.C. and has had a tremendous effect upon the growth and advancement of civilization. There is no metal in all history that shows a more continuous influence on cultural advancement —especially up to the late 19th century—or a wider variety of artistic and practical use from architectural decoration to statuary, weapons, vessels, utensils, and other products. Table 9 analyzes commercial copper-base alloys.

ZINC-BASE ALLOYS

These alloys are widely used by the die casting industry. Parts for electrical appliances, hardware, automobile parts, typewriter parts, housings for small engines, turbine parts, and hundreds of other items are being made from zinc-base alloys. They can be cast readily with a good finish. The material is low in cost and has considerable strength. Aluminum, copper, and magnesium are the elements usually alloyed with zinc. Copper increases the tensile strength, ductility, and hardness of the metal. The tensile strength for zinc alloys varies from 25,000 to 47,000 psi depending upon the alloying element used.

NICKEL-BASE ALLOYS

The nickel content of most nickel-base alloys ranges from 57% to 80%, depending upon the particular alloy and the purpose for which the metal is to be used.

Nickel is a metal almost as bright as silver. Its properties are malleability and ductility. Nickel resists corrosion and for this reason is sometimes used as a protective coating for other metals.

There are many nickel alloys. Nickel is used to a great extent with chromium and molybdenum for parts in automobiles, aircraft, chemical process equipment, and many other applications.

Monel is an alloy of nickel and copper with small amounts of silicon, manganese, and iron. It is made directly from copper-nickel ores.

Copper, aluminum, iron, silicon, and tungsten are commonly used in nickel-base alloys.

TIN-BASE ALLOYS

Tin-base alloys are used with a large number of other metals. Gunmetals and bronzes are alloys of tin and copper.

Tin may be alloyed with other elements such as zinc, antimony, lead, silver, and iron. Tin-base alloys include solders of various types. Tin babbit is used in the construction of bearings containing about 80% to 90% tin and the balance lead and copper. Britannia metal is a tin-base alloy containing about 92% tin and 8% antimony and copper.

Table 9. Copper-Zinc-Tin Casting Alloys*

Name	Cu	Sn	Zn	Pb	Ni	Si	Mn	Al	Fe	Use
Red brass	90		10							Hardware
Yellow brass	70		30							Cartridges
Leaded red brass	85	5	5	5						Machinery castings
Leaded yellow brass	72	1	24	3						Plumbing fixtures
Tin bronze	88	8	4							Bearings, ship hardware
Bell metal	80	20								Bells
Bearing bronze	83	7	3	7						Machine bearings
Silicon bronze	95					4	1			Machinery castings
Manganese bronze	62	1.5	31	1			1.5	1.5	1.5	High-strength parts
Aluminum bronze	78				5		3	10	4	Corrosion-resisting parts
Nickel silver	65	4	6	5	20					Dairy and laundry equipment

* *Cast Metals Handbook*, 3rd edition, American Foundrymen's Association.

Cu—Copper	Pb—Lead	Mn—Manganese
Sn—Tin	Ni—Nickel	Al—Aluminum
Zn—Zinc	Si—Silicon	Fe—Iron

CHECK YOUR KNOWLEDGE

1. Why are ferrous and nonferrous metals important in the present era?

2. Explain the difference between metals and nonmetals.

3. What is an element?

4. Explain the term "alloy."

5. How may alloys be classified?

6. Do nonferrous alloys ever contain iron? Explain.

7. What are homogeneous mixtures?

8. Explain the difference between a compound and a mixture?

9. What is ferrite?

10. Why are metals mixed with other substances?

11. What is a solid solution?

12. Define solute and solvent.

13. What elements are found in commercially pure iron?

14. What is an equilibrium diagram?

15. What are the constituents of Monel metal?

16. Name two important divisions in the study of metallurgy.

17. Metals are divided into what two large groups?

18. Explain the following terms: hardness, brittleness, plasticity, ductility, toughness, and malleability.

19. Heat treatment causes change in the hardness of steel. Explain.

20. What types of metals can be classified as ductile?

21. How is the ductility of a metal measured?

22. What is the difference between yield strength and tensile strength of a metal?

23. What is the basic source of iron and steel?

24. Explain the open-hearth method of making steel.

25. What purpose is served when a stream of oxygen is blown over steel in the open-hearth process?

26. When does refining and purification take place?

27. Describe the electric furnace process of producing steel.

28. Describe the electric furnace, including shape and size.

29. What types of steel are produced by the electric furnace process?

30. What are the results of significant increases of carbon content in plain carbon steel?

31. What are constructional steels?

32. How may the analysis of the various grades of tool steels be obtained?

33. Chromium and nickel are sometimes used together in steel. For what purpose?

34. What effect does molybdenum have upon steel?

35. Explain the SAE and AISI code number systems used to classify steel.

36. In what way is the AISI code number system different from the SAE system?

37. What type of furnace is used for smelting nonferrous metals?

38. Why is it necessary to build aluminum plants near the source of large quantities of electrical power?

39. What is a pot line?

40. What is magnesium?

41. What are the machinability characteristics of magnesium?

42. Describe the most common method of producing magnesium.

43. Why is a great deal of brass used in industrial applications?

44. What is bronze?

45. What effect has bronze had upon the development and growth of civilization?

46. What is the range of tensile strength for zinc-base alloys?

47. How are zinc-base alloys usually cast?

48. What are the principal characteristics of nickel-base alloys?

REFERENCES

American Foundrymens Association, *Cast Metals Handbook*, 6th ed., 1961.

American Society for Metals, Metals Park, Ohio, *Metals Handbook,* 8th ed., 1961.

"Nonferrous Metals Book Issue," *Machine Design*, Cleveland, Penton Publishing Co., September 19, 1963.

Steel Founder's Society of America, *Steel Castings Handbook,* 3rd ed., 1960.

United States Steel Corporation, *The Making, Shaping, and Treating of Steel*, 8th ed., 1964.

In this electric furnace, the proper proportions of copper, zinc, and nickel are melted together. The molten metal is then poured into molds where it hardens gradually, forming bars of nickel silver.

International Silver Co.

Section Three

Metallurgy and Heat

Treatment of Steel

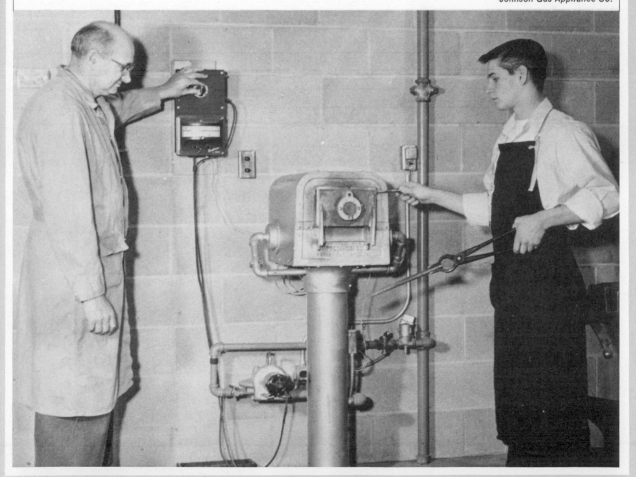

Unit 10.

Introduction to Heat Treatment

The fact that steel has the property of hardening when suddenly cooled from a heated condition has been known for many centuries. The origin of steel hardening cannot be traced exactly, but the Greek poet, Homer, refers to it and the Roman, Pliny the Younger, describes a method which compares in its main points to the fundamentals used in the hardening process of steel today. During the 15th and 16th centuries, the practice of hardening metal became such an art that there developed a great deal of superstition and secrecy among existing craftsmen. Process secrets were handed down from father to son.

Although craftsmen knew how to harden steel, they did not know what steel was or why it hardened. Despite the age-long acquaintance with metals, comparatively little was known about their real nature and the real reasons for their varied behaviors. During the last century, men have endeavored to discover the reasons for metallic behavior and have evolved the science of metallurgy.

Heat treatment, which is an aspect of physical metallurgy, changes the structures of metals by the application of heat.

10–2. Small electric heat treating furnace.

Thermolyne Corp.

FURNACES AND TEMPERATURE CONTROL

Special furnaces are used to heat metal parts during the heat-treatment processes. The source of heat may be oil, gas, or electricity. In order to do a satisfactory job, automatic indicating and control devices maintain a temperature very close to the one selected. 10–1.

The electric furnace may be used for a variety of heat-treating operations. 10–2. It can be equipped with indicators and controls which regulate the temperature automatically in the range of 300° to 2300° F. 10–3.

Furnaces are also made in two-unit combinations, a hardening furnace and a drawing or tempering furnace. 10–4. They are heated with gas and are equipped with an air blower which supports combustion. The furnace on the bottom in the illustration is used for hardening carbon and high-speed steels with a temperature

10–1. Gas-fired, heat-treatment furnace with temperature-indicating controls.

McEnglevan Heat Treating and Mfg. Co.

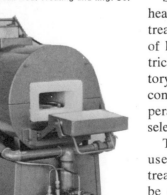

10–3. Temperature-indicating control equipment. Overshoot is minimized and temperature held very closely.

Thermolyne Corp.

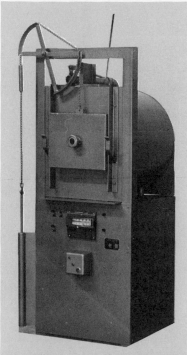

McEnglevan Heat Treating and Mfg. Co.

10–4. Hardening and tempering furnaces.

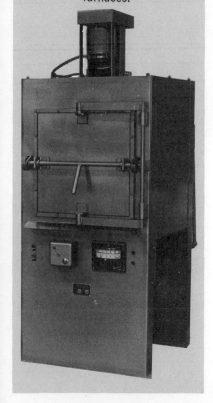

A. F. Holden Co.

10–5. A 3-in-1 salt bath furnace for toolroom use.

range of 1300° to 2350° F. The furnace on the top may be used for tempering or drawing operations, with a temperature range from 400° to 1150° F. Temperature control units are furnished with these units.

A pot-type liquid hardening furnace which is used for salt, lead, and cyanide baths is available for cyaniding operations. 10–5. A unit which controls the liquid bath is usually located near the furnace. Parts which are cyanided are heated in this type furnace in a bath of molten cyanide-carbonate-chloride salts. The parts are then quenched in brine, water, or mineral oil.

Temperature-Indicating and Control Equipment

Modern heat-treating methods for industry require accurate measurement and temperature control to obtain satisfactory results. The days of estimation of temperature by color have long since been discarded. The thermocouple operates on the principle that whenever two wires of dissimilar metals are joined together at one end and heated, an electromotive force is generated at the welded end. The other end is connected to an electrical *pyrometer*. 10–6. There are many types of excellent pyrometers

10–6. A pyrometer is used to accurately tell the temperature inside the furnace. The thermocouple is located in the back, with leads returning to the furnace.

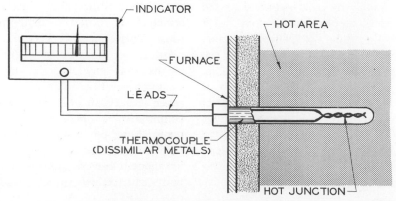

INDICATOR

HOT AREA

FURNACE

LEADS

THERMOCOUPLE (DISSIMILAR METALS)

HOT JUNCTION

available. Some indicate simply the temperature of the furnace by the position of the needle on the dial and are known as indicating pyrometers. 10–7. Other types permanently record the temperature on a graph and are called recording pyrometers. When the hot junction of the thermocouple is heated, a small amount of electrical energy (emf) is developed. The voltage is measured in millivolts. The scale reading on the millivoltmeter usually indicates the temperature in degrees.

The thermocouple is enclosed in a tube made of refractory material to prevent oxidation or damage.

Johnson Gas Appliance Co.

10–7. Temperature indicator and thermocouple used in gas heat-treatment furnace. Also shown is control equipment for furnace.

Unit 11. Grain Structure of Steel

Although metals may exist in various forms (liquid, vapor, or solid), they are normally used in the solid form, and have internal crystalline structure. The atoms align themselves in a geometric pattern upon solidification. The crystals or grain—formed as the metal cools and changes to a solid state—is called freezing. Upon fracture of the metal, the granular structure is noticeable.

The graphic representation of the systematic arrangement of atoms is called a *space lattice*. An X-ray analysis of a steel can be made and type of lattice can be determined, as well as the distance between the atoms.

Scientists have found that the atoms in metals and other crystalline materials have a definite space lattice arrangement. Each type of metal has its own characteristic arrangement of atoms in its space lattice. Iron may have more than one space lattice structure at different temperatures. This change is known as *allotropic* or polymorphic, which means that any material may exist in several crystal forms. The space lattice unit or cell of most common metals may be of four types: (1) body-centered cubic, (2) face-centered cubic, (3) hexagonal close-packed, and (4) body-centered tetragonal. 11–1.

1. The body-centered cubic lattice consists of nine atoms, one at each of the corners of a cube and one at the center. The atoms do not touch each other. Ferrite, also known as alpha iron —as well as molybdenum, vanadium, tungsten, chromium, and columbium—have this lattice structure at room temperature.

2. It will be noticed in the face-centered cubic lattice that the atoms are located at the four corners of the cube, with an atom in the center of each face. Iron (at the gamma or austenite stage), silver, copper, lead, nickel, and aluminum all have this lattice structure at elevated temperatures.

Austenite forms at an elevated temperature, causing carbon in the steel to decompose from its combined state as cementite or iron carbide. The free carbon then dissolves into the solid and forms a solid solution (a solid

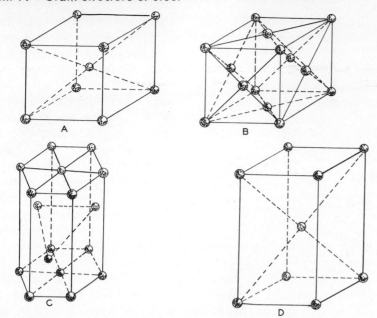

11–1. The most common crystal patterns. (A) body-centered cubic unit arrangement of atoms, (B) face-centered cubic unit arrangement of atoms, (C) hexagonal close-packed unit arrangement, and (D) body-centered tetragonal arrangement.

standing. The form and amount of carbon is important in the heat-treatment process, and the form and distribution of the carbon content is dependent upon changes taking place in the lattice structure at hardening temperatures.

ALLOTROPY

As said, the structural changes produced by thermal treatments are due to a property called allotropy, which indicates the capacity of a metal to change structure internally without external change in shape and without loss of chemical identity. That is, when the lattice changes from one form to another it is in allotropic change.

Gamma iron has its atoms arranged in the face-centered cubic lattice. It is a nonmagnetic crystal form of lron. Gamma iron dissolves carbon. Its grain size depends upon time, temperature, and working.

Alpha iron has a body-centered cubic lattice and is magnetic. If heated to approximately 2535° F., gamma iron changes to a body-centered cubic form (*delta stage*) with an atomic arrangement similar to alpha iron.

When iron is heated to a temperature of 2800° F., it becomes a liquid. While in this state, the atoms seem to gain fluidity and lose any specific lattice arrangement. NOTE: If pure iron is allowed to cool from molten state, the changes are in reverse order.

Certain discontinuous changes in the physical properties of pure iron take place at a temperature of 1414° F. Iron is very magnetic at a temperature a little below this range; however, at higher

which is in effect a solution of two or more materials) of uniformly dispersed carbon in iron. Body-centered (alpha) form of iron (ferrite) will dissolve a maximum of approximately 0.05% carbon, while the above mentioned type will dissolve a maximum of 2.00% carbon.

3. The hexagonal, close-packed lattice has an atom at each of the six corners of the two end faces, one at each center of the end faces, and three spaced equally at the sides. Cadmium, beryllium, magnesium, zinc, and cobalt have this type of lattice arrangement.

Because a lattice arrangement of this type has a close-packed structure, the metals lack ductility and increase in brittleness when subjected to bending operations.

4. The body-centered tetragonal lattice arrangement has atoms

arranged similar to the body-centered cubic lattice, except that the axis is elongated.

Austenite is a solid solution with gamma iron. When steel is heated to the hardening temperature, the grain structure transforms to austenite, which has a face-centered cubic lattice arrangement. Upon quenching at hardening temperature and cooling rapidly below 400° F., a transformation forms another grain structure called *martensite*. Martensite space lattice arrangement is made up of body-centered tetragonal units. Martensite is the hardest and also the most brittle form of steel.

The *cubic forms* of atomic space lattice arrangement are the most important. But in heat-treatment processes of iron and steel a knowledge of all forms is important and will aid in under-

temperatures it loses its magnetic properties.

Transformation temperatures may be defined as temperatures at which changes in phase or allotropic changes take place. The changes from one form of iron to another are not often instantaneous at a specific temperature. Changes take place at a temperature within the upper transformation and the lower transformation ranges.

At the upper transformation range, when iron or steel is heated, a change from one lattice arrangement to another is rather rapid. During the change in form there is a rearrangement of the atoms, and a certain amount of time is necessary for the change to take place. During the heat-treatment process the steel is allowed to "soak" at a predetermined temperature for a period of time. The time element is generally determined by the thickness of the part, allowing for complete transformation.

Heat-treatment operations have a time-temperature cycle which is important to successful results: (1) when the metal is heated to a predetermined temperature, the heating rate is important; (2) the temperature is then held for a given period to permit its thickest section to attain uniform temperature and provide time for internal structural changes to take place; and (3) the cooling cycle.

Upon heating steel to the proper hardening temperature, with the change in the atomic lattice arrangement from the body-centered cubic type to the face-centered cubic type, the grain structure will be very fine at the proper hardening temperature. A fine grain structure is important to create a hard, tough steel.

The grain structure increases in coarseness at temperatures of about 50° to 100° F. above the upper transformation temperature.

GRAIN FORMATION

A grain is a crystal with almost any shape, but has an internal atomic structure based upon the space lattice with which it was born.

The atoms in metal have a tendency to arrange themselves geometrically upon solidification of the metal. This results in branchlike divisions called *dendrites.* 11–2.

Metals cool more rapidly at the outside areas and this is where the individual grains start to form. The initial lattice formations in the solidifying metal form the nuclei for crystals which have a tendency to grow in an orderly form. As the metal cools at a more rapid rate, the grains form rapidly and solidification (freezing) takes place. Numerous such crystals form. The crystals grow by extending in three directions; but when one crystal comes in contact with another, growth of both crystals ceases. The enlarged crystals are irregular by nature, forming part of a grain boundary as crystallization of the metal is completed.

The cooling rate from the liquid to the solid state controls the size of the grains formed. A slow cooling rate produces grains of larger size and fewer in number. With a rapid cooling of the metal, the grain size is smaller and grains are more numerous.

You can see why the temperature of metals must be carefully

11–2. Growth of crystalline grains. Dendrites are shown in figures A, B, and C. Grain boundary is shown in figure D.

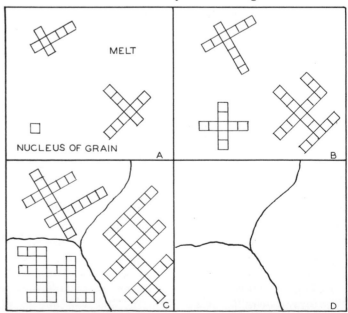

MELT

NUCLEUS OF GRAIN

regulated to control the grain size and condition of metal.

Grain Size

The size of grains in steel depends upon a number of factors, the principal one being the furnace treatment it has received.

Coarse-grained steels are not as tough and have a greater tendency towards distortion than those having a fine grain, although offering better machinability and greater depth hardening qualities. Fine-grained steels are tougher and more ductile and do not distort or crack during heat treatment.

One method of estimating the grain size involves the use of a grain-size comparator in the form of a chart. 11–3.

Grain sizes are designated by a standard number system as shown in Table 11.

Table 11. Grain Size Chart		
ASTM Grain Size	Grains per Square Inch	
Mean		
1	1	1 to 1½
2	2	1½ to 3
3	4	3 to 6
4	8	6 to 12
5	16	12 to 24
6	32	24 to 48
7	64	48 to 96
8	128	96 and over

By polishing the steel and etching with acid, the grain size can be exposed. The fracture method may also be used. Then compare the grain size from a photomicrograph with the specimen on the chart. A comparison can also be made on a metallograph. 11–4. The metallograph projects grain sizes on a screen at a magnification of 100X. The magnified grain is then compared with the grain sizes on the chart.

Fracture Test

A test specimen of fractured high carbon steel is usually turned to a small diameter before heating to the required temperature. The specimen is water or brine quenched after it has been held at a specified temperature for the required period of time. It is then fractured transversely. The surface of the fracture is visually compared with the Shepherd fracture standards, which consist of ten grain sizes numbered from one to ten. Number one is the coarsest and number ten the finest, as will be noted in the illustration. 11–5 (Page 58).

11–3. ASTM grain-size chart-twined grains (flat etch) ASTM designation E112, the average grain size of steel after standard heat treatment. Grain size is measured at 100 magnifications.

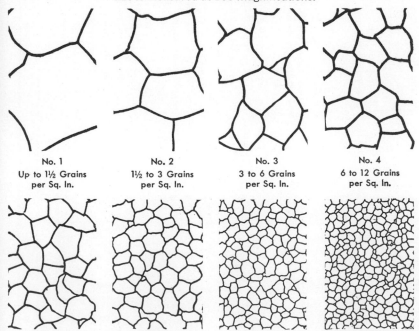

No. 1
Up to 1½ Grains
per Sq. In.

No. 2
1½ to 3 Grains
per Sq. In.

No. 3
3 to 6 Grains
per Sq. In.

No. 4
6 to 12 Grains
per Sq. In.

No. 5
12 to 24 Grains
per Sq. In.

No. 6
24 to 48 Grains
per Sq. In.

No. 7
48 to 96 Grains
per Sq. In.

No. 8
96 Grains and More
per Sq. In.

11–4. Balphot metallograph.

Bausch and Lomb, Inc.

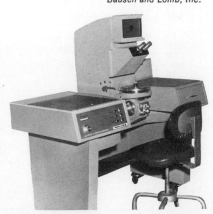

Shepherd Grain Size Fracture Standards

Stereoscope photographs by George K. Manning

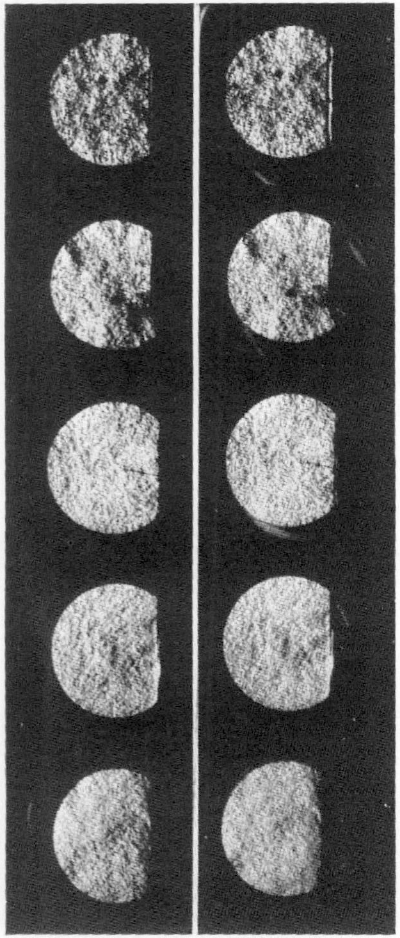

Grain Size 6 to 10

Grain Size

6

7

8

9

10

IN THE AUGUST 1941 issue of METAL PROGRESS the author described a method for vertical illumination of metallurgical macro specimens. The results are clearly superior to those attainable when using oblique light rays, since side shadows are avoided, and THE EDITOR suggested that duplicate photographs made in this manner, merely shifting the camera 2½ in. sideways between exposures, would enable the observer to capture the third dimension.

A useful set of such photographs would be of grain size fracture standards. B. F. SHEPHERD, who is responsible for the standards most used in the United States, kindly permitted them to be published and International Harvester Co. loaned a set for photography.

A third dimensional or stereoscopic effect may be obtained from the double exposures by placing a light piece of cardboard, 6 to 10 in. square, so that one edge rests on the center line between the prints and the other edge touches the observer's nose. (This cardboard may be from 6 to 10 in. square depending on the observer's eyes, and can readily be determined by trial.) First, without any attention to focus, adjust the eyes so that there appears to be only one print rather than two. When this is achieved the details of the fracture will be blurred. Thereupon the eyes may be focused, and the prints will appear to stand up sharply from the dark background and to be rough and jagged, as the fractures actually are. The lighting should be adjusted so that its intensity on each set is approximately the same. Several seconds may be required to achieve superposition the first time, but thereafter the necessary ocular manipulations are more easily performed.

If desired, the prints may be mounted on cardboard and viewed with a stereoscope. In this case the prints should be separated by the distance which is appropriate for the particular instrument to be used.

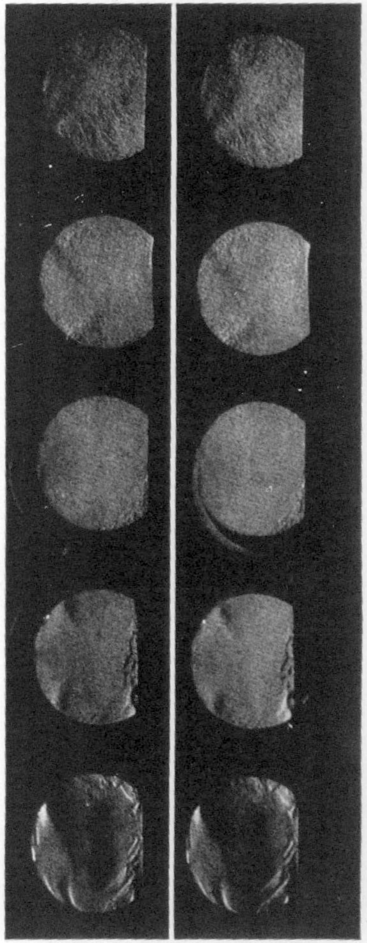

Fig. 11-15.

Grain Size

1

2

3

4

5

Grain Size 1 to 5

Several limitations have to be taken into consideration when making comparisons: (1) length of time the specimen is heated, to determine accurately grain size present; (2) mixed grain sizes, and (3) specimens too large to be through-hardened will give wrong interpretations.

Controlling Grain Size

Steels with grain sizes ranging from 1 to 5 are classed as coarse-grained steels. Those grain sizes ranging from 5 to 8 are classed as fine-grained.

The steelmaker can control the inherent grain size of a steel. He can also control, within certain limits, the grain size that the steel will develop when it is heated above the critical temperature. However, the actual grain size of a given type of steel may vary with heat treatment, temperature, certain processing, such as hot and cold working, and machining.

Unit 12. Heat Treatment of Steel

Heat treatment of steel can be defined as the operation of heating and cooling steel in its solid state at a predetermined rate to alter its physical properties.

Steel may be hardened or softened depending upon the requirements of a particular application. It can be made to resist wear, abrasion, and penetration when properly heat-treated. Other advantages of the heat-treating processes are: (1) to refine grain structure, (2) to relieve internal stresses, and (3) to impart strength and toughness. The steel can be heat-treated in such a manner that a hard surface can be obtained with a ductile interior.

EFFECTS OF CARBON

It was learned long ago that the influence of thermal treatment increases with the carbon content of steel. It is important to know how the amount and form of carbon in the steel affects its hardness.

Steel is an alloy of iron, carbon, and other elements, but the maximum degree of hardness obtained in steel is determined largely by the amount of carbon present. The hardening effect of carbon without the addition of other alloys is principally apparent on the surface. Adding certain alloys to carbon steel has a tendency to retard the critical transformation rate and makes such steel deeper hardening.

As the carbon content is increased up to 0.60%, the maximum hardness obtainable is approached. If the carbon is increased above this percentage, the hardness can be increased only slightly. This is explained by the fact that steels above the eutectoid point (where a pearlitic structure is formed from austenite during slow cooling through its critical temperature) are made up entirely of cementite and pearlite in the annealed state. 12–1.

The properties of very low-carbon steel are those of nearly pure iron. The upper limit of carbon in steel has been determined to be about 1.40%. Beyond this percentage of carbon

12–1. Microscopic structure lamellar or coarse pearlite. Dark streaks are cementite (iron carbide) and light areas are nearly pure iron (ferrite) 1,000X.

U.S. Steel Corp.

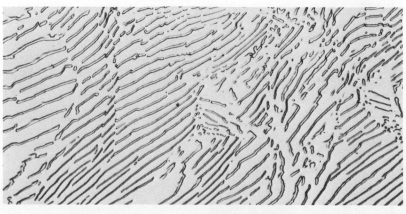

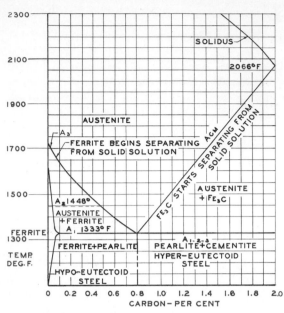

12–4. Partial iron carbide phase diagram.

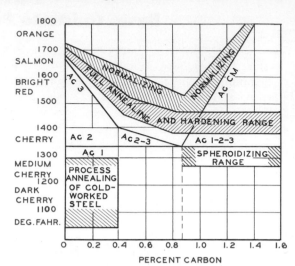

12–5. Critical temperature diagram. The hardening-normalizing-annealing ranges are shown.

there is the possibility that a breakdown of cementite into graphitic carbon and ferrite will occur. This will result in a weak, brittle steel with properties somewhat resembling those of cast iron.

The purpose of increasing the carbon content is to increase the hardness of the steel. The objective would be lost if the carbon were to change from cementite to graphite, as graphitic carbon tends to decrease the hardness and strength of the steel. Naturally, higher percentages of carbon have more of a tendency to graphitize than lower percentages.

12–2. Spheroidized carbides in tool steel (1,500X): C—1.00, S1—:20, Mn—.25, Fe—bal.

Allegheny Ludlum Steel Corp.

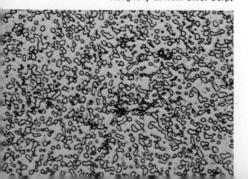

Carbon tool steels contain a high percentage of carbon (from 0.65% to 1.40%) depending upon the use of the steel. Cutting tools are made from this type steel. Even after annealing, it is difficult to machine. The cementite of these steels can be spheroidized (structure found in steel containing balls or spheroids of cementite in a matrix of ferrite) by special annealing treatment. 12–2.

IRON-CARBIDE PHASE DIAGRAM

A knowledge of the heat treatment of steel begins with the study of the iron-carbide phase diagram. The value of steel in its many uses lies in the range of physical properties that can be obtained by changes in chemical composition and proper heat treatment.

When steel consisting of 100% pearlite is heated to a temperature of about 1350° F., which is

known as the eutectoid temperature, the carbide is dissolved in ferrite, forming a new structure which is 100% austenite. 12–3. This temperature is known as the critical temperature, shown in line A_1. If the carbon content is higher or lower than 0.80%, it is known as the *lower critical* or *lower transformation* temperature. 12–4. This is because the individual pearlite grains in the steel all transform to austenite regardless of the original carbon content.

The temperature range shown between the lines A_1 and A_3 is known as the *transformation* temperature range. 12–5.

12–3. Grain structure of an austenitic steel (250X).

TEMPIL°
Basic Guide to Ferrous Metallurgy

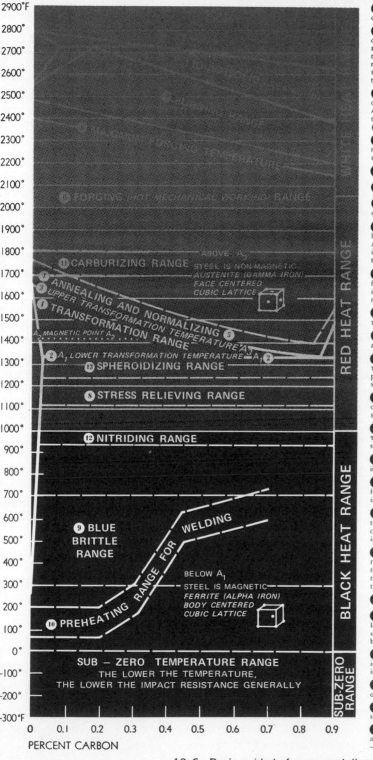

1 **TRANSFORMATION RANGE.** In this range steels undergo internal atomic changes which radically affect the properties of the material.

2 **LOWER TRANSFORMATION TEMPERATURE (A_1).** Termed Ac_1 on heating, Ar_1 on cooling. Below Ac_1 structure ordinarily consists of FERRITE and PEARLITE (see below). On heating through Ac_1 these constituents begin to dissolve in each other to form AUSTENITE (see below) which is non-magnetic. This dissolving action continues on heating through the TRANSFORMATION RANGE until the solid solution is complete at the upper transformation temperature.

3 **UPPER TRANSFORMATION TEMPERATURE (A_3).** Termed Ac_3 on heating, Ar_3 on cooling. Above this temperature the structure consists wholly of AUSTENITE which coarsens with increasing time and temperature. Upper transformation temperature is lowered as carbon increases to 0.85% (eutectoid point).

● **FERRITE** is practically pure iron (in plain carbon steels) existing below the lower transformation temperature. It is magnetic and has very slight solid solubility for carbon.

● **PEARLITE** is a mechanical mixture of FERRITE and CEMENTITE.

● **CEMENTITE** or IRON CARBIDE is a compound of iron and carbon, Fe_3C.

● **AUSTENITE** is the non-magnetic form of iron and has the power to dissolve carbon and alloying elements.

4 **ANNEALING,** frequently referred to as FULL ANNEALING, consists of heating steels to slightly above Ac_3, holding for AUSTENITE to form, then *slowly* cooling in order to produce small grain size, softness, good ductility and other desirable properties. On cooling slowly the AUSTENITE transforms to FERRITE and PEARLITE.

5 **NORMALIZING** consists of heating steels to slightly above Ac_3, holding for AUSTENITE to form, then followed by cooling (in still air). On cooling, AUSTENITE transforms giving somewhat higher strength and hardness and slightly less ductility than in annealing.

6 **FORGING RANGE** extends to several hundred degrees above the UPPER TRANSFORMATION TEMPERATURE.

7 **BURNING RANGE** is above the FORGING RANGE. Burned steel is ruined and *cannot be cured* except by remelting.

8 **STRESS RELIEVING** consists of heating to a point below the LOWER TRANSFORMATION TEMPERATURE, A_1, holding for a sufficiently long period to relieve locked-up stresses, then slowly cooling. This process is sometimes called PROCESS ANNEALING.

9 **BLUE BRITTLE RANGE** occurs approximately from 300° to 700°F. Peening or working of steels should not be done between these temperatures, since they are more brittle in this range than above or below it.

10 **PREHEATING FOR WELDING** is carried out to prevent crack formation. See TEMPIL° PREHEATING CHART for recommended temperature for various steels and non-ferrous metals.

11 **CARBURIZING** consists of dissolving carbon into surface of steel by heating to above transformation range in presence of carburizing compounds.

12 **NITRIDING** consists of heating certain *special steels* to about 1000°F for long periods in the presence of ammonia gas. Nitrogen is absorbed into the surface to produce extremely hard "skins".

13 **SPHEROIDIZING** consists of heating to just below the lower transformation temperature, A_1, for a sufficient length of time to put the CEMENTITE constituent of PEARLITE into globular form. This produces softness and in many cases good machinability.

● **MARTENSITE** is the hardest of the transformation products of AUSTENITE and is formed only on cooling below a certain temperature known as the M_s temperature (about 400° to 600°F for carbon steels). Cooling to this temperature must be sufficiently rapid to prevent AUSTENITE from transforming to softer constituents at higher temperatures.

● **EUTECTOID STEEL** contains approximately 0.85% carbon.

● **FLAKING** occurs in many alloy steels and is a defect characterized by localized micro-cracking and "flake-like" fracturing. It is usually attributed to hydrogen bursts. Cure consists of cycle cooling to at least 600°F before air-cooling.

● **OPEN OR RIMMING STEEL** has not been completely deoxidized and the ingot solidifies with a sound surface ("rim") and a core portion containing blowholes which are welded in subsequent hot rolling.

● **KILLED STEEL** has been deoxidized at least sufficiently to solidify without appreciable gas evolution.

● **SEMI-KILLED STEEL** has been partially deoxidized to reduce solidification shrinkage in the ingot.

● **A SIMPLE RULE:** Brinell Hardness divided by two, times 1000, equals approximate Tensile Strength in pounds per square inch. (200 Brinell ÷ 2 × 1000 = approx. 100,000 Tensile Strength, p.s.i.)

12–6. Basic guide to ferrous metallurgy.

Tempil°

When the carbon content is lower than 0.80%, it is known as hypo-eutectoid steel. The free ferrite is absorbed by the austenite with an increase in temperature. All of the ferrite is dissolved upon raising the temperature, so the structure is 100% austenite.

The temperature necessary to create 100% solution is called the *upper transformation* or *upper critical* temperature, represented by line A₃. 12–6.

With a carbon content above 0.80% a *hyper-eutectoid* steel is obtained. A similar action takes place, with the free carbide gradually dissolving when the temperature increases. This upper critical temperature is represented by the line AcCM.

Of course, by heating the steel above the critical temperature, a 100% austenite structure is produced. At line A₃ the transformation to austenite is shown complete.

Austenite is a solid solution of carbon or iron carbide in iron. Upon transformation of steel to austenite, the carbon which was in a combined state as cementite (Fe_3C) breaks down into pure iron and carbon. The carbon is absorbed in the iron and distributed uniformly. For obtaining maximum hardness upon quenching, this condition is usually required for a fine grain structure.

HARDENING

Hardening is the process of heating a piece of steel to a temperature within or above its critical range and then cooling rapidly.

In the heat treatment of steel, hardening is probably the most important process. The hardening process consists of:

1. Heating to a temperature well above the critical temperature of the particular steel being used without introducing dangerous thermal stresses.

2. Soaking long enough at a temperature to equalize and effect a complete or desirable solution.

3. Cooling uniformly and at a sufficient rate by quenching in a suitable medium under proper conditions.

4. Immediately and uniformly reheating to the required drawing or tempering temperature.

5. Soaking long enough at the tempering temperature to equalize and meet hardness requirements.

There is a difference in steels in their power to harden (hardenability) which depends to a great extent on their carbon content.

The heating operation is performed to change the steel from a soft pearlitic structure to a solid solution structure known as austenite. (The solid solution is, in effect, a solution of two or more materials.) This operation is done by heating any carbon steel to within the temperature range shown in Illustration 12–5, on page 60.

Upon heating to within the gamma range, steels containing less than 1.0% carbon will become 100% austenitic. Steels that contain a greater amount than this percentage will contain an excess of free cementite in the austenite. In the higher carbon steels the amount of free cementite depends upon (1) the amount of carbon in the steel and (2) the

maximum temperatures to which the steel is heated. The line AcCM in 12–5 indicates the solubility of carbon in austenite. This line can be used to determine the amount of free cementite present in the steel at any selected temperature. When carbon steel is heated through the temperature zone, Ac₁-₂-₃, the alpha iron changes to gamma iron. The cementite is dissolved by the gamma iron which refines the grain structure of the steel, forming austenite.

The recommended hardening temperature for hyper-eutectoid steels (steels containing a mixture of pearlite and free cementite) is in the range of 1375° F. to 1450° F.

The next operation in the hardening process is that of rapid cooling of the austenite. This process produces *martensite* which is a relatively hard structure.

MARTENSITE

Martensite is a supersaturated solution of carbon in alpha iron. This type of grain structure, if observed under a microscope, appears fine and needlelike. The hardness of martensite depends upon the amount of carbon present in the steel. 12–7.

It is important that carbon steel be cooled rapidly from the

12–7. Structure of martensitic stainless steel (500X).

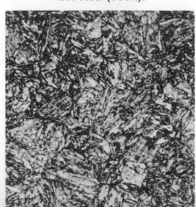

hardening temperature for complete transformation from austenite to martensite. This usually takes place from the hardening temperature to below 200° F. Pearlite and martensite are the only two structures that can be obtained from the usual quenching method in any hardening operation. If a slow quench is used, there is a transformation of austenite to pearlite. The pearlite formed by this type of quench is very fine. 12–8. Under the microscope, at high magnification, a fine lamellar structure is shown. Any further reduction of the quenching rate allows more complete transformation of the pearlite.

As a result, when carbon steels are quenched at hardening temperatures, it is necessary to undercool austenite under 1000° F. during a period of one second to prevent the formation of softer pearlite. After three seconds in a temperature range of 1000° F., the austenite decomposes rather rapidly to pearlite. Therefore, the quenching speed is very essential in the formation of an austenitic structure. Faster cooling than the critical rate will result in a better opportunity to form martensite. It is apparent in the hardening process that the avoidance of a

pearlitic grain structure is important.

The curve shown in the accompanying chart is made up of test points from both carbon and alloy steels. Little variation in the results may be seen. Alloy and carbon steels of the same carbon content cannot both use the same quenching rate. The maximum hardness that can be obtained in any steel represents the hardness of martensite. 12–9. This hardness is approximately 66 to 67 Rockwell C. In order to achieve this level of hardness, a carbon content of at least 0.60% is necessary.

QUENCHING

Quenching may be defined as the controlled cooling operation which allows steel to harden. While the austenizing treatment determines the exact hardness that will be obtained, the quenching cycle is the step that permits the steel to attain that hardness.

Quenching is also a time-temperature dependent reaction, with

equal emphasis placed upon both of these factors. In cooling from the austenizing temperature, the steel must pass rather rapidly through the critical range (approximately 1100° to 1300° F.) in order to insure that the hardening reaction will take place. The minimum rate at which the steel must be cooled to develop full hardness can be termed the critical quenching velocity. This is controlled basically by the analysis of the steel and the austenizing treatment.

The critical quenching velocity is much slower for steels containing appreciable amounts of hardenability agents, such as molybdenum, chromium, and manganese. Steels are commonly classified according to their quenching velocity—water, oil, or air-hardened varieties.

Low- and medium-carbon steels are water-hardening steels. High-carbon and alloy steels are oil-hardening. Special high-alloy steels that require a very slow rate of cooling are air-hardened.

12–8. Fine pearlite in low-alloy steel —35 nital etch (2,000X).

12–9. Relation of maximum quenched hardness to carbon content.

Burns, J. L., T. L., and Archer, R. S. "Quantitative Hardenability". Transactions of American Society for Metals, Vol. 26, 1938, p. 14.

An air blast can be used on special types of tool and die steel; however, in most cases the cooling is carried out in still air rather than by air blast.

The quenching medium for most carbon steels is water that may also be used for cooling low-alloy steels. Shallow hardened steels which need rapid transformation from austenite to martensite are water quenched. For rapid quenching, brine with a solution of 5% to 10% sodium chloride (salt) is used. The temperature of the quenching solution affects the severity of the quench. Water or brine should be kept at a temperature of about 60° to 80° F.

NOTE: *Moderate agitation* in the quenching bath serves to remove a vapor film that is formed by the liquid coming in contact with the hot surface of the metal. Vaporization seems to reduce the cooling rate.

Because of the relatively high alloy content of most tool steel compositions, rarely are quenching difficulties encountered from not maintaining the necessary critical quenching speed. One of the common quenching faults occurs as a result of not permitting the steel to cool sufficiently to permit the completion of the hardening action. This results in incomplete hardening and highly stressed finished parts. Tool steels should always be cooled down to a temperature where the parts can be handled with the bare hands prior to beginning the tempering operation.

Carbon steel parts that have thin sections, such as razor blades, knives, etc., can be satisfactorily hardened by agitating them in oil. *Distortion* and *cracking* can occur in parts by too rapid cooling in a cold quench. Heavy sections of deep hardening alloy steels can be oil quenched, as many of these steels have a slow transformation rate from austenite to martensite. The temperature of the quenching oil should be about 125° F.

HARDENABILITY

The hardenability of steel is defined as that property which determines the depth and distribution of hardness induced by quenching. Hardenability is an inherent characteristic of steel largely determined by the percentage of alloying elements, austenitic grain size, time and temperature during the austenizing, and prior structure.

Hardness is often confused with hardenability. The mere surface hardness of a steel part is dependent upon the carbon content and the cooling rate. The depth to which a certain hardness level exists is hardenability. The hardenability of a certain analysis is a constant when determined by standard procedures. Hardness will vary with the cooling rate.

The cooling rate is dependent upon certain factors: (1) the amount of heat present in the material being cooled, (2) the ratio of the surface area to volume of the object, (3) the efficiency of the heat transfer between the quenching media and the object, and (4) the cooling capacity of the quenching media. The amount of heat present in a part depends upon the heat capacity and temperature of the part. The cooling capacity of the quenching media is controlled by the volume, temperature, specific heat, viscosity, and degree of agitation.

12–10. Jominy end-quenching and method of hardness testing the end-quench hardenability specimen. (A) Specimen being water quenched. (B) Finished quenched specimen after grinding and checking Rockwell C hardness.

Republic Steel Corp.

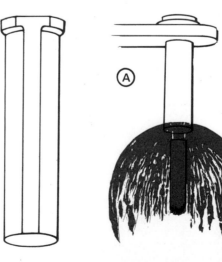
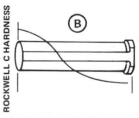

A. Shows Specimen being Water Quenched.
B. Shows Finished Quenched Specimen after Grinding and checking Rockwell C Hardness.

The maximum hardness that can be obtained in a given piece of steel is dependent upon the carbon content. By the addition of various alloys, the rate and depth hardening abilities are increased; however, maximum hardness will not be greater than that of any carbon steel with the same carbon content. The graph shown on page 63 shows the maximum hardness that can be obtained for a given hardness percentage.

The most accurate and convenient method of measuring hardenability is by the end quench method which was developed by Jominy and Boegchold.

A normalized specimen of the steel to be tested is a round bar 1″ in diameter and 4″ long. One end is squared off and machined smooth. The other end is provided with a means for supporting the specimen in a vertical position. The bar is obtained by rolling or forging to a size slightly larger than that required for the test specimen and then machining it to size. Any decarburization should be removed. Most hardenability control tests in the steel industry are performed on cast samples made during the pouring in order to evaluate the hardenability of the steel as melted.

A specially designed fixture with a yoke for supporting the specimen vertically at a distance of ½″ above a ½″ diameter water orifice is used for the test. The bar should be transferred from the furnace to the fixture as rapidly as possible. A vertical jet of water at 40° to 85° F. is quickly turned on the bar. The specimen is held in the fixture for 10 minutes, at which time it should be

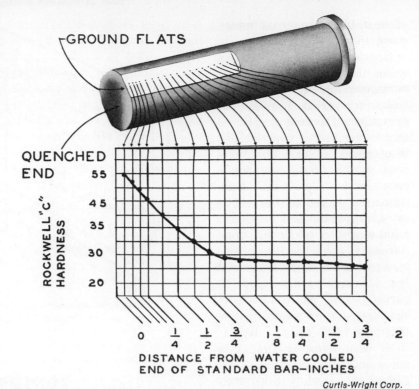

Curtis-Wright Corp.

12–11. Jominy test permits exact determination of the maximum surface hardness and the depth hardness relationship possible in any given lot or heat of steel in a matter of a few hours.

entirely cooled. It is then quenched at room temperature. 12–10.

Two parallel longitudinal flats are then ground on opposite sides of the bar to a depth of 0.015″, which serves to remove any decarburized surface. Rockwell hardness readings are then taken at ¹⁄₁₆″ intervals from a distance of ½″ from the quenched end, ⅛″ intervals to the 1¼″ position, and ¼″ intervals until the hardness falls below RC 20. 12–11.

Readings taken away from the quenched end will show progressively lower hardnesses. A high hardenability steel will show higher hardness readings for some distance from the quenched end.

Hardness readings for a low hardenability steel will show a sharp drop a short distance from the end.

In testing, care must be taken to maintain the specimen flat on the supporting anvils, to keep it free from vertical movement under major load. The flat surface should be centered in relation to the penetrator on the hardness tester, and the spacing should be accurate.

ISOTHERMAL TRANSFORMATION DIAGRAM

Isothermal transformation may be defined as a transformation that takes place at a constant temperature where radiation of heat from the metal body is counterbalanced by an equal evolution of heat from the metal undergoing the transformation.

Iron-iron-carbide phase diagrams are useful in the selection of temperature for parts to be heated for various heat treating operations. This diagram also indicates the type of structure that is obtained in steels that have been slowly cooled; however, it does not give a great deal of information regarding the effects of cooling rate and time and grain structures obtainable in interrupted quenches at certain elevated temperatures. Isothermal transformation diagrams, S-curves (from their shape) or time-temperature-transformation diagrams (T-T-T), are used to show what transformations take place and what constituents are formed in a steel as temperature and time changes on cooling.

Equilibrium is a function of temperature and composition only when sufficient time is allowed. 12–12. Practical heat treatment of material of fixed composition becomes a function of time and temperature. The diagrammatic representation of the approximate relationship between these two concepts is indicated by the two cards, showing how the equilibrium temperatures are lifted from one diagram to the other.

The general shape of a T-T-T curve differs for each steel depending upon: (1) carbon content, (2) alloys in the steel, and (3) austenitic grain size. Each type of steel has its own curve. A martensitic structure is obtained by quenching the steel rapidly so that the cooling curve does not intersect the nose of the transformation curve.

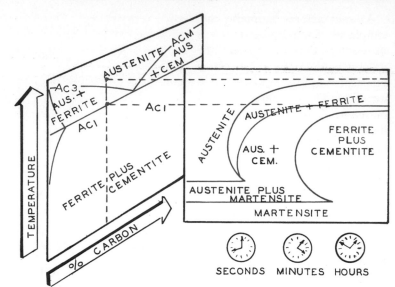

12–12. Illustration showing how the equilibrium temperatures are lifted from one diagram to the other.

Unit 13. Tempering, Annealing, and Normalizing; Surface Hardening

Tempering may be defined as reheating steel, after hardening, to an intermediate temperature range for the purpose of toughening the steel. The hardening phase of heat treatment permits the steel to obtain full hardness, while the tempering phase conditions the steel so that the hardness can be utilized best.

After the hardening operation, the steel is in a highly stressed condition. This hard, brittle condition is produced by the transformation of austenite to a more voluminous structure called martensite, as previously discussed. The steel has a distinct tendency toward cracking in this condition, so it must be handled carefully. Tool and die steels generally are not usable in this condition since they require some degree of toughness in order to withstand the shock that occurs with normal operation. Tempering, which immediately follows the quenching operation, creates this toughness.

In tempering, the steel is reheated to an intermediate temperature, which causes the hard martensitic structure to break down. Some carbon is precipitated from the martensite into the form of fine carbides. In most cases this causes a slight decrease in hardness. At the same time, stress relief takes place within the metal and the very high internal stresses within the steel are eliminated.

As said before, tempering accomplishes its purpose through the combination of temperature and time. 13–1. Low tempering temperatures (around 400° F.) are used when higher strength and more hardness are wanted. High ductility and toughness require much higher tempering temperatures—in a range from 1100° to 1275° F.

The hardened part must not only be heated to a certain temperature, but it must be soaked at that temperature for a definite period of time. After reaching the tempering temperature throughout the entire section, a simple alloy should soak for approximately one hour. For more complex alloys, several hours may be required.

Double tempering is sometimes required for higher alloyed tool and die steels which require hardening temperatures in excess of 2000° F. This is necessary because, from the first tempering operation, upon cooling, additional fresh martensite is formed from the retained austenite. The second tempering operation serves to toughen this newly formed martensite.

Control of time and temperature between quench and temper is very important, as the actual hardening takes place at the end of the quenching cycle. Tempering too soon will interrupt cooling, which does not allow full hardening. Cracking can occur if the quenched part is held at room temperature too long. Stresses tend to build up to a point where cracking occurs. To avoid: (1) allow the steel to cool, after hardening, to a point where the

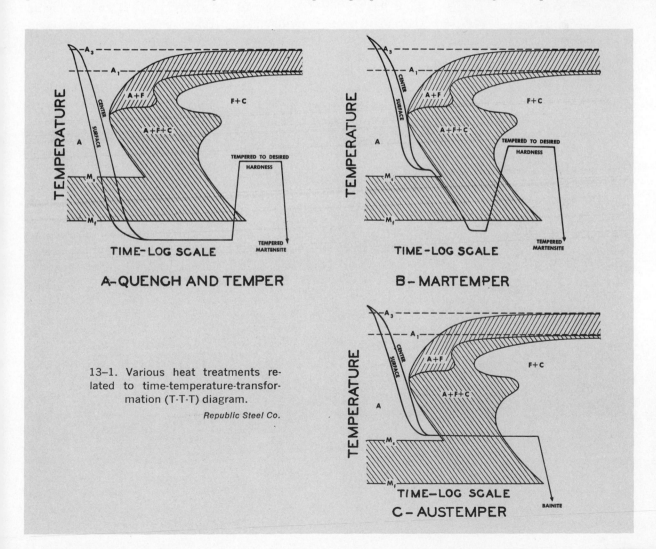

13–1. Various heat treatments related to time-temperature-transformation (T-T-T) diagram.

Republic Steel Co.

Ajax Electric Co.

13–2. Heat treatment of large parts such as this jet aircraft wing flap impart toughness and uniform strength to metal, permitting machining to be done before the heat-treatment cycle with minimum distortion.

13–3(A). Operator unloads container of parts after austenizing.

Ajax Electric Co.

part can be handled with the bare hands and (2) begin the tempering operation immediately after this point is reached.

MARTEMPERING

Martempering is a process which consists of heating the steel above its critical temperature range. The steel is held at this temperature for a certain length of time to enable the surface and center of the steel to arrive at the same temperature. The steel is rapidly quenched from the austenite region to a temperature just above the Ms line (the point at which martensite begins to form). 13–1. A salt bath is usually used —the steel being held long enough to permit temperature equalization—followed by air cooling to room temperature, producing martensite. Martempering minimizes distortion, cracking, and internal stresses that can result from normal quenching in water or oil. 13–2.

AUSTEMPERING

Austempering is a process which utilizes the isothermal transformation of austenite to a hard structure called bainite. The isothermal transformation takes place at a constant temperature where the radiation of heat from the metal body is counterbalanced by an equal evolution of heat from the metal undergoing the transformation. Austempering is an interrupted quenching process. 13–3 (A&B).

The quenching medium is generally a low temperature salt bath having a working range of 350° to 1100° F. Bath temperature is dependent upon the material treated but is controlled within the rapid transforming bainite region above the Ms temperature and below the knee of the T-T-T in Diagram 13–1 which is shown on page 67.

NOTE: Since the operating bath temperature serves to retard the cooling rate, this process is limited to small parts with good hardenability, to avoid the formation of pearlite during the initial quench.

ANNEALING

Annealing involves heating steel to slightly above the critical temperature, followed by rela-

13–3(B). Typical seat belt components after treating (left) and after plating (right). Salt bath austempering leaves metal so smooth that tumbling is the only preparatory step needed before plating.

tively slow cooling of the metal or alloys. 13–4.

Annealing is used to obtain a variety of results, among which are: (1) to soften or alter the grain structure of the steel, (2) to develop machinability, formability, and required mechanical properties, (3) to remove effects of strain hardening resulting from cold work, and (4) to remove internal stresses previously set up in the metal. Specific annealing cycles include *full annealing, process annealing,* and *spheroidizing.*

Full Annealing

The process of full annealing is utilized primarily to produce maximum softness in steel. It relieves internal stresses in steel and improves machinability.

The part is heated uniformly to the full annealing temperature, which is about 50° F. above the A_3 temperature. When there is complete penetration by heat, the temperature is held until conditions are uniform throughout. An allowance of 45 minutes for each inch thickness of the largest section is the usual rule.

The cooling rate must be very slow to obtain maximum softness and ductility. This can be obtained by allowing the part to cool down with the furnace. A good rule is: the higher the carbon content, the slower the cooling rate.

Process Annealing

Process annealing, sometimes called *stress* or *subcritical* annealing, consists of heating the steel to a temperature close to the lower critical range and then cooling it slowly. This is the sim-

plest form of annealing. Its function is to reduce stress and hardness and make minor changes in structure. This process is more rapid than spheroidizing. The usual pearlitic structure is obtained by this method. Heating to a lower temperature lessens the tendency of the steel to scale.

Spheroidizing

Spheroidizing is an annealing process applied to steel when the cementite or carbide is desired in globular or spherical shape. 13–5.

Steel is heated slowly to a temperature just below the critical range, or just below the Ac_1, and held for a prolonged period, usually followed by slow cooling. The final step should consist of holding at a temperature just below the critical (Ar).

The rate of spheroidization is affected by the initial structure. The finer the pearlite, the more readily spheroidization takes place.

This type of treatment is usually applied to high-carbon steels (0.60 carbon content and higher), when machinability is desired and when steel is to be severely deformed.

NORMALIZING

Normalizing is a process which involves heating steel to a temperature above the Ac_3 or the Acm and then cooling in still air.

This process serves to improve machinability and relieve internal stresses due to machining, cold working, and forging. Normalizing also softens hardened steel but not to the degree of softness obtained by the full annealing process.

Ajax Electric Co.

13–4. Low-carbon steel wire is annealed in this pot furnace with over-the-top electrodes. Furnace uses nitrate salt at 1000° F.

The grain structure in normalized steel is less ductile, somewhat harder, and has a finer pearlitic structure than steel that has been fully annealed.

SURFACE HARDENING
Carburizing

One of the oldest known heat-treating processes is carburizing. History tells us that sword blades

13–5. Microscopic structure called spheroidite (2,000X) consists of globular particles of cementite or alloy carbides in a mat of ferrite grains.

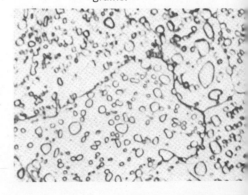

and primitive tools were made by the carburization of low-carbon wrought iron.

The following carburizing processes are commonly used in industrial applications: (1) pack carburizing, (2) gas carburizing, and (3) liquid carburizing.

Today, carburizing is scientifically controlled so that carbon is added to steel to produce a hard steel surface of exact specifications.

The process consists of heating parts in contact with a carbonaceous material to a temperature above the Ac_3 of the steel and holding at that temperature. The steel must be soaked at this temperature long enough for the carbon to penetrate to the proper depth to produce the required hardened surface. The depth of penetration depends upon temperature, time, and the composition of the carburizing material. A carburized depth of about 0.030″ to 0.050″ can be obtained in about 4 hours at a temperature of about 1700° F. The carburizing agent may be a solid, liquid, or gas.

The primary object of carburizing is to secure a hard outside surface and a relatively soft, tough core. This treatment is for low-carbon steels of up to about 0.25% carbon. The steel may or may not contain alloying elements such as nickel, chromium, manganese, or molybdenum.

Pack Carburizing

In the pack carburizing process, the operation is carried out by packing the steel in suitable containers such as steel boxes or pots, with a carbonaceous material.

The substances used are generally commercial solid carburizers that vary in composition. They generally consist of a hardwood charcoal to which an energizer, such as barium carbonate, has been bound by molasses or oiltar. Mixtures of coke (diluent) and charred leather, bone, and charcoal are also used. The energizer usually represents about 20% of the mixture. To increase the rate of heat transfer through the compound, an additional 20% is made of coke.

Since the compound decomposes with use, it is common practice to add 12% to 30% new material to used compounds for a new operation.

In the process, the box, which is made of heat-resistant alloys, is packed and sealed tightly, then placed in the furnace and heated to between 1500° and 1750°F. Within this range a transformation takes place in the steel forming austenite which has the capacity to dissolve large amounts of carbon. At carburizing temperature, carbon monoxide is released and carbon is absorbed by the surface of the steel parts. After carburization, the cooling cycle is carried out in various ways, depending upon the type of steel and desired objectives.

Gas Carburizing

Gas carburizing consists of introducing carbon into the ferrous base material by heating in a gaseous atmosphere.

Commercial gases, natural and propane, and easily vaporized hydrocarbon liquids are used to supply the desired quantity of carbon.

Batch type furnaces are used in this process. This furnace consists of an inner cylinder, made from noncarburizing alloy steel, and a heat-insulated outer cylinder. The space between the cylinders is heated. The parts are placed in the inner cylinder; then carburizing gas or oil is introduced, circulated by a fan. The furnace is sealed and the parts are soaked at the carburizing temperature for the required time for the depth of case desired. The carburizing temperature required is about 1700°F. for case depths of 0.020″ to 0.030″. Longer carburizing periods will produce greater depths.

The parts are then quenched. Finally, they are reheated to a point above the transformation range of the case and quenched to produce a fine, hard structure.

Liquid Carburizing

Liquid carburizing is a method of case-hardening or carburizing steel in molten baths. The baths are mixtures of cyanides, chlorides, and carbonates. 13–6. The case that is produced is comparable with one resulting from pack or gas carburizing. The salts produce both carbon and nitrogen that penetrate the surface.

The carburizing action depends upon sodium cyanide or barium cyanide, which supplies the carbon and some nitrogen.

Liquid carburizing temperatures usually range from 1550° to 1750°F. Faster penetration can be obtained if higher temperatures are used. However, this method increases material cost and causes rapid deteriora-

Ajax Electric Co.

13–6. This gas-fired salt-bath-type furnace is suitable for most salt bath heat treating, including neutral hardening, carburizing, cyaniding, nitriding, high-speed quenching, and drawing. Normal operating temperatures are from 325° to 1650° F.

tion of equipment. Cases as deep as 0.30" can be obtained with a cyanide content of 20% using carburizing temperatures from 1550° to 1650°F.

The advantages of this method can be summarized as follows: (1) uniform case depth and carbon content, (2) rapid penetration depth, (3) rusting, pitting, and corrosion minimized, (4) reduction of time required for the steel to reach carburizing temperature, and (5) low installation cost.

Nitriding

Nitriding is a case-hardening process used to produce an exceptionally hard surface on alloy steel parts in an atmosphere of ammonia gas and dissociated ammonia (separated into constit-uents) mixed in suitable proportions. Special composition steels are used in this process, which is carried out at a temperature range from 900° to 1050°F. The hardening reaction takes place when nitrogen from the ammonia diffuses into the steel and reacts with the nitride formers—chromium, aluminum, vanadium, molybdenum, and tungsten—to produce precipitates of alloy nitrides.

This method of case-hardening is slow compared to other processes. A 50-hour cycle is required to give a case of 0.020". In nitriding large sections, normalizing is recommended prior to nitriding.

Nitriding has advantages over other case-hardening processes. It (1) produces a harder surface, (2) has superior wear resistance, (3) causes minimum warpage and distortion, (4) improves corrosion resistance, and (5) provides high resistance to fatigue.

Common applications are connecting rods, crankshafts, pinions, piston rods, push rods, wrenches, gears, and cutting tools.

Cyaniding

Cyaniding is a process that involves the case-hardening of machined steel parts by heating in contact with molten cyanide salt, followed by quenching in a salt bath, water, or mineral oil, depending upon the type of steel. The salt bath consists of a mixture of 30% sodium cyanide, 40% sodium carbonate, and 30% sodium chloride.

The cyaniding temperature is above the lower critical temperature of the steel, usually from 1400° to 1600°F. Direct quenching is employed. This process is capable of high production, as immersion periods require only 15 minutes to 2 hours. It requires about 30 minutes to case-harden a part from 0.003" to 0.005". The maximum case depth is rarely more than about 0.020" and the average depth is considerably less.

A very thin surface case can be obtained by dipping in a powdered cyanide mixture, followed by quenching.

Cyanide salts are violent poisons if allowed to come in contact with wounds or scratches and are fatal if taken internally. Posionous fumes are generated when cyanides are brought into contact with acids. **Caution:** A method of venting gases is a must during the operation and molten cyanide should never be allowed to come in contact with sodium or potassium nitrates, used in tempering operations, as the mixtures are explosive. *Extreme care* is necessary at all times when using this material.

Carbonitriding

This process is sometimes referred to as *dry cyaniding, gas cyanitriding, ni-carbing,* or *nitrocarburizing.* It is a process of case-hardening ferrous material by heating it in a gaseous atmosphere of such composition that there is a simultaneous absorption of carbon and nitrogen at a rate which will produce the desired properties. A case depth of 0.003" to 0.025" can be produced.

A furnace similar to the one for gas carburizing is used. The

Detroit Flame Hardening Co.

13–7(A). Flame-hardening machine.

13–7(B). Flame hardening a lathe bed.

Clausing Corp.

atmosphere in the closed furnace is enriched with a gaseous compound of carbon and nitrogen. The atmosphere circulates freely in the furnace; the parts absorb both carbon and nitrogen. Carbonitriding is carried on above the Ac temperature of the steel. It is practical up to 1700°F. Quenching in oil is sufficiently fast to attain maximum surface hardness; this moderate rate of cooling tends to minimize distortion. The parts do not come in contact with air, which prevents oxidation and buildup of scale.

Nitrogen increases hardness and resistance to tempering, compared to the conventional carburized case.

Flame Hardening

Flame hardening consists of heating steel or small gray iron castings to obtain a hard surface and a relatively soft interior. This method is well adapted for treating both small and large lots. Flame hardening is used on parts where it would not be feasible to heat the part in a furnace and quench with oil or water, due to the risk of warping and cracking the part. Any cast iron or steel part that requires a high surface hardness and would be difficult to harden by other methods can be heat-treated successfully by the process. The illustration shows one type of flame-hardening machine. Surface hardening by this process is accomplished by applying heat to the surface of the part from an oxyacetylene flame. 13–7(A&B).

Only a thin layer of the surface metal is brought up to the desired temperature. As the

torch heats the metal, a stream of water follows the torch, quenching the heated metal and producing a hardened surface. The depth of hardness is controlled by the speed of movement of the torch. Cylindrical shapes such as gears and shafts can be rotated and the surface heated by the flame of a torch or a series of burners, as shown in the illustration. 13–8. The machine setup for flame hardening a gear is also shown. 13–9.

Steel to be hardened by this method should have a carbon content of at least 0.40%. The

13–8. Various methods of flame hardening.

Detroit Flame Hardening Co.

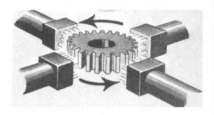

PROGRESSIVE METHOD

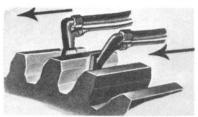

SPINNING METHOD

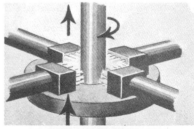

COMBINATION—SPINNING AND PROGRESSIVE

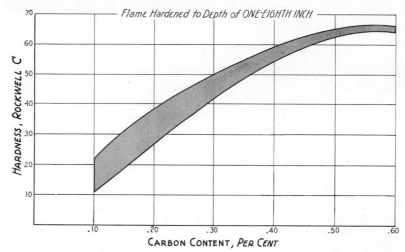

Detroit Flame Hardening Co.

13–10. Hardness range of plain carbon steels flame hardened to a depth of ⅛".

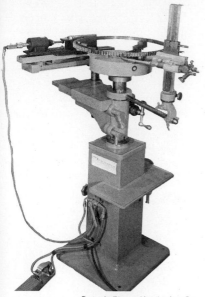

Detroit Flame Hardening Co.

13–9. Showing the setup and machine for flame hardening the teeth of a gear.

hardness of the case will depend upon the type of steel used and the quenching medium. Hardness of Rockwell C50 to C60 is common.

The chart shows the hardness range of plain carbon steel that has been flame hardened to a depth of ⅛". 13–10. A typical hardness curve for flame-hardened, medium-carbon steel is also illustrated. 13–11.

Induction Hardening

Induction hardening is a heating process by which induction heat is developed within the surface by magnetically inducing an electric current in the surface. This differs from conventional heating methods where heat is applied at the surface and diffuses inward.

In the past two decades induction hardening has been used extensively. 13–12 (A&B) on page 74. From the metallurgical viewpoint, it differs from most other hardening processes in two important respects; (1) extremely rapid heating rates are used and (2) time and temperature prior to quenching are essentially zero. These conditions provide an absolute minimum of time for metallurgical changes associated with hardening, which include formation of austenite upon heating, austenite grain growth, and solid solution of any alloying elements.

Steels to be induction hardened are those which austenize readily due to the extremely short heating times. A fine dispersion of carbide will dissolve more readily than coarse carbide.

Medium-carbon steels (0.45% to 0.50%) are normally se-

13–11. Typical hardness curve for flame-hardened medium-carbon steels.

Detroit Flame Hardening Co.

TYPICAL HARDNESS CURVE
FOR FLAME HARDENED
MEDIUM CARBON STEELS

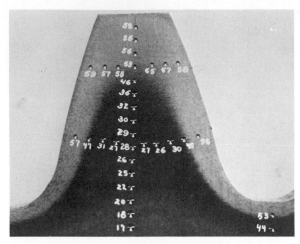

Tocco Induction Hardening, Div. Ohio Crankshaft Co.

13–12(A). Section of a gear that has been induction hardened.

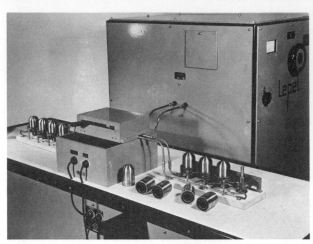

Lepel High Frequency Labs, Inc.

13–12(B). Induction-hardening machine. Note the inductor coils around parts to be hardened.

lected for high-frequency induction hardening, the most common being AISI 1045 and AISI 1050. These grades can be readily induction hardened to provide minimum surface hardness of Rc 58 to 60, respectively. They are less susceptible to cracking than steels of higher carbon content, and may be water-spray quenched.

However, all ferrous metals containing sufficient combined carbon can be induction hardened succesfully. Some suitable materials are given in Table 13.

Surface hardening by the induction method is accomplished by using an inductor block, or heating coils, encircling the part and passing a high-frequency alternating current (500 to 15 million cycles per second) through the block of coils. The inductor block acts as a primary coil of a transformer. It is placed around, but does not touch, the part to be hardened.

The high-frequency current passed through the block or coil

Table 13.* Recommended Induction Hardening Temperatures and Minimum Surface Hardness for Various Materials Successfully Induction Hardened[a]

Metal	Hardening Temp. deg. F.	Quench	Rc Min[b]
Carbon and Alloy Steels[c]			
0.30% C	1650 to 1700	Water	50
0.35	1650	Water	52
0.40	1600 to 1650	Water	55
0.45	1600 to 1650	Water	58
0.50	1600	Water	60
0.60	1550 to 1600	Water or Oil	64 or 62
>0.60	1500 to 1550	Water or Oil	64 or 62
Cast Irons[d]			
Gray Iron Pearlitic	1600 to 1700	Water	45
Malleable	1600 to 1700	Water	48
Nodular	1650 to 1700	Water	50
Stainless Steel[e]			
Type 420	2000 to 2100	Oil or Air	50

(a) Metals listed in this tabulation are typical of those successfully induction hardened and the listing is indicative rather than inclusive.

(b) Minimum surface hardness, Rockwell C.

(c) Free-machining and alloy grades with equivalent carbon contents may be induction hardened. Alloy steels containing carbide-forming elements (chromium, molybdenum, vanadium, or tungsten) should be heated 100° to 200°F. above the temperatures indicated.

(d) Combined carbon should be 0.40 to 0.50% min; hardness will vary with amount of combined carbon present.

(e) Other martensitic grades of stainless steel, types 410, 416, and 440, have been induction hardened.

*Lepel High Frequency Laboratories, Inc.

Lepel High Frequency Labs, Inc.

13–13. High-frequency current passes through the coil and sets up magnetic flux lines, which induce an electric current which cuts through the flux field.

13–14. Induction hardening a ring gear made of C-1045 steel.

General Electric, Industrial Heating Dept.

sets up magnetic flux lines which induce an electric current which cuts through the flux field. 13–13. In the case of a transformer, both the primary winding, to which the power is applied, and the secondary winding, in which current is induced, are portions of complete low-resistance circuits. In induction hardening, the "secondary," or part to be heated, supplies sufficient resistance to electrical current to generate heat.

The primary frequency used depends upon the depth of heating desired, the power required, and the size of the part.

After reaching the hardening temperature, the electric circuit is opened and at the same time the part is automatically spray quenched under pressure. Oil and water are the common quenchant. Caustic, brine, or air may be used.

Since heating cycles for both quenching and induction tempering are very short, precise timing with automatic equipment is necessary.

The illustration shows the method of induction hardening a ring gear made of C–1045 steel. 13–14. The operator loads the gear on a rotating column, locks the gear into position, and presses the cycle-start button. The rest of the operation is automatic. One tooth at a time is hardened. The inductor automatically moves into position around the tooth. The induction heater automatically turns on and heats the tooth for a period of 2.5 seconds to a temperature of 1575°F. The heater goes off, the inductor retracts, and the tooth is automatically

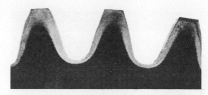

Tocco Induction Hardening, Div. Ohio Crankshaft Co.

13–15. Showing the depth to which the gear teeth have been hardened by the induction method.

oil quenched and the gear indexed. The cycle is repeated for all the teeth. A depth of ⅛" can be obtained by this method. 13–15. A flexible ventilating pipe removes the fumes into a central system.

Copper tubing is used almost exclusively in the high-frequency induction heating coils. Annealed tubing with an outside diameter of ³⁄₁₆" to ¼" and a 0.030 wall is easy to work with, permits a sufficient water flow for cooling, and is rigid enough for most applications.

Induction heating is very efficient for brazing and soldering operations. Cutting torches, carbide tipped tools, structural frames, musical instruments, jewelry, ice skates, and other items

13–16. Cutting tools and work coils for carbide tip brazing.

Lepel High Frequency Labs, Inc.

13–17. Drying impregnated motor field windings.

are frequently fabricated by brazing. 13–16. Many other heating and melting operations are done by the induction process. 13–17.

Production rate from the induction hardening process is high because of the high initial cost of equipment. 13–18.

Induction hardening differs from ordinary case-hardening in that analysis of the surface steel is not changed. Extremely rapid heating has no effect upon the inner core. The hardness compares to the conventional heat-treatment process.

13–18. Production induction hardening.

Unit 14. Testing

HARDNESS TESTING

A hardness test is a means of determining resistance to penetration and is sometimes used to obtain a quick estimate of tensile strength. There are several methods of determining hardness, ranging from a file to hardness testers. The most common of these testers are the Rockwell and the Brinell.

The hardness of metals or metal parts is designated by a number. There are several common hardness number systems, depending upon the hardness-testing instruments being used. The most common systems are:

Rockwell C scale (RC or Rc)
Rockwell B scale (RB or Rb)
Rockwell Superficial hardness scales
Brinell hardness number (BHN)
Vickers scale
Shore scleroscope hardness number
Knoop hardness scale

It is possible to test the approximate hardness of a piece of metal with a small, fine-toothed file. Case-hardened objects, quenched shapes, and surface-hardened parts may be tested in this manner. Close comparisons to Rockwell hardness readings can be made with this test, despite the variables involved by individual handling of the file. NOTE: This method of testing is difficult to evaluate quantitatively which makes the use of instruments necessary for testing the exact measurement of hardness. The data in Table 14–A may serve as a guide when using a file for testing the hardness of parts.

Table 14-A. Estimating Hardness With a File	
Rockwell C Hardness No.	Action of File on Steel
20	File removes metal easily with slight pressure
30	File starts to resist cutting metal
40	File cuts with difficulty
50	File barely cuts metal
70	File is not able to cut metal

Rockwell Hardness Test

The Rockwell testing machine is generally used on harder steels and on small samples when the Brinell impression becomes too large to be practical. 14–1.

In the Rockwell hardness test, a hardness value is obtained by using a direct reading testing machine which measures hardness by determining the penetration depth of a diamond point or steel ball into the specimen being tested. Deep penetration indicates a low hardness number while a shallow penetration indicates a higher hardness number. First a minor load of 10 kilograms is applied. This sets the penetrator on the specimen

14–1. The hardness of a test specimen is being checked on a Rockwell hardness tester.

and serves to hold it in position. A major load is then applied which increases the depth of penetration. The major load is then removed, leaving the minor load still acting on the specimen. The Rockwell number is proportional to the difference in penetration between the minor and major loads and then can be read directly on the barrel dial through a magnifier.

The most common scales used in hardness testing of steel are the Rockwell B and C scales. The C scale is used for testing hardened steels using a diamond penetrator. Softer materials such as unhardened steel, cast iron, and nonferrous metals are generally tested using the B scale. The B scale uses a smaller major load (100 kilograms or 220.5 pounds) and a $\frac{1}{16}$"-diam. steel ball as a penetrator. The B hardness numbers are read according to the red figures in the dial.

Rockwell superficial hardness scales are useful in testing excep-

Table 14-B. Rockwell Hardness Scales

SCALES—Normal Tester

The symbol for use as a prefix to the value read from the dial depends upon the load, type of penetrator, and scale from which dial readings are taken, and these symbols are shown below.

Scale Symbol	Penetrator	Major Load kg.	Dial Figures	Typical Applications of Scales
B	$\frac{1}{16}$" ball	100	red	Copper alloys, soft steels, aluminum alloys, malleable iron, etc.
C	diamond cone	150	black	Steel, hard cast irons, pearlitic malleable iron, titanium, deep case hardened steel, and other materials harder than B 100.
A	diamond cone	60	black	Cemented carbides, thin steel, and shallow case hardened steel.
D	diamond cone	100	black	Thin steel and medium case hardened steel and pearlitic malleable iron.
E	$\frac{1}{8}$" ball	100	red	Cast iron, aluminum, and magnesium alloys, bearing metals.
F	$\frac{1}{16}$" ball	60	red	Annealed copper alloys and thin soft sheet metals.
G	$\frac{1}{16}$" ball	150	red	Phosphor bronze, beryllium copper, malleable irons. Upper limit G 92 to avoid possible flattening of ball.
H	$\frac{1}{8}$" ball	60	red	Aluminum, zinc, lead.
K	$\frac{1}{8}$" ball	150	red	Bearing metals and other very soft or thin materials. Use smallest ball and heaviest load that does not give anvil effect.
L	$\frac{1}{4}$" ball	60	red	
M	$\frac{1}{4}$" ball	100	red	
P	$\frac{1}{4}$" ball	150	red	
R	$\frac{1}{2}$" ball	60	red	
S	$\frac{1}{2}$" ball	100	red	
V	$\frac{1}{2}$" ball	150	red	

SCALES—Superficial Tester

The symbol for use as a prefix to the value read from the dial depends upon the load, type of penetrator, and scale from which dial readings are taken, and these symbols are shown below.

Scale Symbol	Penetrator	Load in Kilograms
15N	"BRALE"	15 kg.
30N	"BRALE"	30 kg.
45N	"BRALE"	45 kg.
15T	$\frac{1}{16}$" ball	15 kg.
30T	$\frac{1}{16}$" ball	30 kg.
45T	$\frac{1}{16}$" ball	45 kg.
15W	$\frac{1}{8}$" ball	15 kg.
30W	$\frac{1}{8}$" ball	30 kg.
45W	$\frac{1}{8}$" ball	45 kg.
15X	$\frac{1}{4}$" ball	15 kg.
30X	$\frac{1}{4}$" ball	30 kg.
45X	$\frac{1}{4}$" ball	45 kg.
15Y	$\frac{1}{2}$" ball	15 kg.
30Y	$\frac{1}{2}$" ball	30 kg.
45Y	$\frac{1}{2}$" ball	45 kg.

tionally high surface hardness, such as case-hardened or nitrided surfaces of razor blades, clock springs, small cutters on electric shavers, and plug and ring gages.

The Rockwell superficial hardness scales (Table 14–B) include both the N and T scales. The initial load is 3 kilograms and the major load may be 15, 30, or 45 kilograms, depending upon the thickness of the hard surface. A special Brale penetrator, N diamond, is used when measuring N scales, while a $\frac{1}{16}$″-diam. ball penetrator is used with the T scales. 14–2.

Operating Instructions for Normal Tester

1. Select the proper penetrating point and insert in the bottom of the plunger rod. Place the proper anvil in the elevating screw.

2. Place the specimen upon the anvil table and elevate the specimen into contact with the penetrator until the small pointer is nearly vertical and slightly to the right of the dot; then elevate still further until

14–2. Penetrator points used on Rockwell hardness tester. (A) 120° diam. point. (B) $\frac{1}{16}$″ diam. ball point.

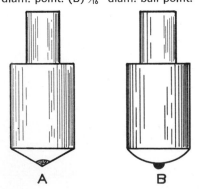

A B

the large pointer points vertically upward. You have now applied 10 kilograms, which is the minor load.

3. Set the dial to zero—i.e., the line marked set—by turning (with the thumb) the knurled ring located below the capstan handwheel.

4. Push down on the depressor bar to apply the major load. (The dial does not indicate the hardness number while the major load is applied.)

5. Watch the pointer until it comes to rest.

6. Pull the crank handle forward, lifting the major load but leaving the minor load applied.

7. Read the Rockwell hardness number. The reading is recorded as follows:

● If using the $\frac{1}{16}$″ ball penetrator and a load of 100 kilograms, the reading is taken from the red scale and the letter "B" is prefixed to the number to signify the condition of the test.

● If the test is made with the Brale penetrator with a load of 150 kilograms, the reading is taken from the black scale and the letter "C" is prefixed to the number.

8. The handwheel is turned to lower the specimen; the specimen is removed from the anvil.

Brinell Hardness Test

The Brinell hardness test utilizes a specified load that is applied to a smooth surface of the specimen or part under test through a hard ball. 14–3. The ball is 10 millimeters in diameter. It may be a hardened steel ball, hultgren ball, or a carbide ball. For the standard Brinell hardness test on hard

Tinius Olsen Co.

14–3. Brinell hardness tester.

materials, a 3,000 kilogram load is used, and a 1,500 or 500 kilogram load is used for thin sections or soft materials. The diameter of the indentation is then measured through a microscope which has a calibration lens. This diameter is used as the basis for calculation of the Brinell hardness number.

A system of weights, levers, and screws applies the load on a Brinell hardness tester, which may be hand operated or motorized.

Vickers Scale

There are other hardness testers available to check hardness of very thin sections and microstituents found in metallographic examination. 14–4. The values obtained are normally referred to as the Vickers Diamond Pyramid hardness numbers. In this test, a specified load is applied to the surface of the material through the square-based pyramidal diamond having specified face angles. The resulting permanent impression is then measured. A wide variety of test specimens may be tested by this method—large bars, rolled sections, and very small pieces in metallographic mounts.

Shore Scleroscope Hardness Test

The scleroscope is a portable instrument for testing hardness. 14–5. A diamond-tipped hammer is allowed to drop by gravity from a fixed height down a glass tube upon the specimen being tested. The resulting rebound is read against a graduated scale. The rebounding is caused by elasticity; however, since elasticity is closely associated with hardness, the hardness is measured indirectly. In other words,

the amount of rebound is a test of the elastic limit of the specimen more than of its tensile strength; thus, the instrument does not measure exactly the same type of hardness that indentation methods measure. 14–6 (Page 80).

On some instruments the height of rebound is recorded on a dial. The accuracy of the reading is dependent upon the technique of manipulation. The dial instrument tester shows the equivalent Rockwell C numbers as well as the Brinell hardness numbers.

Microhardness Testers and the Knoop Hardness Scale

Microhardness testers are widely used to determine the hardness of individual grains or

constituents in the microstructure of metals, according to the Knoop hardness scale. 14–7 shown on page 80.

In this test a diamond penetrator is pressed into the surface of the specimen. It is essential that the surface be free of surface irregularities such as scale and nicks. A given force is applied to the penetrator for a given period of time with the depth of penetration depending

14–5. Model C-2 Shore scleroscope on a clamping stand. A diamond-tipped hammer drops through a glass tube upon the specimen being tested.

Shore Instrument & Mfg. Co., Inc.

14–4. Three types of hardness testing equipment in a steel laboratory. From left to right: Brinell, Tukon, and Vickers.

Republic Steel Co.

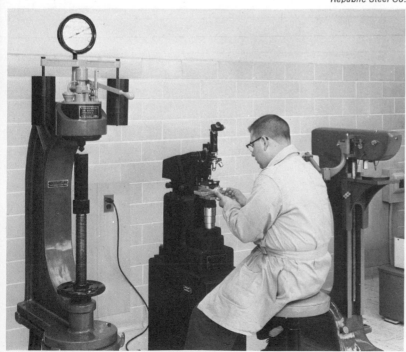

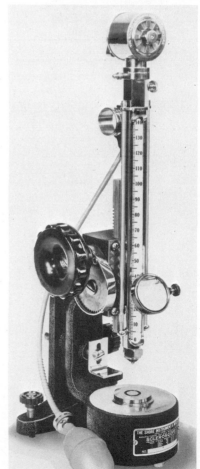

Shore Instrument & Mfg. Co., Inc.

14–6. Model D Shore scleroscope testing the hardness of a standard test block.

14–7. A microhardness test being performed on a test specimen with a Tukon hardness tester.

Republic Steel Co.

upon the amount of load applied and the hardness of the specimen. The pressure applied is in the range of 25 to 3,600 grams. This pressure is so low that the indentation must be measured with a microscope, which is part of the tester. The hardness is determined by the size of the indentation. 14–8.

The advantages of this type of testing are: (1) the dent produced is so small that it does practically no damage to the surface of the specimen. (2) it may be used to test the hardness of very small or thin parts. (3) it may be used to test minerals too hard to test by other methods.

The Knoop hardness number is based upon a relationship between the load and the long dimension of the indentation in the surface. A conversion chart which includes these factors is supplied with the tester.

TENSILE TESTING

The tensile test is used to determine the mechanical properties of a material when it is subjected to a slowly applied force tending to pull it apart. 14–9. A tensile test evaluates the ultimate strength level, yield point, yield strength, and factors which determine the ductility of the specimen.

Tests are usually conducted on symmetrical specimens less than a square inch in area, which are subjected to a uniaxial tensile stress resulting from a load applied to the ends. The shapes of standard representative test specimens most commonly used are outlined in ASTM E8–57. However, full test specimens,

Republic Steel Co.

14–8. Diamond shapes are Knoop hardness impressions. Microstructure illustrates a case produced by nitriding for 48 hours at 975° F. and 30% ammonia dissociation.

14–9. Tensile testing (stress-strain) equipment being used in a steel laboratory.

Republic Steel Co.

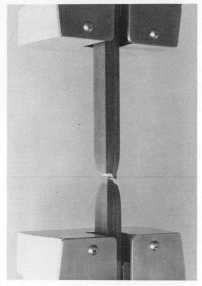

Tinius Olsen Co.

14–10. A tensile test on a steel specimen, which will fracture when ultimate tensile strength is exceeded.

14–11. Top acting tension and compression testing machine of 5,000 to 40,000 pounds capacity.

Physical Testing Machine Div., Service Diamond Tool Co.

such as rods, small bars, and wire are used whenever practical.

In making the test, the load on the specimen, applied in a specific manner, can be removed when a specified stress or strain has been reached, or it may be continued until the test specimen is ruptured. 14–10. The maximum load is recorded and the result indicates the ultimate tensile strength of the material. 14–11. Various stages of the tensile tests provide data for determining the elastic limit, yield point, yield strength, tensile strength, and proportional limit. 14–12. The percent of elongation in a given gage length, reduction percent of area, and modulus of elasticity are also obtained in the test.

IMPACT TESTING

This is a dynamic test of a specimen which has been machined, ground, and notched, then placed in an impact testing machine.

The specimen is struck and broken by a single blow which measures the energy in foot-pounds required to break it. The specimen is usually notched to concentrate the stresses at the base of the notch. If the material distributes the stress uniformly, the impact value in terms of foot-pounds of energy absorbed will be high. Three tests are normally performed; then an average value of the tests are made.

Impact testing is generally performed by two types of machines: the Izod and the Charpy.

In the Izod test, the specimen is gripped at one end in a vertical position and is broken by a

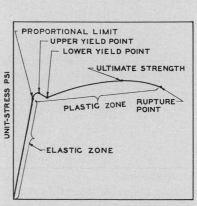

14–12. Stress-strain diagram for low-carbon steel.

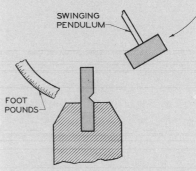

14–13. Specimen mounted for Izod impact-toughness test.

14–14. Specimen mounted for Charpy impact-toughness test.

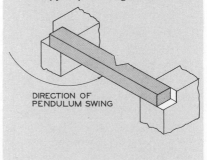

blow delivered at a fixed distance from the notch (about 22 millimeters). 14–13 (page 81).

The Charpy specimen is supported freely at its ends and is hit at a point behind the notch. 14–14 (page 81). The type of notch being used is very important. The V-notches should be cut with a specially formed milling cutter or with a specially prepared grinding wheel.

The blow to the specimen is applied by means of a freely swinging pendulum in both machines.

FATIGUE TESTING

Machine parts can fail due to a repetition of stresses even though well below the stress which the part is capable of withstanding under static load application.

The endurance level of a metal is the stress level at which a metal can withstand, without failure, an infinitely large number of repeated alternating stresses. This stress level is always below the elastic limit of the metal. The stress can be located by fatigue testing machines.

There are many different types of testing machines for the determination of this endurance level, ranging from small laboratory models to large actual-part, fatigue-testing devices.

The most commonly used type of fatigue test is the *rotating beam test*. In this test the specimen is rotated while being subjected to a bending movement. The purpose of the rotation is to cause an alternate shift of the uniform bending movement between load points from

tension to compression every 180° of rotation.

Another commonly used test is the *R. R. Moore fatigue test*. The specimen being tested is rotated under load at 10,000 rpm so that very rapid stress alternations occur. In this test it is very important that care be taken in preparation of the specimen. Careful machining and preparation of the gage length is very essential, as fatigue failure is very sensitive to· surface influences.

Numerous test specimens have to be prepared to determine the endurance limit. The first specimen is tested at relatively high stress so that it will fail from a small number of stress applications. By testing a number of specimens and reducing the unit tensile stress, a load will be found where the number of reversals necessary to produce failure is greater than an arbitrary number of reversals previously selected. If the load

cycles approach 10 million in number, for instance, the specimen may be considered to have indefinite life. This point is then known as the *endurance limit* or *strength*.

Another fatigue test is the *bend test*. In this test the metal is bent back and forth and not rotated. It is used on flat rolled products.

Failures are plotted, using semi-logarithmic paper with the values of stress (S) as the ordinate and the number of reversals to cause failure (N) as the abscissa; the result is called an SN diagram.

SPARK TESTING

Spark testing is often used to identify unknown types of steel. This is a general test that cannot take the place of chemical analysis. In this test a study is made of the sparks formed when the steel is held against a high-speed grinding wheel. The sparks are observed under subdued

14–15. Metals can be identified by the spark pattern which is generated by grinding.

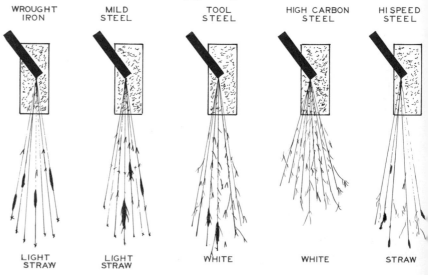

WROUGHT IRON	MILD STEEL	TOOL STEEL	HIGH CARBON STEEL	HI SPEED STEEL
LIGHT STRAW	LIGHT STRAW	WHITE	WHITE	STRAW

lighting conditions. Identification is made by the characteristics of the spark created. Sparks made by known metals are compared with sparks from the metal being tested for identification.

The quantity of spurts, or spark-explosions, depends upon the carbon content of the metal. The volume of sparks produced with carbon steel is quite large. Wrought iron, which has a very low carbon content, will produce very few spurts. 14–15. Tables that show the characteristics of sparks can be secured from manufacturers of grinding wheels.

Check Your Knowledge

1. Define heat treatment.

2. Why do modern heat-treating methods require accurate measurement and temperature control?

3. For what purposes are indicating pyrometers used?

4. Describe each of the cubic space lattice units.

5. What is austenite?

6. What is meant by allotropic change in grain structure?

7. What controls grain size?

8. Why should the temperature of metals be carefully controlled in the heat treatment process?

9. What is a fracture grain size test?

10. What limitations have to be taken into consideration when making comparisons of grain sizes?

11. Explain the relationship between the carbon content and the degree of hardness obtainable by heat treatment.

12. What happens when steel consisting of 100% pearlite is heated to a temperature above 1350°F.?

13. Explain the term critical temperature.

14. What effect does carbon in steel have upon the rate of transformation?

15. Describe how martensite is formed.

16. What is essential in the formation of a martensitic structure?

17. What effect do hardenability agents have upon the critical quenching velocity?

18. What means are used to aid cooling of parts having heavy sections?

19. Describe the end quench method of measuring hardenability.

20. What is an isothermal transformation diagram and for what purpose is it used?

21. What is the purpose of tempering?

22. Describe the tempering operation.

23. What effect do time and temperature have upon tempering?

24. Describe the process of martempering.

25. State the results of the annealing process.

26. What is austempering? How does it differ from ordinary tempering?

27. Why must the cooling rate be very slow in austempering?

28. Distinguish between spheroidizing and normalizing.

29. How is the pack carburizing process performed?

30. What kind of carbonaceous materials are used for pack carburizing?

31. Describe the gas carburizing method.

32. Briefly describe the cyaniding process.

33. How is flame hardening carried out?

34. How does induction heating differ from conventional heating methods for hardening?

35. Is this method of hardening applicable for fast production processes? Explain.

36. What is a hardness test?

37. Explain the Rockwell hardness tester.

38. Explain how a Brinell hardness tester operates.

39. What is a tensile test? Describe the method used.

40. What type of specimens are used in tensile testing?

References

Chalmers, Bruce, *Physical Metallurgy,* 2nd ed., Princeton, N.J., D. Van Nostrand Co., Inc., 1962.

Dieter, G. E., Jr., *Mechanical Metallurgy,* New York, McGraw-Hill Book Co., 1961.

Doan, G. E., *The Principles of Physical Metallurgy,* 3rd ed., New York, McGraw-Hill Book Co., 1953.

Grossman, M. A., *Principles of Heat Treatment,* Metals Park, Ohio, American Society for Metals, 1957.

Hultgren, R., *Fundamentals of Physical Metallurgy,* Englewood Cliffs, N.J. Prentice-Hall, Inc., 1952.

Pouring cupola iron into a converter with a 60- or 75-ton transfer ladle.

Section Four

Foundry Processes

As previously noted, one of the oldest industries in the world is the casting of metals. Metal castings were made by the Egyptians as early as the year 4000 B.C. The columns that supported King Solomon's temple in Israel were made of cast bronze, 27′ high and 5′ 9″ in diameter, the thickness of the metal being about 4″. Later the Greeks and then the Romans cast metal bells and ornaments for their temples.

Although the first use of metal castings was for ornamental purposes, as man became more skillful he developed metal weap-

ons for defense against his enemies. After that the art of founding progressed slowly until cast iron was developed and scientists began the kind of study known today as metallurgy.

In the year 1642 the first iron casting was made in Colonial America by the Saugus Iron Works. It was an iron cooking pot. From this single foundry engaged in the manufacture of cooking utensils has developed one of the largest industries in the United States. There are an estimated 390,000 workers employed in the nation's more than 5,000 foundries.

Most foundries specialize in casting a particular metal, since somewhat different methods and equipment are needed for diverse casting. However, some foundries do cast several types of metals. These have very little mechanized equipment. They are usually small and produce small amounts of different kinds of castings for special needs.

Large, highly mechanized shops typically produce large quantities of identical castings. For example, such a foundry may produce thousands of identical castings for automobile manufacturers. Materials and finished castings in these plants are moved with mechanized conveyors and cranes.

The conveniences found today in the modern home depend to a large extent on foundry products. Products such as bathtubs, sinks, wash basins, soil pipe, heating equipment, cooking utensils, and parts for washers and dryers generally use cast metal in their construction.

shrinkage allowances in the construction of the pattern. Different metals, when cast, have different shrinkages. Table 15 shows the shrinkage allowance for the most common metals. This shrinkage is readily calculated by the patternmaker. He constructs the pattern oversize to allow for it.

Table 15. Metal Shrinkage in Fractions of an Inch per Foot	
Monel metal	$3/16$
Cast iron	$1/8$
Aluminum	$3/16$
Brass	$3/16$
Magnesium	$3/16$
Bronze	$3/16$
Copper	$5/32$
Steel	$1/4$
Nickel	$3/16$
Malleable iron	$1/8$
Zinc	$5/16$
Tin	$1/2$
Lead	$5/16$

Unit 15.   Patternmaking

A pattern for a metal casting is a form used to make a cavity in sand. A pattern can be made from wood, metal, plaster, plastic, or any other material that will retain its shape during the molding process. NOTE: A metal pattern is used for production runs due to the fact that it has a much longer life than a wood pattern; however, a wood pattern is constructed first, as the master pattern. The permanent metal pattern, usually aluminum, is cast from it, then machined to dimensions.

Most metals expand when heated and contract when cooled. Therefore it is necessary for the patternmaker to provide for

The patternmaker also has to make allowances for machining the finished casting. This is controlled by the *degree of finish* desired, *type of metal* used, and the *shape and size* of the casting.

All vertical surfaces of a pattern must be provided with *draft* (tapered sides) to facilitate withdrawing from the sand. 15–1. This tapering allows a slight clearance for the pattern as it is lifted from the sand. Draft varies from 3° for small, thin patterns to ½° to 1° for thicker ones. NOTE: Interior openings may need a larger allowance.

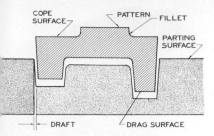

15-1. Draft is necessary to facilitate the removal of the pattern from the sand.

As mentioned before, *allowances for finish* are also made on a pattern, sufficiently oversize to permit the machining of surfaces to dimensions.

The standard finish allowance for ferrous metals is $\frac{1}{8}''$. For nonferrous castings the allowance could be as low as $\frac{1}{16}''$. On large castings, where warp must be compensated, the finish allowance might run as high as $\frac{3}{4}''$.

Sometimes it is necessary to rap the pattern to facilitate its removal from the sand. This causes the cavity in the mold to enlarge slightly and permits easy removal of the pattern from the sand. This is known as *shake*. Shake allowance should be taken into consideration in the construction of the pattern. (See Unit 20, page 107.)

Wooden master patterns are made from a variety of woods. Sugar pine is the most commonly used, as it has a close grain and carves easily. Honduras mahogany is generally used for patterns which have to withstand a great deal of rough handling. Other woods are maple, cherry, walnut, northern pine, and Mexican cedar.

PATTERN CONSTRUCTION

In the construction of a wooden pattern, accurate layout is important. The method for withdrawing the pattern from the sand must be carefully considered so that proper *draft* can be built in. Corners have to be *filleted* to eliminate the development of shrinkage cracks and to prevent the sand from sticking in the corners and spoiling the cavity in the mold.

The construction of a simple pattern is shown in the illustration. The following steps should be pursued. The casting can be made from aluminum or brass, so allow for the proper shrinkage of the metal. 15-2.

Procedure for Making a Split Pattern

1. Check the drawing carefully; note that this pattern will be easier to mold if made of the split variety.

2. Secure two sugar pine blocks of the proper size and glue together with a piece of paper between the blocks. Let the glue dry.

3. With dividers scribe a circle on the block, allowing enough stock for turning to the proper dimensions.

4. Mount the block on a faceplate of a wood-turning lathe and turn the recess on the bottom.

5. Reverse the block on the faceplate and turn block to the shape and size as shown in the drawing. Sand smooth.

6. Remove block from the faceplate and separate the two halves. This can be done with a thin knife blade.

7. Drill two holes and place dowel pins in one of the halves. Drill corresponding holes in the other block directly opposite the holes drilled for the dowel pins. NOTE: Be sure the two halves separate easily when pulled apart.

8. Give the pattern two or three coats of thin shellac.

Fillets

It is necessary that sharp corners be avoided on castings because: (1) they are difficult to produce, (2) in cooling of the metal the grains have a tendency to align themselves at right angles to the cooling surfaces causing a weak area to develop in the corner, and (3) sharp corners are easily destroyed by the movement of the molten metal poured into the sand mold. All sharp corners should be eliminated in the construction of the pattern. This can be accomplished by the use of *fillets*. There is no

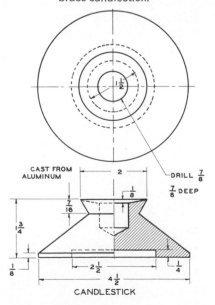

15-2. Pattern for an aluminum or brass candlestick.

possibility of a hole developing in a corner if a fillet is used.

Fillets can be made of a variety of materials, the most common being wax. Wax is applied with a fillet iron, which is a ball-like tool that has been heated slightly to melt the wax. 15–3. Wooden fillets are used for long straight angles. Leather fillets are commonly used because they are easily applied. Fillets are classified in size by 16ths of an inch radius variations.

TYPES OF COMMON PATTERNS

In the following, several of the most common types of patterns are described.

Wood and metal patterns can vary a great deal, depending upon the purpose for which they are going to be used. The most common types of patterns are the one-piece flat back, split, multipiece, loose-piece, cored, sweep-pattern, and match-plate.

One-Piece Flat Back Pattern

This pattern has a flat surface on the cope side, making possible a straight line parting on the joint between the cope and drag of the mold. 15–4. NOTE: *Part-*

Sebree Photography, Canton, Ill.

15–4. An example of a one-piece flatback pattern.

ing surface is a line at which a pattern or mold separates. The *cope* is the top half of the flask, having aligning pin guides. The *drag* refers to the bottom half of the flask, having aligning pins.

Split Pattern

For castings that are intricate in design or of unusual shape, making removal from the sand difficult, a split pattern is employed to form the mold. 15–5. This pattern is made in two parts, one producing the lower half of the mold and the other the upper half. The parts are generally turned on a wood lathe

Sebree Photography, Canton, Ill.

15–5. Split pattern. This pattern is made in two parts to facilitate easy removal from the mold.

so that they are symmetrical. The cope and drag portions of the pattern are accurately fitted together with wood or metal dowel pins.

Multi-Piece Pattern

This pattern is constructed of three or more parts. 15–6. The

15–6. A cross-sectional view of a three-part (multi-piece) pattern in a three-part flask. Metal is poured into the sprue and flows to the cavity through the runner gate. The cheek is the part of the flask located between the cope and the drag.

15–3. Applying a wax fillet to a pattern. Heated fillet iron is drawn along wax to form proper radius.

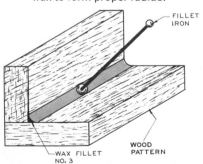

FILLET IRON

WAX FILLET NO. 3

WOOD PATTERN

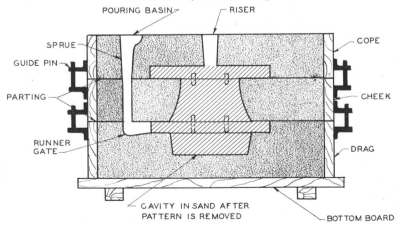

POURING BASIN

RISER

SPRUE

GUIDE PIN

PARTING

RUNNER GATE

COPE

CHEEK

DRAG

CAVITY IN SAND AFTER PATTERN IS REMOVED

BOTTOM BOARD

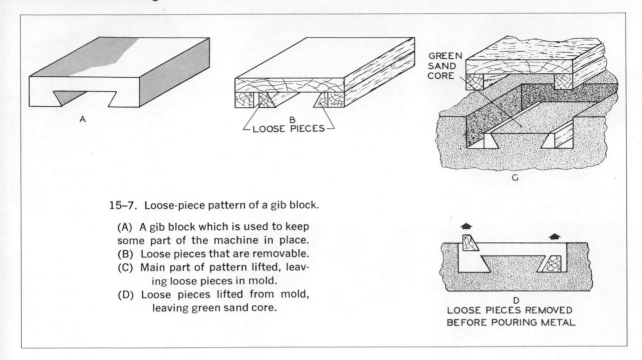

15–7. Loose-piece pattern of a gib block.

(A) A gib block which is used to keep some part of the machine in place.
(B) Loose pieces that are removable.
(C) Main part of pattern lifted, leaving loose pieces in mold.
(D) Loose pieces lifted from mold, leaving green sand core.

pieces may be actual body parts of the pattern and other parts such as *bosses* (projections on a pattern), hubs, or loose pieces such as *cope* or *drag prints* (projections on a pattern that form a seat in the mold for a dry sand core). The parts that make up the multi-piece pattern are held together with dowel pins.

Loose-Piece Pattern

This pattern may be used when projections or overhanging parts occur. Without the loose piece on the pattern, projections may make it difficult or even impossible to withdraw the pattern from the sand. 15–7. The pattern is made with a loose piece or pieces fastened only with vertical dowels or pins. When the mold is being made, the loose pieces remain in the sand until the main pattern is removed.

Each loose piece can then be extracted through the cavity which has been created by the withdrawal of the main pattern.

Cored Pattern

Many castings require holes, recesses, or indentations. Some types of patterns are made with parts—*core prints*—added to the surface. These form a seat in the mold and leave impressions in the sand for a dry sand core. In some cases, core prints are removable and are fastened to the pattern with dowels. After the pattern is removed from the sand, a baked dry sand core is placed in the seat made by the core prints. After the molten metal is poured, a cavity is left in the casting, the shape of the core. 15–8 (A, B & C). Figs. B & C shown on page 90.

15–8(A). Cored pattern. Core prints on the end support the pattern in the mold.

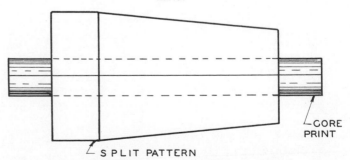

15–8(B). An example of a cored pattern. The dark part of the pattern forms the seat for the core in the mold.

Sebree Photography, Canton, Ill.

15–8(C). Expert craftsmen are required to construct a pattern of any size or shape in a modern pattern shop.

Mesta Machine Co.

Sweep Pattern

While it is not ordinarily thought of as a true pattern, this can function as a pattern in forming symmetrical molds and cores. The sweep is a form made of wood, which is revolved around a central axis and shapes a mold in the sand. 15–9. The sweep is used for rough castings, such as sewer covers or catch basins.

Match Plate

This pattern is used on molding machines for quantity production of castings. A single pattern or a number of patterns can be mounted on a plate. The plate can be made of wood but more often it is of metal, aluminum being the most common. Flat back patterns are mounted with one half on the drag side, while split or two-piece patterns are mounted with one half on the drag side and the other half on the cope side—exactly opposite. The sprue bases, runners, and gates are fastened to the drag side, eliminating the necessity of cutting flow channels (depressions in the sand which carry the molten metal to the cavity) by hand. 15–10 (A, B & C).

A match plate pattern has an advantage in that it is easier to store and use than is a loose-piece pattern. Another distinct advantage is that the *gating* system (provision for easy passage of the flowing metal into the mold) can be mounted on the match plate. This eliminates cutting gates and flow channels by hand, a time saver in production molding.

15–9. (A) Sweep pattern rotates around post forming the mold cavity. (B) Core is placed on chaplets in the mold cavity and molten metal flows around core into mold cavity, causing chaplets to fuse into casting as in (C).

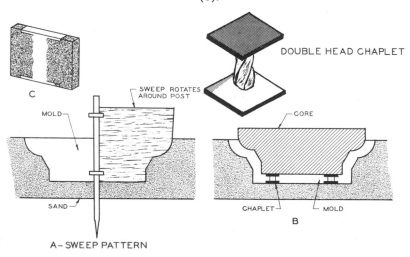

15–10(A). In a match plate pattern the sprue and riser bases are fastened to the plate. If the pattern is cored, core prints are also attached.

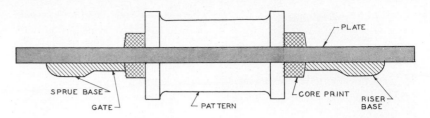

SPRUE BASE
GATE
PATTERN
PLATE
CORE PRINT
RISER BASE

15–10(B). Match plates.
Accurate Cast Products, Inc.

15–10(C). Match plate with master pattern. One half of the pattern is located on each side of the plate.

Accurate Cast Products, Inc.

Unit 16.   Foundry Sands

Many deposits of various grades of molding sands are found on earth. These natural sands are composed of silicas (silicon dioxide) which are very *refractory* (heat resistant) and usually contain a small amount of organic matter. The grains of silica sand neither melt nor fuse together easily, nor do they crack into smaller particles when they come into contact with molten metal.

However, pure silica sand lacks binding qualities and, therefore, is not suitable to be used alone for molding. By adding bentonite (a clay product used primarily as an admix to molding and core sands as a bonding material), the necessary binding quality can be obtained.

Molding sand must possess qualities that enable it to be tempered and formed into definite shapes. It must have the required chemical composition so that fusion will not take place from the high heat of the metal. Natural molding sand needs 6% to 9% moisture for good molding. Foundry sand should possess a certain amount of porosity to permit the escape of natural gases when the molten metal contacts the sand.

Natural sands used in general molding work contain only the binder which was mined with them and they are used as found, with water added.

Sand texture is regulated by sifting it through wire-mesh screens of different sizes. It is selected for use according to grain size and its ability to withstand the high heat of molten metal (refractoriness). The clay bond is an important factor in molding sands. Too small an amount of clay packs the sand too tightly and does not permit the gases to escape from the mold, which can cause defective castings. As the bonding materials are burned away after prolonged use, new bonded sand has to be added from time to time. As the clay bond is burned out, molding sand becomes inactive. The sand will feel "rotten," in that it will not hold together when squeezed by hand. Addition of new sand causes a portion of its clay to mix with the used sand and bring it to "life." New sand should be added until, when a small quantity of the mixture is squeezed into a lump in the hand, the lump will separate into pieces without crumbling.

TYPES OF SAND

Albany No. 1

The most common type of molding sand used in school foundries is Albany No. 1—combined with water. The analysis of this sand is shown in Table 16.

Table 16. Analysis of Albany No. 1 Sand	
Silica	80.88%
Alumina	14.93%
Iron oxide	1.32%
Combined water	2.54%
Inert materials	1.32%

Water tempered sand has to be used and properly cared for each day if good quality castings are to be obtained. Difficulties are often encountered in schools because the sand is not used for several days at a time.

Oil Binder

Another type of sand that is recommended for schools is a sand-oil-binder combination. Water tempering is not necessary. In fact as little as ¼ of 1% of moisture is detrimental to the mixture. The physical properties of the sand are indicated by its grade and type. These properties will determine the surface finish of the casting.

A wash silica sand with a fineness number of 100 to 180 is satisfactory. A sand with low clay content is best, as excess clay absorbs too much moisture during the molding operation and releases it during the pouring of the metal.

● The binders for waterless sand can be purchased from foundry supply houses, under the names of Petro-Bond and Neo-Bond.
● The oil used in the oil-bonded sand has a viscosity index of less than 50 or 55 and an aromatic content of 10 to 20%.
● A small quantity of methyl alcohol is mixed with the sand as a catalyst.

A good formula for a waterless sand is:

100 pounds of sand.
  5 pounds of Neo-Bond or Petro-Bond binder.
  3 pounds of oil.
  4 ounces methyl alcohol.

Dry-mix the sand and binder for at least 2 minutes. Add 3 pounds of oil to the sand mixture and mull (mix) for 5 minutes. Add the methyl alcohol and mull for 5 minutes.

This sand can be stored until ready for use. Any flask can be used with oil-bonded sand but a steel flask will give the best results.

The molder will get better results if dry parting agents (see page 93) are used; spread evenly over the patterns.

Synthetic Sand

Sand adapted for molding is either natural (already mentioned)—found as deposits in old lake and river beds, wind driven deposits, deposits left by glaciers, and marine deposits—or it may be synthetic. The proper grade of washed sand is selected and is mixed with clay or bentonite in a power mixer. 16–1. An adequate amount of water is added. NOTE: These synthetic sands are worked at a lower moisture content than natural molding sands. Whereas natural molding sand needs 6 to 9% moisture for good molding, a synthetic sand can be worked at a moisture content of 2 to 5%. Less gas is generated with this type of sand.

Sand Grain

The determination of grain in sands depends upon the type of work to be molded. Only in recent years have both physical and chemical properties of molding sand been recognized as playing an important part in the

16–1. Sand conditioning machine.
Royer Foundry & Machine Co.

production of clean sand castings, free from imperfections.

Core Sands

Sands that are used for core making have very little or no clay bond. The sand grains may be either sharp or round, are bright in color, glassy in appearance, and are of pure silica. Core sand must have the property of resisting fusion to the casting in order to produce a smooth casting.

Core sands have these sources —glacial, wind-deposited, and water-deposited. After the sand is mined, it is washed and all clay removed. It is then graded to various sizes in rotary screens.

Large cores require a coarse, open silica due to the fact that a large amount of gas is developed. When the finish of the core surface must be smooth, a fine core sand is necessary.

All cores must have sufficient refractoriness to withstand the heat until the molten metal has filled the cavity. A thin coating of graphite or similar material helps the core to withstand the intense heat until the metal has cooled. NOTE: The binding material in the core should be burned out so that the core can be removed easily from the casting.

Facing Sand

Facing sand is a mixture of new sand, old sand, and sea coal. The primary purpose of facing sand is to form a smooth, highly heat-resistant surface as an insulating layer between the sand and molten metal. This insulation prevents the metal from

"burning-in." As a result, good surfaced castings are obtained, while blasting and cleaning costs are minimized.

In molding processes there is a distinction between *blacking* and facing sand. Blacking consists of graphite with a small amount of clay mixed with it to make it stick to the mold. It is applied to the finished surface of the mold or core.

Core Binders

In making cores, the sand is mixed with a binder to hold it while it is being baked in a core oven. Binders can be water soluble, oil, pitch, or rosin. Foundry molasses also makes a good core binder.

Parting Compounds

To prevent the green sand from sticking to the pattern in a molding operation, it is necessary to provide a material that will allow the sand to separate from the parting surfaces of the cope and drag. This is accomplished by using a material known as parting compound. A non-silica parting compound, made from powdered phosphate rock, has all the desirable qualities necessary and does not have any of the undesirable features of silica dust. Parting compounds that were used in the past have been abandoned as they were a health hazard to the molder.

Core Paste

Core paste is a material used to cement the two halves of a core together. It is also used to repair cores that have been broken. For school use a core paste can be made of flour and water, similar to wallpaper paste.

Unit 17. Sand Testing

Controlling sand mixtures in modern foundry operations is an important part of the casting procedure. At one time, the molder was responsible for testing the quality of the molding sand. His experience as a molder had to guide him. Today, high-quality production quotas and competitive costs have made it necessary to use more scientific methods.

The properties of molding sand are changed by continued subjection to high temperature, contamination from foreign materials, washing action in tempering, and change and distribution of grain size. It is therefore important that periodic tests be made. Two types of tests are used—mechanical and chemical —the mechanical being favored.

Sands are tested for the following properties: (1) refractoriness, (2) permeability, (3) strength, (4) grain size and shape, and (5) moisture content. When tested for *refractori-*

ness, the sand must resist a high temperature without fusing.

PERMEABILITY TEST

Sand has to have sufficient porosity to permit the gases generated in the mold by the molten metal to escape. Permeability is measured by the quantity of air that passes through a sand sample in a prescribed time and under standard conditions.

The smoothness of a casting depends upon the grain size of the molding sand. As previously mentioned, coarse-grained sands are more permeable. However, when coarse-grained sands are *added* to a sand of fine grain, the permeability initially decreases and then increases.

In a permeability test, the sand specimen is prepared in a machine known as a *sand rammer.* 17–1. A predetermined weight of sand is placed in a steel speci-

men tube. The tube is placed in the rammer and a 14-pound weight is dropped on the sand three times. This operation compacts the sand to a standard hardness. The sand is then placed in an electric permeameter. 17–2. A simple lever arrangement is used to expand a ring to form an airtight seal within the specimen tube.

The time it takes for 122 cubic inches of air to pass through the rammed specimen determines the permeability of the sand. If the pressure is maintained at a constant value between 0.014 and 0.14 psi, the permeability number (p) is defined as:

$$p = \frac{7.13}{P \times T}$$

where P = air pressure, psi
(pounds per
square inch)
T = time (minutes)

The time required for the air to pass through the specimen is read directly on the dial. The value must conform to permeability standards as shown in Table 17.

17–2. Electric permeameter.

SURFACE HARDNESS OF GREEN SAND MOLDS AND CORES

The illustration shows an instrument used to test the surface hardness of green sand molds and cores. 17–3. The hardness test can be made within a few seconds. This tester is simply pressed against the mold surface and the resultant reading is given

17–3. Mold-hardness tester for measuring surface hardness of green sand molds.

17–1. Sand rammer.

Table 17. Permeability Numbers	
Castings	Permeability Number
Cast iron (light)	15–65
Cast iron (medium)	65–100
Cast iron (heavy)	75–150
Malleable iron (medium)	50–100
Steel (medium)	125–200
Aluminum	8–15
Brass	8–20

on the dial. Excessive pressure on the tester will not alter the reading.

The principle is similar to that of the Brinell hardness tests. A ½"-radius ball point is loaded with a spring load of 980 grams. The softer the mold surface, the greater the penetration of the point into the mold. Penetration of the ball point is indicated on a reversed dial in 1,000ths of an inch.

The green hardness tester finds practical application in standardizing the degree of ramming (compacting the sand) in the foundry; also for comparison of ramming as practiced in a group of foundries, and for investigating the uniformity of ramming obtained from certain machine settings. Recommended mold hardness readings are:

Soft-rammed molds	below 70
Medium-rammed molds	70 to 80
Hard-rammed molds	above 80

TESTING FOR SAND STRENGTH

In testing sand strength the compression test is most common. It tells the foundrymen how strong the green molding sand is.

In general, the higher the compression strength of sand the more easily molds may be made.

The test is suitable for the control laboratory. It takes only a few minutes for tests of the compression strength, moisture, and permeability of sand. In industries where a conveyor system is used for handling molding sands these three tests are performed every half hour.

The Universal sand strength machine is used to test the strength of sand, which is governed by the amount of bonding material in the sand. 17–4. The machine can be used both for testing green core sand and for measuring the dry compression strength of molding sand. A sand specimen is prepared in a sand rammer and transferred to the sand strength machine where tensile, shear, and compression tests are made.

TESTING FOR MOISTURE CONTENT

Any testing system of sand control includes a periodic check on moisture content.

The moisture content of foundry sands will vary depending upon the type of molds being made and the type of metal being poured.

The moisture test is very important, because the foundryman can, from the test, standardize the percentage of moisture required in the various grades of sands in use. Every molding sand has an optimum moisture range; it is advisable to have the moisture content as close to this amount as possible. If the moisture in molding sand is too high, blow holes will appear in castings. The lower the moisture percentage, the less chance hot metal has to form excessive steam that causes the holes.

A moisture teller has a fan that drives air down past large capacity heating elements, then the heated air is dispersed through a sand sample and out through the 500-mesh bottom of the drying pan. 17–5. The high velocity of the air dries the 50-

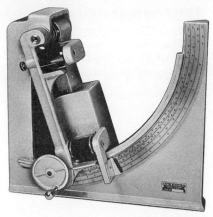

Harry W. Dietert Co.

17–4. Universal sand strength machine. Sand specimen is transferred to this machine, where tensile, shear, and compression tests are made.

gram sample of molding sand in 3 or 4 minutes.

A precision balance registers the loss of weight after moisture is removed. The percentage of moisture is thus determined. The moisture content should vary from 2 to 8%, depending upon the type of molding being done.

17–5. Moisture teller.

Harry W. Dietert Co.

THE FINENESS TEST

The fineness test of molding sand is of great value to the foundryman because the fineness of sand affects the permeability factor and bond strength very much. Coarse sand gives a rough finish to the smaller castings. Large castings require a coarse and open sand; whereas small castings require a finer sand. Brass and aluminum require a finer sand than cast iron.

The fineness test is carried out by means of a set of standard sieves (National Bureau of Standards) that are graded and numbered according to the fineness of their mesh. The screening operation is accomplished by stacking the sieves one on top of the other with the sand placed in the coarsest sieve on the top.

The sieves are vibrated in a power-driven shaker for 15 minutes and the weight of the sand retained on each sieve is obtained and converted to a percentage basis. The fineness and weight of the sand which is retained in each sieve is noted. The fineness number is obtained by adding all the products and dividing the total by the percentage of sand retained.

Unit 18. Cores and Core Making

Cores consisting of a body of specially prepared sand are made for the purpose of producing a cavity in or on a casting. A good example is the cavity made for the water jacket in a water-cooled engine block.

Cores are of three types: (1) green sand cores which are formed by the pattern itself from the same sand as is used in the rest of the mold, (2) dry sand cores which are made from special sand formed in a core box, and (3) a type of core known as a "chill," which will be described in Unit 19. 18–1.

Core making resembles molding except that cores are formed in a box constructed by the patternmaker. The core receives its shape from the core box.

Cores are usually made of clean river sand, which is mixed with a binder (common mixture of 40 parts of river sand to 1 part linseed oil) and baked in a core oven. Other binders such as wheat flour, dextrin, rosin, and pulverized pitch are also used. These are soluble in water.

The core may be rammed or packed by hand in the box. In foundries where core blowing machines are available, the sand is blown or jolted into the core box. Large cores are made on molding machines the same as molds. Compressed air blows sand through a core plate which has holes arranged to pack the sand firmly and evenly in the core box. 18–2.

After the core is packed, the excess sand is struck off, and a drier plate is placed over the core box. The box is inverted, releasing the core, which is then baked in an oven suitable for the size of the core. Core ovens are of various types: (1) shelf, (2) rack, (3) car, (4) drawer, and (5) continuous. 18–3. Core ovens are normally heated by gas because this type of fuel is clean, low in cost, and controlled easily. 18–4. There are many types of dry sand cores and they are made in many sizes and shapes. 18–5. Some of the most common are described as follows:

Vertical core stands vertically in the mold. The part of the core that is located in the cope usually requires considerable taper so that it will not tear the sand when the cope part of the flask is placed on the drag.

Balanced core is supported in the mold on one end. The core

18–1. Dry sand core.

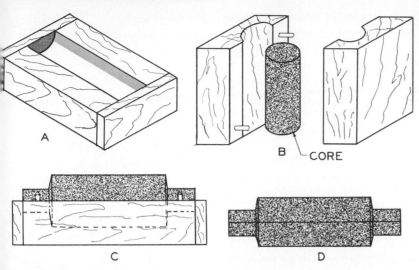

18–2. Cores can be one piece or made in two pieces and cemented to-gether: (A) core box, (B) core which has been tamped in the core box, (C) core with core prints, and (D) two halves of core cemented together.

Foundry Equipment Co.

18–4. Dry sand cores on a conveyor entering an oven for baking. Note the size of the cores.

18–3. Core oven for baking dry sand cores. The cores on the rack are moved into the oven where they are dried.

Foundry Equipment Co.

18–5. Various types of dry sand cores.

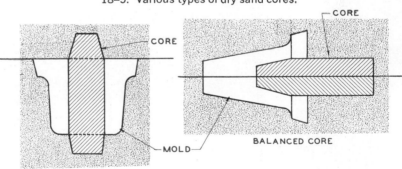

VERTICAL DRY SAND CORE

BALANCED CORE

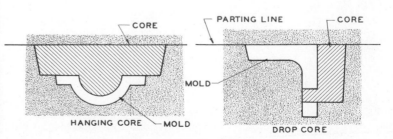

HANGING CORE

DROP CORE

print (projection) on the pattern must be made long enough so that the core will not fall into the mold. In other words, the part of the core that rests in the mold cavity should balance the part which rests in the core seat. (The core seat is the impression made in the sand by the core print.)

Hanging core is employed when the entire pattern is rammed in the drag and the core must be suspended from the top of the mold.

18–6. Chaplets: (A) double-head chaplet, (B) perforated chaplets, and (C) single-head, wrought-iron, fitted-style chaplets.

W. L. Jenkins Co.

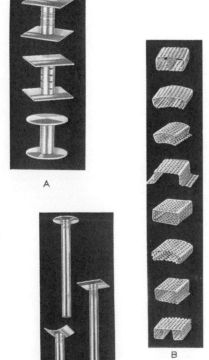

Drop core is used when a cavity or hole is not in line with the parting surface (the surface between the cope and the drag) and must be formed below the surface.

If a core does not stay properly positioned in the mold when the molten metal is poured, the walls of the castings will not be of the required thickness. Sometimes a core needs internal support in the mold. *Chaplets* are used to support cores that have a tendency to sag, shift, or sink. Chaplets are usually made of the same metal as the casting and become part of the casting by fusion. Chaplets have a height equal to the space between the core and mold cavity. They come in a variety of sizes and shapes to fit molding conditions. (Also see Unit 15.) 18–6.

A core known as a *chill* is not made from sand, but from metal. The chill has a slight taper. It is placed on a "seat" left by the core print. As the molten metal

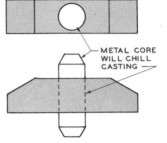

18–7. Chills are inserted in molds to speed up the solidification of the metal and to prevent internal defects.

strikes the chill, a smooth, hard surface is formed on the casting which eliminates machining. External chills are used to prevent metal shrinkage where a smooth, unmachined surface is required and where machining is not practical. 18–7.

Unit 19. Foundry Tools and Equipment

Most large foundries today are highly mechanized. The molding line is designed for high-production work, using a car-type mold conveyor serving fourteen, 4½′ molding stations. 19–1(A).

Many facilities are provided to save the molder's time and help increase productivity. Each man has his own overhead sand hopper gates, which are operated by a knee valve, and his own core racks constantly filled at his side. With the molding machine before him and sand directly overhead, with core rack at hand and the endless car-type conveyor, and with the molds being automatically carried away as fast as he completes them,

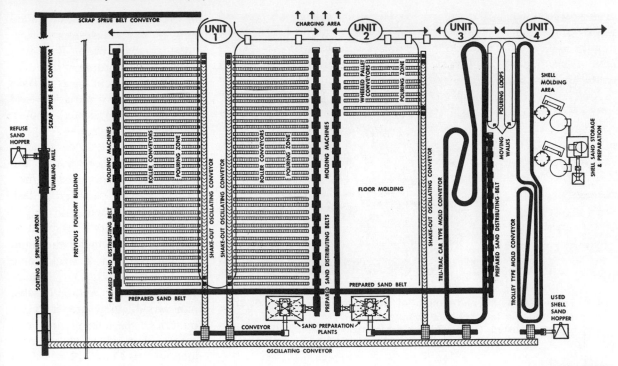

SCRAP SPRUE BELT CONVEYOR

CHARGING AREA

UNIT 1   UNIT 2   UNIT 3   UNIT 4

REFUSE SAND HOPPER

SCRAP SPRUE BELT CONVEYOR

TUMBLING MILL

SORTING & SPRUING APRON

PREVIOUS FOUNDRY BUILDING

MOLDING MACHINES

ROLLER CONVEYOR

POURING ZONE

PREPARED SAND DISTRIBUTING BELT

SHAKE-OUT OSCILLATING CONVEYOR
SHAKE-OUT OSCILLATING CONVEYOR

ROLLER CONVEYOR

POURING ZONE

MOLDING MACHINES

PREPARED SAND DISTRIBUTING BELTS

WHEELED PALLET CONVEYORS

POURING ZONE

FLOOR MOLDING

PREPARED SAND BELT

SHAKE-OUT OSCILLATING CONVEYOR

TRU-TRAC CAR TYPE MOLD CONVEYOR

PREPARED SAND DISTRIBUTING BELT

POURING LOOPS

MOVING WALKS

SHELL MOLDING AREA

SHELL SAND STORAGE & PREPARATION

TROLLEY TYPE MOLD CONVEYOR

USED SHELL SAND HOPPER

PREPARED SAND BELT

CONVEYOR

SAND PREPARATION PLANTS

OSCILLATING CONVEYOR

Link Belt Co.

19–1(A). Schematic diagram of a mechanized malleable iron foundry consisting of two gravity roll lines, a pallet line, continuous car-type mold conveyor system, and a high-speed shell mold line.

the molder works under ideal conditions.

Each molder has a mechanical counter at his station to indicate the number of completed molds that he has deposited on the conveyor.

Completed molds are taken from this area to the weight and jacket shifting zone. Here the weights on top of the poured molds and the jackets confining the molds are removed and transferred across the line to be used on newly made molds.

Three men can pour simultaneously while standing on a moving platform, which consists of a double strand of chain with checkered floor plate slats and which travels at the same speed as the conveyor. 19–1(B). This

assures a constant relationship between the pourer and the mold, with the men pouring "on the move."

After pouring, the molds pass through a short section of exhaust tunnel where hot gases and fumes are exhausted through a stack. Weights and jackets are removed as the molds approach a fan-ventilated cooling room, where additional steam and gases are exhausted and cooling of molds is accelerated.

The conveyor makes several loops within this area, then upon reaching the far end of the room, automatically dumps molds on a shakeout screen. 19–2 (Page 100). The dumping is done through the action of a roller on one side of the mold car that rides

19–1(B). Three men can pour simultaneously while standing on a moving platform.

Link Belt Co.

Link Belt Co.

19–2. Following pouring and removal of jackets and weights, molds are conveyed through a fan-ventilated cooling room where steam and gases are exhausted. Then molds are automatically discharged.

the cope and drag which is called the *"cheek."* Flasks are designated as two-part of three-part flasks, etc., according to the number of component parts. Flasks of more than two parts are used for more complicated molds. (See Fig. 15–6, page 88.)

The snap flask is constructed with a hinge on one corner and a lock on the opposite corner. 19–3(A). This permits the flask to be removed before the metal is poured. Before the metal is poured into the mold, the mold is enclosed with a steel frame or jacket. 19–3(B). Because steel flasks are more durable than wood, they are used by foundries specializing in large castings that call for heavy production. 19–4 and 19–5. Wood is suitable for school foundries. 19–3(A).

Molding and bottom boards, made of either wood or metal, support the flask while the mold is being made. 19–6(A). The bottom board supports the drag half of the flask. The molding board is placed on top of the cope before the flask is rolled over.

up and over a dumping cam located at the discharge point. Bottom boards are not discharged here but stay on the conveyor and are returned to the molding area.

FLASKS

A flask is a box which holds the sand in which the pattern is rammed-up in the making of a mold. Made of either wood or metal, flasks are parted horizontally into two or more sections. In a mold composed of two parts, the lowermost—or the one which is molded first—is called the *"drag,"* and the uppermost—or the one on the top half of the flask is called the *"cope."* A flask that consists of more than two parts has a section between

19–3(A). Cherry snap flask. The upper part is the cope; the lower part is the drag.

Adams Co.

19–3(B). Steel jacket.

Adams Co.

OTHER TOOLS AND DEVICES

Bellows or compressed air blows excess parting material and loose sand from the mold cavity. 19–6(B).

Riddles are used by the molder to sift sand over the pattern in order to insure a smooth casting. 19–7(A). Riddles are usually round in shape and their sizes are denoted by the diameter of the frame and by the number of meshes per inch in the screen. A No. 4 riddle has 4 meshes per inch, etc. Some foundries use motor driven riddles to speed up the work. 19–7.(D).

A *draw pin* or *spike* is a pointed piece of steel which can be stabbed into the pattern to lift the pattern from the mold.

Draw screws are devices used to lift the pattern from the sand after the mold has been rammed. 19–7(B). The draw screw is threaded either for the pattern

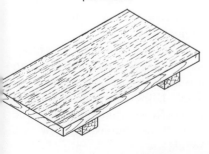

Shanafelt Mfg. Co.

19–4. Special pressure-proof flask.

19–5. Steel flask used in foundries where large castings are made. The weight of this flask is 2,210 pounds.

19–6(A). Mold board used to support flask.

19–6(B). Bellows used to blow excess sand and parting material from the mold cavity.

19–7(A). Riddle used to sift sand over pattern.

McEnglevan, Inc.

19–7(D). Motor-driven riddle.

19–7(B). Drawing devices to lift pattern from sand.

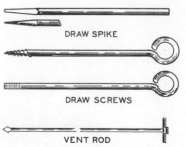

DRAW SPIKE

DRAW SCREWS

VENT ROD

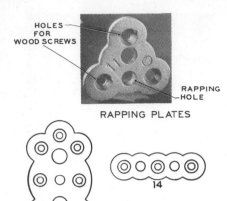

HOLES FOR WOOD SCREWS

RAPPING HOLE

RAPPING PLATES

14

17

19–7(C). Rapping plates fastened to pattern to be used with draw screws and rapper.

or for a draw plate fastened to the pattern. 19–7(C).

Vent wire or a *rod* is used for making openings (vents) in the mold. The rod is ⅛″ to ¼″ in diameter and is thrust into the mold in all directions for the purpose of allowing the free escape of gases and steam generated by the evaporation of the moisture in the sand.

Slicks, spoons, lifters, and cornering tools are used for repairing and finishing molds. 19–8.

Slicks and *spoons* are of many types, depending upon their shapes: oval, spoon, heart and spoon, and double spoon. Many other types are used by molders, depending upon the design of the mold.

Lifters are used for patching deep sections of a mold and removing loose sand from mold pockets.

Rammers of hardwood are often used in pairs for packing sand in the mold around the pattern. The molder generally uses bench rammers, one in each hand, as he rams up the mold. The wedge-shaped peen-end forces the sand sideways in the flask. Pneumatic rammers are

American Foundrymen's Society

19–9. Pneumatic sand rammer being used to pack sand into a foundry mold.

used in many foundries to speed up the work. 19–9.

Trowels are made in many different styles and sizes, each one suitable for a particular job, such as making joints and finishing, slicking, and smoothing the mold. 19–10.

A *gate cutter,* as previously noted, is a piece of sheet metal used to cut an opening between the sprue or riser and the mold cavity to provide an opening for the molten metal to flow to the cavity. 19–10.

A *water brush* or *molder's bulb* is used to moisten the sand around the pattern. 19–11(A). This helps prevent the sand edges from crumbling when the pattern is removed from the mold.

The *shake bag* is used to dust parting compound on the mold and pattern.

19–8. Corner tools, slicks, spoons, and lifters are used for smoothing and repairing the mold. Bench rammers are used to tamp sand around the pattern in the flask.

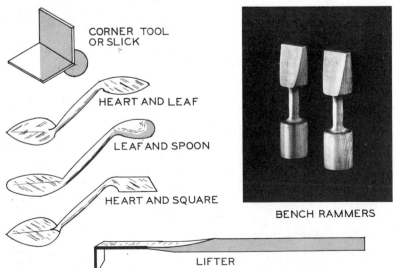

CORNER TOOL OR SLICK

HEART AND LEAF

LEAF AND SPOON

HEART AND SQUARE

LIFTER

BENCH RAMMERS

FINISHING TROWEL   GATE CUTTER

19–10. LEFT: Trowel for finishing, slicking, and smoothing the mold. RIGHT: Gate cutter for cutting gates which permits molten metal to flow to mold cavity.

WATER BRUSH   SHAKE BAG   SPRUE OR RISER PIN

19-11(A). Some tools used by moulders.

ing "washing" of the sand as the metal enters the mold.

Types of Gates

There are three types of gates used in molding operations: (A) parting, (B) top, and (C) bottom. 19–11(B).

The *parting gate,* as shown, is made between the cope and the drag. Care has to be taken in pouring to see that the molten metal dropping into the drag does not cause washing of the mold.

A *top gate* has a cup strainer made of ceramic material placed in a gate for casting of steel, iron, brass, and bronze. A strainer provides a means to control the metal flow and permits only clean metal to enter the mold. An ad-

Riser pins and sprue pins are very similar in appearance. The riser pin forms an opening to supply the mold with additional metal to compensate for metal shrinkage.

A *sprue pin* is rammed in the cope of the mold to make an opening through which the molten metal is poured. A *sprue cutter* can be used instead of the sprue pin in production molding. A sprue cutter is a hollow tube pushed through the top to the joint of the mold. The tube is then withdrawn, leaving an opening.

A *strike-off bar* is a metal or wooden bar used to remove excess sand from the mold after ramming is completed. (See Unit 20.)

GATING

The purpose of a gating system is to permit pouring the molten metal into the mold with as little turbulence as possible; to permit the mold cavity to be filled completely; to control the flow of metal; and to help the metal solidify properly between the sections.

There should be no change in the direction of the gating system that would lead to a slower filling of the mold cavity. This would cause the metal to solidify before reaching all parts of the cavity.

Whenever possible the gating system should be a part of the pattern, allowing the sand to be properly rammed and prevent-

19-11(B). Three main types of gates or molds: (A) parting gate, (B) top gate, (C) bottom gate.

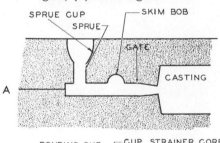

SPRUE CUP   SKIM BOB
SPRUE   GATE
A   CASTING

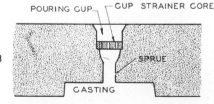

POURING CUP   CUP STRAINER CORE
B   SPRUE
CASTING

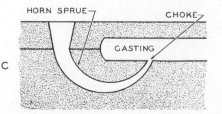

HORN SPRUE   CHOKE
CASTING
C

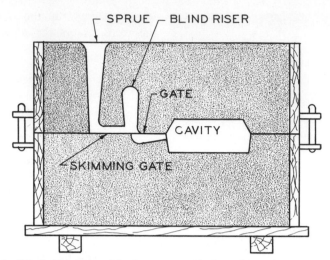

SPRUE — BLIND RISER

GATE

CAVITY

SKIMMING GATE

19–12. Blind riser located in the cope half of the flask. Note that height must be well short of the cope. Also see next drawing.

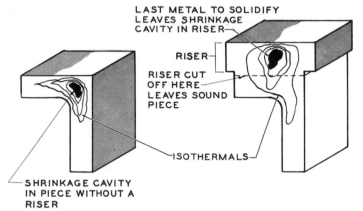

LAST METAL TO SOLIDIFY LEAVES SHRINKAGE CAVITY IN RISER

RISER

RISER CUT OFF HERE LEAVES SOUND PIECE

ISOTHERMALS

SHRINKAGE CAVITY IN PIECE WITHOUT A RISER

19–13. Shows the purpose of a riser on a casting. The riser is removed after the metal solidifies.

the riser is not large enough, the metal in it will freeze before the casting proper solidifies, and the shrinkage that occurs in the casting will not be replenished by a fresh supply of molten metal from the crucible or ladle, a riser that begins to fill will indicate when the mold is full. Also generated steam and gases can escape through the riser and serve to collect slag or loose sand.

Dome-like risers, called *blind risers,* can be formed in the cope half of the flask. 19–12. These are placed directly over the gate which feeds the metal into the mold cavity, to facilitate the flow of hot metal to the casting.

Shrinkage occurs when metal solidifies in the area where the metal stays molten the longest. By adding a riser adjacent to the casting, this condition can be avoided and any cavity caused by the shrinkage will take place in the riser, the gate, or the sprue. 19–13.

CHILLS

Chills are metal parts that are placed in molds for the purpose of speeding up the solidification of the metal. 19–14. The chill (as the name suggests) carries away heat from the solidifying metal at a rapid rate.

There are two types of chills in common use—the external and the internal chill. The external chill does not become a part of the casting as is the case with internal chills. NOTE: The chill should be of the correct size and shape because too rapid cooling of the metal can cause defects in the casting. (See Unit 18, page 96.)

vantage of this type of gating is that a favorable temperature gradient can be had; however, there is a possibility of mold erosion in this type of gating.

A *bottom gate* permits the metal to flow evenly from the drag into the bottom of the mold cavity. One of the disadvantages is that the metal has a tendency to cool before it reaches the riser and does not properly feed molten metal back into the mold until all of the casting has solidi-

fied. NOTE: The riser should contain the hottest metal in the hottest part of the mold.

RISERS

Risers are provided in a mold to feed back the molten metal into the casting. This compensates for any shrinkage of metal. It is good practice to place the riser as close as possible to the heavy section of the casting. The riser should be large enough to supply all the metal needed. If

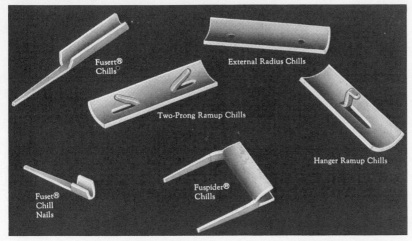

L. W. Jenkins Co.

19–14. Typical chills used in foundry operations.

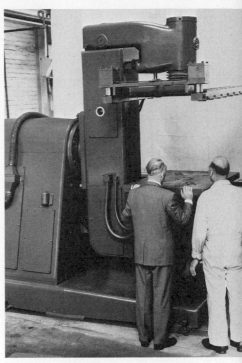

British Molding Machine Co. Ltd.

20-1. Molding machine.

Unit 20. Fundamental Processes of Molding

Sand molding is done by the green sand and dry sand processes and may be classified as: (1) bench molding, (2) floor molding, (3) pit molding, and (4) machine molding.

Bench molding is for small work done on the bench. *Floor molding* is done when castings become too large to handle on a bench. The work is done on the foundry floor.

Pit molding is done in a pit instead of a flask. Extremely large castings are molded in this fashion. The pit acts as the drag part of a flask, and a separate cope is used above the pit.

Machine molding is done on machines that are capable of performing a large part of all molding that is done in the foundry today. 20–1. The machine re-

places many hand operations such as ramming the sand in the mold, rolling the mold over, lifting and drawing the pattern from the mold, and other operations. *Bench* and *machine molding* will be the two types of molding described in detail in this text.

MAKING A MOLD OF A ONE-PIECE PATTERN ON THE BENCH

1. The first step in making a mold on the bench is to place the pattern with the parting surface downward on the molding board. 20–2. The pattern is checked to see that the draft is pointing upward so that, when the flask is turned, the pattern may be removed without breaking the mold.

2. The drag half of the flask is placed on the molding board with the pins pointing downward.

3. Parting compound is dusted over the pattern and molding board.

4. Fine facing sand is riddled to a depth of about 1″ over the pattern.

5. The flask is filled level full with unriddled, tempered sand from the bin or floor. The sand

20–2. Pattern is placed on bottom board preparatory to making the mold.

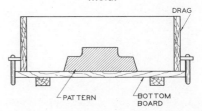

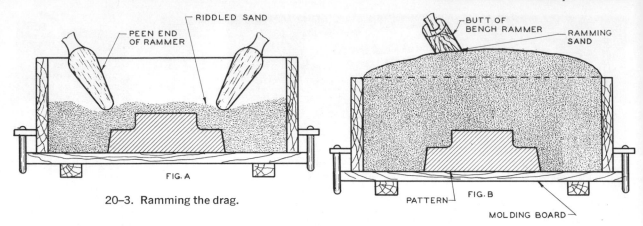

20–3. Ramming the drag.

is peen-rammed around the outer edge of the pattern and the inside edge of the flask. 20–3.

6. After peen-ramming is completed, the flask is filled heaping with sand. Correct ramming is important as sand packed too hard will have insufficient openings to permit steam and gases to escape.

7. The surplus sand is removed. The sand is leveled even with the top of the flask, using a strike-off bar. 20–4.

8. Loose sand in the amount of ¼″ is placed on top of the flask to form a bed for the bottom board. The bottom board is then placed on the sand and rubbed firm to the bed. Next, the mold is turned over so that the cope may be placed in position.

9. The molding board is removed and the surface of the mold around the pattern is smoothed with a trowel. The cope part of the flask is placed in position with the pins on either side holding it.

10. To provide a place for the molten metal to enter the mold, a sprue pin is placed as close to the pattern as practical. 20–5. Then a riser is placed in the drag near the heaviest section of the pattern from about the same distance as the sprue pin.

11. The surface of the pattern and also of the sand surrounding it is covered with a fine coating of parting compound. The parting prevents the tempered sand from sticking to the pattern when the cope is rammed and will also enable the cope to be lifted from the drag without the two sticking together.

12. Next, sand is riddled over the pattern and the cope is filled with sand from the bin. The sand is rammed and the excess sand is removed with the strike-off bar. To insure the escape of gases when the molten metal is poured, small

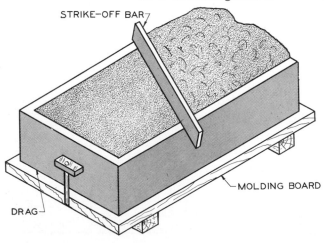

20-4. Sand being leveled.

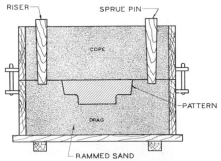

20–5. Sprue pin and riser in place.

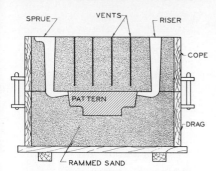

20–6. Small vents are made in the mold to facilitate escape of gases. Sprue and riser pins are removed from the cope.

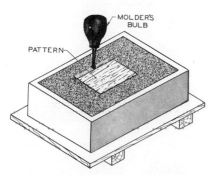

20–7. Dampen sand around the pattern with water brush or swab. This will help keep the sand from breaking away when the pattern is withdrawn.

20–8. With a rapper, strike the draw screw in such a manner that a slight opening is observed between the pattern and the sand on all sides. This is called shake allowance.

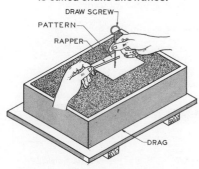

vent holes are made through the sand to within ½″ to ¼″ of the pattern. 20–6.

13. The sprue and riser pins are removed from the cope. A funnel-shaped pouring basin is formed around the sprue opening.

14. The cope half of the mold is carefully lifted off and set to one side.

15. Before the pattern is withdrawn, the sand is moistened with a water brush (molder's bulb) or swab so that the edges will not break off when the pattern is withdrawn. 20–7.

16. A draw screw or spike is inserted into the pattern and rapped lightly from all angles, loosening the pattern slightly. 20–8. The pattern then can be withdrawn by lifting with the draw screw or spike.

17. Any repair work on the mold can then be done with a trowel or slick. 20–9.

18. Next a gate is cut with a gate cutter, from the mold cavity

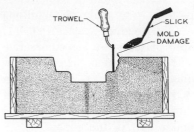

20–9. Damaged molds can be repaired with trowels and slicks. Some moisture is added to the sand used to make the repair.

to the sprue opening. The cross-section area of the gate should be less than that of the sprue in order to flow clean metal to the hole. Gates can be cut before the pattern is withdrawn.

19. Then, with bellows or an air hose, all loose sand is blown from the sprue, riser, and the mold cavity.

20. The cope is replaced on the drag. The mold is ready to receive the molten metal. 20–10.

MOLDING A SPLIT PATTERN

The chief purpose in the construction of a two-piece split

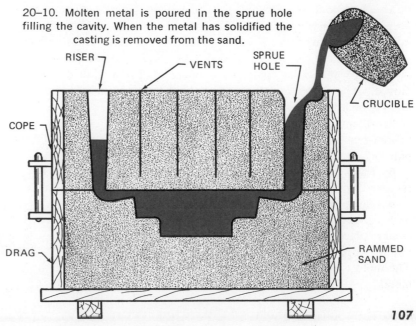

20–10. Molten metal is poured in the sprue hole filling the cavity. When the metal has solidified the casting is removed from the sand.

pattern is to make the molding of the pattern easier. 20–11. Split patterns are sometimes fastened to a match plate for production molding. A split pattern is molded with the lower half of the pattern in the drag and the upper half in the cope.

The method is as follows:

1. The drag half of the pattern is placed on the molding board with the flat side down.

2. The drag is rammed up by the same method as molding a one-piece pattern.

3. The drag is then turned over and parting compound is dusted on the pattern and the surface of the mold. Next, the cope half of the pattern is placed on the drag half of the pattern. Be sure the cope half withdraws easily. If not, the pins are sanded slightly.

4. Parting compound is shaken over the surface of the pattern. The cope half of the flask is placed on the drag and the sprue and riser pins placed in position.

5. The mold is rammed as previously described in molding a one-piece pattern.

6. The mold is vented and the sprue and riser pins removed. The cope is removed and set on edge.

7. A molder's bulb is used to moisten the edges around the pattern.

8. Each half of the pattern is removed with a draw screw.

9. Next, the gates are cut with a gate cutter. If a core is necessary, place it in the core seats and the cope is placed in position. The mold is ready for the molten metal.

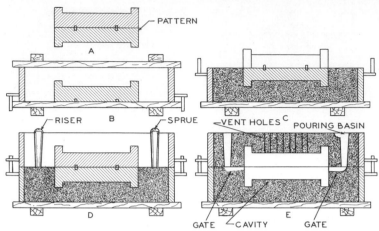

20–11. Molding a split pattern. (A) Pattern. (B) Drag or lower half of pattern. (C) The drag rolled over after ramming sand about the pattern. (D) Assembled mold after pattern is withdrawn from sand and central core inserted for metal to be poured.

Unit 21. Machine Molding

Modern molding machines have largely taken the place of hand operations. Today's labor costs and competition place emphasis on high production rates in our modern foundries. A molding machine with efficient flask and pattern equipment, operated by a skilled molder, will complete all the molding operations necessary to meet today's demands.

Machine ramming is more uniform and produces more and better molds than hand ramming. The pneumatic rammers serve to (1) pack sand firmly and uniformly in the mold and (2) make it easier to manipulate the flasks, pattern, and mold.

21–1. Operating principles of machine molding.

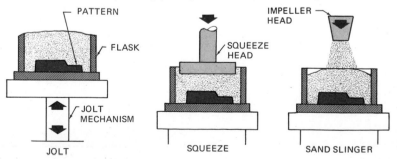

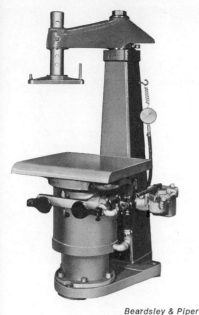

Beardsley & Piper

21-2. Jolt-squeeze machine.

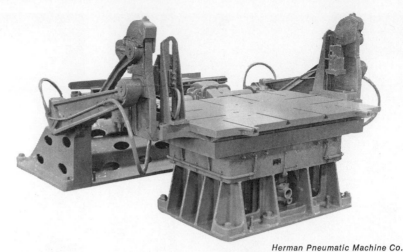

Herman Pneumatic Machine Co.

21–3. Jolt-rollover molding machine.

Molding machines are of many different kinds, models, and sizes. They perform molding operations in various ways. 21–1. In general, they fall into three classes: (1) jolt-squeeze, (2) jolt-rollover, and (3) sand slinger.

JOLT-SQUEEZE MOLDING MACHINE

This machine consists of a table controlled by two pistons in air cylinders. The mold is jolted by the action of the pistons. 21–2. This raises the table and jolts it on a bumper pad. The operation packs the sand in the lower parts of the flask. A cylinder then raises the table upward against the squeeze head and compresses the sand on top. NOTE: A vibrator attached to the machine can be removed without damaging the mold.

JOLT-ROLLOVER MOLDING MACHINE

This type of machine can mold the cope or drag. 21–3. In operation, a pattern is set on a table and the flask is filled with sand and jolted. The excess sand is then struck off and the bottom board clamped to the flask. The mold is then raised by the machine and is rolled over onto a conveyor. The flask is freed from the machine and the pattern vibrated and raised from the mold. It is then returned to loading position.

THE SAND SLINGER

The sand slinger's function is to pack sand into the mold. 21–4. The prepared molding sand is placed in the hopper at the top of the machine, then is transferred to an impeller by a belt conveyor. The mold hardness can be controlled by changing

21–4. Sand slinger-motive type.

Beardsley & Piper

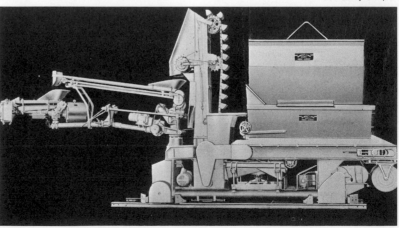

Osborn Mfg. Co.

21–5. Molder fills the cope with sand from an overhead hopper.

Osborn Mfg. Co.

21–6. After the cope is filled with sand and rammed, the machine squeezes the cope and drag. The flask being run here is 24″ x 33″ with 8″ cope over 6″ drag.

the speed of the impeller. The arm of the sand slinger is mounted on a swivel. This enables the operator to direct the sand easily into all parts of the mold.

21–7. With the cope clamped, drawn, and swung out of the way at the left, the heavy pattern plate is easily drawn by the operator.

Osborn Mfg. Co.

MODERN MOLDING MACHINE OPERATIONS

The drag and match plate patterns are assembled on the molding machine table. The drag is filled with molding sand; then a valve is pressed by the operator, causing the machine to jolt-ram the drag.

The bottom board is bedded and clamped to the drag and rolled over by the trunnion (opposite projecting pivots) on the flask.

Then the cope is lowered on the flask and filled by hand from an overhead hopper. 21–5.

Next the squeeze board is set in place, and the sand squeezed by operating a hand valve which actuates the piston.

The squeeze board is removed and the sprue is cut in the cope. The cope is lifted from the drag on the return stroke of the piston. 21–6.

21–8. Completion of mold on the portable jolt-squeeze molding machine.

American Foundrymen's Society

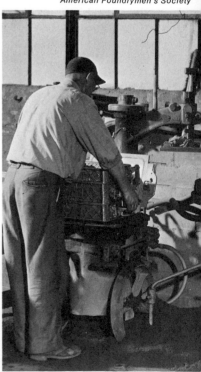

The cope is then swung to one side and the pattern is vibrated. This will permit a clean and also an accurate lifting from the mold. 21–7.

If cored holes are required, the cores are set in the mold.

The next operation swings the cope back to a closing position, and the drag is raised until the mold is closed. 21–8. The clamps on the cope are released and the table lowered. The mold is complete; another can be made.

Unit 22.

Melting and Casting Metals

There are many types of furnaces for melting metals. The principal types are listed in Table 22–A.

CUPOLA FURNACE

The cupola furnace is used for melting pig iron and scrap metal for use in the foundry. 22–1 (Page 112). The bulk of the gray-iron and malleable-iron base for castings also is melted in this furnace.

The cupola consists of a vertical stack, lined with refractory material provided with an air blast at the bottom. Cupolas are made in many sizes, commonly about 4′ to 7′ in outside diameter and 30′ to 40′ high.

In preparing a cupola for use, the slag and refuse from the previous day's run are cleaned from the lining and from around tuyeres (air-blast nozzles). The refractory lining is repaired or replaced, as required. The bottom doors are propped shut. All cracks are closed with fire clay, and a layer of black molding sand is rammed over the bottom, sloping toward the tap hole.

The breast opening is plugged with a mixture of fire clay and sand and a small tap hole about 1″ in diameter is made.

Wood is placed on the sand bottom to ignite the coke bed. All of the tuyeres are open when the fire is started, to provide a draft. The charge of coke is built up to its proper height above the tuyeres. NOTE: This is important, as it determines the height of the melting zone and affects the temperature and oxidation of the metal.

Pig iron and scrap are charged through the door, which is located 15′ to 25′ above the bottom. After the initial charge has become hot, alternate layers of coke and iron are added to make a ratio of 8 or 10 parts of iron by weight. Flux is usually added to remove the impurities in the iron, protect the iron from oxidation, and reduce the slag to a more fluid state. Limestone is generally used as a fluxing material, but sometimes soda ash or fluorspar is added for extra cleansing action. About 75 pounds of limestone is used per ton of iron. During the heating process slag that is formed on top of the metal flows continuously from the slag hole by means of the spout located at the rear of the cupola.

Table 22-A. Furnaces Used for Melting Metals

Type of Furnace	Type Refractory Lining	Use
Air or reverberatory	Acid	Malleable cast iron, nonferrous metals
Bessemer converter		Pig iron refining
Blast		Pig iron
Cupola	Basic	Cast irons
Crucible	Graphite or silicon carbide	Nonferrous
Direct-arc	Acid or basic	Cast irons, nonferrous metals
Indirect-arc		Cast irons, nonferrous metals
Induction	Acid or basic	Nonferrous alloys, high purity metals, cast irons
Open-hearth	Acid or basic	Steel
Side-blow converter		Carbon and alloy steel castings

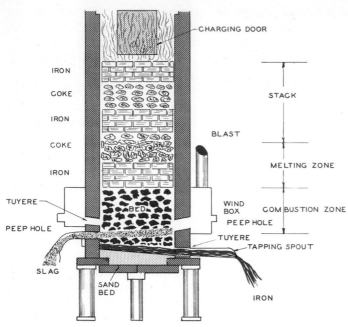

CHARGING DOOR

IRON

COKE

IRON

COKE

IRON

TUYERE

PEEP HOLE

SLAG

SAND BED

BED

BLAST

WIND BOX

PEEP HOLE

TUYERE

TAPPING SPOUT

IRON

STACK

MELTING ZONE

COMBUSTION ZONE

22–1. Cupola furnace used for melting pig iron.

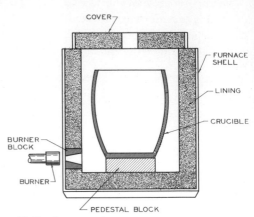

COVER

FURNACE SHELL

LINING

CRUCIBLE

BURNER BLOCK

BURNER

PEDESTAL BLOCK

22–3. Cross section of a stationary crucible furnace.

It usually takes about an hour before the charge is heated uniformly. Then the tuyeres are closed and a forced draft started. The molten metal begins to accumulate on the hearth, or bed, after a few minutes. Next the tap hole is plugged with a wad of clay. NOTE: The cupola must be kept filled to the charging door by the addition of successive charges.

Tapping of the metal is done by removing the clay in the tap hole. The metal is drawn off into a ladle for pouring into molds.

The tap hole is then closed with a clay plug or *bot.* The operation is repeated until the end of the run. At the completion of the run, the blast is shut off and the prop under the bottom doors is removed; then what remains in the cupola is dropped to the floor, where it is left to cool.

CASTING NONFERROUS METALS

Most melting of nonferrous metals is done in oil or gas fired crucible furnaces of two basic types—stationary and titlting. 22–2.

Crucibles

Stationary furnaces use a "lift-out" or "pull-out" crucible, lifted out by tongs, either hand or motor operated. The crucible is set in a ring carrier called a *shank.* With the shank, the crucible is carried by hand or trolley to the molds where the metal is poured. The sizes customarily used may vary from a No. 20 crucible, capacity 60 pounds of brass, to a No. 400, holding 1,200 pounds of brass, or larger. 22–3.

Tilting furnaces, use fixed crucibles which remain in the furnace during the entire life of the crucible. 22–4(A). Crucibles range in capacities of from 180 to 3,000 pounds of brass or bronze, with the majority in the range of 600 pounds (No. 200 crucible) to 1,200 pounds (No. 400 crucibles). NOTE: Capacities in pounds for aluminum are $1/3$ of the above figures.

Crucibles are made in two general classes—ceramic bonded and carbon bonded. 22–4(B). Both classes contain graphite and silicon carbide as the re-

22-2. Crucible melting furnace.

McEnglevan Heat Treating & Mfg. Co.

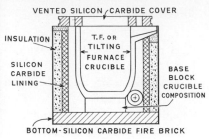

VENTED SILICON CARBIDE COVER

INSULATION

SILICON
CARBIDE
LINING

T.F. OR
TILTING
FURNACE
CRUCIBLE

BASE
BLOCK
CRUCIBLE
COMPOSITION

BOTTOM - SILICON CARBIDE FIRE BRICK

Crucible Manufacturers Assn.

22–4(A). Installation of crucible in tilting furnace with specially vented cover.

Vesuvius Crucible Co.

22–4(B). Carbon-bonded crucible with factory-attached lip.

22–5. Graphite crucible used for melting nonferrous metals.

American Refractories & Crucible Co.

fractory conductor of heat. 22–5. The burner is located in the bottom of the furnace with the center line approximately on the same level as the top of the pedestal block or crucible rest. It should fire on a tangent to the inside furnace wall to eliminate any possible impingement on the crucible. NOTE: Be sure to use the size crucible for which the furnace is designed.

Ladles

Melting operations conducted in tilting furnaces require ladles to transfer the molten metal from the furnace to the molds. NOTE: Steel hand ladles used for pouring aluminum must be coated on the inside to prevent the molten metal from sticking to the ladle.

The ladles are lined with a refractory material to protect the steel shell. 22–6. Large ladles have a graphite or silicon carbide liner with suitable insulation placed between the liner and the shell. The insulation aids in holding the metal at a constant pouring temperature. This type of ladle is carried in a shank.

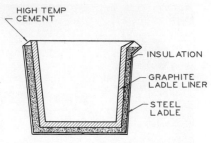

HIGH TEMP
CEMENT

INSULATION

GRAPHITE
LADLE LINER

STEEL
LADLE

22–6. Assembly of a graphite ladle liner.

Tongs

Correctly fitted tongs are necessary for efficient and safe handling of the molten metal. 22–7. The tongs must clear the top edge of the crucible without pinching, and the blades of the tongs must bear evenly against the sides of the crucible. The bottom blades should contact the crucible below the bilge so that there is a lifting hold.

There are various types of crucible tongs. The type usually used has double prongs, the "grab" or "claw" type.

Side-operated and vertical lift-out tongs are equipped with stops which limit the maximum pressure on the crucible. 22–8 (Page 114).

22-7. (A) Side operated and vertical lift-out tongs, both equipped with stops, limiting maximum pressure on the crucible. (B) Hand lift tongs. (C) Tongs that fit will increase crucible life.

Crucible Manufacturers Assn.

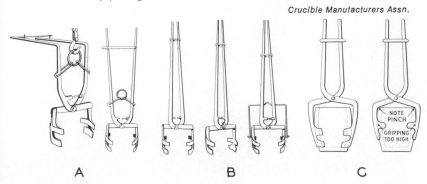

A   B   C

22–8. Vertical lift-out tongs.

Shanks

A shank consists of a rigid steel ring with steel rods extending from opposite ends of the outside diameter to serve as a carrying handle. 22–9. The roundness and taper should be checked frequently. The crucible has to fit the shank so that the point of contact is just below the bilge in order to insure proper balance when pouring the molten metal. 22–10. A crucible that rides high over the shank is top-heavy.

TIPS ON USING A CRUCIBLE

● When charging the crucible with scrap such as gates, risers, etc., be sure that none of the metal is hanging over the edge of the crucible, as it will drop into the base of the furnace when it melts.

● Ingots and scrap should never be wedged or jammed into a crucible, as the metal expands when heated and the resulting expansion can easily crack the crucible. **Safety Caution:** Do not drop additional metal into the *melted* charge. It can splatter, causing terrible burns.

● The metal is fed into the crucible as fast as it will take it.

● A chemical flux can be added for the purpose of purifying metal, but a minimum amount should be used. The best method is to add a small amount just prior to pouring. This does the least harm to the crucible.

METAL TEMPERATURE AND POURING

As soon as the metal has reached the correct temperature,

22–9. Crucible shank with safety lock.

22–10. Safety single-end pouring shank with bail.

the crucible is removed from the furnace and the metal poured into the mold. 22–11. The correct temperature of the metal can be determined by an immersion-type pyrometer. 22–12. NOTE: Allowing metal to "soak" after it has reached the correct pouring temperature does not improve it and also is hard on the crucible. Overheating is harmful to the metal and shortens the life of the crucible as well as causing inferior castings.

The required temperature depends upon: (1) the type of alloy and casting and (2) the size and shape of casting. Light castings generally require hotter metal than large castings with heavy sections.

After the crucible is removed from the furnace, all slag and dross are skimmed from the metal before pouring.

CLEANING CASTINGS

After a casting has been poured and cooled to the proper temperature, it is shaken from the mold.

Nonferrous castings require very little cleaning, as they are poured at a much lower temperature than iron or steel and sand does not adhere to the surface to any great extent. The sprues, risers, and gates are removed with a metal-cutting band saw or a sprue press. Power brushing is usually sufficient to clean the surface.

The gates and risers on iron castings are broken off, but a cutting torch or high-speed cutting wheel is necessary to remove these from steel castings. Iron and steel castings acquire a coating of sand and scale dur-

McEnglevan Heat Treating & Mfg. Co.

22–11. Metal being poured into mold with a single-end shank.

ing the casting process which is difficult to remove. Castings such as these can be cleaned by various methods. (1) Castings are placed in a rotating, cylindrical, tumbling mill and are cleaned by a tumbling action of the castings one upon another. 22–13 (Page 116). (2) Another method utilizes a machine which consists of a cleaning barrel formed by an endless apron conveyor. 22–14.

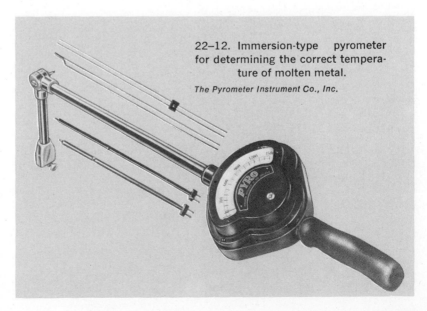

22–12. Immersion-type pyrometer for determining the correct temperature of molten metal.

The Pyrometer Instrument Co., Inc.

The castings are cleaned by blasts of metallic shot. 22–15. (3) Sand-blasting units are used to blow sharp sand against castings placed inside a blasting cabinet. The blast removes all foreign particles from the castings. (4) Large castings are often cleaned by streams of water (under considerable pressure) which washes away the sand. (5) Castings that require a plating or galvanizing operation require pickling with a weak HCl acid solution.

CAST IRON

Like steel, cast iron is an alloy or a series of alloys containing various percentages of iron, carbon, silicon, and minor elements. It has a high carbon content and low ductility. The carbon content is much higher than found in ordinary steels, amounting to 2.5% to 4.0%. Silicon plays a most important role. The silicon content has more effect on cast iron than it does on steel. Manganese, phosphorous, and sulphur, in varying percentages, are also present in cast iron. Sometimes special alloying elements such as nickel, chromium, copper, and molybdenum are added to alter the mechanical and chemical properties of cast iron. Cast iron may be classified as: (1) gray cast iron, (2) white cast iron, and (3) malleable cast iron.

Gray Cast Iron

Gray cast iron is the most widely used of all cast materials. It is so called from the characteristic gray fracture, as opposed to the lighter colored fractures of

Wheelabrator Tumblast

22–13. "Tumblast" for cleaning castings.

22–14. Continuous conveyor for blast cleaning castings.

American Foundrymen's Society

most steels. The gray color is due to the carbon in the form of flake graphite. It has good machinability and high compression strength. Castings range in size from those weighing as much as 100,000 pounds to small parts weighing only a few ounces.

As has been noted, gray iron is essentially an alloy of iron and carbon. The other elements present are useful in that they affect the iron and carbon structural components.

"The matrix, which is the base metal structure of gray iron, somewhat resembles steel. 22–16(A&B). However, gray iron contains graphite flakes. These flakes are without strength and break up the continuity of the matrix. They also impart the dark gray fracture color and add greatly to the machinability of the metal."* The final properties of gray iron are largely controlled by the size, shape, and

* James Aston, *The Encyclopedia Americana.*

distribution of graphite flakes. The carbon present is in the form of graphite. Large flakes of graphitic carbon have a tendency to produce soft, weak castings. Fine short flakes result in a stronger casting.

The foundry metallurgist can control the properties of the iron by controlling the amount, size, and distribution of graphite flakes. He does this by: (1) regulating the ratio of carbon to silicon (the more silicon present the more and larger the graphitic flakes), (2) adding steel to the melt, (3) controlling the temperature (fast cooling will reduce the graphitization), and (4) adding special alloys to the melt.

Ordinary gray iron contains about 3.5% carbon and about 1.75% silicon. The groundmass (fine-grained base) structure of gray cast iron is pearlite and ferrite; therefore it is quite tough. 22–16(A&B). However, the groundmass structure is

Ford Motor Co.

22–15. Automobile cylinder blocks shown in a shot-blast cabinet.

broken up by the graphite flakes which makes the metal brittle. The graphite in gray iron has a tendency to improve the machinability of the metal, so gray iron castings find many applications such as automotive cylinder blocks, pistons, gears, pulleys, and machine tools.

22–16(A). Pearlite gray iron etched to bring out the fine pearlite structure which forms the matrix of this iron.

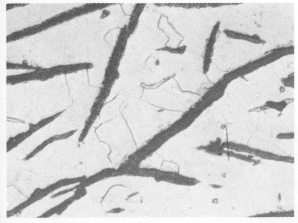

A

22–16(B). Ferritic matrix of gray iron.

B

Pearlite Gray Iron

A casting consisting of pearlite (a very fine lamellar structure of ferrite and cementite—Fe_3c—and graphite), or pearlite gray iron, is the best possible structure for strength and good machinability.

Of course, pearlite in gray iron is the same as pearlite present in steel. This pearlitic condition is developed by carbon present in the combined form (cementite) and will combine with the ferrite constituent, upon cooling, through the critical range of the iron.

The properties of gray iron are influenced by the pearlite in the following manner: (1) As the amount of pearlite increases, the strength of the metal is also increased. (2) The finer the cementite and ferrite layers, the stronger the iron. (3) Increased strength is gained by a finer grain size.

Ferrite and Steadite Ranges

A highly *ferritic* gray iron is not ductile because there is less pearlite and more graphitic carbon present. Highly ferritic gray iron has less strength and is much softer.

Phosphorus content of most gray iron is rather low, being within the approximate range of 0.10% to 0.90%. *Steadite* is a eutectic structure of alpha iron and iron phosphide, formed by the presence of phosphorus. Steadite is hard and brittle; however, it affects the strength of the metal very little.

White Cast Iron

White cast iron has much of its carbon in the combined condition (cementite) and, consequently, is hard and brittle. As said, white cast iron is so named because it shows a white fracture.

White cast iron that has gone through a slow cooling process in the mold has a structure of pearlite and free cementite resembling high-carbon steel. However, this iron contains more free cementite. By the addition of elements such as nickel, chromium, and molybdenum it is possible to obtain a much harder iron. The addition of alloys produces a structure which is usually in the range of martensite and free cementite. 22–17. The alloying, hardening agents serve to prevent the formation of pearlite from austenite during the cooling process.

Farm machinery parts and industrial equipment—which require wear resistance, strength, and hardness—are made from alloyed white iron.

Chilled Cast Iron

Chilled cast iron refers to gray iron castings which have a very hard, wear-resistant surface layer of white cast iron. If gray iron is poured into molds and rapid cooling of the outer surface takes place, the carbon does not have an opportunity to graphitize and remains combined. The rapid cooling prevents the formation of coarse, soft pearlite, adding to the hardness of the casting. Martensite may be formed if cooling is fast enough.

The molds into which the metal is poured may be metal, or they may be equipped with metal chill plates which create a rapid cooling and a hard surface.

Chilled iron castings are used for railroad car wheels and other parts that call for a strong resistance to wear.

Malleable Cast Iron

Malleable cast iron is produced by a process of heat treating white cast iron. The purpose of the malleabilizing or annealing process is to change the combined carbon or cementite of the white cast iron to a graphitic carbon (temper carbon) which is found in malleable iron.

Malleable cast iron contains about 2.5% carbon and about 1.25% silicon. The silicon content is low enough to solidify as white cast iron. There is enough silicon present, however, to promote graphitization in the subsequent heating or annealing

22–17. Martensite white cast iron. Structure is martensite with cementite. (Etched magnification approximately 250X.)

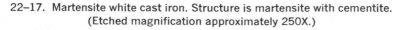

U.S. Steel Corp.

process to which the casting is subjected.

Thus there are two stages: (1) heating to graphitize the massive cementite and (2) heating to graphitize the last remnants of pearlitic cementite. In malleable iron, the graphite is present in the form of rounded "nests" instead of elongated sharp flakes as in gray iron. Because of this and also because the matrix or base of malleable iron is entirely composed of soft ferrite, malleable iron is very tough and not brittle.

Malleable iron is used where greater toughness and shock resistance are required, as in farm implements. It is used in some automobile parts, hardware, pipe, and pipe fittings. Camshafts, gear housings, differential housings, and brake pedals are made of this type of iron.

Procedures

White iron castings are used in the production of malleable iron by a process which involves a high-temperature, annealing treatment.

The metal for white iron castings is melted in the air furnace, cupola, or electric furnace. Accurate control of the metal can be secured by using two furnaces such as the air furnace and cupola together, thus permitting a continuous flow of the metal at the right temperatures.

In the annealing process the white iron castings are packed in pots or rings. The castings are surrounded by a packing material such as sand, blast furnace slag, or other forms of iron oxide. The packing material serves to support the castings and protect

them from warping during the annealing process.

The packed castings are placed in the furnace or furnaces and gradually heated to about 1650°F., for a period of 48 to 60 hours. Next the temperature

Table 22-B. Chemical Composition of Malleable Iron Percentage	
Carbon	1.00 to 2.00%
Silicon	0.60 to 1.10%
Manganese	Under 0.30%
Sulphur	0.6 to 0.15%

Table 22-C. Average Properties of Malleable Iron*	
Tensile strength	54,000 lbs. per sq. in.
Yield point	36,000 lbs. per sq. in.
Elongation—2″	15% maximum
Brinell hardness	115
Izod impact strength	9.3 foot pounds
Fatigue endurance limit	25,000 lbs. per sq. in.

* C. Johnson and W. R. Weeks, *Metalurgy*, 4th edition. American Technical Society.

is gradually reduced to about 1350°F. and held at this point for about 14 hours. The containers are then removed from the furnace and allowed to air cool. After cooling, the castings are removed from the containers.

The average chemical composition and physical properties of malleable iron are shown in Tables 22–B and C.

Black-Heart Malleable Iron

Black-heart malleable iron is ductile in nature. Because of the presence of graphitic carbon, when fractured, the structure will show black, with a lighter decarburized surface. 22–18. It is not necessary to use a chemically active carbonaceous packing material in the black-heart annealing process. The graphite present

22–18. Black-heart malleable iron, etched to show ferrite grains. The dark spots are graphitic or temper carbon. (Etched magnification approximately 200X.)

U.S. Steel Corp.

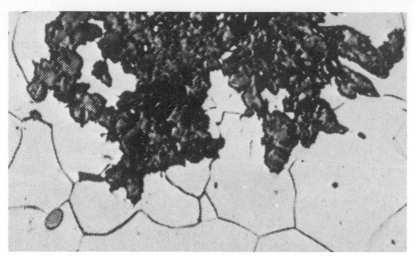

22–19. "Flake-graphite-aggregate." Temper carbon in white-heart, malleable iron containing sufficient manganese to balance sulphur content (300X).

by the additional magnesium present. This type of iron is used where improved physical properties are desired, extensively in farm implements, crankshafts, camshafts, and parts for heavy machinery. The metal has good machinability, can be annealed, and is hardened by induction- and flame-hardening methods.

WROUGHT IRON

Modern wrought iron is of high purity, except for many minute threads of iron silicate slag which give it a fibrous character that makes it easy to work. 22–20.

Corrosion resistance is attributed to the barrier effect of the

in the annealed iron is quite different from that found in gray iron. In black-heart malleable iron the graphite takes the nodular form of *temper carbon*.

The two principal constituents of this iron are ferrite and nodular graphite. Carbon and silicon control is quite important in the manufacture of black-heart malleable iron.

White-Heart Malleable Iron

White-heart malleable iron fractures with a light appearance. 22–19. Carbon and silicon content control is not important. The carbon is burned out during the process of annealing by using an iron oxide. Decarburization can be eliminated if carbonaceous packing material is used. This type of iron has neither the machinability nor the mechanical properties of black-heart malleable iron.

Nodular or Ductile Cast Iron

Nodular or ductile cast iron (also known as spheroidal

graphite iron) contains free carbon in ball-like form. Each nodule of graphite is surrounded by a matrix of ferrite, or ferrite and pearlite. Nodular iron is produced by adding a small amount of magnesium alloys to gray iron, to produce graphite. The amount added depends largely upon the sulphur present.

In this process the sulphur is eliminated by being converted to magnesium sulphide. The graphite is changed to a nodular form

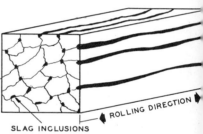

22–20. Microdistribution of the slag in wrought iron. Many threads of iron silicate slag give this a fibrous appearance.

22–21. Cross section of puddling furnace.

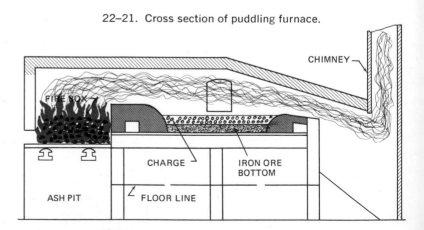

120

slag threads, which may amount to 350,000 threads per square inch of cross section. Wrought iron contains less than 0.1% of carbon, with 1% to 3% of finely divided slag.

It is produced by the puddling process. 22–21. The puddling furnace capacity ranges from 300 to 1,500 pounds. This furnace is somewhat similar to the open hearth furnace, with combustion taking place at one end only. The furnace is lined with iron oxide, which is in the form of ore or scale.

The furnace is charged with cold pig iron. As this melts, the carbon and other impurities are eliminated by the iron oxide lining. After this the metal has a higher melting point and begins to form a pasty mass, which is a mixture of relatively pure iron and slag. This is stirred and shaped into balls and removed from the furnace. A mechanical squeezer is used to squeeze the slag from the mass and the iron is rolled into bars which are cut into alternate layers at 90° angles. The bars are then heated to welding point and rolled into desired shapes.

Wrought iron, the forerunner of steel, was used by the Egyptians to make nails and hasps prior to 1600 B.C. Due to the fact that it still has many uses it has not been completely replaced by steel or other metallic materials. Ductility, corrosion resistance, and the resistance to various stresses are properties that make it desirable for household pieces and ornamental work in the form of bars, pipe, plates, and sheets.

Check Your Knowledge

1. How important are foundry products to our way of life?

2. Do all metals have the same shrinkage upon cooling? Explain.

3. Why is it necessary in making a master pattern to make allowances for machining?

4. Why is a pattern sometimes made in two parts? Name this type of pattern.

5. What is a multi-piece pattern?

6. Explain the terms "cope" and "drag."

7. What is draft on a pattern and what is its purpose?

8. Why is pure silica sand in itself not suitable for molding?

9. Discuss the effects of moisture on molding sands.

10. Explain the use of parting sand.

11. How is sand restored to its best condition and prepared for use?

12. Is a binder necessary in the construction of cores? Why?

13. Why is it necessary to use scientific methods for testing the correct mixtures for sand?

14. Explain the permeability test.

15. Why is it necessary that molding sands have sufficient porosity?

16. What effect does sand grain size have on the smoothness of a casting?

17. How is the surface hardness of a mold determined?

18. Discuss the factors relating to permeability.

19. Why is the moisture test of various molding sands so important?

20. How does the grain size of sand affect the permeability and bond strength?

21. What is a core?

22. Why is it necessary to use a core binder in the construction of cores?

23. Why are green sand cores preferred to dry sand cores?

24. What are the qualities that a dry sand core should possess?

25. Why and how are cores baked?

26. Sometimes a core needs an internal support in the mold. Name the device used to support the core.

27. What is the function of a jacket?

28. Why is it necessary to vent a mold?

29. What effect do gases in the mold have on the quality of the casting?

30. What is the function of a riser in the molding operation?

31. What is the purpose of a gating system?

32. What hand molding operations are replaced by machine molding in today's modern foundry?

33. Describe how a typical mold is made.

34. Discuss machine molding procedure from the time the mold is made until the finished casting is made.

35. What are the advantages of using a sand slinger?

36. What are the constituents of cast iron and how do they vary in gray, white, and malleable iron?

37. What are the effects of silicon and manganese in gray cast iron?

38. *What products are made of chilled cast iron?*

39. *What is malleabilizing?*

40. *Describe the process used in making wrought iron.*

41. *Describe the cupola and how it operates.*

42. *What is the purpose of a fluxing material?*

43. *Describe the difference between a ladle and a crucible.*

44. *Why should ingots and scrap not be wedged in a crucible?*

45. *What methods are used in cleaning castings?*

References

American Foundrymens Association, *Cast Metals Handbook,* 6th ed., 1961.

American Society for Metals, Metals Park, Ohio, *Casting Design Handbook,* 1963.

Cook, Glenn J., *Engineered Castings,* New York, Mc-Graw-Hill Book Co., 1961.

Flinn, Richard A., *Fundamentals of Metal Casting,* Reading, Mass., Addison-Wesley Publishing Co., Inc., 1963.

United States Steel Corporation, *The Making, Shaping, and Treating of Steel,* 1961.

A view of the casting shop in a rolling mill.

International Silver Co.

Section Five

Special Casting Processes

ALL cast metals can be produced by sand molding processes. However, sand molds are completely destroyed as a casting is made. The following units will describe processes that will produce castings more uniformly and precisely and at lower costs, in most cases, than sand casting.

Kux Machine

Unit 23.

Permanent Mold Casting

Permanent mold casting is produced with metal molds plus hydrostatic pressure (pressure of liquid at rest). The method is impractical for larger castings and also when using metals with high melting temperatures. Nonferrous metals such as aluminum, zinc, lead, magnesium alloys, and certain bronzes can be successfully cast by this method.

The mold consists of two or more pieces held together with screws, C-clamps, toggles, or other devices that can release the product when it solidifies.

Generally, permanent molds are made of close-grain alloy cast iron parts with hinges at one end and clamped together at the other end. The molds are usually coated with a wash of an adhesive refractory *slurry* (heat-resisting wet mixture) and lampblack which helps to keep the castings from sticking and reduces the chilling effect upon the metal.

After the mold has been prepared, it is closed and all cores or loose members are locked in place. 23–1. Both sand and metal cores can be used in molds of this type. The metal, at the predetermined temperature, is gravity poured into the mold through the gate opening. 23–2. After the casting has sufficiently cooled, loose members are withdrawn, the mold opened, and the casting removed. The molds are then blown out and coated; the cores set and the molds are ready for pouring again.

Major uses include the casting of pistons and other parts for automotive, diesel, and marine engines. Many applications are also found in other industries that produce such items as washing machine gear blanks, vacuum cleaner parts, fan casings, parts for portable tools, outdoor lighting fixtures, and gear housings.

Permanent mold castings have a good surface finish and sharp detail. Uniformity is obtained with products weighing from 1 ounce to 50 pounds. Tolerances can be maintained from 0.0025″ to 0.010″.

Permanent mold casting lends itself to automation, so a high production rate can be obtained.

23–1. Permanent molding machine. This view shows the mold box in open or strip position.

Sutter Products Co.

23–2. Permanent mold in position for pouring operation.

Sutter Products Co.

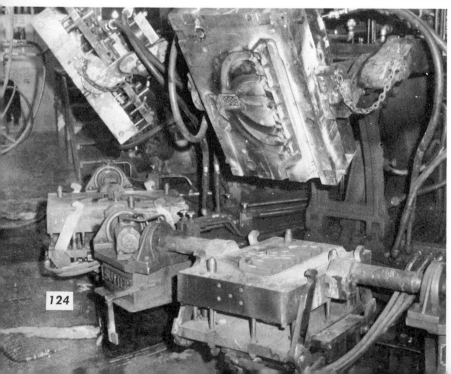

Unit 24. Die Casting

Well over a million tons of nonferrous metals—aluminum, zinc, magnesium, and brass—went to market in the form of die castings this year.

They made their appearance in a great variety of end products created by virtually the full spectrum of metal-consuming industries.

Die-casting production is entering the million-ton stage, with ferrous alloys becoming prominent in the picture.

A high standard of living would not be economically possible if it were not for die castings. Household appliances, automobiles, small tools, and electric motors—these things and many more are all made possible by the die-casting industry.

Die casting can be defined as *the process of forcing metal, by pressure—hydraulic or pneumatic—into a metal die or mold.* The pressures, which range from 80 to 40,000 psi (pounds per square inch) are held until the solidification of the metal occurs.

Die-casting machines may be classified as (1) hot-chamber and (2) cold-chamber. 24–1.

HOT-CHAMBER PROCESS

In the hot-chamber process, the melting pot is included with the machine. 24–2. The molten metal is forced into the mold by means of a plunger or compressed air. 24–3 (Page 126).

Both the metal plunger and the die mechanism are hydraulically operated in the plunger type machine.

The plunger operates in one end of a gooseneck casting which is submerged in the molten metal. The metal is introduced by gravity into the gooseneck. After the molten metal is ladled into the machine the rest of the operations are automatic. The downstroke of the plunger creates pressure which causes the metal to be forced along into the die cavity. Upon solidification of the metal, the pressure is relieved and the dies are opened. The finished casting is ejected by knockout pins.

The operating pressures in this machine range from 5,600 to 22,000 psi.

Process Details

Air operated machines are equipped with a gooseneck cast-

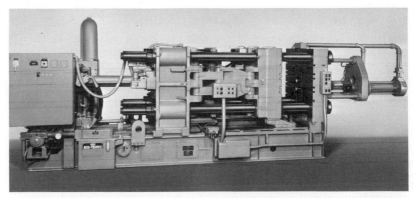

Reed-Prentice Div., Package Machinery Co.

24–1. 600-ton, cold-chamber, die-casting machine.

24–2. 400-ton, hot-chamber, die-casting machine.

Reed-Prentice Div., Package Machinery Co.

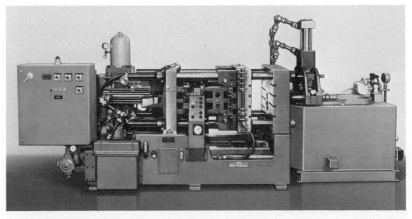

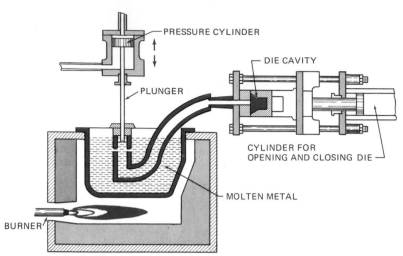

24–3. The hot-chamber or plunger type die-casting machine is used primarily for casting zinc alloys. The melting pot is built into the machine and the cylinder that leads to the die chamber always contains molten metal.

ing that is operated by a lifting device. 24–4. The start of the casting operation begins with the gooseneck being lowered into the molten metal where, as just noted, it is filled through the nozzle by gravity. The raising mechanism lifts the gooseneck until it comes into contact with the opening of the die cavity and locks itself into position for the casting operation. Compressed air is then admitted into the die, where solidification takes place. After the metal solidifies, the air pressure is released and the gooseneck returns to its original position to receive more

24–4. Cross section of a pneumatic die-casting machine, having a horizontal nozzle in position for filling a die by air pressure without a plunger.

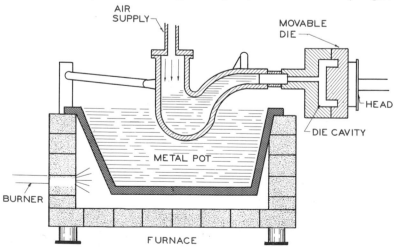

metal. The dies are opened and the casting is ejected. The operation is then repeated. Air pressures range from 80 to 600 psi.

COLD-CHAMBER PROCESS

1. One style of cold-chamber, die-casting machine consists of cylindrical pressure chamber, generally operated hydraulically, that conveys pressure to a ram or piston. In sequence, the dies are closed and a predetermined amount of molten metal is ladled into the cylinder. The plunger is actuated and forces the metal into the closed sections of the die. 24–5. After the metal solidifies, the cores are removed, the dies opened, and the casting is ejected from the stationary half of the die. A cold-chamber machine may be used for making castings of aluminum, magnesium, or brass. From 100 to 150 pieces per hour can be produced by this method.

2. Another style of cold-chamber machine uses metal in a semiliquid or plastic state, which permits the operation at a lower temperature than if using molten metal. 24–6. Longer die life is obtained. The process reduces the high temperature required to heat such metals as brass and bronze, which have a higher melting temperature than either aluminum or zinc. Overheating of dies is eliminated by being able to use the metal in a semiliquid state, and less die damage occurs. The dies are water cooled to protect them from overheating.

The metal is ladled by hand to the compression chamber. It will be noted that the compression chamber is part of the die. Metal is poured into this chamber at the upper part of the die and forced under pressure into the die cavity. The ram is moved out, the dies open, and the casting is ejected.

The sprue and excess metal are removed in the finishing operation.

DIE-CASTING DIES

A die for die casting is normally made in two parts. One part is the front cover portion; the other serves to eject the metal. Each is equipped with dowel pins or other device to align the two parts, much like a split pattern. The two die sections meet at the parting line and are joined by a locking mechanism when in the closed position. In cooling, the casting shrinks onto core pins and projections which are attached to the ejector portion of the die. When the molten metal has cooled, the ejector plate in the movable part of the die is advanced sufficiently to force the casting from the cavity. The casting falls clear, and the cycle of operations is repeated.

Dies may be classified as follows: (1) single-cavity die, (2) multiple-cavity die, (3) combination, used with (4) a unit die. A *single-cavity* die produces one casting per cycle of operation. In large production runs a *multiple-cavity* die is used to produce several castings at the same time. A *combination* die has cavities of two or more different shapes which are cast at the same time. A *unit die holder* holds several die elements at the same time.

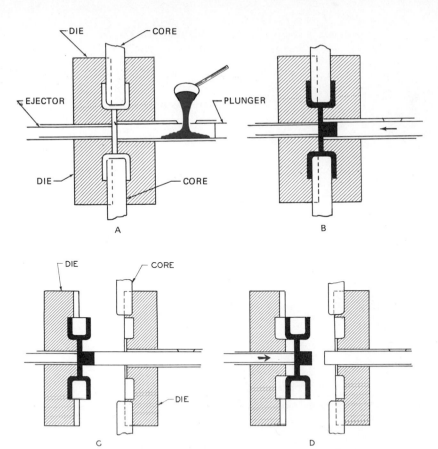

New Jersey Zinc Co.

24–5. (A) Ladling molten metal into cold chamber. (B) After molten metal is forced into die. (C) Cores are withdrawn, die opened, and plunger advanced to eject piece. (D) Plunger withdrawn and ejector advanced to force gate of castings from ejector half of die.

24–6. Die-casting machine designed to use metal in a semi-liquid or plastic state, showing compression chamber in dies.

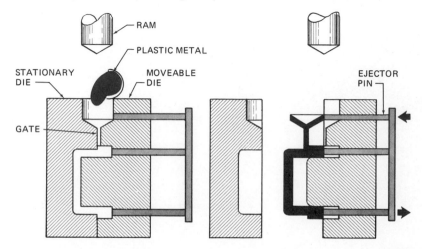

Newton-New Haven Co.

24–7. Die castings for use in mechanism of a fine rifle.

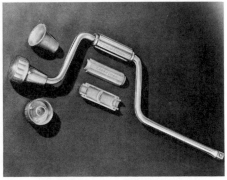

Newton-New Haven Co.

24–8. Zamak 3 alloy is used to construct a wrench by die casting.

24–9. Die castings made from aluminum alloy and Zamak alloy.

Newton-New Haven Co.

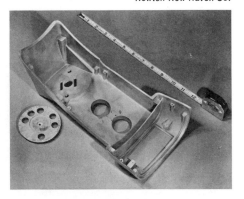

ADVANTAGES OF DIE CASTING

Die casting lends itself to rapid and economical quantity production of parts. The result is a low cost per piece. Another result is excellent reproducibility from part to part, with closer dimensional tolerances than probably any method other than machining processes could provide. Excellent surface finish is also possible. Generally, aluminum die castings are about on a par with heat-treated sand castings, as far as tensile and yield strengths are concerned.

The most useful property of die castings is their fatigue strength. In this they are substantially superior to sand and permanent mold castings, and are about on a par with forgings.

Die castings can be produced with much thinner sections, and with smooth surfaces. Complex shapes require fewer pieces with fewer operations. The process is best adapted to nonferrous alloys such as zinc, aluminum, magnesium, copper base, lead, and tin.

Large aluminum die castings can be made as heavy as 125 pounds with present equipment. The illustrations show many of the products that can be produced by die casting. 24–7 through 24–11.

DIE-CASTING METALS AND THEIR ALLOYS

Zinc-Base Alloys

As mentioned, the die-casting industry uses a wide range of nonferrous alloys. Among the most widely used are zinc alloys. Some of the alloying constituents used with zinc include aluminum, magnesium, and copper.

Commercial zinc alloys are strong, ductile, and have good resistance to shock at normal operating temperatures. They will stretch under moderate stresses.

Zinc alloys can be plated with nickel or chromium for decorative purposes. This practice is extensively used in the automotive industry, where many zinc die castings are used in grille parts, door handles, and other parts.

Organic coatings, lacquers, paints and enamels can also be used.

Zinc alloys have the lowest melting point of any die-casting alloys—in the range of 715° to 750° F. This means a reduced heating time and cost, and less damage to costly steel dies.

Zinc used in the manufacture of industrial-quality zinc alloys has a purity of about 99.00%, with lead, tin, and cadmium held to close tolerances to insure structural stability.

Added to the zinc, as alloying agents, are tin and aluminum in small quantities.

Aluminum-Base Alloys

Many of the die castings that are produced by industry today are made from aluminum alloys, which are light in weight and have a good surface finish. They have good resistance to corrosion. However, they are more difficult to die cast than zinc-base alloys.

Die life is shorter due to the fact that the molten alloys of aluminum have a tendency to attack the steel in the die if kept in contact with the die over a prolonged period of time. Hence the cold-chamber process (described early in this unit) is normally used.

Silicon, copper, and magnesium are the principal elements used as alloys with aluminum. Aluminum-copper is perhaps the most common.

Copper-Base Alloys

Heat-resisting, alloy steel dies are necessary if die castings are to be made of brass or bronze. Rapid deterioration of the dies can occur when these alloys are used in die casting. The temperatures of these metals range from 1600° to 1900° F.

In order to prolong die life, copper-base alloys are melted in an auxiliary furnace and ladled to a plunger-type, cold-chamber machine.

The cost of producing brass die castings is higher than that of other alloys because of the short life of the dies. Hardware, aircraft, marine and automotive fittings, gears, and numerous other products are made from this alloy.

Magnesium-Base Alloys

Magnesium-base alloys are the lightest in weight. Magnesium is normally alloyed with aluminum, but it may contain small amounts of zinc, copper, and nickel.

Magnesium alloys are die cast in cold-chamber machines much the same as aluminum alloys. The casting temperature ranges from 1200° to 1300° F. This alloy has good machinability combined with excellent mechanical properties and is used for spacecraft accessories, aircraft parts, motor and instrument parts, portable tools, household appliances, and many other products.

Newton-New Haven Co.

24-10. A smooth uniform finish and contours are obtained in this aluminum die casting.

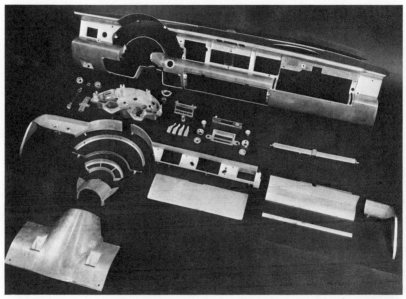

New Jersey Zinc Co.

24-11. Die-cast instrument panel for Chrysler New Yorker—the heaviest zinc die casting ever produced. Completely assembled, it has 36 die-cast parts.

	Table 24-A. Properties of Die-Casting Metals			
Type	Tensile Strength (psi)	Yield Strength at 0.2%	Brinell Hardness	Density Lbs./Cu. In.
Zinc alloy	40,000 to 50,000		75 to 85	0.26
Aluminum alloy	30,000 to 40,000	14,000 to 24,000	60 to 80	0.098
Magnesium alloy	30,000 to 33,000	21,000	60 to 65	0.063
Brass	45,000 to 60,000	25,000 to 30,000	120 to 130	0.30

The strengths shown in table are for standard test specimens.

129

Table 24-B.

Fabricating Characteristics, Die-Casting Alloys*

ALLOY	Resistance to Hot Cracking	Pressure Tightness	Fluidity Mold Filling Capacity	Resistance to Corrosion	Machining	Polishing	Electro-plating	Anodizing (Appearance)	Chemical Oxide Coating Protection
13	Excellent	Very Good	Excellent	Good	Fair	Poor	Good	Poor	Good
A13	Excellent	Very Good	Excellent	Good	Fair	Poor	Good	Poor	Good
43	Very Good	Good	Good	Good	Fair	Fair	Very Good	Fair	Good
L214	Fair	Poor	Poor	Very Good	Very Good	Excellent	Fair	Very Good	Excellent
218	Poor	Poor	Fair	Excellent	Excellent	Excellent	Poor	Excellent	Excellent
360	Excellent	Excellent	Excellent	Very Good	Fair	Good	Excellent	Good	Good
A360	Excellent	Excellent	Excellent	Very Good	Fair	Good	Excellent	Good	Good
380	Very Good	Very Good	Very Good	Fair	Good	Good	Excellent	Good	Poor
A380	Very Good	Very Good	Very Good	Fair	Good	Good	Excellent	Good	Poor
384	Very Good	Very Good	Very Good	Good	Fair	Poor	Poor	Poor	Good

Chemical compositions for aluminum general-purpose casting ingot:

Alloy 13—12.0 Si   360—9.5 Si   0.5 Si
     43—5.0 Si   380—3.5 Cu 8.5 Si
   214—3.8 Mg   384—4.0 Cu 12.0 Si
   218—8.0 Mg

Values are in percent. Aluminum and normal impurities constitute remainder.

* Reynolds Metals Co.

Strength at Elevated Temp.	Gas Welding	Arc Welding	Resistance Spot & Seam Welding	Brazing	TYPICAL MECHANICAL PROPERTIES			APPLICATIONS
					Ultimate Tensile (psi)	Yield Strength (psi)	Elonga-tion (%)	
Good	Fair	Fair	Fair	No	39,000	21,000	2.0	Excellent casting characteristics and very good corrosion resistance. Good mechanical properties. Typewriter frames, outboard motor pistons, dental equipment. A general-purpose alloy for large intricate parts with thin sections.
Good	Fair	Fair	Fair	No	—	—	—	Similar to 13 alloy with impurities more closely controlled. Same general applications as 13, but which require higher elongation than provided by 13 alloy.
Poor	Fair	Fair	Fair	No	30,000	16,000	9.0	Excellent castability and pressure tightness, good weldability. General purpose medium strength castings.
Very Good	Fair	Fair	Fair	No	—	—	—	Hardware, support brackets. Good corrosion resistance.
Fair	Fair	Fair	Fair	No	45,000	27,000	8.0	Excellent resistance to corrosion and tarnish as well as excellent strength and ductility. Does not cast as well in intricate parts as 13 alloy. Responds well to alumiliting.
Excellent	Fair	Fair	Fair	No	44,000	27,000	3.0	Excellent casting characteristics. Good mechanical properties and corrosion resistance. Cover plates, instrument cases, general-purpose castings.
Good	Fair	Fair	Fair	No	41,000	23,000	5.0	Impurities controlled to lower limits than in 360 alloy. Has somewhat better elongation than 360.
Very Good	Fair	Fair	Fair	No	45,000	26,000	2.0	Good casting characteristics and mechanical properties. General purpose castings.
Very Good	Fair	Fair	Fair	No	46,000	25,000	3.0	Impurities controlled to closer limits than in 380 alloy.
Good	Fair	Fair	Fair	No	46,000	27,000	1.0	Pistons.

Unit 25.   Centrifugal Casting

Centrifugal casting is accomplished by pouring molten metal into a revolving mold. 25–1. The metal is held against the wall of the mold by centrifugal force until it solidifies. In some types of centrifugal casting, cores are used to form cavities on the inside of the casting. Products of this method have superior physical properties and greater accuracy than can be obtained by sand casting. This process owes most of its development to the cast-iron pipe industry.

There are three methods of centrifugal casting: (1) true cen-

trifugal, (2) semicentrifugal, and (3) centrifuge.

Cast-iron and cast-steel pipe, tubes, liners, and other cylindrical products are produced by the process known as true *centrifugal* casting. 25–2. The mold is rotated about its horizontal or vertical axis by mechanical means. 25–3. A rapid rate of rotation creates a force that holds the molten metal against the inside surface of the mold until solidification takes place. 25–4. The inside surface of the mold contains a liner made of refractory materials. No core is re-

quired in this method of casting. The wall thickness of the pipe is controlled by the amount of metal poured into the mold.

Speeds for this method have to be correctly estimated for the production of sound, cylindrical castings. Speeds range from 50 to 3,000 revolutions per minute, depending upon the size of the casting.

There are several types of molds used in centrifugal casting. Of course, the type used depends upon the casting required and the type of machine that produces the casting. The molds are contained in shells made of iron or steel and are rotated by a driving mechanism. The mold proper is made up of a dry core sand which is rammed in the shell, or a separate container may be made from core sand, which is then baked and placed in the metal shell. Only one mold can be made at a time by this method.

In centrifugal casting of nonferrous metals, permanent molds of alloy steel or alloy iron are used. The inside of the mold is tapered so that the solidified casting may be withdrawn easily.

The end of the shell is covered with a plate and the metal is poured into the mold. This type of mold, spun about on a vertical axis, is used for shorter castings such as gears, track wheels, sheaves, and small marine propellers. 25–5.

A *semicentrifugal* method is employed when a number of small- or medium-sized castings as in stack molding, are produced in one mold. 25–6. It combines a gravity feed with centrifugal distribution. This method can

25–1. Centrifugal casting machines. Here pipe is manufactured in 16′ lengths and in diameters from 14″ through 48″ inclusive.

American Cast Iron Pipe Co.

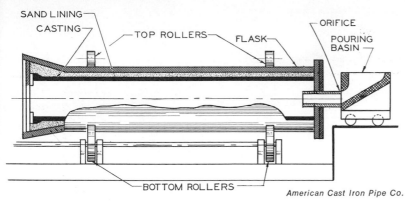

SAND LINING — CASTING — TOP ROLLERS — FLASK — ORIFICE — POURING BASIN — BOTTOM ROLLERS

American Cast Iron Pipe Co.

25–2. Cross section of centrifugal casting machine for steel or cast iron pipe.

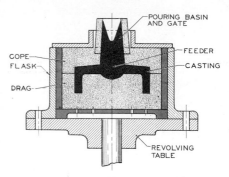

POURING BASIN AND GATE — COPE FLASK — DRAG — FEEDER — CASTING — REVOLVING TABLE

25–6. Semicentrifugal casting method—cross section. Small- or medium-sized castings can be produced by this method.

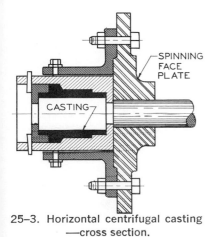

SPINNING FACE PLATE — CASTING

25–3. Horizontal centrifugal casting —cross section.

produce solid castings and the center cavity can be machined in a separate operation.

The semicentrifugal method produces a dense, strong outer casing.

When the design of the centrifuge machine influences the way the force is used, it is called centrifuge casting.

Centrifuge casting is produced with mold cavities of a number of castings located on the periphery (outside) of a circle and spun by a centrifuge around its center. 25–7. Gates are so arranged that the metal flows by

centrifugal force to these cavities from a *central pouring riser* or gate. Suitable dry sand cores produce internal cavities. For many years, gold dental inlays have been produced by this method.

25–7. Centrifuge method of casting. Mold cavities of a number of castings are arranged on the periphery of a circle and spun around its center.

American Cast Iron Pipe Co.

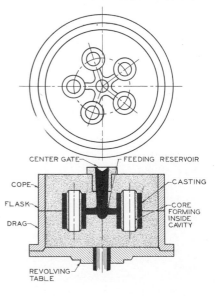

CENTER GATE — FEEDING RESERVOIR — COPE — CASTING — FLASK — CORE FORMING INSIDE CAVITY — DRAG — REVOLVING TABLE

25–4. Horizontal water-cooled centrifugal casting machine.

Centrifugal Casting Machine Co.

25–5. Vertical centrifugal casting machine.

Centrifugal Casting Machine Co.

Unit 26. Investment Casting

26–1. Investment casting: the solid mold and shell methods.

1. Pattern

Wax or plastic is injected into a metal die to form a disposable pattern.

3. Molding

A. Solid Pattern

A metal flask is put over the cluster of patterns and sealed to a base plate to form a container. A hard setting moulding material is then poured into the flask, completely investing the pattern cluster. This mold solidifies in air.

4. Pattern Removal

The flasks and shells are then placed in ovens to bake at a moderate temperature in order to slowly melt the embedded patterns. The cavity left in the mold, after the pattern material has completely flowed out, will receive the poured molten metal.

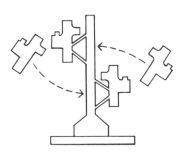

2. Gating

Patterns are gated to a sprue to form a tree or cluster, and a base of the pattern material is attached to the tree.

B. Shell Pattern

The ceramic shell (or mold) is formed by dipping the clustered patterns in a ceramic slurry and then sprinkling them with a refractory grain grain (stuccoing). This procedure is repeated until the required thickness of the mold, or shell, is achieved.

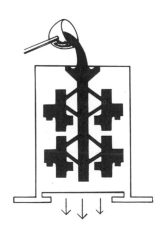

5. Casting

The flask or shell is inverted and the metal is poured into the hot mold. To help fill in the cavity completely, pressure, vacuum, gravity or centrifugal force is usually applied.

Investment casting, or the "lost-wax" process for molding metals, was known as early as the 14th century in Italy. Metal plaques, medals, and even statues were cast in molds formed by wax patterns. However, the process had limited use until the second decade of this century, when it was applied to fine dental work. In the early thirties the jewelry industry began to use the process. During World War II investment casting was used in the production of complex military parts and small turbine blades. Since then the process has been widely adopted, for making a wide variety of products.

Early artisans formed the object in wax by hand. The wax pattern was then covered by a plaster "investment." The plaster was allowed to harden, and the mold was heated in an oven, melting the wax—which escaped through a vent—and drying and hardening the mold further. The remaining cavity, with intricate details of the original wax pattern, was then filled with metal. After a suitable period of cooling, the plaster investment was then broken away from the metal casting.

Today's method of investment casting involves the making of a model of the part to be cast from steel or brass. From this model a die is cast. The dies usually must be made with several impressions of the same part.

The die halves are clamped together and a liquid wax is forced into the cavities under pressure. After the wax solidifies, the wax patterns are carefully removed. 26–1.

Wax runners or sprues are next formed to join the several

26–2. A variety of small, intricate cast parts made by the investment casting process.

American Foundrymen's Society

patterns together. This cluster of patterns is supported in a metal container or flask. An investment of wet plaster slurry, or sand mixture called investment, is poured around the wax pattern.

The flask is placed on a vibrating machine, which firmly packs slurry around the patterns. After the investment sets, the mold is ready to be placed in an oven and baked for several hours to melt the wax and further dry the mold.

The hardened mold now contains the cavities which are identical in shape to the wax pattern and which are ready to be filled with molten metal. When the mold is sufficiently cool after pouring, the investment material is broken away and the finished casting removed.

Precision investment casting has many advantages: (1) fine surface finish and close casting tolerances (from ± 0.003″ to ± 0.005″), (2) extremely complex shapes can be cast, and (3) can be used to replace die casting when small parts are involved.

There are also some disadvantages to this process: (1) the process is expensive due to high engineering costs because of increased die design time, (2) the process is limited to small castings with a limit of 35 pounds, and (3) skilled workers are needed to produce dies and molds.

Products made by this process include parts for motion picture projectors, turbine and compressor blades, turning vanes for jet aircraft, parts of postage meters, binoculars, rock drills, and automotive and diesel engine parts. 26–2 (Page 135).

Unit 27.

Investment Casting by the Solid or Mono-Shell Process

An important advancement in the manufacture of precision castings is the Mono-Shell molding process, patented by the Howmet Corporation, Misco Division. 27–1. The wax patterns and clusters are made by conventional methods, but, instead of investing a massive mold around a wax pattern ("lost-wax" process), the cluster is dipped into a ceramic slurry, stuccoed, and dried. The dipping process is repeated a number of times until a ¼″ ceramic shell is built up around the entire wax cluster. The wax is removed by firing the shell to 1900° F. Upon cooling, the shell can go into immediate use.

These molds are more versatile than conventional invested molds. Preheating of the shells can vary from room temperature to 1900° F. They can also be surrounded by backup material, or can receive molten metal without backup material if rapid cooling is desired. The materials used are more refractory than the type used in silica investment castings. A description of the modern investment casting process as applied to an air-cooled turbine blade is given below. 27–2. (See illustration.)

1. A wax pattern of the part is made by injection of wax around a ceramic core that forms the air cooling passages in the turbine blade.

2. Individual wax patterns are assembled into a wax cluster for economical manufacture.

27–1. Pattern, ceramic shell mold and casting cluster in the Mono-Shell molding process.

Howmet Corp.

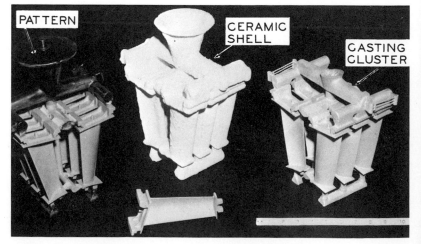

3, 4. A refractory shell is built up on wax cluster by alternately dipping in fine refractory slurry and then stuccoing with coarse refractory particles.

5. Wax is melted out of ceramic shell and the shell is heated to a high temperature.

6. The hot ceramic shell is filled with high-quality alloy that is melted and poured inside of vacuum chamber.

7. Individual blades are cut from the metal cluster that has had the ceramic shell removed, after which individual blades are cleaned and polished.

8, 9, 10. Inspection includes X-ray examination for possible internal flaws, fluorescent penetrant inspection under black light for tiny surface defects, and complete gaging to insure that the airfoil is perfect.

AUTOMATION IN MONO-SHELL MOLDING

To match the efficiency of the shell molds themselves, the machinery that makes the molds must also be efficient. On a production basis, these machines must be capable of turning out molds which are of uniform thickness, have desired physical characteristics, and good surface finish.

The 12-station machine shown in the illustration is capable of producing 480 molds per hour yet requires only one person to operate it. 27–3 (Page 138).

The single station machine is capable of turning out 40 shells per hour. 27–4 (Page 138). Pattern size is 22″ × 28″, but molds of smaller size can be made by including metal dividers in the pat-

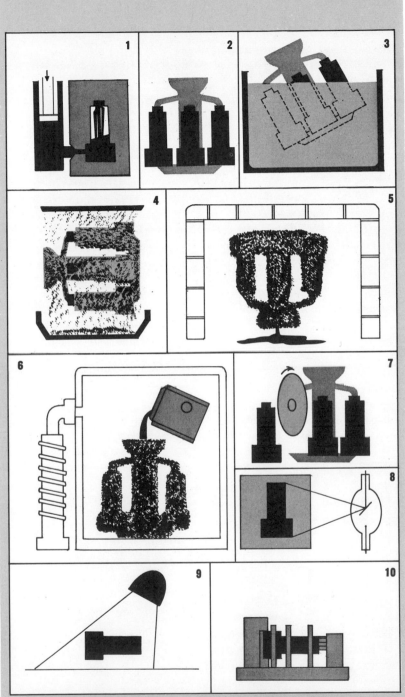

Howmet Corp., Austenal Microcast Div.

27–2. Modern investment casting process as applied to high-quality, air-cooled turbine blade for a supersonic aircraft.

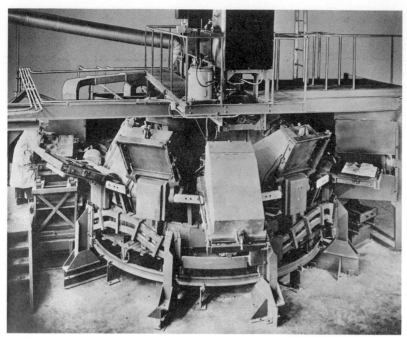

Mechanical Handling Systems, Inc.

27–3. Twelve-station rotary shell-molding machine and sand-blending machine.

27–4. Automatic, single-station, shell-molding machine which performs all steps for completing a mold, from sand blending to curing, in one continuous sequence of operations.

Mechanical Handling Systems, Inc.

DUMP BOX

MOBILE OVEN

CONTROL PANEL

PATTERN HOLDER SWING GATE

OVEN TRACKS

Mechanical Handling Systems, Inc.

27–5. After initial preheat, the single motor-driven unit moves the pattern assembly to engage the dump box at the rear. Air-operated latch on the box seals it to pattern assembly.

27–6. A timer switch raises the pattern and box after shell is set. Excess sand falls off, and the pattern and box return to horizontal position.

Mechanical Handling Systems, Inc.

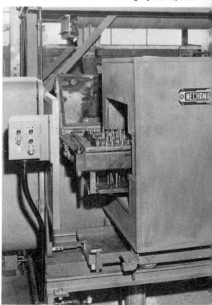

tern plate. The shell mold can then be broken into two or four sections.

The main elements of this machine are the *control panel, oven, sand* and *resin dump box,* the *pattern assembly,* the *gear segment,* and *motor housing.* In operation, the sand supply system is installed to feed automatically during the time the dump box is in the disengaged position.

The three main operating cycles which take place in response to one push button are: (1) the dump cycle, in which the sand is deposited on the pattern, (2) the cure, during which the mold is baked, and (3) stripping the mold from the pattern. 27–5 through 27–7.

The pattern plate and sand mixture hopper movements are controlled by a gear segment driven by an electric motor. Only two air cylinders are used—one for latching the pattern to the sand hopper and one for raising the stripper actuating mechanism which engages the stripper plate and removes the cured mold from the pattern. 27–8.

ADVANTAGES OF THE MONO-SHELL PROCESS

As said, production molding is a mechanical process, accomplished by machine and requiring only one skilled operator.

Molds produced by this method are more accurate than those made by conventional methods.27–9 (Page 140). They have smooth, dense surfaces, yet they allow free passage of gas when the metal is poured, thus preventing blow holes and defects caused by gas. 27–10 (Page 140).

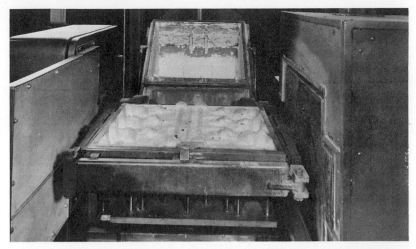

Mechanical Handling Systems, Inc.

27-7. Automatic timer returns oven to right side after predetermined curing period. Completed shell is ready for ejection as automatic sequence ends.

27–8. In the only manual operation, the operator actuates the air-operated stripper plate. On engaging the pattern assembly, a cam lock releases ejector pins, raising the shell for removal by the operator.

Mechanical Handling Systems, Inc.

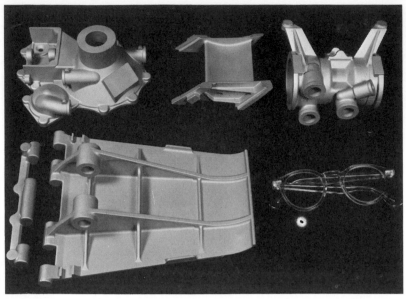

Howmet Corp., Austenal Microcast Div.

27-10. Typical rotating investment cast components. These are gas-turbine and turbo-charger wheels.

Howmet Corp.

27–9. Investment castings made by the Mono-Shell process.

Unit 28.

Shell Molding

28–1(A). Shell molding machine. Notice the shell molds at the base of the machine.

Shell Process, Inc.

The shell molding process is one of the more recent methods for the production of metal castings. 28–1(A). It consists of making molds and cores in the form of thin bonded sand shells on a hot pattern.

The mold is made of a mixture of dried silica sand and thermosetting resin. The sand and resin are mixed in a mulling machine.

A metal pattern is used. 28–1(B). This is heated to a temperature of approximately 450° F. and sprayed with a silicone release agent before being placed on top of the dump box.

The box is rolled over and the sand mixture drops on the pattern. This mixture is held there for a period of 15 to 30 seconds and then returned to its original position. Excess resin-sand material falls back into the dump box. 28–2. The pattern now has a coating of the sand mixture about ⅛″ to 3/16″ thick. Next it is placed in an oven and the shell cured and hardened. The finished mold is ejected from the pattern and the mold halves, the drag and cope, move onto a closing machine where they are assembled with clamps, resin adhesives, or other devices. 28–3.

Shell-O-Matic, Inc.

28–1(B). Metal pattern for shell molds.

Shell Process, Inc.

28–4. Metal that has been poured into shell molds. After the metal has solidified, the mold is broken away.

Shell Process, Inc.

28–2. Steel pattern plate used in shell molding process. A mixture of sand and resin is applied to the heated plate. Heat melts the resin, which binds the sand into a smooth mold.

28–3. The pattern moving to a station where a resin and sand mixture will be deposited on it to form the shell mold.

Shell Process, Inc.

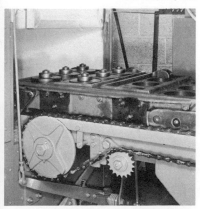

The metal can then be poured into the molds. When the metal has solidified, the mold is broken away from the casting. 28–4. The casting is ready to be cleaned by shot blasting.

Castings produced by this method have close tolerances.

The surface finish is so fine that finish machining is unnecessary, or can be held to a minimum.

A shell mold weighs only a fraction as much as a conventional mold, thus reducing material handling load per pound of casting produced.

Unit 29. Plaster Mold Casting

For years, plaster mold casting had limited use until a method was found to make the plaster more permeable so that gases could escape the mold. The recent improvement in the plaster mixture—to accomplish a combination of quick drying and increased porosity—has accelerated use of the method.

A method being used at the present consists of adding slurry to an agent that is first beaten to a foam. Bubbles are created.

When the mold is dried below 400°F., the walls of the bubbles break as the plaster sets, providing the necessary porosity.

Production of plaster mold castings begins with the preparation of very accurate brass patterns, either hand-gated or split, mounted on aluminum cope and drag plates. 29–1. *This operation is basically manual,* as extreme care is needed to insure exact conformation and size. The plaster molds are also handled man-

141

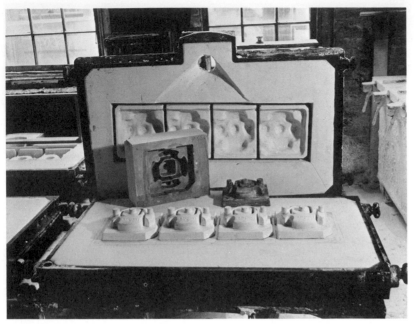

Scientific Cast Products

29–1. Dump core box, plaster pattern, plaster "reversal," and plaster mold.

to the bottom of the crucible to insure complete cleansing. Nitrogen provides the agitation needed for degassing; chlorine reacts chemically with nonmetallic solids and dissolved gases to produce clean metal.

In pouring the metal into the molds, small crucibles are purposely used to permit more accurate control of metal temperatures. NOTE: Molds are maintained at preheated temperatures until pouring; if allowed to cool, molds must be reheated, a procedure that will affect the accuracy of the castings.

The handling of materials and the methods used in the plaster mold process naturally result in remarkably smooth castings. For the same reasons, the process produces castings of exceptional uniformity regardless of quantities involved. Smooth finish and uniformity reduce machining time. On some products machining is eliminated entirely.

The surface finish on plaster mold castings will average 90–125 microinches; on high copper-base alloys, an average of 125–160 microinches. (A microinch is one millionth of an inch.)

Plaster mold castings can be held to very close tolerances. Over limited areas, tolerances as low as ±0.005″ can be held.

In designing a part for plaster mold casting, the draft is very important. This requires approximately 0.005″ to the inch, although the figure can be reduced as the height of the part increases.

Sizes of parts to be cast are limited only by the size of existing foundry equipment. At present the largest flask measures 12″x17″x9″.

ually, each half of the mold being poured very slowly so that distribution of the material will be uniform.

Precision and accuracy are important. The correct proportions of plaster and heated water are carefully determined by weight, after which the two are mixed at regulated speed for a predetermined length of time.

The instant the mixture reaches the desired consistency, it is rushed to the pouring area. The plaster mixture must be poured slowly at first to insure smooth, even distribution. Brass patterns and runners are used in the drag side of the mold.

Moving quickly now, to finish pouring before the mixture starts to set, the cope side is poured. Modern plastic patterns and brass risers are used on this side of the mold. Again, manual operation

at this stage is essential for smooth castings, accurate in the finest details.

Next, the plaster molds are arranged in huge twin ovens, ready for baking. During the first 3 hours of baking, oven temperature is maintained at 320°F., then cycled up to a maximum of 600°F. for an additional 11 hours. Oven temperatures are regulated automatically during the entire 14-hour period. After baking, the completed plaster molds are ready for the molten metal.

Degassing of the molten metal is also a very important step. An exact mixture of nitrogen and chlorine gases, in specific proportions measured in flow meters and precisely dispensed through flow control valves, is injected into the molten aluminum with a graphite lance which penetrates

Check Your Knowledge

1. Explain permanent mold casting.

2. Describe a permanent mold.

3. What are some of the major uses of permanent mold castings?

4. What are some of the advantages of this type of casting?

5. How important a part does die casting play in modern industrial processes?

6. What is die casting? Explain the process.

7. Explain the difference between hot-chamber and cold-chamber die casting.

8. By what means is the metal injected under pressure into a die-casting mold?

9. What means are used to heat the metal in a hot-chamber machine?

10. Compare the advantages of gravity-type permanent molds and die castings.

11. What is the difference between a multiple-cavity die and a combination die?

12. How large can die castings be made?

13. What is centrifugal casting and why is this process used?

14. Make a comparison between centrifugal casting and sand casting.

15. Describe the process of centrifugal casting.

16. What is the difference between centrifugal and centrifuge casting?

17. Why is investment casting called the "lost-wax" process?

18. Compare the method used by early artisans with modern investment casting methods.

19. Explain the complete process of investment casting.

20. Name the disadvantages of investment casting.

21. Name some products produced by this method of casting.

22. Explain the difference between the Mono-Shell investment casting process and the conventional method.

23. Why are these molds more versatile than the conventional method?

24. Describe the machine used in this process.

25. Name some of the advantages of this process.

26. How is shell molding done?

27. Why is the shell-mold process adaptable to automation?

28. How does shell molding differ from the investment process?

29. How close are the tolerances that can be obtained by this process?

30. What are the advantages of this process over sand casting methods? Disadvantages?

31. What improvements in plaster mold casting have accelerated its uses?

32. Describe fully the plaster mold casting process.

33. What metals are suitable for this type of casting?

34. Name some of the products made by this process.

35. What are the advantages of plaster mold casting?

References

American Society for Metals, *Metals Handbook,* 8th ed., Vol. 1, 1961.

Bart, R. L.; Hurd, D. T.; and Stoltenburg, J. P., *"The Pressure Die Casting of Irons and Steels,"* Modern Castings, July, 1967.

Cook, Glenn J., *Engineered Castings,* McGraw-Hill Book Co., 1961.

Herman, Robert H., *How to Design and Buy Investment Castings,* Investment Castings Institute, 1960.

Schaum, J. H., *"New Technology Expands Centrifugal Casting Horizon,"* Modern Castings, April, 1962.

A 6,000 pound, double-frame hammer used in conjunction with a floor-type manipulator.

Section Six

Hot-Working Metal

THE mechanical hot-working of metals consists of shaping metals above the recrystallization temperature. 30-1. For steel, as shown in the illustration, recrystallization starts around 950° to 1300°F. However, most hot-working of steel is ordinarily done at a temperature considerably above this range. Until the lower limit of the recrystallization range is reached there is no tendency for the metal to harden during the mechanical process. Metals such as lead, tin, and zinc have a low recrystallization range and can be hot-worked at near room temperature.

The metal is in a plastic state during all hot-working operations and can be formed into desired shapes by mechanical working processes. There are several advantages to hot-working metal: (1) Porosity that occurs in cast ingots is largely eliminated. (2) The toughness of the metal is increased because the grain structure is refined. (Large grains are broken up and reformed into smaller crystals.) (3) Less energy is required to change the shape of the metal when hot-worked. (4) Hot-

Ajax Mfg. Co.

working improves the ductility; resistance to impact and strength is increased. (5) Slag and other inclusions are pressed into fibers and distributed through the metal. (6) Hot-working pushes the metal into extreme shapes, causing the continual deformation of the crystals, thereby eliminating ruptures and tears in the metal. (7) Hot-working processes are more economical than cold-working.

Hot-working has a few disadvantages, namely: (1) Higher temperatures produce oxidation and scaling of the surface. (2) Close tolerances are difficult to maintain. (3) Equipment and heat-resistant tools are expensive.

The following principal methods of hot-working metals will be described in this section:

A. Rolling

B. Forging
 1. Hammer or smith forging
 2. Drop forging
 3. Upset forging
 4. Press forging
 5. Roll forging

C. Special forging techniques
 1. Bending
 2. Piercing
 3. Ring rolling
 4. Swaging

D. Finishing operations
 1. Trimming
 2. Punching
 3. Coining, sizing, and ironing

E. Pipe and tube manufacturing
 1. Pipe piercing
 2. Plug rolling
 3. Reeling
 4. Pipe welding

F. Hot extrusion

G. Hot spinning

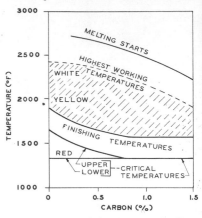

30–1. Range of forging and rolling temperature for carbon steel.

Unit 30.   Rolling

After the steel making process is completed, the molten metal is poured into ingot molds where it cools and solidifies. At the proper time, the mold is removed from the ingot. This first solid form of steel usually ranges from 5 to 25 tons in weight.

The outside of the ingot cools and solidifies faster than the inside. At the time the mold is stripped from the ingot the outside of the ingot is comparatively cool, but the interior is extremely hot, in a semi-molten state.

ROLLING TEMPERATURE

Before rolling can take place, the temperature through the ingot has to be the same. This is ac- complished by heating in a special gas-fired furnace or *soaking pit*. The ingot is heated to 2200°F. and kept at that temperature for 4 to 8 hours, till soft and plastic enough to be shaped by rolling mills, when it is removed from the pit.

Following soaking, the hot ingot is brought to the blooming mill for an initial reduction on rolling mill stands. 30–2. The rolling process consists of passing the hot ingot between two rolls which rotate in opposite directions at a uniform speed. 30–3. The distance between the rolls is adjusted so that they are always slightly closer together than the thickness of the steel passing through. The ingot gets longer and thinner as it passes between the rolls.

Semi-finishing mills are of three principal types: blooming mills, slabbing mills, and billet mills. Blooms are the form of semi-finished steel that is processed into structural steel and railroad rails. They are either square or rectangular in cross section. 30–4.

Mesta Machine Co.

30–2. A two-high reversing slabbing mill (entry side) rolling a 20-ton ingot into slabs.

30–3. Delivery side of a two-high universal slabbing mill.

Mesta Machine Co.

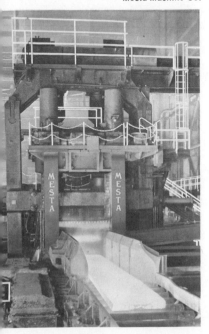

Blooms can be further reduced in size to billets before being processed into finished products. Billets are used to make bars and rods. Rods may be further drawn to wire.

The rolls are mounted in heavy housings, or roll stands. 30–5. A stand with two rolls is called two-high; a stand with three rolls, one above the other, is three-high. The ingot is carried to and through the stands on a path of rollers. These rollers, which are rotated by electric power, are mounted on the long table of the mill. The rolls are made from steel or cast iron and are shaped according to the type of rolling that is required. These shapes may be flat or grooved to roll definite shapes. 30–6. They may be as much as 5' in diameter.

TWO-HIGH AND FOUR-HIGH DESIGN

Blooms and slabs are frequently made on two-high or four-high *reversing* mills. Since the direction of rotation of the rolls can be reversed, the ingot is passed back and forth between the rolls, which are brought

30–4. How a bloom is shaped into a rail.

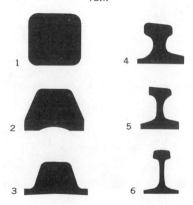

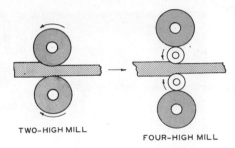

TWO-HIGH MILL
FOUR-HIGH MILL

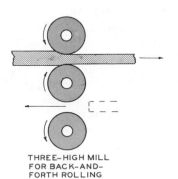

THREE–HIGH MILL FOR BACK-AND-FORTH ROLLING

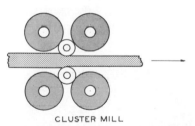

CLUSTER MILL

30–5. Roll arrangements used in rolling mills.

30–6. Types of rolls. Rolls are made from steel or cast iron.

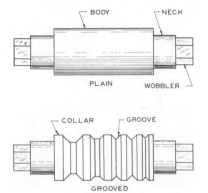

BODY — NECK

PLAIN — WOBBLER

COLLAR — GROOVE

GROOVED

Mesta Machine Co.

30–7. Continuous bar and billet mill.

30–8. Bar mill showing intermediate, leader, and finishing stands, with transfer and manipulators. Insert shows position of rolls as mounted in machine.

Mesta Machine Co.

closer together at each pass, until the steel has been reduced to the desired size. The ingot is passed between the bottom and middle rolls, then raised and passed between the middle and top rolls.

CONTINUOUS DESIGN

Billet mills may be of continuous design. 30–7. The mill consists of a series of roll stands arranged one after another. The steel being rolled passes successively through each stand and emerges from the last stand as a finished billet. 30–8. The final billet size after the required number of passes is approximately 2"x2". This is the raw material for shapes such as tubes, bars, and material for forgings. The illustration shows the number of passes required to reduce a billet to round stock. 30–9.

Hot-rolling not only reduces the steel to the desired shape and size but improves the quality of the material. Steel consists of a mass of metallic crystals or grains. In the ingot these grains are relatively large and the distribution is such that the steel is not suitable for most purposes. The hot-rolling process creates a smaller grain, making the steel denser and tougher and leaving it in more workable condition. Hot-working thus improves the quality of the steel while the ingot is being reduced to bloom, billet, or slab, and also during the finishing operations that follow.

As shown in the illustration, the arcs AB and A'B' are in contact with the rolls. There is a wedging action on the billet which is overcome by the frictional forces acting upon the

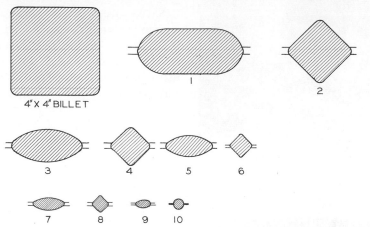

4" X 4" BILLET

1 2 3 4 5 6 7 8 9 10

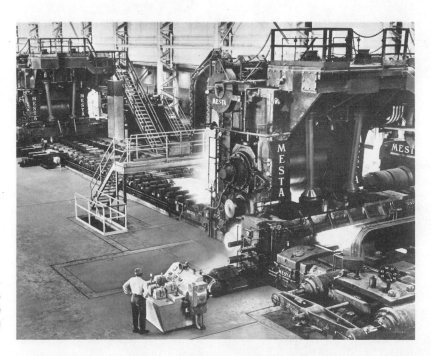

30–10. Effect of hot rolling on grain structure.

Carnegie-Illinois Steel Corp.

30–9. Number of passes and sequence required in reducing the cross section of a 4″ x 4″ billet to round stock.

arcs and drawing the metal through the rolls. 30–10.

After the rolling operation has been completed, irregular ends are cut off by powerful shears. The billets and slabs are then cut to shorter lengths that are more easily handled in the finishing mills.

PLATES

Plates range in thickness from about ³⁄₁₆″ to over 12″. Plates are used in the fabrication of girders, components of bridges and buildings, aircraft fuselage and wings, hulls and decks of ships, as well as machinery parts and housings.

Plates are rolled from slabs, using two types of plate mills—*sheared* or *universal*.

Mesta Machine Co.

30–11. Four-high continuous roughing mill stands on an 86″ hot strip mill. Steel slabs up to 130″ long are reduced to a thin, narrow strip a quarter of a mile long.

The slab is placed in a furnace and slowly heated to rolling temperature. The hot slab is removed from the furnace and taken to the plate mill where it is rolled to the required thickness and width. Next, it is passed through the leveling rolls for final flattening and then sheared or gas-cut to size.

SHEETS AND STRIPS

Automobile companies use large quantities of sheet and strip for the manufacture of auto bodies. Metal furniture, desks, chairs, household appliances, containers of various types, and many other products use sheets and strips.

30–12. Continuous hot strip finishing stands.

30–13. Four-high, two-stand cold temper mill rolling coils of steel strip.

30–14. Five-stand tandem cold mill.

Sheets are made by hot-rolling in a continuous hot-sheet mill. 30–11. The slab is heated to the proper rolling temperature. From the furnace the hot slab is pushed onto a line of revolving rollers which carry it to a scale-breaker which breaks up the scale formed by the heating process. The scale is washed away by a powerful water spray. The slab is then squeezed down to about one-fifth its original thickness by passing it through roughing stands. This process also stretches the metal to about five times its original length.

At this time, a second scale-breaker is used and a shear cuts off the uneven ends formed during the roughing.

Six huge roll stands, called finishing stands, form the material to about 50 to 60 times its original length. 30–12. A trap door directs the fast-moving steel down into a coiler. 30–13. In less than 20 seconds the material is wound into a heavy coil which is ejected and moved by conveyor to storage.

Sometimes steel is cut into sheets by a *flying shear* which is equipped with rotating knives.

A great deal of the sheet rolled on the hot-sheet mill is further processed on the *cold reduction mill,* which can produce a thinner sheet than possible on the hot mills. 30–14. Besides finishing the steel to more accurate dimensions, cold-rolling produces a smooth, bright finish as well as improved mechanical properties. Cold-reduced sheets, after further processing, are used in forming automobile bodies and metal buildings of all types.

31–2. Pneumatic, motor-driven forging hammer.

Unit 31. Forging

HAMMER OR SMITH FORGING

Though forging is one of the oldest metalworking processes, techniques for designing and producing steel forgings have made great changes in the past few decades. Today metal is not always heated for forging; instead, a great deal of work is done in various forms of presses.

The process starts with the rolling of the ingot (Unit 30), and the steps involved in producing a forging combine to produce a refined grain with a fiberlike structure. Forging produces parts with unbroken grain flow following the contour of the part, making a stronger product than one that has been cast or machined from the solid. 31–1.

Metal can be forged by impact or pressure. When metal is forged by impact of hammers, the part can be formed by dies which are flat or only slightly shaped—smith forging.

Smith forgings are sometimes called blacksmith, hand, hammered, or flat die. The forgings are generally produced with steam hammers or motor-driven pneumatic or helve hammers. 31–2.

The rate of production is relatively slow. However, with an experienced and skilled operator, forgings with a high degree of accuracy can be produced. This type of forging is used where the quantity is too low to make it practical to justify the production of structural dies.

DROP FORGING

Drop forging is a process consisting of hammering heated metal bars or billets into closed impression dies. The resulting products are known as drop forgings, compression-die forgings, or closed-die forgings. The metal used in this process can be carbon or alloy steel, alloys of copper, aluminum, magnesium, and nickel.

Equipment

The equipment used in drop forging operations consists of a steam hammer, a gravity drop (31–3) or board hammer (including the piston-lift which can use steam), and a set of forging dies designed for the part to be produced. In the steam hammer the ram and hammer are lifted by steam. (Furnaces to heat the metal are also necessary.) The force of the blow is controlled by throttling the steam. It is possible to obtain approximately 300 blows per minute with this type of hammer. Generally, a finished

31–3. A battery of motor-driven drop hammers.

31–1. Forging produces parts with uninterrupted grain flow following the contour of each part.

CAST   MACHINED FROM SOLID   FORGED

forging cannot be entirely formed by one blow because of the limitations of directions in which the metal can be forced at one time. Therefore the operations are divided into a number of steps and each step changes the form of the part until the final desired shape is obtained. Many products cannot be completely formed on one set of dies, and therefore it may be necessary to use more than one set of dies to secure the final shape.

Steam hammers range in capacity from 500 to 50,000 pounds and are usually of double housing design. 31–4. Most steam hammers today are double acting and considerably more energy can be obtained at the die from a steam hammer than with a board or gravity drop hammer.

Action of Board Drop Hammer

The force of gravity is employed in the board drop hammer. 31–5. The ram is raised to striking position by means of boards, the lower ends of the boards are wedged into the ram. The upper ends pass between one or two pairs of rolls. With the two rolls, in a pair, rotating in opposite directions, the boards and ram are raised when the rolls move together. As the ram reaches the top, the rolls separate and the boards are released.

The ram is operated by a treadle, which, when depressed, causes the ram to fall. 31–6. As long as the treadle is held down, the board drop hammer will automatically deliver blows at a uniform rate. The force of the blow can be varied by changing the distance of the fall, by unclamping and moving the dogs on the front rod. The force of the blows is determined entirely by the weight of the ram, or falling weight, which in most commercial forging plants is between 600 and 6,500 pounds.

Piston-Lift Action

The piston-lift hammer uses compressed air or steam to lift the ram, then lets it fall by gravity similar to the board drop hammer. The ram is lifted by a

31–4. A 50,000-pound steam drop hammer.

Erie Foundry Co.

31–5. A 1,500-pound "FV" board drop hammer.

Erie Foundry Co.

31–6. This ram is operated by treadle.

Crescent Niagara Corp.

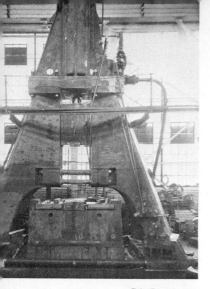

31–7. The ram is lifted by either steam or compressed air in this 16,000-pound double-frame hammer.

steel rod connecting it to the piston. 31–7. A separate air circuit operates a clamp which holds the ram in a raised position between strokes. A series of short- and long-stroke blows can be obtained and the operator does not have to regulate the stroke heights. The rate of the piston-lift hammer is faster than the board drop hammer.

Forging Dies

Forging dies are constructed from high-grade carbon or alloy steel and must resist heat, abrasion, and pressure. 31–8. They must withstand severe strains, have a long wear life under high-production conditions, and minimize checking.

The majority of die-blocks are heat-treated before impressions are machined to avoid warping or cracking. 31–9(A). The cavities are such as to allow for shrinkage in the workpiece when it cools. A parting line must be selected and draft applied to the

part. In selecting the parting line and position in which the stock will be placed in the dies, the resulting grain flow must be considered.

On drop forgings the standard amount of draft is about 7°. The die is also supplied with generous fillets, radii, and ribs to prolong its life.

Locking surfaces or pins can be provided so that the two dies will match the same way each time they come together.

Steps in forging a connecting rod are shown in the illustration. 31–9(B). The dies, shown in the first illustration, contain impressions for several operations. Preliminary hot-working beginning operations are pictured in the second illustration at A, B, and C for forming the connecting rod. At D is shown the shaping of the rod into the first definite form. The appearance of the connecting rod after several blows by the finishing die is shown at E. The completed connecting rod, shown at F, is then

31–8. The construction of a forging die for a crescent wrench.

31–9(A). A set of forging dies.

31–9(B). Successive steps in forging a connecting rod.

A   B   C   D   E   F   G

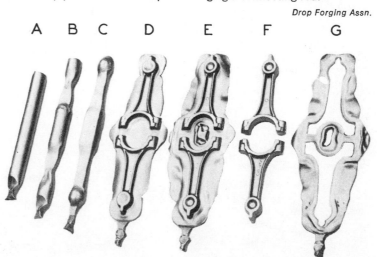

The Hill Acme Co.

31–10. Upset forging machine.

ready for the heat-treating operation.

The illustration G represents the flash that has been trimmed from the rod by a trimming press. For this operation, special trimmer dies are used and the centers are punched out at the same time. Since the forgings are covered with scale after the forging operation, they are cleaned by pickling in acid, tumbling, or shot peening. The size and composition of the forging control the method used. NOTE: If the part has become distorted during the forging operation, it may have to be sized or straightened.

Forging produces the best combination of physical characteristics for parts which will

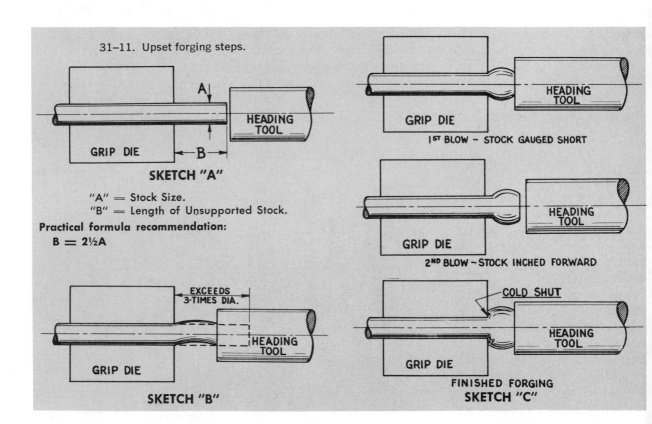

31–11. Upset forging steps.

SKETCH "A"

"A" = Stock Size.
"B" = Length of Unsupported Stock.
Practical formula recommendation:
B = 2½A

GRIP DIE   HEADING TOOL

EXCEEDS 3-TIMES DIA.

SKETCH "B"

1ST BLOW – STOCK GAUGED SHORT

2ND BLOW – STOCK INCHED FORWARD

COLD SHUT

FINISHED FORGING
SKETCH "C"

be highly stressed. The rolling of the ingot combined with forging produces a refined grain with a fiberlike structure. This introduces flow lines and directional properties.

UPSET FORGING

The upsetter or forging machine was originally developed to form bolt heads. 31–10. This original purpose has been broadened to include a variety of forging work including not only upset but displacement operations.

The operation consists of placing a bar which is heated on one end against a movable stock gage in the first groove of a stationary die. (See illustration.) Some machines are equipped to feed the heated stock automatically. The moving die closes, gripping the bar holding it while the header advances and upsets (expands) the projecting unsupported end. 31–11. The stock is moved to the next die station, and the cycle is repeated. Various shapes can be formed. The impressions may be in the gripping die, punch, or in both. 31–12. The number of grooves in the die is governed by the number of steps required to complete the part.

The size of the upset forging machine is indicated in inches—a holdover from the original bolt-making days. 31–13. Sizes range from ½″ to 9″.

The weights of machine or upset forgings range from less than 1 pound to 500 pounds. The forgings are uniform in size and weight and the process is rapid. The dies are without draft and are well-fitted. Straight holes may be hot-pierced. Very little

Ajax Mfg. Co.

31–12. Set of typical upset forging dies for forging axles.

machining is required to finish the part.

PRESS FORGING

Presses for forging steel are of massive, rigid construction with steel frames and heavy crankshafts with eccentrics to operate the pitman (connecting rod) and ram. 31–14 (Page 156). Press forging differs in operation from hammer and drop forging because of its slow, squeezing action rather than impact blows.

31–13. A 5″ high-duty forging machine and the type of products produced on this machine.

National Machinery Co.

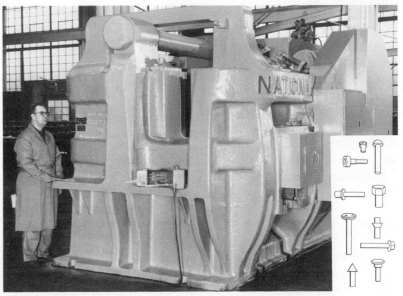

31–14. A 3,000-ton forging press.

National Machinery Co.

National Machinery Co.

31–15. Reducer roll preforms forging blanks in a wide variety of shapes, lengths, and sizes for finish forging on the same heat.

Some of the advantages are: (1) Dies have less draft. (2) Forgings can be made nearer to desired sizes. (3) Vibration and noise are not as great. (4) Greater porportion of total work put into the machine is transmitted to the metal. (5) Press production of the metal is faster and therefore more economical. (6) Forgings are symmetrical in shape, with closer tolerances and smooth surfaces.

Maximum pressure occurs at the end of the stroke, forcing the metal to the desired shape. The press is rated on the basis of the *force in tons* applied to the bottom of the stroke. The rating of forging presses, based on the estimated pressure at this point, varies from 200 to 6,000 tons.

Hydraulic forging presses move the ram by pressure of a fluid, usually oil. The control is extremely flexible, permitting adjustment of length of stroke and pressure attained.

ROLL FORGING

Stock can be drawn out to long slender sections in forging rolls. 31–15. The roll dies are semicylindrical. 31–16. The stock is placed between them when they are in the open position and rolled toward the operator, who again places the stock between rolls for the next pass. 31–17.

Tapered or straight work can be forged at high speed. Products such as axles, leaf springs, crowbars, airplane propellors, chisels, and tapered tubing can be produced by roll forging. This process can be used as a preliminary to finish forging in a hammer or press.

A smooth-finished surface characterizes the parts. Tolerances are equal to other forging processes. A thorough hot-work-

31–16. Operation of a roll forging machine.

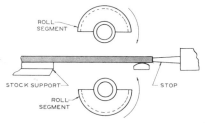

ing of the metal with good physical properties is possible.

Circular products are rolled between dies in a roll mill. The blank is pierced at one end in order to position it on the vertical die. Wheels, brake drums, gear blanks, and turbine rotors are produced by this method of forging.

When the blank is loaded, the vertical die moves forward under forging pressure and both dies revolve. A combination of the initial pressure and the rolling action shapes the part to the die.

31–17. Typical No. 3 forging roll. *Ajax Mfg. Co.*

Unit 32.

Special Forging Techniques

There are several forging processes or techniques that do not fit easily into any of the previously discussed forging operations. A brief explanation of a few of these are discussed in the following paragraphs.

BENDING

Bending is often done as a part of a hammer or press forging operation. It has been found that bending large parts is more economical for the manufacturer if done on separate equipment. The long-stroke equipment is normally used for bending operations. Special mechanical or hydraulic presses known as bulldozers are used for bending large parts such as engine crankshafts.

PIERCING

Piercing is sometimes combined with other basic forging operations. Special multi-ram presses are used for moving auxiliary punches. Highly complex parts such as large valve housings, shells, and seamless tubing can be produced by this method.

Piercing produces hollow bodies with thick walls. Whether the steel flows radially or whether it is displaced axially between the container wall and punch surface is largely dependent upon the dimensions of the container, workpiece, and the punch diameter.

RING ROLLING

Ring rolling is a special forging process performed on a

vertical two-high mill with one of the rolls driven. 32–1. A thick-walled ring is used as the starting part. This has been preformed by the process of forging, punching, or some other type of preparatory operation.

32–1. Ring rolling process: (A) work roll, (B) idling roll, (C) workpiece—a ring, (D) guide rolls which insure proper position of the ring during rolling, and (E) base plate which supports the ring.

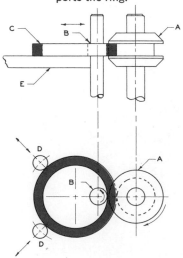

157

32–2. Swaging machine.

Fenn

Deformation of the ring takes place between the driven roll and the idler roll. The thickness of the ring decreases and the diameter of the ring increases. By decreasing the distance between the idler roll and work roll, a continuous wall-thinning and deformation takes place. A variety of profiles can be obtained by shaping the forming rolls. Sizes up to 15′ in diameter are possible.

32–3. How swaging machine operates.

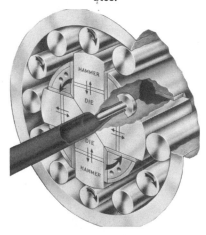

SWAGING

Swaging is a special type of forging in which metal is formed by a succession of rapid hammer blows. It is easily the most economical method to point, size, shape, taper, bond, or form metal parts, hot or cold. Metal is formed—not machined—so there are no wasteful chips. Accurate sections are produced to plus or minus .001″. Swaging actually improves grain structure, giving the part greater strength and an unusually fine finish. Unskilled operators can perform a complete swaging operation in just a few seconds with almost no training. Setup or changeover is simple and fast. One employee can operate two or more machines.

How Swaging Machines Function

In a *rotary* swaging machine, forming dies backed by hammer blocks revolve around the work. 32–2. As the spindle revolves, centrifugal force throws the hammers and dies outward against a series of rollers surrounding the spindle. Each time the hammer blocks strike diametrically opposed rollers, they are driven inward, causing the die halves to close and compress the metal being swaged. As the hammer blocks pass out from under the rollers, the dies are again thrown open. 32–3.

In a *stationary die* swaging machine, the spindle assembly remains stationary and the roller cage rotates. Thus, a stationary die swager is not limited to round cross sections. 32–4. Two types are available—simultan-

eous- and alternate-blow. The most versatile is the alternate-blow type.

FINISHING OPERATIONS

After a part has been forged generally there is some finishing to be performed, such as trimming, punching, coining, sizing, and ironing.

Trimming

It is necessary that the flash formed on impression die forgings be removed before the forging leaves the forge shop. The thick flash of hot forgings is usually trimmed while the metal is hot because this does

32–4. Simultaneous-blow machines are used to form circular cross sections. Rectangles and hexagons are formed on alternate blow machines.

Simultaneous Blow

Alternate Blow

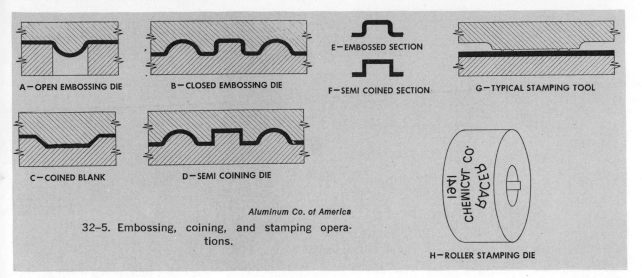

A—OPEN EMBOSSING DIE

B—CLOSED EMBOSSING DIE

E—EMBOSSED SECTION

F—SEMI COINED SECTION

G—TYPICAL STAMPING TOOL

C—COINED BLANK

D—SEMI COINING DIE

Aluminum Co. of America

32–5. Embossing, coining, and stamping operations.

RACER
CHEMINCL CO.
1941

H—ROLLER STAMPING DIE

not require as much power as with cold forging. However, this means that the trimming press is not used as much because it is tied up with a forging hammer. Separate trimming presses are sometimes used, and cold trimming is efficient for smaller parts, making a full utilization of the trimming press possible. When suitable, the flash can be removed by grinding, milling, sawing, or by shot blasting or tumbling.

Punching

Punching and trimming are closely associated operations. Punching is an internal operation, such as punching out holes. Often punching and trimming are done at the same time which does increase the accuracy of the cuts, relative to each other.

Coining, Sizing, and Ironing

Coining and sizing are restriking operations in which compression is applied to bring the forging to correct dimensional

size and impart a smooth finish to surfaces of forgings where a small amount of metal flow is involved and flash is not usually formed. 32–5. These operations are conducted on powerful presses after the forging has cooled to room temperature.

It is often sufficient to restrict coining or sizing to certain areas of the forging, such as the ends

of a connecting rod. Parts finished by coining and sizing are levers, links, brackets, connecting rods, and many other machined parts.

Ironing is a finishing process used to improve the surface finish of a part. It is a cold operation, and the quality of the finish is comparable to a machined surface.

Unit 33.

Pipe and Tube Manufacture

Two methods of making pipe and tubular products are piercing, which is a seamless process, and welding.

ROLL PIERCING

Roll piercing is done on a unit which consists of two barrel-shaped rolls set at an angle to each other in order to induce a spiral feed, with a "piercer point"

between them so positioned as to serve as a guide. 33–1 (Page 160). A solid round billet enters from the left side as shown in the sketch, is gripped by the rolls and then simply rolled spirally up over the cone-shaped piercer point. A section through the mill near the back of the piercer point is shown at the right. You will note stationary cross-hatched

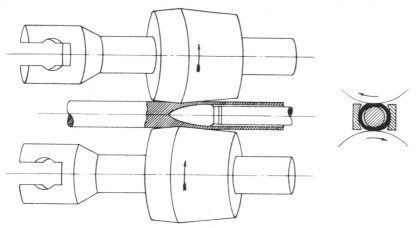

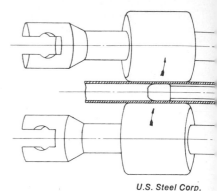

U.S. Steel Corp.

33–3. Reeling machine.

U.S. Steel Corp.

33–1. Sequence of operations in the production of seamless tubing, with a two-roll piercing machine.

guides positioned at the top and bottom of the pass. Their function is to prevent "ballooning." After a complete billet has been spirally rolled over the piercer point, the point is fully retracted out of the tube by means of the attached bar. The tube is then lifted out of the delivery trough and the bar, with piercer point attached, moves forward to its piercing position, ready for the next billet.

PLUG ROLLING

The purpose of the plug rolling mill is to further elongate the tube by thinning the wall. 33–2. It is essentially a two-high mill with round, closed grooves in the rolls. Within the center line of the pass a stationary plug is positioned which, in effect, serves as a mandrel over which the tube is rolled. Normally, two passes are used through the mill for each tube. After the first

pass, the plug is lifted out of the mill. Then the main rolls are opened up and pinch rolls, as shown in the lower portion of the sketch, are raised to propel the tube back out of the mill. Next, the tube is rotated approximately 90°, a slightly larger plug is put in the mill, and the tube is rolled a second time. Finally the tube is again propelled out of the mill and is ready for the next operation.

REELING

The rolls in the reeling machine are positioned for spiral motion similar to those of the piercer. 33–3. However, these

33–2. Plug rolling mill.

U.S. Steel Corp.

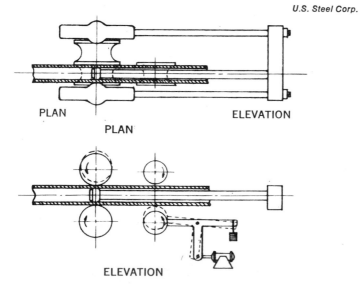

PLAN   ELEVATION

PLAN

ELEVATION

33–4. Sizing mill.

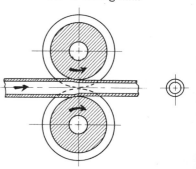

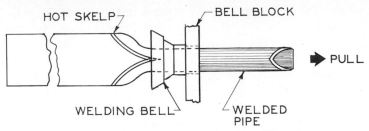

33-5(A). Bell drawing method of welding pipe.

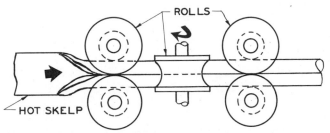

33-5(B) Skelp being formed into continuous butt-welded pipe.

rolls are cylindrical in shape as is the plug positioned between them. Basically, the function of this machine is to provide close tolerance wall thickness rather than to do any significant amount of hot-working.

SIZING

A sizing mill can consist of as many as seven—or as few as one—consecutive two-high stands of driven rolls. 33–4. Sequential stands are usually positioned with their axes 90° apart from the prior stand. In this way, a final and close tolerance diameter is achieved.

WELDING STEEL TUBING OR PIPES

Tubes or pipes can be: (1) butt-welded, (2) lap-welded, (3) resistance-welded, or (4) fusion-welded. The diameters of tubing made by these processes range from 1/8″ to 150″.

Butt-Welding Pipe

Butt-welded pipe ranging from 1/2″ to about 4″ in diameter is usually joined by the continuous process. Heated strips of steel, called skelp which have edges beveled slightly are fed into a furnace and heated to welding temperature. One end of the skelp is gripped by tongs which engage a draw chain. This pulls the skelp through a welding bell which forces it into a circular shape, and the edges are welded together. 33–5(A&B). The pipe

is then passed through finishing and sizing rolls to fashion it to shape and remove any scale.

For continuous butt-welding, the skelp is used in coils, and the ends are welded together to make a continuous strip. The edges are heated to welding temperature. The skelp passes through a series of grooved rolls and is formed into pipes.

Lap-Welding Pipe

In this type of weld, the edges of the skelp are beveled as it comes from the furnace. 33–6. Then the plate is formed into a cylinder with the edges over-lapping. Next, it is reheated and passed over a fixed mandrel, which fits the inside diameter of the pipe. The combination of heat and pressure welds the lapped edges together in a uniformly sound weld. Extruded flash metal is removed from both the inside and outside of the pipe. Sizing and finishing rolls are used to give the pipe accurate size. Lap-welded pipe ranges in size from 2″ to 16″ in diameter.

Electric Resistance-Welding

Pipe measuring from 5 9/16″ to 16″ inclusive is made by the electric resistance-welding

33–6. Lap-welding pipe from bent skelp.

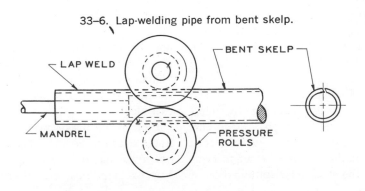

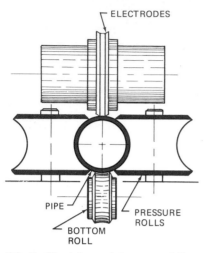

33–7. Electric resistance-welding method. Rolls on both sides and below the electrodes force the heated tube edges together, forming the weld.

process. 33–7. Coils of skelp of a gage corresponding to the thickness of the pipe wall desired are used. NOTE: The width of the skelp is slightly greater than the actual dimension required. The skelp is edge-trimmed to the required width and the edges shot blasted which provides a clean surface for the welding operation.

After the edges of the skelp have been cleaned, it enters a series of forming rolls which gradually form the skelp almost into a tube, with the edges not quite closed. The metal is then passed into the welding rolls. Rolls on the sides and bottom force the edges together to form a tube.

The electrode is in the form of circular discs. The formed stock is fed beneath the electrodes and the high voltage current travels from one electrode to another across the seam, heating the steel. The combination of

pressure and heat welds the edges together.

Next, the pipe is cut to the desired length and passed through more sets of rolls which bring the pipe exactly to the specified diameter.

Electric-Fusion Welding

Electric-fusion welded pipe is made in sizes ranging up to 150″. The larger sizes are usually constructed in locations where the pipe is to be used.

Large pipe is made from steel plates about 40′ long and some-

times over 1″ thick. All four edges of the plate are beveled prior to the welding operation. Next, the plate is formed to a cylindrical shape and temporary tack welds are made. Then a large electric-fusion welding machine is used to complete the weld.

Pipe from 16″ to 42″ in diameter is used for the transmission of oil and natural gas. Water lines are made as large as 9′ in diameter for special purposes such as penstocks for hydroelectric projects.

Unit 34. Hot Extrusion and Spinning

Hot extrusion consists of heating suitable metals and alloys to the proper temperature and placing the heated stock in the cylinder of an extruding press. The pressure obtained by a moving ram or piston forces the plastic metal through a die of specified shape. The metal, which is very near the melting point, is squirted through the die (similar to squirting toothpaste from a tube). It solidifies upon exit from the die. Molding trim, tubes, rods, structural shapes, and brass cartridges are examples of this type of extrusion. Shapes that cannot be formed by rolling can be successfully extruded.

One of the major problems in hot extrusion is the effect the hot metal has on the equipment. Various methods are used to

protect the dies. The die may be changed and allowed to cool for each piece. The ram and mandrel may be sprayed with cool water while idle. Table 34 shows the temperatures of some metals used in this process.

Table 34. Temperatures for Hot Extrusion	
Material	Temperatures
Magnesium	650°– 800°F.
Aluminum	800°– 900°F.
Copper alloys	1650°F.
Steel	2200°–2400°F.

A great deal of extrusion is done on horizontal hydraulic presses ranging in size from 250 to 5,500 tons. However, in recent years presses with a capacity to 25,000 tons have been constructed.

HOT SPINNING

This process is used to shape or preform circular parts over a revolving form called a *mandrel* or chuck on a machine similar to a lathe. 34–1. The product is formed by means of a roller or pressure tool coming in contact with the surface of the rotating metal. The pressure of the tool causes the metal to flow and shapes the metal to the mandrel, similar to the conventional spinning process. A great deal of frictional heat is generated during the operation which helps to maintain the metal in a plastic state. The method is used to form circular and cylindrical shapes and is considerably more economical than forming parts by the use of stamping and forming dies.

Lukens Steel Co.

34–1. Head spinning machine. World's largest steel heads are produced on this machine. Heads range up to 21½' in diameter and 6½" thick.

CHECK YOUR KNOWLEDGE

1. Name some of the advantages of hot-working metal.

2. Has the hot-working of metal any disadvantages? If so name them.

3. What is an ingot?

4. Describe the rolling process.

5. Why are steel ingots not cooled and stored until ready for rolling?

6. Explain the difference between a bloom and a billet.

7. What governs the shape of a roll?

8. What is a two-high reversing mill?

9. Describe a billet mill.

10. Describe the process of making sheets.

11. What effect does forging have upon the grain structure of steel?

12. Describe the process of drop forging.

13. What is the advantage of a steam hammer over a board or gravity drop hammer?

14. What is a board hammer? Describe its operation.

15. What is a forging die?

16. What was the original purpose of the upsetter or forging machine?

17. Describe this method of forging?

18. How is the size of a forging machine indicated?

19. What advantages does press forging have over drop forging?

20. What products are made by roll forging?

21. Name some special forging processes.

22. Describe the ring rolling process.

23. What is swaging?

24. Name some of the products finished by coining and sizing.

25. What is the purpose of plug rolling?

26. What is meant by reeling?

27. Describe a sizing mill.

28. Describe the butt-welding process for welding pipe.

29. What are the main applications for hot extrusion?

30. What is hot spinning?

REFERENCES

American Society for Metals, Metals Park, Ohio, *Metals Handbook,* 8th ed., 1961.

American Society of Tool and Manufacturing Engineers, *Tool Engineers Handbook,* 2nd ed., New York, McGraw-Hill Book Co., 1959.

Chambersburg Engineering Company, *Impact and Die Forging.*

Everhart, J. L., *Impact and Cold Extrusion of Metals,* New York, Chemical Publishing Co., Inc., 1962.

Larke, Eustace C., *Rolling of Strip, Sheet, and Plate,* 2nd ed., Metals Park, Ohio, American Society for Metals, 1963.

United States Steel Corporation, *The Making, Shaping, and Treating of Steel,* 8th ed., 1964.

Section Seven

Cold-Working Metal

COLD-WORKING is a plastic deformation of metals below their recrystallization temperatures. The result is strain or work hardening of the material.

While hot-working refines the grain structure, cold-working has a tendency to fragment the grains and distort the grain structure. Cold-working processes necessitate higher pressures

than hot-working. Recrystallization does not occur in the cold-working temperature range and, therefore, there is no recovery from grain fragmentation or structure distortion.

The metal hardens with increased cold-working, to a point where further working of the metal is not possible until after a stress relief or complete anneal. Yet cold-working increases the metals strength as well as hardness, producing preferred grain orientation with directional properties. As you can assume, cold-working reduces ductility to a marked degree.

Cold-working has the following distinct advantages over hot-working: (1) Tool and die life is prolonged. (2) Closer dimensional tolerances can be obtained. (3) Smoother surface finishes are obtained. (4) It saves material. (5) Structure and other properties are made more uniform by stress relieving and intermediate annealing.

Heavier equipment is necessary for cold-working than for hot-working.

Unit 35. Cold-Rolling

Cold-rolling is used to produce a smooth and bright finish on metal that has been previously hot rolled. 35–1. The cold-rolling process improves the hardness and tensile strength of plate, strip, bar, rod, flat wire, and other shapes.

After hot-rolling, the materials are cleaned by placing them in a weak solution of hot sulphuric acid and water. This pickling operation serves to remove scale. The steel is then rinsed in water and dipped in a hot solution of lime and water. A protective coating is formed on the steel after the lime solution has dried.

After the cleaning operations are completed, the steel is cold-rolled on two-high, three-high, or continuous mills. Plates, bar stock, shafting, and similar materials are rolled on equipment with rolls designed for this purpose. Cold-rolling gives the product a smooth finish and imparts surface skin to the metal which increases its strength and wear resistance.

It is sometimes necessary for the metal to be passed through the rolls several times to obtain the desired size. NOTE: Numerous rollings tend to increase the hardness of the metal, so annealing may become necessary

before the metal can be finished to the proper size. After annealing, pickling is necessary before the metal can be passed through the finishing rolls.

TUBE DRAWING

Cold-drawing operations are used to finish seamless and welded steel tubing. Certain qualities such as surface smoothness, dimensional accuracy, and improved physical properties can be obtained by cold-drawing tubing. Smaller diameters and thinner wall sections can be obtained by this method than by hot-drawing.

The cold-drawing process begins by pickling and washing hot-formed tubing to remove the scale that has been formed by hot-drawing. The tubing is then coated with a suitable lubricant preparatory to the drawing operation. The drawing is then performed on a drawbench.

A swaging operation is performed on one end of the tubing to reduce its diameter so that it can enter the die. The tube end is then gripped by tongs fastened to a drawbench. Next, the tube is drawn through the die which is smaller than the outside diameter of the tube. Dies are made from wear-resistant materials such as tungsten carbide, diamond, or high-grade alloy tool steel. The tube is drawn over a fixed mandrel which controls the inside diameter and the wall thickness. NOTE: The mandrel is omitted if the inside diameter and wall thickness is not important.

The length of the drawbench may be more than 100' and the pulling power for operating the drawbench may range from 50,-000 to 300,000 pounds.

Tube drawing is very severe, as the metal is stressed above its elastic limit to permit flow through the die. 35–2. Due to the cold-hardening of the metal, one or several annealing operations are often necessary before the drawing operation is completed.

COLD-DRAWING WIRE FROM ROD

Wire is made by pulling rod through tapered holes or dies slightly smaller in diameter than the rod itself. In this way the diameter of the rod is decreased while the length is increased. The usual arrangement is to cold-draw the rod through a series of successively smaller dies, until the finished wire is of the desired diameter.

In preparing the rod for drawing, the first step is to remove the oxide scale which has been formed by hot-rolling. This is done by pickling the coiled rod in hot dilute sulphuric acid. When the scale has been removed, the rod is bathed in water which washes away the acid. The rod is then dipped in a lime solution and baked in an oven to fix the lime coating. This coating serves as a base for the lubricant that eases the rod through the dies.

The prepared coil is placed on a reel at the wire drawing machine; the end of the rod is pointed and started through the tapered die. 35–3 (Page 168).

The end of the rod is gripped by tongs on a drawbench and pulled through the die far enough so that the wire may be

Aluminum Co. of America

35–1. A 60" five-stand cold finishing mill. Sheet previously hot-rolled is precision rolled to .008" to .016" in thickness.

35–2. Tube forming mill with cut-off.

Brand K Machinery, Inc.

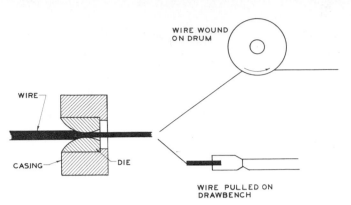

WIRE WOUND ON DRUM

WIRE

CASING   DIE

WIRE PULLED ON DRAWBENCH

35-3. Wire-drawing.

As the wire moves along from die to die, each succeeding drum must rotate faster to accommodate the lengthening of the wire. On leaving the last die, the smaller sizes of wire must travel as fast as 20 miles an hour.

The tremendous strain of cold-drawing hardens steel so that it cannot be drawn any further. The wire's ductility and capacity for cold-working are restored by annealing during intermediate stages of drawing and after the final drawing.

Much of the wire is coated to prevent rust or corrosion, either by hot-dip galvanizing or aluminum-coating.

attached and wound on a power-driven drum or reel, which pulls the wire through the die and forms it into a coil.

In continuous wire-drawing, the wire is drawn through a series of dies and around a series of drums. Continuous wire-drawing is similar to continuous rolling, in that the steel is gradually reduced in cross section and its length proportionately increased.

Unit 36. Cold-Heading

Cold-heading is a high-speed, automatic operation for upsetting or cold-forming wire with dies or punches. The operation is scrapless, thus insuring the most efficient use of materials. Today, 80% of all special fasteners and small parts are made by this process.

In producing cold-headed parts and fasteners, materials are formed at room temperature to predetermined shapes. 36–1. Materials, usually in wire form, are fed automatically into cold-heading machines where they are cut to the proper length and then positioned so they can be struck with one or more blows

and formed into desired shapes. 36–2. Speeds of production range from 70 to 450 pieces per minute. Shown in the illustration are four basic methods of forming a head: (1) shaped between punch and the die, (2) shaped by the punch, (3) shaped by the die, and (4) shaped by both the punch and the die. 36–3.

DIES
Solid Die

The solid die is a solid cylinder with a hole of the proper dimension and shape extending axially through its center. Wire is fed into a machine by feed

rollers against a wire stop. A cutoff knife and finger move laterally to cut and transfer the wire blank to a position in front of the die, where the first heading punch moves forward, pushing the blank into the die, which forms the head. 36–4. A knock-out pin, inserted through the back of the solid die, ejects the finished part.

Open Die

The open die consists of a matched pair of square blocks with semicircular grooves which form a round hole extending axially through the die when the matching faces are put together. Wire is fed through the die against a wire stop. The die closes on the wire and moves laterally, shearing off the wire. The wire stop swings clear and the heading punches move forward to form the head.

National Machinery Co.

36–1. This cold-former processes parts up to 1⅛" in upset diameter and 3⅛" long. Extruding, piercing, upsetting, and trimming can be done in one continuous automatic operation.

COLD-HEADING PROCESS

The illustration shows the progressive steps of a multiple-blow machine: (1) the wire cutoff, (2) the first upset, (3) upsetting the large round head, (4) trimming a straight-side hexagon head, (5) pointing the lower body diameter, and (6) rolling the thread so that this part comes off the machine complete except for supplementary heat treating or plating. 36–5.

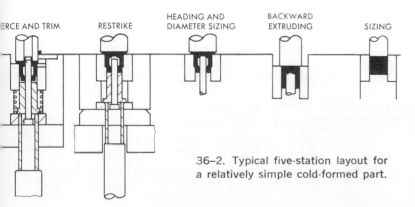

PIERCE AND TRIM   RESTRIKE   HEADING AND DIAMETER SIZING   BACKWARD EXTRUDING   SIZING

36–2. Typical five-station layout for a relatively simple cold-formed part.

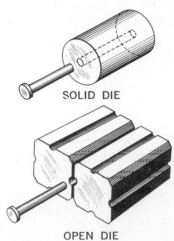

SOLID DIE

OPEN DIE

36–4. Cold-heading dies.

36–5. Progressive stages of a part produced in one cold-heading machine.

Elco Tool and Screw Corp.

36–3. Four basic methods of forming a head.

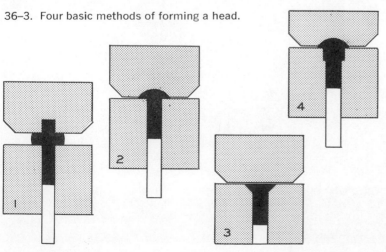

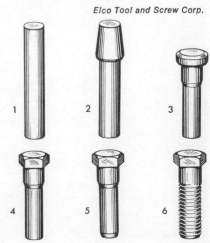

Advantages

Because there is no scrap created in the cold-heading process, the overall part cost is reduced. Additional economies are realized in high production speeds possible with modern cold-heading equipment, plus the fact that often several parts, such as stampings, forgings, castings, wire products, etc., can be combined and cold-headed as a single part to help assembly technique. 36–6. This combining of parts greatly reduces in-place costs by eliminating multiple assembly and related handling operations.

Fasteners or parts made by cold-heading are stronger than parts made by many other methods of manufacture. 36–7. This is because the grain flow lines in the original wire form are upset to follow the configurations of the part being formed, insuring greater strength with higher resistance to fractures at high-fatigue points. As a result, parts do not have the tendency to shear or rupture under heavy loading or torque. In other processes, such as turning, the metal grain flow pattern is unaltered. This cutting away of material to produce a desired shape weakens the part in critical load areas.

Wire shapes are almost unlimited. Shapes include round,

National Machinery Co.

36–6. Parts made by the cold-heading process.

square, "D" section, grooved, keyed, and hexagon in various diameters.

Workable materials include low- and high-carbon steels, alloy steels, stainless steels, brass, bronze, and aluminum.

36–7. These enlarged part cross sections illustrate how the metal grain flow lines within cold-headed parts follow the shape of the part being formed. This creates stronger fasteners and metal parts that will not have the tendency to rupture and fatigue.

Elco Tool and Screw Co.

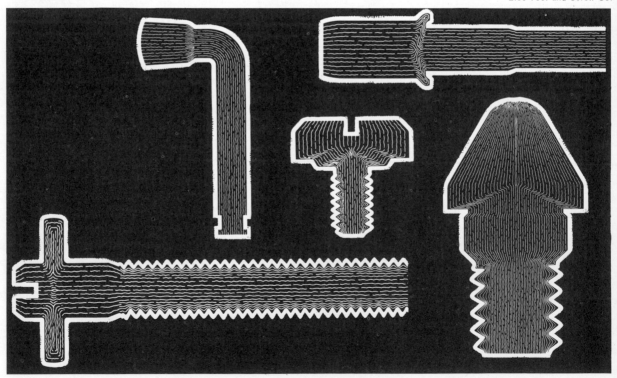

Unit 37.　Metal Spinning

Since colonial days in America, and previously abroad, metal spinning has been used to produce such items as cooking utensils, lighting fixtures and other products from soft metals such as copper, brass, and pewter. 37–1.

Conventional spinning is one of the simpler methods of metal forming for sheet or plate. 37–2(A). Essentially, it involves shaping a circular disc over a mandrel. The mandrel is mounted on the headstock of a heavy-duty lathe. The disc is clamped to the mandrel by tailstock pressure, and forming is done by manipulating a blunt tool or an anti-friction roller to shape the metal tightly against the mandrel. 37–2(B). The finished piece is necessarily concentric about an axis.

Spinning removes no metal from the workpiece. It merely pushes the metal from one area to another—"flowing" the metal disc into a desired shape. 37–3 (Page 172). For this reason, parts requiring maximum uniformity of wall thickness are produced by controlled processing. This makes possible maintenance of specified thickness limit either by spinning, by supplementary methods, or both. The chart illustrates the interesting "flow" of metal during spinning and how it is controlled.

Spinning is basically a low- or medium-quantity method of

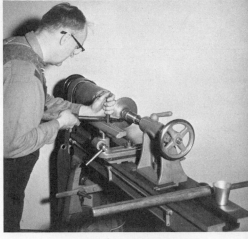

Haag Machine Co., Inc.

37–2(A). Conventional spinning on a small lathe.

37–1. An example of a product produced by the conventional metal spinning process.

Sebree Photography, Canton, Ill.

37–2(B). Power spinning an elliptical head, spun from ⅝" thick tool steel. Application of heat is used in this case. Spinning is accomplished through the medium of a hydraulically controlled servo-mechanism.

Phoenix Products Co., Inc.

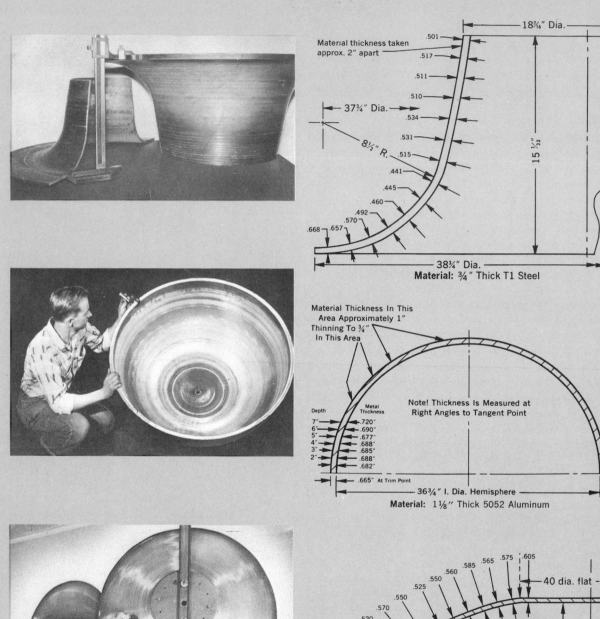

Material thickness taken approx. 2" apart

.501
.517
.511
.510
.534
.531
.515
.441
.445
.460
.492
.570
.668 .657

18⅞" Dia.

37¾" Dia.

8½" R.

15½" / 32

38¾" Dia.

Material: ¾" Thick T1 Steel

Material Thickness In This Area Approximately 1" Thinning To ¾" In This Area

Note! Thickness Is Measured at Right Angles to Tangent Point

Depth	Metal Thickness
7"	.720"
6"	.690"
5"	.677"
4"	.688"
3"	.685"
2"	.688"
	.682"

.665" At Trim Point

36¾" I. Dia. Hemisphere

Material: 1⅛" Thick 5052 Aluminum

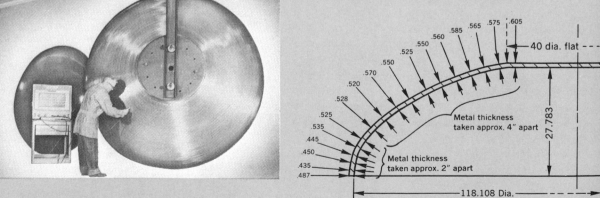

.585 .565 .575 .605
.525 .550 .560
.550
.570
.520
.528
.525
.535
.445
.450
.435
.487

40 dia. flat

Metal thickness taken approx. 4" apart

Metal thickness taken approx. 2" apart

27.783

118.108 Dia.

Material: .625" Thick H-11 Tool Steel

Phoenix Products Co., Inc.

37–3. Chart shows the "flow" of metal during conventional spinning and how controlled (at left).

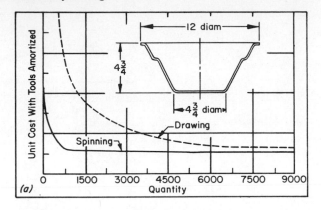

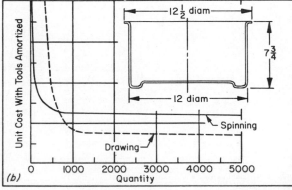

Phoenix Products Co., Inc.

37–4. Comparison of two metal forming methods for two different shapes. Cone (a) is 0.050″ thick, 3003 aluminum; shell (b) is 0.040″ thick 6061 aluminum.

forging, Rotoforming, shear spinning, compression spinning, and various others.

The power spinning process combines two basic metalworking techniques: sheet metal spinning and heavy metal extruding. It consolidates the flow-shaping principle of spinning on the lathe with high-pressure flowing of metal in an extrusion process. Each machine manufacturer has its own name for the process. The Lodge & Shipley Company call their process Floturning. It will be explained in this unit.

Floturn Process

The Floturn process is a method of rotary metal forming which produces parts which are round in cross section, but which may be straight-sided cones, contoured cones, or cylindrical-shaped parts. In a sense, the Floturn process utilizes a 3-dimensional variation of the basic rolling process that is used in a steel mill to produce flat sheet, starting with a thick slab.

It might be thought that Floturning is very similar to conventional spinning; however, there is a basic difference between spinning and Floturning. Conventional spinning utilizes a relatively thin piece of material and produces the shape of the finished part from the diameter of the starting blank, while the Floturn process does not change the diameter or the *shape* of the starting blank, but produces a finished shape by working from the thickness of the starting blank, producing a part considerably thinner than the starting blank. The illustration shows a comparison between spinning

forming. It is especially suited to prototype or pilot production. 37–4. Costs are lower compared to deep draw dies. Tools are usually made from low-cost hardwood or metal. They have fewer components than draw dies. When several sizes of a similar item are required for prototype samples, tools may be recut at a considerable savings.

The size and shape of the part, the type of alloy, and tooling must all be considered when determining cost, as shown. Cone shapes are always more economical as spinnings, although typical shapes which can be spun range from simple flanged heads or covers to parabolic, hemispherical, and nozzle shapes. 37–5, shown on page 174.

POWER SPINNING

Power spinning is rapidly taking the place of conventional spinning in many applications. Closer tolerances can be held by power spinning to meet tighter specifications that are often required in aerospace and other critical components.

The power spinning process is known by many names: Floturning, Hydrospinning, Spin-

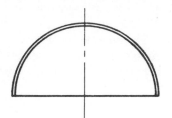

Hemispherical—common shape; very well adapted to spinning.

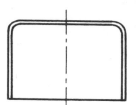

Cylindrical shell—with or without taper, best produced at low cost in small or medium production lots.

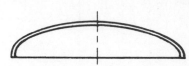

Flanged and dished head—easily and economically produced by spinning. Many variations of this basic shape are possible—spherical or elliptical dish of various depths, angled flanges, curved flanges, lips, or stiffening beads.

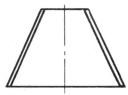

Cone—one of the most economical shapes, even in high-production quantities, due to low tool cost and high production rates.

Flanged cover or head—considered one of the simplest shapes that can be produced by spinning methods. The result is a seamless part with the desired corner radius, far superior to that produced by ordinary two-piece sheet metal methods.

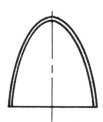

Parabolic or nose shape—usually has a depth/diameter ratio exceeding 1.0 which is very costly to produce by deep draw methods due to high-cost tooling and multiple operations.

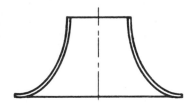

Nozzle or venturi—adapted to spinning in a wide range of sizes—small diameter, heavy wall parts or large diameter, thin wall parts.

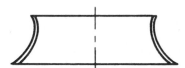

Re-entrant and flared—usually costly and difficult to draw or shape by sheet metal or deep draw methods; relatively simple and economical to spin. Sheet metal methods require two- or three-piece welded construction. Spinnings are seamless.

Stepped cover—stepped offsets give added stiffness, enabling the use of thinner material; therefore overall costs are lower and the weight is lighter.

Phoenix Products Co., Inc.

37–5. Basic shapes that can be spun. Variations or combinations are numerous.

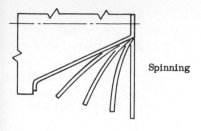

Spinning

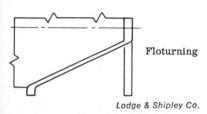

Floturning

Lodge & Shipley Co.

37–6. Comparison between spinning and Floturning a conical part.

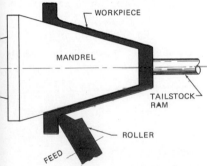

WORKPIECE

MANDREL

TAILSTOCK RAM

ROLLER

FEED

Lodge & Shipley Co.

37–7(A). Principle of the Floturn. The thickness of the part depends on its side angle as well as the thickness and shape of the blank. The heavy work roller displaces metal, forming it to the shape of the mandrel.

37–7(B). Basic formula of the Floturn process.

Floturn, Inc.

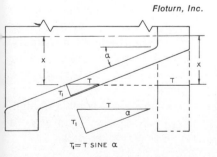

$T_1 = T$ SINE α

and Floturning a conical part. 37–6.

The Floturn process should not be confused with swaging or upsetting operations because the material is not reduced in diameter as in swaging, or gathered to increase thickness as in upsetting.

The illustration shows the basic arrangement of the elements of a Floturn machine, so as to produce a straight-sided, uniform-thickness cone from a flat blank. 37–7(A).

Lingren's formula states that finished wall thickness (T_1) equals flat blank thickness (T) times the sine of ½ the included cone angle (a).

Expressed as a formula: $T_1 = T$ sine a. 37–7(B).

Cold-working during power spinning refines and elongates the grain structure in the direction of flow. This results in an increase in tensile strength and fatigue resistance of the metal. Hardness is also increased. High forming pressures are employed in power spinning, but, despite this fact, the surfaces have no minute tears or ruptures, and microstructure analysis of stressed parts reveals no fractures developing in the crystalline structure.

How Floturning Is Done

The Floturn machine is simple and easy to operate. The carriage bed is angled in a predetermined relationship to the mandrel. 37–8. The blank is clamped to the mandrel with the tailstock or other clamping device. 37–9. Then, with the blank rotating at the end of the mandrel and the roller positioned at the be-

Lodge & Shipley Co.

3-78. The carriage bed is angled at a predetermined relationship to the mandrel.

37-9. The blank is clamped to the mandrel with the tailstock.

ginning of its tracer-controlled path, the feed is started. 37–10.

The roller contacts the blank and begins to flow the metal to the precise shape of the mandrel. 37–11. Since the mandrel and the blank are rotating and the roller is being fed, the forming pressure is applied in a continuous spiral manner. The blank is gradually and quickly flowed to the mandrel's shape. 37–12.

The blank metal thickness is reduced as calculated in advance. This reduction may range as high as 75% in a single pass of the roller, depending upon the roller setting, which is determined by the design of the part.

The Floturn machine handles blanks up to $\frac{5}{16}''$ in thickness, 42" in diameter, and up to 50" in length. 37–13. It has been proven in a wide range of metals:

- Steel-sheet, plate, or forgings.

- All 300 and 400 series of stainless steels.

- Timken 16–25–6 and 17–225; "Hastalloy" B, C, and X.

- "Universal Cyclops Uniloy" 19–9; titanium TI–14–A.

- "Inconel," "Inconel X," Monel and K-Monel.

- Molybdenum and tungsten.

In addition to the smaller machine, Lodge & Shipley has manufactured a machine for the Allison Division of General Motors which will Floturn cylindrical and conical shaped missile parts up to 6' in diameter and 7' long.

This machine stands 14' high, 47' long, and 27' wide. It weighs 190,000 pounds.

Lodge & Shipley Co.

37–10. Start of automatic duplication operation. The tracer (left foreground) and roller (center background) are at the beginning of the cycle.

Lodge & Shipley Co.

37–11. As the tracing stylus nears the mid-point on the template, the roller—which is hydraulically controlled by the tracer—is in a similar position.

37-12. As the tracer and roller complete the operation, the finished part conforms perfectly to the shape of the template.

Lodge & Shipley Co.

Lodge & Shipley Co.

37–13. Typical consumer, industrial, aircraft, missile, and space parts made by the Floturn process, using both exotic and common metals in sizes up to 5' in diameter and 6' in length.

A pivoting fixture can be mounted on the forming roll carriage that permits facing, turning, and cutting off shear formed parts while they are still mounted on the arbor of the Floturn machine. Aluminum parts are turned as thin as 0.032" after cold forming to a thickness of 0.056".

A good example of the value of combining machining with shear forming is the production of the inner and outer "spikes" which serve as baffles to control the air intake for jet engines on the B–58 Hustler aircraft. 37–14.

The ability to repeat parts of uniform size, shape, and tolerance on large production runs is a feature of the Floturn machine. The vertical Floturning machine is capable of extremely high-production runs with practically no scrap. 37–15.

37–15. Vertical Floturn machine.

Lodge & Shipley Co.

37–14. Inner and outer spikes, which control air intake for jet engines, are shear formed and machined on Floturn machines.

Lodge & Shipley Co.

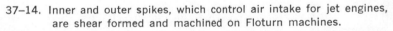

177

Unit 38.

Thread and Form Rolling

Thread and form rolling is a simple process confined almost entirely to external threads. It is referred to as a cold forging process because most rolling is done on cold blanks. Today, thread and form rolling is generally accepted as a preferred method for producing uniform, smooth, precise threads of superior physical qualities.

Hardened steel dies are used to roll the threads. 38–1. The threaded faces of the dies are pressed against the periphery of a plain cylindrical blank and reform the surface of the blank into threads as the blank rolls on the die faces, as shown. The working faces of the dies have a thread form which is the reverse of the thread to be produced. In penetrating the surface of the blank, the dies displace the material to form the roots of the thread and force the displaced metal radially outward to form the crests of the thread. The blank has a diameter partway between the major and minor diameter of the thread.

A comparison of a cut and rolled thread is shown in the illustration. In the thread rolling process, no material is removed. 38–2.

Reed Rolled Thread Die Co.

38–3. Cylindrical rolled thread die machine.

PHYSICAL CHARACTERISTICS OF ROLLED THREADS

Thread rolling of the surface increases the tensile strength of the metal.

The shear strength of the threads is increased by rolling because the fibers of the material are not severed as they are in other methods of screw production. The threads are re-formed in continuous unbroken lines that follow the contours of the threads, as in forging.

Resistance to fatigue is considerably improved in the thread rolling process because rolling between smooth dies leaves the threads with smooth burnished roots and flanks, free from tears, chatter, or cutter marks.

Most of the threads produced today are rolled on thread rolling machines or automatic screw machines, and automatic lathes. 38–3. Thread rolling machines use flat and cylindrical dies.

38–1. Hardened steel dies are used to roll threads.

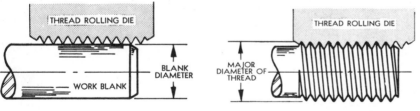

38–2. A comparison of cut and rolled threads.

Reed Rolled Thread Die Co.

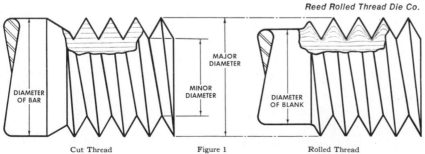

Cut Thread   Figure 1   Rolled Thread

Automatic screw machines can use cylindrical thread rolls.

There are several types of thread rolling machines—reciprocating (flat die), rotary planetary, and cylindrical die.

In *reciprocating* machines two dies are used—one stationary and one moving. A thread is rolled on one blank at a time during the forward stroke of the machine.

Rotary planetary machines have one central rotary die on a fixed axis and one or more stationary concave segment dies located to the outside of the rotary die. 38–4.

Cylindrical die machines are made with two or three dies with diameter capacities up to 5″. 38–5. The two-roll system resembles the motions of centerless grinding.

All of the commonly used thread forms can be produced by thread rolling, including screws, bolts, and precision heat-treated aircraft or space parts. Component parts of various shapes and materials with precision threads, knurling, splines, serrations, grooves, burnished surfaces, and other special forms

can be produced by form rolling.

Rolling produces much the same finish on the work regardless of the properties of the material being rolled. A comparison of thread finishes commonly produced by the various threading methods is shown in Table 38.

Rolling has long been conceded to be the fastest method of producing screw threads.

Thread rolling machines may be manually loaded or arranged with semiautomatic or completely automatic feeding devices.

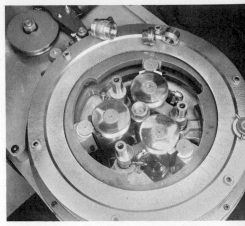

Reed Rolled Thread Die Co.

38–5. Three-cylindrical-die thread rolling.

Table 38. Comparison of Common Thread Finishes*

Type of thread	Surface roughness-microinches							
	250	125	63	32	16	8	4	2
Screw machine chased threads								
Milled threads								
Ground threads								
Rolled threads								

* Reed Rolled Thread Die Co.

38–4. (A) Reciprocating (flat die) machine technique. (B) Rotary planetary machine technique.

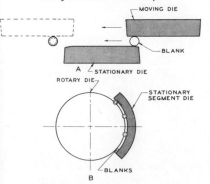

Unit 39.   Stretch Forming

It is rather difficult to form shallow shapes with large areas from thin sheet metal because drawing alone does not stretch the metal beyond its elastic limit to give it a permanent set.

Stretch forming or drawing is used to overcome this difficulty by stretching the metal beyond its elastic limit while it is forced into shape.

STRETCH FORMING

In stretch forming, the forming die is bolted to the circular table. 39–1 (Page 180). The extrusion, sheet, or shape to be stretch formed is gripped at one end by powerful, serrated gripper jaws mounted on the table. The opposite end of the material is gripped by similar jaws mounted on the main hydraulic ram of the machine.

Tension is then applied to the material through the stretch action from the main ram and its gripper head through the material and to the table-mounted gripper head. While this tension is maintained upon the part, the form die, rigidly attached to the table, is rotated into the work, forming the material only a fraction of an inch at a time and causing the part to assume configurations of the die. The ram and gripper head are free to swivel during the stretch forming operation so that the tension force is kept tangential to the part and to the form-die contact surface at all times while the part is being progressively formed.

The principal advantage in stretch forming is that it virtually eliminates spring-back.

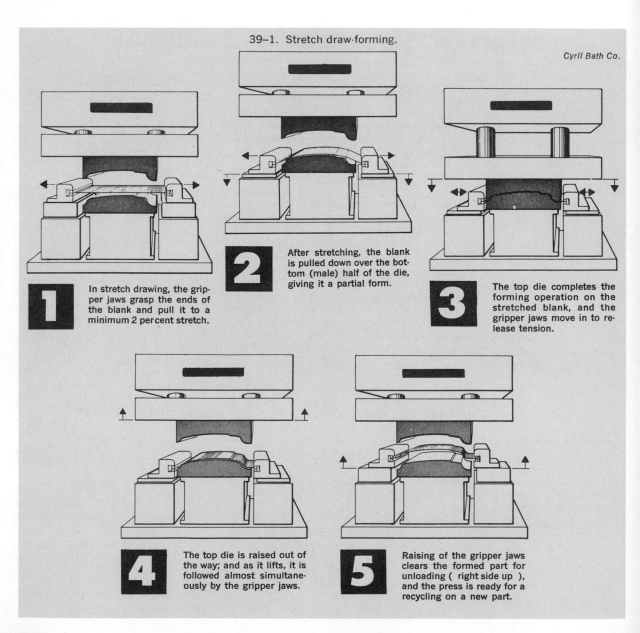

39–1. Stretch draw-forming.

Cyril Bath Co.

1 In stretch drawing, the gripper jaws grasp the ends of the blank and pull it to a minimum 2 per cent stretch.

2 After stretching, the blank is pulled down over the bottom (male) half of the die, giving it a partial form.

3 The top die completes the forming operation on the stretched blank, and the gripper jaws move in to release tension.

4 The top die is raised out of the way; and as it lifts, it is followed almost simultaneously by the gripper jaws.

5 Raising of the gripper jaws clears the formed part for unloading (right side up), and the press is ready for a recycling on a new part.

Unit 40. Riveting, Staking; Sizing, Coining, and Hobbing

RIVETING AND STAKING

Riveting and staking are operations used to fasten parts together. Solid rivets are placed through drilled holes. As shown, a punch shapes one end of the rivet, drawing the two parts together. When hollow rivets are used, their ends are curled over the edges of the part.

Staking is accomplished by upsetting one end of the part. 40–1. Then it is indented, curled over, and spread by a punch with a sharp point or sharp edges in the form of a ring.

SIZING, COINING, AND HOBBING

Sizing is an operation by which parts of malleable iron, forged steel, powdered metals, and nonferrous soft metals such as aluminum are finished to thickness by squeezing.

Coining is performed in dies which raise images or creates impressions on the surfaces of flat metal objects, such as coins. The operation is limited to soft alloys. High-pressure presses set up with dies are used in this cold-working process.

A *hob* is machined from tool steel to the desired form of the part to be molded, heat-treated, and polished. 40–2. The operation consists of pressing the hob by means of a hydraulic press—capacity from 250 to 8,000 tons—into a blank of soft steel mounted in a cavity of a specified size. A retaining ring prevents the mold from spreading out of shape. This method of cold-forming can produce identical cavities economically.

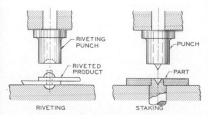

40–1. Riveting and staking process used to fasten parts together.

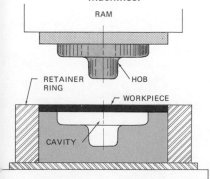

40–2. Hobbing: a method of mold-making for plastic and die-casting machines.

Unit 41. Cold Roll-Forming; Plate Bending: Shot Peening

COLD ROLL-FORMING

This is a high-production process for fabricating flat metal strip to a desired uniform shape. The strip metal is passed through a machine containing several pairs of rolls. It is progressively formed to a desired uniform shape in cross section. The metal passes through the rolls at speeds ranging from 50 to 300′ per minute.

A set of rolls mounted on a cold roll-forming machine, is used for each different application. 41–1 (Page 182). Each set of rolls bends the metal to a certain point. The complexity of the part determines the number of rolls necessary to complete the product.

Roll-forming machines can be used to form hot- and cold-rolled carbon steel, stainless steel, and numerous other alloys. Many of the nonferrous metals and alloys can be formed including brass, copper, bronze, zinc, and aluminum.

Sections can be produced in any thickness up to 3/8″ and in widths ranging from less than 1″ to a maximum of 60″. Most cold roll-formed products (excluding welded pipe and tubing) are made from flat rolled metal—usually coiled strip—less than

.125″ thick and less than 20″ wide.

High production of roll-forming machines—20,000′ to 40,000′ of formed sections per 8-hour day, with one operator—helps the equipment pay out in minimum time.

Among the many products made by this process are window moldings, sections for hollow metal doors and trim, window frames and sash, drawer slides, and track for sliding garage doors.

Roll-formed moldings are also widely used in the application of floor and wall coverings. 41–2. Transportation equipment, drip and garnish moldings for automobiles, buses, and railway coaches are typical cold roll-forming applications.

PLATE BENDING

Plate bending is done on rollers that have a bending capacity for light-gage sheet metal to material up to 1¼″ in thickness. 41–3.

The roll-bending machine is made up of three rolls, two of

41–1. Cold-forming machine.

41–2. Radial draw-former.

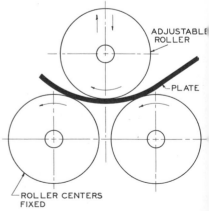

Yoder Co.

Cyril Bath Co.

41–3. Plate bending.

ADJUSTABLE ROLLER

PLATE

ROLLER CENTERS FIXED

which are held in a fixed position and one of which is adjustable. The metal plate is passed through the fixed rolls and the final diameter of the part is determined by the adjustable roll. By moving the adjustable roll to a closer position to the fixed rolls, the diameter is decreased.

SHOT PEENING

Shot peening is a cold-working process used to improve the fatigue resistance of metal by surface compression. Small steel shot is blasted against the surface at high velocity, the result being small indentations which create a slight plastic flow of the surface metal to a depth of a few thousandths of an inch. This method produces compressive stresses which offset the effect of tension stresses within the metal. Hardening and strengthening of the metal also takes place.

Machine parts such as gears, rods, crankshafts, and camshafts can be improved by shot peening. Many parts which have irregular surfaces are difficult to treat by other cold-working processes. Fillets around shafts and gear teeth, where stress is concentrated, can be successfully treated by this method.

Unit 42. Cold Extrusion

Cold extrusion is a process that forces unheated metal to flow through a shape-forming die. The metal is plastically deformed under compression at room temperature while within the die cavity formed by tools.

Extrusion differs from drawing in that the metal is pushed in a compression manner rather than pulled under tension.

In cold extrusion the thickness of the walls is identical all around. Ribs, flutes, and fins located inside or outside must be axi-symmetrically located.

There are many advantages to the cold-extrusion process: (1) a saving of metal, (2) low labor cost, (3) improvement of physical properties, (4) allows for close tolerances, (5) less expensive metals can be used, and (6) better inner and outer surfaces can be obtained.

Metals such as brass, copper, lead, aluminum, steel, magnesium, tin, titanium, and zinc can be formed by cold extrusion.

METHODS OF EXTRUSION

There are three basic methods of cold extrusion: (1) forward extrusion, (2) backward extrusion, and (3) a combination of the two processes.

Forward Extrusion

This is sometimes known as the Hooker process. In this process the confined metal is forced to flow downward in the direction of the punch travel. The process is generally used to produce thin-walled tubular parts with heavy flanges, straight tubular shapes, and extrusions of stepped, multiple diameters. Forward extrusion is best applied to parts having a cup diameter of 1″ or more. The production of rods and other solid shapes is also possible with forward extrusion.

In forward extrusion the workpiece is placed in a close-fitting die. The punch is forced downward, displacing the metal forward through a restricted opening in the bottom of the die, and the metal is forced to flow a considerable distance beyond the end of the punch. Cupped or tubular parts of the punch extension serve as a mandrel that controls the wall thickness and inner contour of the extruded part.

Backward Extrusion

This is a process that forces the metal confined in the cavity to flow in a direction opposite to that of the punch travel. The slug (workpiece) is contained in a closed die. The descending punch enters the slug and the pressure displaces the metal upward through the opening between the punch and die.

This is generally used for extruding symmetrically shaped parts having a closed end.

Combined Extrusion

This uses a combination of forward extrusion and backward extrusion. The metal is confined inside a matrix between the lower and upper punches. This forces the metal to flow both up and down. The extruded part is lifted from the die on the upward stroke of the slide by a lift-out on the bed of the press.

Some advantages of this type of cold-working are that it: (1) is fast, (2) can complete parts in few steps, (3) can produce large quantities with low unit cost, (4) causes low waste of material, (5) can make parts with small radii, and (6) requires minor tooling. 42–1.

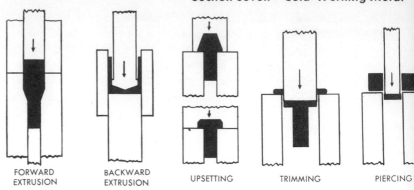

FORWARD EXTRUSION   BACKWARD EXTRUSION   UPSETTING   TRIMMING   PIERCING

42–1. The most common cold-forming operations.

Unit 43. High-Energy-Rate Forming Methods

High-energy-rate forming can be accomplished by several processes known as explosive forming, Dynapak, electro-hydraulic forming, and magnetic forming.

Explosive forming is a high-energy-rate method of forming metal by the sudden high-velocity release of the powerful energy of explosives. The rapidly applied shock waves and gas pressures are great enough to shape the metal upon which they act. Used in the aircraft and missile industry to shape high-strength materials, this method is especially useful for shaping materials that are difficult to form by conventional methods or for parts that are too large for existing presses.

Explosive forming may be done by gas pressure, shock wave, or a combination of the two. The method is largely controlled by the shape of the cavity

in the die in which the explosive charge is fired. There are two distinct methods of explosive forming. 43–1.

1. Pressure forming with propellant type explosive.

2. Shock forming with detonating explosives.

In pressure forming, a closed system is necessary. The propellant must be confined in order to burn and control the pressure generated.

Open and semi-open systems are generally used with the shock forming method in forming large parts. Pressure can be applied directly. The media through which the energy of the explosion is transmitted include air, oil, water, and talc. These pressure transfer media also serve as shock and noise dampeners.

In using this technique the bottom of the die is vented to remove the air between the

43–1. Forward head closure for the Polaris missile, sized in an open die. The die with workpiece was lowered into the tank of water which was the transfer medium for the shock waves from the explosive.

Propellex, Div. of Chromalloy

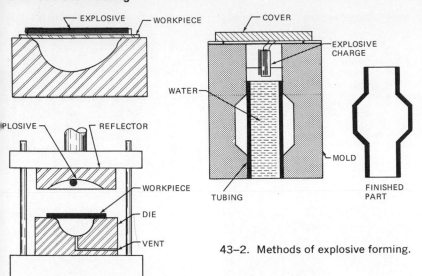

43–2. Methods of explosive forming.

workpiece and the die to prevent surface damage to the work.

The type of explosive mixture and container size controls the gas pressure and deformation rate, which is critical.

One of the most common methods used in the aircraft industry in forming cones, cylinders, tanks, etc., is shown in the illustration. In this explosive process, water is the intermediate medium. 43–2.

43–3. Hydrospark forming a metal tube to the contour of the die.

The Tool Engineer

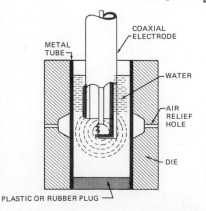

In this technique, explosive forming utilizes the pressure wave generated by the explosion in the water to force the material being formed against the walls of the die. The explosive is placed in the center at approximately water level, and a cover placed on top of the die. The air is pumped from between the die and the workpiece and the explosive detonated. The cylindrical part is forced against the walls of the die.

There are two basic types of explosives: (1) low-energy and (2) high-energy. Low-energy explosives are materials which burn rapidly rather than explode.

High-energy or detonating explosives are set off by the shock of a primary explosive. They expand more rapidly and create a great deal of shock per unit of weight.

Dynapak high-energy-rate forming makes use of high-pressure gas instead of explosives. These machines use compressed nitrogen under pressure.

One company uses a new method of high-energy-rate forming called *Hydrospark forming:* A "spark bomb" creates a high-energy shock wave that forms metal parts in 40-millionths of a second. 43–3.

Unit 44. Flo-Peeling

Flo-peeling is a cold-working process developed by the Lodge and Shipley Company. 44–1 (Page 186). It causes the metal to flow outward from the shape being worked, to a point where a flange of the material appears. As this continues, the flange breaks off, leaving a smooth, cylindrical shaped billet ready for the extrusion press.

Flo-peel involves point deformation of material, exceeding the yield point, so that it shears and flows as directed by the roller shape.

The process has particular application in shapes involved in extrusion work where the preparation of hot-formed billets is a problem. The billets must be machined before they can be extruded with smooth surfaces. Ordinarily this work is done on a lathe with carbide cutting tools. 44–2.

In Flo-Peeling, cuts are made up to ¼″ deep on stainless steel with peeling tools, which are rugged rollers designed to present a continually changing area of contact. Wear is eliminated and heat is not a major factor.

Not only is this a more rapid process but tool life is no longer a problem as the roller applies a different work "point" continuously.

Flo-peeling has been successfully applied to metals such as titanium alloys, nickel and cobalt alloys, stainless steels, carbon steel, aluminum, copper and brass.

Lodge & Shipley Co.

44–1. Flo-peeling stainless steel. This operation causes the metal to flow outward from the shape being worked.

Lodge & Shipley Co.

44–2. Three stages of billet preparation via peeling. Left is rough billet. Center shows action of peeling and chip formation. Right shows finished billet. Time to machine: 2½ minutes.

Check Your Knowledge

1. What is meant by cold-working metals?

2. What are the effects of cold-working metal?

3. Describe the operation of tube drawing.

4. How is wire made?

5. What is cold-heading? What are its uses and advantages?

6. Describe the process of cold-heading.

7. Explain the difference between conventional spinning and power spinning.

8. Describe the process of thread rolling.

9. Distinguish between riveting and staking.

10. Describe sizing, coining, and hobbing.

11. What is cold roll-forming?

12. Describe the plate bending process.

13. For what purpose is shot peening used?

14. Compare the process of extrusion with that of drawing.

15. Name three types of cold extrusion.

16. Explain how Flo-peeling differs from single-point tool turning on an engine lathe.

References

Begeman, Myron L., and Amstead, B. H., *Manufacturing Processes,* New York, John Wiley & Sons, Inc., 1963.

Campbell, J. S., Jr., *Casting and Forging Processes in Manufacturing,* New York, McGraw-Hill Book Co., 1950:

Wick, Charles A., *Chipless Machining.* New York, Industrial Press, 1960.

Young, J. F., *Materials and Processes,* 2nd ed., New York, John Wiley & Sons, Inc., 1954.

Section Eight

Forming Metal on Presses

M OST cold-working operations today are performed on mechanical presses.

Presses are made in many varieties and sizes depending upon the needs of industry, yet the principal features are very much

the same for all sizes. A press is a production machine and in order to perform the required operations must be equipped with certain tools called punches and dies. Some presses are better adapted for certain types of operations than others, but most shearing, forming, and punching operations can be done on any standard press, provided the proper tooling is used. This is economical in industrial practices because the same press can be used for a variety of operations, especially on short-run of parts.

Rapid production of parts is a feature of today's presses. Modern presses can draw mild steel at least 50% faster than ever before; they can operate multiple station dies at hundreds of strokes per minute (spm), or punch out small parts at speeds up to 2,000 spm.

Today, few shops can afford to use slow presses with simple, single-operation dies. Instead, the trend is toward progressive dies and transfer mechanisms, and presses that produce a complete part at each stroke. Presses are becoming sophisticated precision machine tools.

Due to the fact that most presses are capable of doing a great variety of work, it is quite difficult to place them in any special classification. Operations such as bending, piercing holes, shearing, blanking, and stamping are often done on the same machine. However, presses can be classified according to: (1) design of frame, (2) method of applying power to the ram, and (3) operations performed.

ally operated, with speeds from 65 to 150 fpm (feet per minute).

When a long stroke is needed, *rack and pinion* presses are best. A uniform motion can be obtained and the movement of the slide is slower than in crank presses. Operation is very similar to that of a standard *arbor* press.

Screw presses are used for squeezing and impact operations such as coining. A long stroke is obtainable with this press. The stroke delivers a blow upon the stock without shock. Its operation is relatively slow. The *knuckle-joint* press is best for coining, squeezing, and forging work. A great deal of force with a short stroke can be obtained with this type of press. Link mechanisms are used in knuckle-joint presses because of the high mechanical advantage that is obtained near the bottom of the stroke.

FRAME AND BED DESIGN

Press frames are made of both iron and steel. The *frame* supports and guides the "slider,"

Unit 45. Press Types

All presses are made up of certain basic parts: frame and bed, rams or slides, ram drive, transmission, and power source. 45–1.

In selecting a press, the type of operation to be performed, the size of the part to be made, the speed at which the part is to be produced, and the power required must all be taken into consideration. *Eccentric* (crank type) presses can be used for blanking, punching, and trimming operations. If *drawing* operations are to be required, a press with slower speeds than those for the above operations is necessary. Most presses for this type of work are hydraulic-

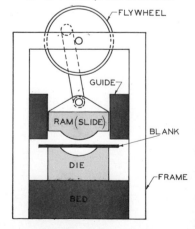

45–1. Power press elements.

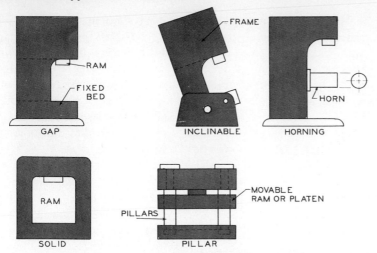

45–2(A). Some frame designs used in presses.

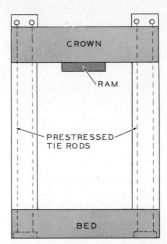

45–2(B). Straight side type frame.

which is reciprocated by a link connecting it to a rotating crankshaft. A *flywheel* and clutch store and control the flow of energy. This energy is supplied continuously at a relatively constant rate to the crankshaft but is consumed periodically in each blow of the descending *slide* or *ram.*

The hollow *bed,* located on the lower part of the press frame, is strengthened by heavy ribs. The bed can be equipped with scrap chutes and pressure springs. The die is frequently supported by a bolster plate which is located on top of the bed.

The drive mechanism is located in the frame as well as the ways or tracks which serve to guide the reciprocating ram in a fixed path. Variable speed drives of the electric or belt type are being used on high-speed presses to facilitate the use of different dies at their optimum speeds. Because belt changes on older style presses were located where they were

difficult to get at and these changes were time consuming, newer machines have the drives mounted outboard.

Presses are rated in tons of force which they are able to exert on the workpiece. The crankshaft transmits the entire load from the prime mover and flywheel to the punch and workpiece. The frame must be strong and rigid enough to avoid distortion; there must be no crown deflection.

The day when a press was selected primarily on tonnage rating and tooling space is past. The technology of stamping is changing too rapidly and production speeds are also increasing. To meet today's requirements, presses must be automated, or at least be made to run automatically.

The most common types of press frames are shown in the illustration. 45–2(A&B).

O.B.I. PRESS

One of the most versatile machine tools in any shop is the

O.B.I. press (open-back, inclinable, punch press). 45–3 (Page 190).

With proper dies and tonnage selection, O.B.I. presses are suitable for almost all stamping operations, such as blanking, forming, drawing, perforating, embossing, coining, notching, and shearing. The inclinable feature permits the press to be tilted so that the workpieces easily fall out of the back of the press.

Variable speed motors are often desirable on these machines. This feature allows the speed to be changed while the machine is in operation and eliminates the downtime and manpower previously required to change pulleys each time a different speed was desired.

GAP PRESS

The gap press has a rigid C-type frame on an integral (unified) base. This press permits handling long and wide parts and also provides plenty of clearance around the dies. Gap

189

presses can be used for the usual stamping operations.

HORNING PRESS

A horning press is used on cylindrical objects, for seaming, punching, riveting, flanging edges, and embossing. This press is equipped with a large round post (*horn*) instead of a bed. The table may be taken off the press or swung out of the way to one side so that the horn can be put into use.

KNUCKLE-JOINT PRESS

This press is equipped with a knuckle-joint mechanism for moving the slide. The upper link is hinged at the upper part of

the frame and fastened to a wrist pin at the other end. The lower link is fastened to the same wrist pin and the other end of the slide. Another link is also used when the two knuckle links are moved into a straight-line position and a great deal of force is exerted downward.

These presses are quite massive in size, as they are used for coining, sizing, and embossing operations that require a heavy, squeezing action.

STRAIGHT-SIDE MECHANICAL PRESS

To withstand heavy loads, presses of this type have strong rigid frames.

The principal components of a single-action, straight-side press are: the bed, uprights, crown, tie rods, crankshaft, pitmans, flywheel, clutch, and brake. 45–4.

The bed is a heavy weldment or casting which provides support for the dies and other parts of the machine.

The uprights are columns supporting the crown of the press. They also guide the slide in precision gibs as it reciprocates.

The crown is located on top of the uprights, and houses the press-drive mechanism.

Tie rods serve to tie the crown and bed of the press together. They resist the forces that tend to separate them as the slide is forced on the workpiece.

The crankshaft, with the high-speed shaft and intermediate shafts required for gearing, is located in the crown.

The pitmans connect the slide and crankshaft. From one to four are used, depending upon work requirements.

The flywheel, is belt-driven by the motor, rotating continuously while the press is in operation. Flywheel inertia is the direct source of energy required to produce parts.

The clutch is used to engage and disengage the flywheel. Thus the press cycle can be controlled without stopping the flywheel and dissipating energy by stopping the press.

The brake provides for stopping the press quickly, usually at the top of the stroke.

The loads imposed upon the dies are exerted in a vertical direction; stresses are taken up in the heavy side frame. Because

45–3. Open-back, inclinable (O.B.I.), geared production press.

Walsh Press & Die Co.

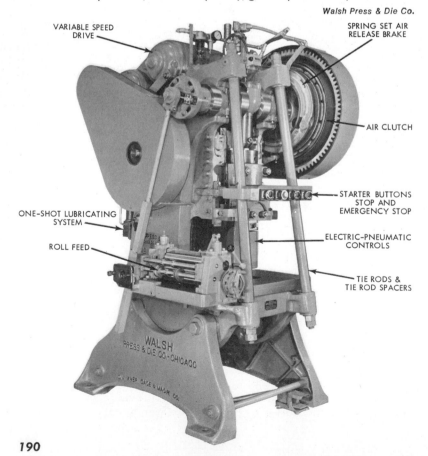

VARIABLE SPEED DRIVE

SPRING SET AIR RELEASE BRAKE

AIR CLUTCH

STARTER BUTTONS STOP AND EMERGENCY STOP

ONE-SHOT LUBRICATING SYSTEM

ROLL FEED

ELECTRIC-PNEUMATIC CONTROLS

TIE RODS & TIE ROD SPACERS

Erie Foundry Co.

45–4. Straight side mechanical press.

Fulton Iron Works Co.

45–5. Coining and embossing press.

45–6. Hydraulic press.

HPM, Div. of Koehring Co.

of this fact there is very little tendency for the punch and die to get out of alignment.

In presses of this type, methods of operation differ as do the ways of supplying power to the ram. A single crank eccentric is generally used on smaller presses to furnish the power. For large work additional cranks distribute the load on the slide uniformly. Single-action, four-point presses of straight-side design are widely used on automotive body panels and larger parts.

Modern straight-side presses are ruggedly built by welded steel fabrication methods and have the strength to resist deflection without being bulky or cumbersome.

Some presses, designed for one or two types of operations, may be identified by the operation performed, such as coining or embossing. 45–5.

HYDRAULIC PRESS

Hydraulic presses are especially adapted to deep drawing operations because of their slow, uniform motion and infinite adjustment of stroke speed, length, and pressure. 45–6. Hydraulic presses push or "squeeze" the work, while mechanical presses actually strike the work. This difference determines their suitability for given applications.

Being slower in operation, hydraulic presses are not suited for production work where speed is of great economic importance.

Hydraulic press frames are made in such basic styles as straight-side, column type, solid, or gap frame. Column type presses are built in a variety of sizes from 25-ton trimming presses to 4,000-ton, or larger, forming presses. Hydraulic presses are built for a variety of applications such as deep-draw forming, straightening, plastic molding, die spotting, and powdered metal compacting. They are not ordinarily used for heavy blanking or punching operations. The break-through shock created by the punch is damaging to this type of press.

TURRET PRESS

A turret press consists of upper and lower turrets carrying different size punches and dies. 45–7. The punches are located in a turret on top with a circle of dies below. Indexing of turrets is done in unison, thus making it easier to position punches and dies under the ram to produce a variety of different shaped holes. (Indexing is a term generally used to describe the process employed to move and accurately locate the workpiece in a series of positions for identical operations performed in sequence at different points on the workpiece.) The table has lead screws so that the stock can be positioned under the punches.

For producing identical parts, a fixed template is prepared by means of which all holes are accurately punched. The illustration shows the variety of work that can be done on a machine of this type. 45–8.

Turret punch presses of the tape-controlled variety are available in capacities of 15 to 150 tons wih multi-station turrets. 45–9. Numerical-positioning controls operate the table, turret, and press-tripping function to produce 65 holes per minute with accuracy to plus or minus .004".

HIGH-PRODUCTION TRANSFER PRESS AND OTHERS

Transfer presses are fully automatic presses for producing such things as ice cube trays,

Di-Acro, Div. of Houdaille Ind., Inc.

45–7. Industrial 18-turret power punch press.

45–8. Typical parts which have been pierced, notched, or nibbled on a turret punch press.

Warner & Swasey Co.

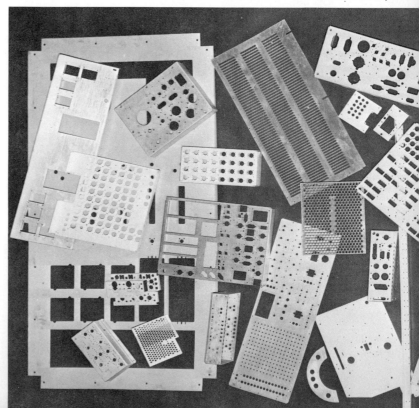

oil pans, and headlight housings for automobiles at a rate of 500 to 1,500 pieces per hour. The stock is fed into the machine from rolls, continuously. The stock is moved from one position to the next by a synchronized mechanism.

Today, numerous small parts are being manufactured in large quantities on high-production presses. 45–10. New developments in products affect the kinds of presses being built. Semi-conductor parts have, for example, created a demand for small, extremely accurate progressive dies for high-speed units. Some presses employ a series of stations, each being an individual press unit with one or more slides. In this type of operation, individual stations perform one or more operations on the workpiece, moving automatically from one station to the next. 45–11. The parts are transferred individually or are transferred in a strip and cut off at the end.

PRESS BRAKE

The illustration shows a press brake arranged for corrugating and shaping metal. 45–12 (Page 194). Essentially a gap press, it can handle wide sheets and accommodate several dies.

Presses of this type are especially suited for making long, straight bends. Press brakes range from 4′ to 30′ in length and power-driven press brakes have capacities which range from

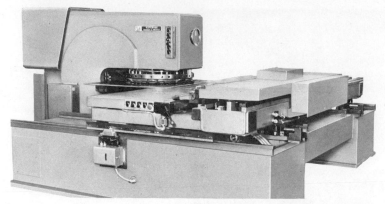

Warner & Swasey Co., Wiedemann Div.

45–9. A 15-ton, tape-controlled turret punch press. Produces 65 holes per minute with accuracy.

Niagara Machine and Tool Works

45–10. Automatic two-point straight-side press with rack-and-pinion, double-roll feed, and scrap chopper.

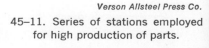

Verson Allsteel Press Co.

45–11. Series of stations employed for high production of parts.

Peck, Stow, & Wilcox Co.

45–12. Press brake for corrugating and shaping sheet metal.

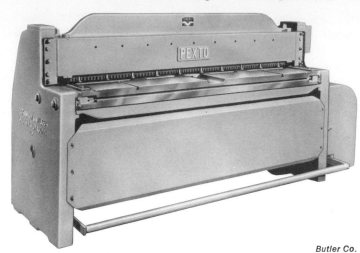

Butler Co.

45-13. Power squaring shears.

20 tons to about 1,000 tons. Metal thickness that can be worked ranges from light sheet metal up to ½″ mild steel plate. An eccentric drive mechanism with a short stroke is generally used.

The press brake is ideally suited for such operations as corrugating, seaming, notching, embossing, wiring or curling, and shaping cylindrical or tapered tube sections.

Air-bend dies (see Unit 47 under Bending and Forming Metal) and flat dies are the most commonly used on the press brake.

SHEARS

Shearing machines can be classified as (1) the blade shear, (2) the billet or structural shear, and (3) the nibbler. These machines are designed merely to cut off metal with a blade. 45–13.

The blade shear or squaring shear is made both for manual and power operation. This machine is adapted for cutting wide sheets. The ram is provided with a long blade held at an angle so that a gradual cut is made across the sheet metal. Hydraulic fingers hold the sheet firmly while the sheet is being cut. Manually, the blade is operated by a foot treadle, which powers the fingers to hold the sheet in place, while the shearing blade makes a progressive cut across the sheet.

The billet or structural shear cuts flat and round bars and certain types of structural shapes as provided for by the openings in the frame.

The nibbler is a machine used for thin-gage sheet-metal work. Its action can be compared to the action of a scissors cutting progressively along either a curved or straight line.

Unit 46. ## Press Drives and Feed Mechanisms

Presses are constantly being improved and streamlined. Large flywheels and counterweights formerly caused excessive wear on the clutch and brake. On modern presses the drive is made as light as possible to reduce the mass to be controlled. Gear ratios have not been changed but changes have been made in the sizes and locations of the gears. The weight of the gear has been considerably reduced and the energy has been stored in the flywheel and not in the gear and clutch. These changes provide faster starting and stopping of the press.

Easier maintenance has also been achieved by changing the

location of the drive. Flywheels are placed outside, where belt changing is made easier and more rapidly. Improvements have been made in clutches and brakes, which are quite different from types that were in use only a few years ago. Wear is taken up by self-compensating devices, eliminating the need for maintenance and adjustment.

New flexibility has been built into modern press drives by providing adjustable-speed drives which permit the presses to be run faster for blanking jobs, and slower for drawing operations.

PRESS DRIVES

Variable speed drives of the electric or belt type are advantageous on high-speed presses. This makes it possible to use different dies at their most favorable speeds. The drive can be mounted on the crown of the press and controlled at floor level.

The *single crank* is the most common drive mechanism used on mechanical presses. In this type of drive the down stroke is accelerated. The maximum velocity is reached at midstroke and is then decelerated.

The outer rams of double action presses are driven by *cams* and *toggle* mechanisms. 46–1. This type of drive serves to make the outer dwell (delay) hold the stock during part of the stroke.

Where some special movement is desired cams are used. This type of drive resembles somewhat the eccentric drive, with the exception that roll followers are used to provide motion to the slide.

The *eccentric drive,* which can be compared to a crank drive, is used when a shorter stroke is desired. It gives greater rigidity and less deflection to the frame. A press frame is subject to many stresses; reactions and deflections are a natural result.

In the *screw drive* the action resembles that of a drop hammer. The slide is accelerated by a friction disk coming in contact with a flywheel. The downward movement of the flywheel increases the speed; the slide motion is accelerated. All stored energy in the slide is absorbed by the workpiece.

Hydraulic drives are used on some types of presses where large pressures and slow speeds are required as in drawing, forming, and pressing operations. The ram on a hydraulic press is actuated by oil pressure on a piston contained in a cylinder.

FEED MECHANISMS

Various devices are provided on presses for the protection of the operator. Feeding mechanisms feed stock to the dies without endangering the hands of the operator; in addition, they provide uniform and rapid machine feeding, which is very important to high production.

Automatic high-speed presses are generally equipped with a double-end roll feed which operates in connection with coiled stock and scrap reels. 46–2 (Page 196). The roller feed device pulls strip stock from the stock reel through the die. Scrap is wound on a power scrap winder. In operation the rolls are actuated through a linkage from an eccentric located on the crankshaft. The upward movement of the ram causes the rolls to turn and feed the proper amount of stock for the next stroke of the ram. With some

46–1. Different types of drive mechanisms used in presses.

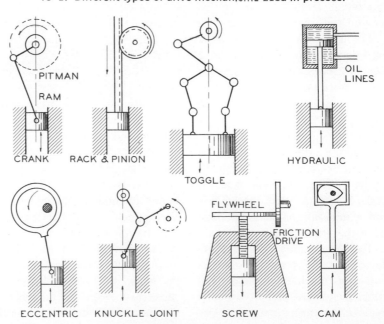

PITMAN
RAM
CRANK   RACK & PINION   TOGGLE   OIL LINES   HYDRAULIC

ECCENTRIC   KNUCKLE JOINT   FLYWHEEL   FRICTION DRIVE   SCREW   CAM

F. J. Littell Machine Co.

46–2. Automatic high-speed press equipped with double-end roll feed.

Unit 47.   Press Operations

A large variety of operations can be performed on a single press set up with the proper dies. 47–1. The tools used, punches and dies, work together as a unit. The punch is attached to the ram (slide) of the press and, in operation, is forced into the die cavity.

SHEARING

Shearing can be classified as: (1) cutting along a straight line with a general purpose shearing machine and (2) die-shearing, employing punches and dies of various shapes. There are two general types of shears: (1) the square shear which employs two long straight blades, one held stationary and the other blade moving down vertically and (2) the rotary shear with two round rotating blades—B in the illustration. 47–2(A&B).

Shearing operations that are normally done with dies include blanking, shaving, trimming, piercing, notching, perforating, slitting, and lancing.

Shearing metal with a punch and die consists of using a punch that has the same configuration as the opening in the die block. The punch is smaller on each side, by an amount known as the break clearance. As the punch is fed downward and contacts the stock, the pressure causes a stress to be set up adjacent to the punch and die edges, result-

ing in fractures on both sides of the stock. 47–3. NOTE: It is extremely important that the break clearance is correct and the edges are sharp. The kind, hardness, and thickness of the stock will govern the amount of clearance necessary. Too small or too large a clearance will prevent the fractures from meeting, thus producing a jagged break. From 5% to 8% of the thickness of the stock is generally accepted as the proper clearance. 47–4.

The shear force can be reduced by placing an angle on the punch or die, which will cause a progressive cutting angle.

47–1. Here a press is forming a punched shape in sheet metal, imposed on a die that can be changed for other shapes.

roller feed devices, the scrap from the operation is sheared to short lengths to facilitate easy handling. Straightening rolls are used if heavy stock is being processed. These can be used as feeding rolls.

The *dial station* feed can be used for feeding parts that have been formed on other presses. This feeding mechanism consists of a round table with several equally spaced stations. The table is indexed through an eccentric on the crankshaft similar to the roller-feed unit. At each stroke of the ram, the dial indexes one station and the loading and unloading of parts is done from the front of the machine.

There are many other feeding devices, such as arms with suction cups, mechanical hands, and magazines which feed pieces of material one at a time to the die.

BLANKING

Blanking refers to the operation of cutting out sheet metal "blanks" or flat shapes. This operation cuts the blanks from the metal sheet or strip on a single-action press equipped with tools consisting of a punch, corresponding die, and a stripper or knockout plate to keep the stock from being pulled upward by the punch on the return stroke. A method for aligning the stock and for spacing successive cuts is also necessary.

Piercing, punching, notching, and perforating metal are similar operations to blanking. 47–5. However, the amount of metal removed is much smaller than in blanking. In all these operations the metal removed is scrap.

Excess metal that has been left around the edges after other operations have been completed is removed by *trimming* dies. (The excess metal is known as "flash.") Trimming dies are quite similar to blanking dies. The workpieces are forced through the dies with punches.

Shaving is a sizing process that resembles trimming. Shaving serves to smooth and square blanked or pierced edges.

Slitting is cutting sheet metal, coiled stock by passing sheet through slitting rolls.

BENDING AND FORMING

Bending and forming operations are usually performed on crank, eccentric, or cam-operated presses. Straight bending is accomplished in a press brake. (See Unit 45.) Bending operations such as seaming, curling, and folding are similar but are slightly more complex.

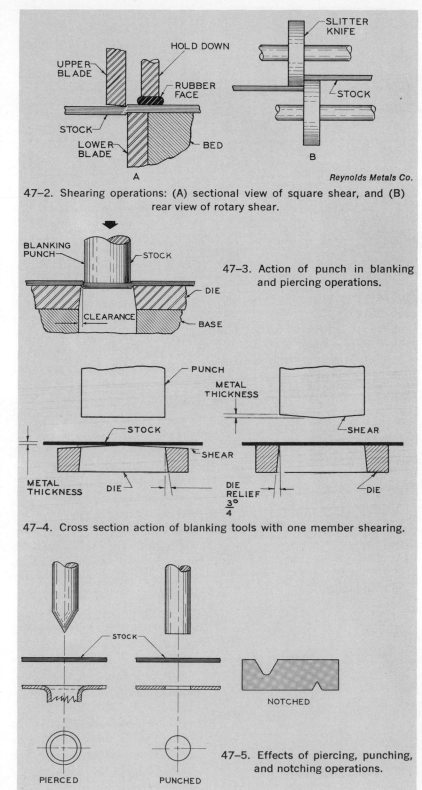

47–2. Shearing operations: (A) sectional view of square shear, and (B) rear view of rotary shear.

Reynolds Metals Co.

47–3. Action of punch in blanking and piercing operations.

47–4. Cross section action of blanking tools with one member shearing.

47–5. Effects of piercing, punching, and notching operations.

197

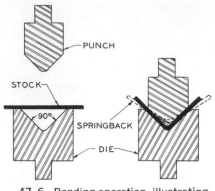

47–6. Bending operation, illustrating spring-back.

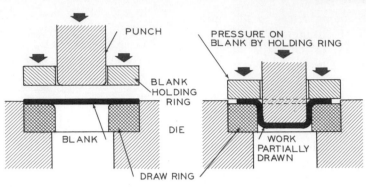

47–8. Function of blank holder and punch during drawing operation.

The fundamental processes of forming single bends in a press brake is called "air bend." In this method the stock contacts the dies at only three points. The die angles are made at 85° for working mild steel. All manufacturers rate their press brakes on this type of bending operation.

Bottoming dies strike solidly. They produce a more accurate bend but are not used on sheet material over 16 gage.

Using low-alloy high tensile steel, the designer has to make allowances for greater spring-back. 47–6. He has to take into consideration that the elastic properties will require greater radii than mild steel, to eliminate fracture.

47–7. Forming a part by drawing.

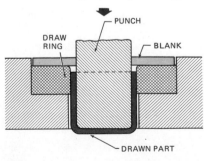

DRAWING

Drawing consists of pressing or stretching a flat blank or sheet over a die having the interior shape of the workpiece to be produced. 47–7. Since the perimeter of the blank is greater than the part to be drawn, its reduction—as the metal is forced through the die opening—sets up a higher compressive stress, which has a tendency either to thicken or buckle the blank.

There are three types of drawing methods: (1) single-action, (2) double-action, and (3) triple-action.

Single-action presses draw blanks of sufficient thickness so that the flange or wall will thicken rather than wrinkle when drawn. Brake drums, cartridge components, and gas containers are made by this method. Additional draws may be made on a cup-shaped part, with dies that reduce shell diameter and also control wall thickness.

Double-action drawing is the most common form of drawing and involves the shaping of thin sheets. An outer member, or blank holder, keeps the sheet flat

to prevent wrinkling, while a drawing punch forces the sheet into the die against the draw ring of the blank holder. 47–8.

Deep draws are usually accomplished by a double-action press fitted with a blank holder slide with a dwell motion and a drawing-slide crank. This crank is driven and guided within the blank holder.

Hydraulic presses are also made with double action to produce deep drawn parts. This type of press is suitable because of its slow action, speed control, and a pressure that is uniform.

Some stampings in automobile plants are made on *triple-action* presses, automobile doors for example. The blank holder produces the flange and a draw punch draws the edges and shapes the door while a lower slide rises and forms the window opening.

RUBBER FORMING

Rubber forming of aluminum —commonly known as the "Guerin process"—is widely used for production of aluminum parts in limited quantities. 47–9.

Hydraulic press rams with rubber pads housed in substantial retainers are normally used.

Only male dies are required as the rubber acts as the female die. The male dies are placed on a die slide which can be moved into position under the ram of the press. The developed (cut-to-size) blanks are located by gage pins when placed in position on the die. In operation, the rubber pad descends, forcing the rubber to flow around the dies and thus forming the part.

Several parts can be formed simultaneously by placing a number of male dies under the rubber pad. The size of the rubber pad is one determining factor in the number of parts that can be formed at one time and another is the available press tonnage and capacity. The following formula can be used in figuring the total rubber pad forming pressure:

Rubber pad forming
$$\text{pressure (psi)} = \frac{P \times 2{,}000}{A}$$

P = Capacity of press in tons

A = Area of pad in square inches

Male dies can be made of aluminum, Kirksite, plastic, Masonite, or steel.

Rubber will not flow into corners, so the forming die has to be made of sufficient height to take care of this. .

MARFORMING

The Marform process is somewhat similar to the Guerin process, using a rubber pad on the movable platen of the press to envelop the part, with a stationary punch located below.

47–10. The blank is laid on the punch and blank holder plate. The platen is lowered by controlled hydraulic pressure and the rubber pad envelopes the punch, forcing the metal blank around it as the press closes. Typical parts made in this manner are spherical domes, flanged cups, conical and rectangular shells. Marforming is suitable for deep drawing because better definition can be obtained on shallow forms.

HYDROFORMING

This process uses a flexible die backed by oil pressure which can be increased or decreased as desired. 47–11. The blank is laid on the holder over the punch. The dome is lowered until the diaphragm covers the blank. Next, oil pressure is applied and the punch is raised; then the oil pressure is increased to form the blank to shape. *Sharper* detail can be obtained by this method than by the Marforming process.

HYDRODYNAMIC PROCESS

The hydrodynamic process is a flexible punch forming process for shallow forming of thin metal with inclined rather than vertical sides. 47–12. The operation is usually performed on a hydraulic press. Water or oil is used as a pressure medium. In the forming operation fluid is admitted through an opening in the plate, its pressure forcing the stock into the die cavity. The pressure is uniform over the entire blank area. One of the advantages of this type of forming is that a variety of odd-shaped and tapered parts may be produced.

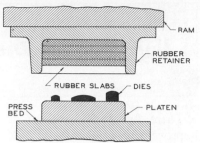

47–9. Press arrangement for rubber forming.

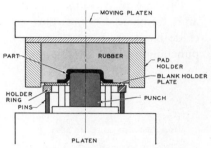

47–10. Setup of Marform process.

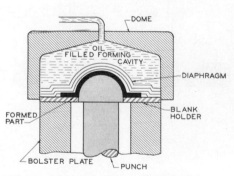

47–11. Hydroforming—a flexible die forming process.

47–12. Hydrodynamic forming process.

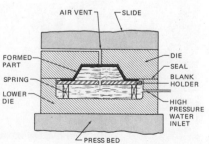

199

Unit 48.   Dies and Die Sets

There has been considerable improvement in the making of dies during the past few years, largely through the use of new and better quality materials.

Dies are of two kinds, cutting and forming. Cutting dies include blanking, parting, piercing, punching, cutoff, and shaving.

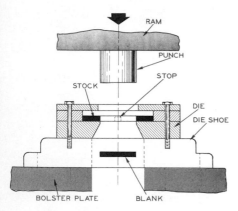

48–1. Setup of a simple blanking die.

Forming dies can be classified as curling, bending, and drawing.

Blanking punches and dies are made of hardened high-carbon steel, tungsten carbide, or chromium oil-hardened die steel. 48–1. The stock, in the form of strip or sheet, is fed into position over the die. The die is made with an opening the same size and shape as the blanks to be produced. The upper edge of the die contains the cutting edge. Proper clearance, which is of critical importance, is provided between the punch and die. A stripper is provided so that the stock can be removed from the punch on the ram's upstroke.

In blanking, piercing, and other shearing operations it is necessary that the upper and lower dies be in close alignment. Clearances of the punch and die shearing edges are only a few

thousandths of an inch; nonalignment could result in considerable damage to the punch and die. Therefore the dies are mounted in sets for most production work. 48–2. The die set consists of a punch holder, die shoe, and leader pins. 48–3. Standardized die sets are made in various types and sizes so the die maker may select the correct size and shape for most work. 48–4.

Alignment of the punch and die is maintained by using leader pins between the top and bottom of the die set. Fastening the upper plate of the die set to the slide and mounting the base to the bolster plate enables a punch to enter a die without damage.

It is not always possible to make a die that can be attached directly to the bed of the press. In this case it is necessary that a *bolster* be used. A bolster consists of a steel or cast-iron plate that can be attached to the bed of the press. The die shoe is attached to the bolster. Bolsters are made in various thicknesses so that the die can be raised to accommodate the ram's stroke.

48–2. Punches and dies mounted on a die set.

Di-Acro, Div. of Houdaille Ind., Inc.

48–3. Magnetic perforating die mounted in a die set.

S. B. Whistler & Sons, Inc.

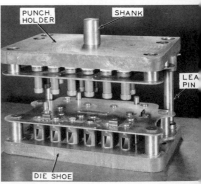

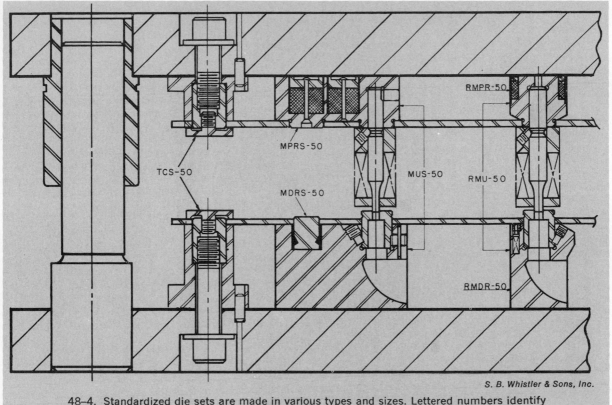

S. B. Whistler & Sons, Inc.

48–4. Standardized die sets are made in various types and sizes. Lettered numbers identify manufacturers' parts.

PROGRESSIVE DIES

Higher production rates can be secured through the use of progressive dies. 48–5. A series of stations is set up for production work. The stock is generally in the form of strip. Each station performs an operation on the stock, which then advances to the next station where the proper dies are located for the next operation. In production work the strip is fed through a feeding and straightening machine. 48–6 (Page 202). This unit is set up in perfect alignment with the punch press, so that the material will feed into the dies squarely. Dies are arranged so that free passage of the material is maintained

48–5. Setup of progressive blanking and piercing die.

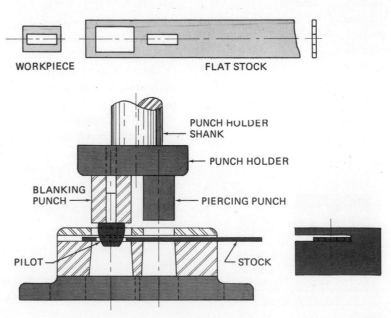

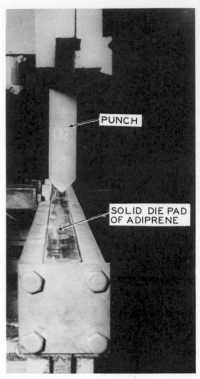

E. I. duPont de Nemours Co.

48–8. Press brake setup to form metal using an Adiprene die pad and a punch.

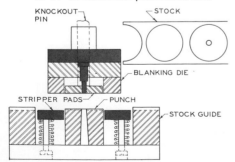

F. J. Littell Machine Co.

48–6. Strip stock is fed through feeding and straightening machines.

during its feeding cycle. With automatic feeding on automatic presses, the slide is reciprocated continuously. The individual die stations are usually mounted along a straight line with progressive dies.

48–7. Combination punch and die.

KNOCKOUT PIN
STOCK
BLANKING DIE
STRIPPER PADS
PUNCH
STOCK GUIDE

COMBINATION DIES

Parts such as washers are produced with combination or compound dies, which combine two or more operations at one station. 48–7. The strip stock is moved progressively through the die with the blanking punch contacting the stock slightly before the piercing punch so that the strip will be held in position for the punch.

URETHANE (ADIPRENE) DIE PADS

For simple and complex forming on a press brake, a solid die pad made of urethane (Adiprene) can accommodate a range

48–9. Part being formed using the solid die pad on a press brake.

E. I. duPont de Nemours Co.

of metals, metal gages, and punch shapes. 48–8. Because the urethane forms the metal tightly around the punch under continuous pressure, it offers a number of production advantages—high accuracy, no scoring of the part, no blank slippage during the stroke, elimination of springback, compensation for variations in the thickness of the metal, minimum metal fracture, low tool cost, and fast setups. 48–9.

A die pad retainer encloses the pad and concentrates the pressure upward, flowing to the exact contour of the punch and then returning to its original dimensions. The only critical provision for deflection control is that the die retainer have an air space channel beneath as shown in the illustration. 48–10.

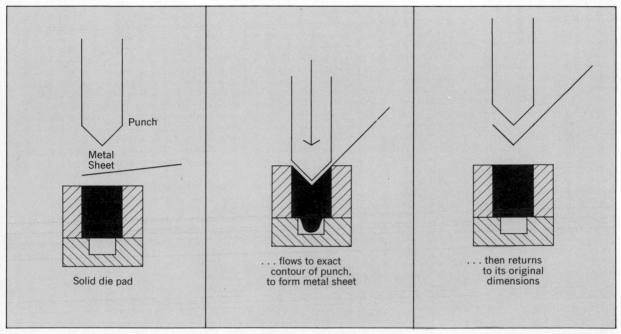

Punch

Metal Sheet

Solid die pad

. . . flows to exact contour of punch, to form metal sheet

. . . then returns to its original dimensions

E. I. duPont de Nemours Co.

48–10. Steps in using the solid die pad and punch. Note that the die retainer has an air space channel beneath the pad.

Check Your Knowledge

1. How are presses classified?

2. What are the trends in press operation today?

3. What type of material is used in the construction of press frames?

4. What is a bolster plate?

5. What is the advantage of a variable speed drive over the belt type?

6. How are presses rated?

7. Describe a gap press.

8. What is a horning press and what type of operations can be performed on this press?

9. Describe a turret press and state its advantages.

10. What are the advantages of transfer presses over other types?

11. How do hydraulic drives compare with mechanical drives for presses?

12. What are the advantages of a knuckle-joint press?

13. Describe briefly the following press operations: blanking, piercing, shaving, and drawing.

14. What is meant by the Guerin process?

15. Describe the Marform process.

16. Make a comparison of the

hydroforming and hydrodynamic process of metal forming.

17. Why is it important that upper and lower dies be in perfect alignment?

18. Describe a progressive die and a compound or combination die.

19. Describe the common way of feeding stock mechanically into presses.

References

Eary, D. F., and Reed, E.A., *Techniques of Pressworking Sheet Metal,* Englewood Cliffs, N.J., Prentice-Hall, Inc., 1958.

Kalpakjian, Serope, *Mechanical Processing of Materials,* Princeton, N.J., D. Van Nostrand Co., Inc., 1967.

Le Grand, Rupert, "Mechanical Presses," *American Machinist,* Special Report No. 568, May 10, 1965.

Siebert, Leo, "How to Specify Perforated Metals," *Machine Design,* March 17, 1966.

United States Steel Corporation, *The Making, Shaping, and Treating of Steel,* 8th ed., 1964.

Horizontal cold forming press.

Section Nine

Measurement and Inspection

THE Egyptians can be credited with being the first people to set up standards of measurement known as the Royal Cubit. To secure stability and durability the Royal Cubit was made of black granite. It was a line-measuring unit subdivided by lines so that increments as small as 1/448 of a cubit could be established. Working cubits were regularly calibrated to the Royal Cubit, a practice that helped make possible the structural wonders of Egyptian architecture.

Feet, fingers, arms, and even seeds were used as European standards later during the 13th century. Queen Elizabeth established the Bronze yard measurement standard in the year 1558, which was a standard up to the year 1824.

L. S. Starrett Co.

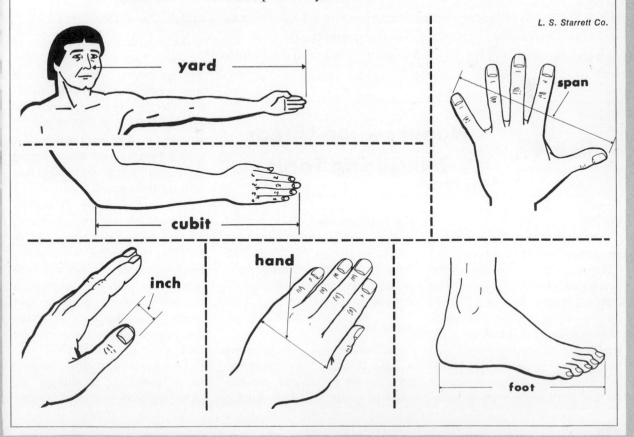

yard

span

cubit

inch

hand

foot

The French adopted the metric unit of length in 1790, based on a straight line between the North Pole and the Equator and passing through Paris. This was divided by 10 million to establish 1 meter.

The international prototype meter, a standard form made of platinum and 10% iridium, was developed in France. It is located at the International Bureau of Weights and Measures, near Paris.

By an act of Congress in 1866, the metric system was officially recognized in the United States. However, its use was not made mandatory in this country. (With so many countries using metric today, the United States is now taking steps toward probable conversion to this system.) In 1893, the Mendenhall Act recognized the international prototype meter as the legal standard and established its relationship to the yard as one yard equaling 3,600/3,937 of a meter, one meter equaling 39.370000″, and one inch equaling 2.540 centimeters.

The modern international inch is based on the wave length of monochromatic light from Krypton 86 gas. The length of a single wave is 0.0000238″, giving an absolute standard which never changes. Measurement of these microscopically small light waves is done by a process, interferometry, using the interferometer. (See Optical Flat, Unit 52.) Another method, spectroscopy, uses angstrom units of length, each measuring less than 4 billionths inch.

Unit 49. Nonprecision Linear Measuring Tools

RULES

The common rule is the basic measuring tool from which many other measuring tools have been developed. Rules range in size from as small as a ¼″ length for measuring grooves, keyways, and recesses to as much as a 12′ length for measuring larger surfaces. Steel rules are graduated in either the English or metric system, with some rules combining both systems. 49–1. English system graduations are commonly as fine as ¹⁄₁₀₀″ in decimals or ¹⁄₆₄″ in fractions. Metric graduations are as fine as ½ millimeter.

Combination Set

A combination set represents a rule developed by means of attachments to achieve the ultimate in utility. 49–2. It consists of a graduated, hardened steel blade with a sliding try square that also combines a miter and bevel. It serves the multiple uses of a rule, square, miter, depth gage, and level. 49–3. A bevel protractor is also a part of the combination set and can be used in connection with the blade which makes it possible to read or layout angles from 0 to 180°. An auxiliary center head can be substituted for the square head for finding centers of cylindrical parts. 49–4(A).

Hardened steel squares are used as master squares and in checking close work, where extreme accuracy is required. The beams and blades are hardened, ground, and lapped to insure parallelism and straightness. 49–4(B).

Calipers and Dividers

An *outside caliper* is used to measure outside diameters. 49–5. The caliper has two curved legs pointing in the same direction. If the legs are joined together at the top with a nut, it is called a *firm-joint* caliper. A *spring-joint* caliper has a spring at the top which maintains tension on the legs.

The *inside caliper* is usually used for internal measurements of cylindrical workpieces. 49–6.

When the caliper is set to the work, care should be taken to bring the points into contact without excessive pressure that might cause the legs to spring and introduce an element of error.

The hermaphrodite caliper, which combines a straight divider leg and a curved caliper

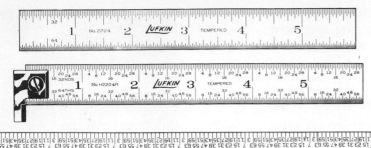

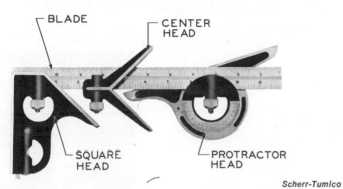

49–1. Various types of rules.

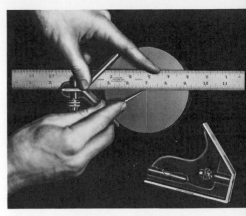

49–4(A). Locating the center of a round workpiece with the center head of a combination set.

BLADE

CENTER HEAD

SQUARE HEAD

PROTRACTOR HEAD

Scherr-Tumico

49–2. Combination set with square head, protractor head, and center head.

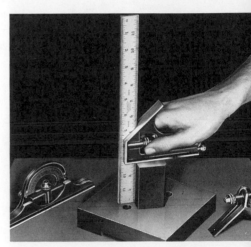

49–4(B). Using the square of a combination set to measure a part on a die.

CHECKING A 45° ANGLE

CHECKING FOR SQUARENESS

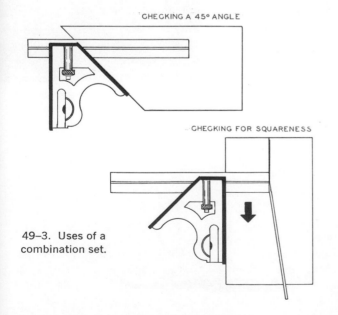

49–3. Uses of a combination set.

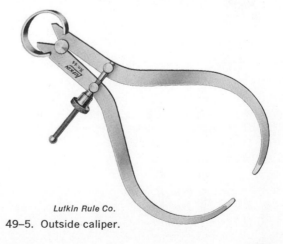

Lufkin Rule Co.

49–5. Outside caliper.

207

leg, is used for scribing parallel lines from an edge or for locating the center of cylindrical work. 49–7.

The dividers are used for measuring dimensions between lines or points; for transferring lengths taken from a steel rule; and for scribing circles and arcs. The contacts are sharp, hardened points at the ends of straight legs. Close measurements are made by visual comparison.

Telescoping Gage

Telescoping gages may be preferred to the ordinary leg caliper for measuring internal diameters, because the head of this gage expands across the inside of the hole and may be locked and then measured with a micrometer. 49–8. NOTE: The ends of telescoping heads are ground with a special radius equal to the radius of the smallest hole in which it can be used.

ANGULAR MEASURING INSTRUMENTS

Protractors

Measuring the angular relationship of two or more lines can be performed by a variety of tools depending upon the degree of accuracy required. Simple angles may be measured with a common protractor, which may be either semicircular or rectangular in shape but with a half circle graduated in degrees so that angles can be measured or laid out.

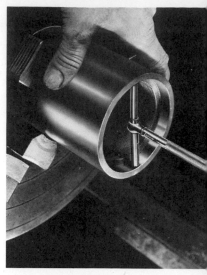

49–8. Telescoping gage.

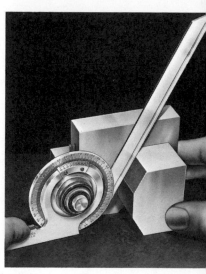

49–9(A). Universal bevel protractor.

Lufkin Rule Co.

49–6. Inside caliper.

49–7. Hermaphrodite caliper.

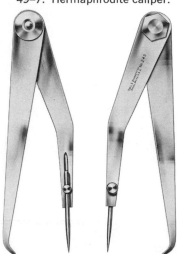

49–9(B). The reading is 50°20′.

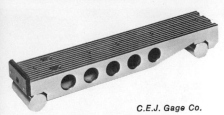

C.E.J. Gage Co.

49–10. Sine bar.

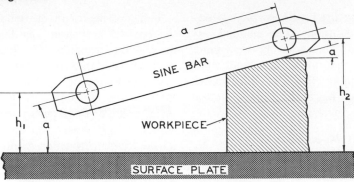

49–12. Application of the sine bar.

Universal Bevel Protractor

A universal bevel protractor measures angles in degrees and minutes. 49–9(A&B). The dial of the protractor is graduated both to the left and right of zero up to 90°. The vernier scale is also graduated to the right and left of zero up to 60 minutes, each of the 12 vernier graduations representing 5 minutes. Any size angle can be measured.

Sine Bar

The sine bar is a precision device for measuring angles and

49–11. Setting a sine bar with a micrometer.

Kingman-White, Inc.

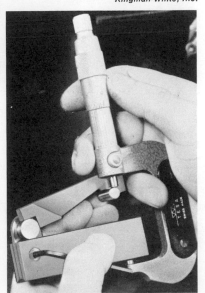

locating work at a desired angle to some other surface or line. 49–10. NOTE: It is always used in conjunction with some true surface from which measurements can be taken, preferably a clean surface plate. The sine in a right triangle is the ratio of the side opposite a given angle to the hypotenuse. 49–11.

The principle is the computation of the exact degree of angularity which a 5″ bar makes with a plane surface to determine the precise vertical height at one end.

With the workpiece resting on a surface plate, distances h_1 and h_2 to the center of the cylindrical pins are measured with gage blocks. 49–12. (See illustration.) Each hypotenuse a is a fixed property of the bar. Then,

$$\text{Sine} = \frac{h_2 - h_1}{a}$$

The angle can be obtained from a trigonometric table after the sine has been computed from the measurements.

Sine Plate

The sine plate, which is very similar to a sine bar, operates on the same principle. It has hard-

ened precision rolls, hinges, and gage block surfaces. 49–13.

In using the sine plate, angles are established by placing gage blocks on the smooth surface underneath the roll. The sine plate may be used on a surface plate or may be clamped to a machine table. Tapped holes are provided on the top and sides for various clamping setups.

The illustration, at top, shows a magnetic sine plate, employing fine-pole, permanent magnets. It

49–13. Sine plates.

Ex-Cell-O Corp.

can be used with surface grinding operations. The center illustration shows a non-magnetic plate for inspection and light machining. The lower illustration shows a heavy-duty sine plate for tough machining.

Direct Measure—
Taper Micrometer

This measuring instrument makes it possible to inspect tapered parts ten times faster than with older conventional methods. 49–14. Both internal and external tapers can be checked without the need for sine bars or more elaborate equipment.

It is not necessary to remove the tapered part from the lathe or grinding machine. The taper micrometer is relatively inexpensive. Incorporating within itself the sine-bar principle, it gives actual value of the taper of small angles. Larger tapers can be obtained from micrometer readings with no more mathematical knowledge than is needed for converting from included angle to taper. Under production conditions, of course, the desired upper and lower limits for various tapers can be readily specified in terms of precise micrometer readings.

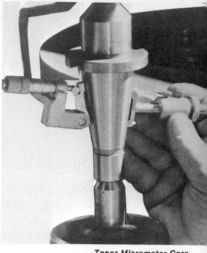

Taper Micrometer Corp.

49–14. Direct measurement of a taper with the taper micrometer.

<table>
<tr><td>

Unit 50.

</td><td>

Precision Measuring Instruments

</td></tr>
</table>

MICROMETER CALIPER

The smallest measurement in common fractions that can be made with the fixed caliper and steel rule is $\frac{1}{64}''$. To measure in thousandths and ten-thousandths, a micrometer caliper is necessary.

The pitch of the screw thread on the spindle of a micrometer is $\frac{1}{40}''$ or 40 threads per inch. One complete revolution of the thimble advances the spindle face toward or away from the anvil face $\frac{1}{40}''$ or .025".

The *longitudinal line* on the sleeve is divided into 40 equal parts by vertical lines that correspond to the number of threads cut on the spindle. Each vertical line designates $\frac{1}{40}''$ or .025"

and every fourth line designates .100". Thus the line marked "1" represents .100", the line marked "2" represents .200", etc.

The *beveled edge* of the thimble is divided into 25 equal parts with each line representing .001" and every line numbered consecutively. Rotating the thimble to the next higher line moves the spindle $\frac{1}{25}$ of .025" or .001". Twenty-five divisions indicate a complete revolution, .025" or $\frac{1}{40}''$.

EXAMPLE:

What is the reading if the edge of the thimble is between the .125" and the .150" lines, and the line on the thimble is the coinciding line? 50–1 (Page 211).

SOLUTION:
Micrometer reading =
sleeve + thimble =
.125 + .015 = .140

CAUTION: Dirt between the anvil and spindle will cause the micrometer to read incorrectly. The *test* of an accurate caliper is to clean and bring the anvil and spindle together carefully. If the zero line on the thimble and the axial (longitudinal) line on the sleeve fail to coincide, wear has taken place either in the screw or contact surfaces.

Micrometer calipers are made in a wide range of sizes and in matched sets. The one shown in the photo is equipped with a ratchet stop and locknut. 50–2. The ratchet stop is used to rotate the spindle when taking a measurement and insures consistent, accurate gaging by limiting the spindle pressure on the workpiece. The locknut makes it possible to lock the micrometer spindle at any desired setting. A slight turn of the knurled lock-nut ring contracts a split bushing around the spindle and makes the micrometer a fixed gage.

When very accurate measurements are required, a micrometer which has an extra scale added to the sleeve is used, enabling the micrometer to be read in ten-thousandths of an inch. This scale consists of a series of lines on the sleeve parallel to its axis. 50–3(A).

Ten divisions on the sleeve mark the same spaces as nine

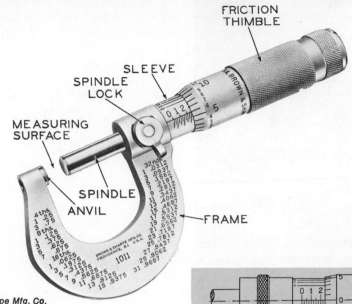

Brown & Sharpe Mfg. Co.

50–3(A). The 1″ micrometer graduated in ten-thousandths of an inch.

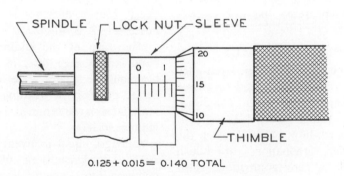

0.125 + 0.015 = 0.140 TOTAL

50–1. Micrometer caliper reading.

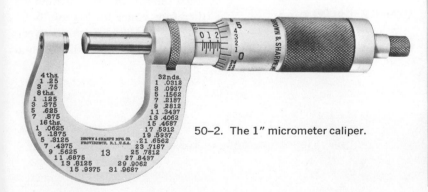

50–2. The 1″ micrometer caliper.

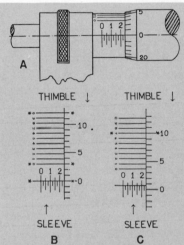

Fig. A & B—Reading .2500″

Example: Refer to figures A and B above.
The "2" line on sleeve is visible, representing .. .200″
There are two additional lines visible,
  each representing .025″ ....2 x .025″=.050″
Line "0" on the thimble coincides with the
  longitudinal line on the sleeve, representing.. .000″
The "0" lines on the Vernier coincide with lines on
  the thimble, representing................. .0000″
The Micrometer Reading is.................. .2500″

Fig. C—Reading .2507″

Example: Refer to figure C above.
The "2" line on sleeve is visible, representing... .200″
There are two additional lines visible,
  each representing .025″ ....2 x .025″=.050″
The longitudinal line on the sleeve lies between
  the "0" and "1" on the thimble indicating
  ten-thousandths of an inch are also to be
  added as read from the Vernier......... ......
The "7" line on the Vernier coincides with a
  line on the thimble, representing..7 x .0001″=.0007″
The Micrometer Reading is................. .2507″

L. S. Starrett Co.

50–3(B). Reading a micrometer graduated in ten-thousandths of an inch.

50–4. Micrometer depth gage.

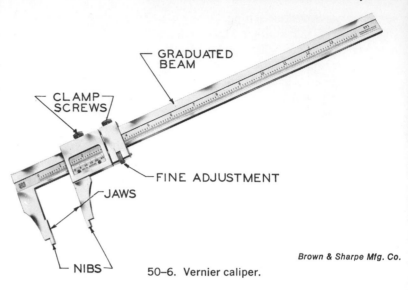

GRADUATED BEAM

CLAMP SCREWS

FINE ADJUSTMENT

JAWS

NIBS

Brown & Sharpe Mfg. Co.

50–6. Vernier caliper.

divisions on the beveled edge of the thimble. Therefore the difference between the width of one of the ten spaces on the sleeve and one of the nine spaces on the thimble is one tenth of a division on the thimble. Since the thimble is graduated to read in thousandths, $\frac{1}{10}$ of a division would be .0001 or one ten-thousandth. 50–3(B) (Page 211).

MICROMETER DEPTH GAGE

A micrometer depth gage is used to measure the depth of such work as holes, slots, recesses, and keyways. 50–4.

The tool consists of a hardened, ground and lapped base combined with a micrometer

head. Measuring rods with individual length adjustment are inserted through a hole in the micrometer screw and brought to a positive seat by a knurled nut. The screw has a 1″ movement.

VERNIER DEPTH GAGE

The type of vernier depth gage shown provides readings over a range of 6″ and 12″. 50–5. The vernier plate, 1.225″, provides readings in .001″ when the vernier graduations are flush with the zero graduation, eliminating parallax. A spring pressure clamp holds the blade firmly in measuring position.

VERNIER CALIPER

A vernier caliper consists basically of a main or beam scale

with a supplementary sliding jaw. 50–6. On the main scale, each unit is divided into forty parts, so that each part is $\frac{1}{40}$ or .025″. For convenience in reading, every fourth division is numbered—1, 2, 3, 4, etc.

The zero of the sliding jaw scale is the gage line; its location on the main scale determines part of the reading. The remainder is determined by the vernier scale.

A length equal to twenty-four main scale divisions or .600″ is divided into twenty-five equal parts on the vernier scale, every fifth division being numbered. Each space on the vernier is therefore equal to $\frac{1}{25}$ of .600″ or .024″. The division between the scale division (.025″) and

50–5. Vernier depth gage.

Brown & Sharpe Mfg. Co.

50-7. Micro-height gage.

50-8. Vernier height gage.

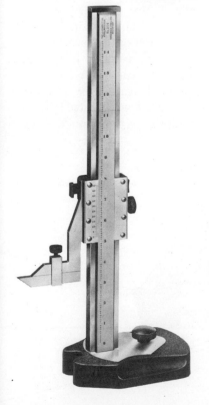

one vernier division (.024) equals .025" less .024" or .001". If the tool is set so that the 0 line on the vernier coincides with the 0 line on the beam, the line to the right of the 0 on the vernier will differ from the line to the right of the 0 on the bar by .001"; the second line by .002", etc. The difference will continue to increase .001" for each division until the line 25 on the vernier coincides with line 24 on the beam.

MICRO-HEIGHT GAGE

The micro-height gage is a precision measuring tool developed to increase the effectiveness of diemakers, toolmakers and inspectors in taking height gage measurements. 50-7.

This gage is read direct from the thimble and barrel graduations. Each graduation represents one hundred thousandths of an inch (.100") and each graduation on the thimble represents .001". The lead screw has a ten-pitch thread. The index line on the cover plate is used only for quick reference in relation to the .100" on the barrel. Accuracy of reading is always determined by the position of the thimble graduations in relation to the reading line on the barrel.

VERNIER HEIGHT GAGE

The vernier height gage consists of a stationary part mounted on a base. 50-8. The stationary part, the beam, is graduated and contains a movable part—a vernier slide assembly—which can be lowered or raised to any position along the beam and adjusted in thousandths of an inch by

means of the vernier plate fine adjusting nut.

Set up with a steel scriber, the gage can be used to mark off vertical distances and locate center distances. Replacing the scriber with a dial indicator, it can be used as an inspection gage for comparing heights from a surface plate.

Another type of height gage (Pla-check) that can be used for many purposes is shown in the illustration. 50-9. Operations

50-9. Pla-Chek height gage scribing on blued plate.

Step 1

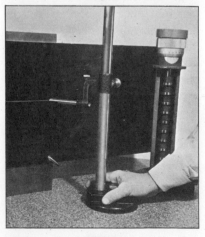

Step 2

Cadillac Gage Co.

50–10. Height gage used in gaging hole location.

Opto-Metric Tools, Inc.

50–11. Toolmaker's microscope.

Scherr-Tumico Co.

50–12. Optical comparator.

such as gaging hole locations, gaging inside diameters, layout, gaging height, and inspection are performed. 50–10. This gage is accurate to within .00005″ up to 18″.

TOOLMAKER'S MICROSCOPE

Many optical instruments have been devised for inspecting and measuring purposes. The toolmaker's microscope is one of these devices. 50–11. It is an instrument of extreme accuracy that can measure parts without contact or pressure. The part being viewed is greatly enlarged, the magnification being from 10 to 50 times, and the image is not reversed as in an ordinary microscope.

In operation the microscope is focused to show, at the focal plane, a clear image of a magnified portion of the workpiece. The portion to be measured is brought under the crossline as viewed in the microscope. The table is then moved so that the line in the eyepiece is aligned

with the opposite end of the dimension. The location of the table is then read. The difference of the two readings is the dimension obtained.

OPTICAL COMPARATOR

The optical comparator projects a magnified image of the object being measured onto a screen where it is compared to a drawing or master chart.

The optical comparator is used when the workpiece is diffi-

cult to check by other methods. 50–12. Extremely small or odd-shaped parts which would be difficult to interpret by other methods can be checked with this inspection device.

A light from a lamp passes through a condenser lens and is projected against the workpiece. The shadow created by the workpiece is transmitted through

50–13. Principle of an optical comparator.

Jones & Lamson, Div. of Waterbury Farrel

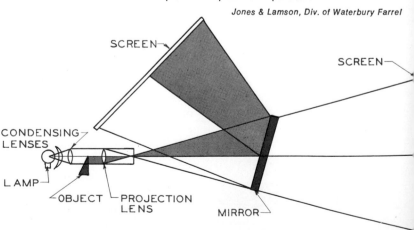

SCREEN

SCREEN

CONDENSING LENSES

LAMP

OBJECT PROJECTION LENS

MIRROR

a projecting lens system which magnifies the image and casts it onto a mirror. The image is then reflected to the viewing screen and further magnification takes place.

A master form mounted on the viewing screen can be used to compare the accuracy of the enlarged image of the part being inspected.

Optical projectors are commonly available with projection magnifications of 10X, 20X, 31.25X, 50X, 62.5X and 100X. 50–13.

It is possible to check tolerances of 0.001″ and smaller quite rapidly on these comparators as the lens magnification enlarges small dimensions to greatly enlarged sizes.

parallelism, and surface finish in grades AA, A, and B.

Gage blocks are used singly or in combinations to check and set micrometers, vernier calipers, snap gages, and indicators; or they may be used directly on workpieces to check center distances, slot widths, and shoulder clearances. With auxiliary holders and special gage blocks, called end standards, they can be made up into gages and layout instruments for checking parts directly or making accurate layouts.

Gage blocks can be wrung together by thoroughly cleaning the gage surfaces, then engaging a small part of the gaging surfaces, and sliding the blocks into full contact while pressing them firmly together. Any traces of air and foreign material are wiped away by this method. 51–2(A, B, C & D) (Page 216).

The manufacturer provides a handbook of tables listing various combinations of gage blocks

Unit 51. Gage Blocks and Gages

A gage block is a reference standard of measurement. Instead of lines for reference as on a ruler, the gage block is made with two reference surfaces. 51–1. It is a small rectangular or square block of hardened steel so carefully machined on the gaging surface that it has almost an optical finish. Each block is engraved with the size in decimals of an inch to which it has been machined. Acceptable gage blocks are within less than four millionths of an inch of their designated size when measured at 68°F.*

A standard set of 81 gage blocks includes the following:

One ten thousandths series—
0.1001–0.1009 inch inclusive—9 blocks.
One thousandths series—
0.101–0.149 inch inclusive—49 blocks.

Fifty thousandths series—
0.050–0.950 inch inclusive—19 blocks.
Inch series—1.000–4.000 inches inclusive—4 blocks.

Federal specifications classify gage blocks according to allowable tolerance for length, flatness,

51–1. Gage blocks.

---

* DoAll Company, "The Facts of Gage Block Life."

51–2(A). When wringing gage blocks, be sure gaging surfaces are clean. To start, overlap gaging surfaces about ⅛″ and slip blocks as shown.

51–2(B). While pressing blocks together, slide one over the other past center.

51–2(C). Slide back to center position.

Do All Co.

51–2(D). Blocks will now adhere.

for any dimension from .0001″. The use of this handbook eliminates calculation and provides an alternate choice of blocks for each dimension.

In building up a specific gage block combination, use as few blocks as possible. Start by selecting blocks which will eliminate the last figure to the right of the decimal point.

In the example here (1.4672), first eliminate the 2 in the last place by selecting a .1002 block. The remainder is 1.3670. The 7 is eliminated with a .117 block. The 5 as well as the 2 of the remaining .250 is eliminated with a .250 block, leaving 1.000, which is eliminated with a single block.

EXAMPLE:

1.4672		
.1002	.1002	(block 1)
1.3670		
.117	.117	(block 2)
1.250		
.250	.250	(block 3)
1.000		
1.000	1.000	(block 4)
0.000	1.4672	requires four blocks

Unit 52. Surface Measurements

Many types of instruments are in use for checking the accuracy of a surface or the condition of a finish.

SURFACE PLATE

A great deal of this work is done from a surface plate which establishes the reference plane from which all precision measurement starts, is transferred, or is interpolated. 52–1. Used in conjunction with other fixed gages, the plate becomes a functional gage in itself.

Measurement always starts from a reference point or plane. Linear measurement begins at a reference point and ends at a measure point. For angular measurements the reference point must be a plane.

Since a plane has three reference points, it is perfectly flat. But this is only theoretical because it has only length and

52–3. Surface gage being used to locate distance from base.

Do All Co.

52–1. Granite surface plate, sine plates, and sine bar. The sine plate uses the same principle as the sine bar.

52–2. Surface gage.

Brown & Sharpe Mfg. Co.

width. The points of contact of a three-legged stool exemplify a true plane. A stool having four legs of equal length and position will reveal the flatness of that plane. To make a plane usable, it must have thickness to support both the measuring tool and the workpiece. Such a plane is called a surface plate.

The surface plate is as essential for positional accuracy as the length standard is for linear accuracy.* The reference surface must have known accuracy before it can become the common plane or starting point for angular measurements, height gages, and gaging accessories.

Cast iron and steel, as a material for surface plates, has been largely replaced by granite. Granite surface plates have flatness within millionths of an inch. They do not rust, are non-mag-

netic, and are harder than metal plates.

SURFACE GAGE

A surface gage is used to transfer measurements, check the accuracy or parallelism of surfaces, and is used in layout work for scribing lines on vertical or horizontal surfaces. 52–2. It is also useful in inspection work as a height gage or depth gage.

This instrument has a base with a ground bottom surface. Two gage pins are located in the base for linear work and it has a v-groove in the base for circular work. 52–3. The spindle is adjustable to any angle above or below the base. It has an extra fine adjustment plus a wide range.

OPTICAL FLAT

Interferometry is the interpretation of the fringe patterns that result when rays of light interfere with each other. Measurements can be made to the

* DoAll Company, "How to Use a Surface Plate," 1966.

217

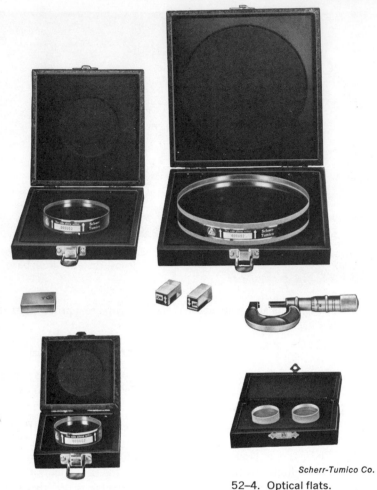

millionth of an inch by interferometry. For this type of measurement there is a choice of two classes of tools: (1) simple inexpensive optical flats or (2) complex interference instruments, generally called *interferometers*. The first will be explained in this unit.

An optical flat and monochromatic light combine to give us a simple method of interferometry. When the flat is placed on a lapped surface, separated dark bands appear. By interpreting the form and relationship of these bands, variation in surface flatness and size may be determined in millionths of an inch.

Optical flats are flat lenses that have been very accurately polished from natural quartz. 52–4. The surfaces have a light-transmitting quality with a low coefficient of expansion and resistance to corosion. These lenses are usually about ⅝″ thick and 2″ in diameter, although they can be obtained in various sizes and shapes up to 12″.

Scherr-Tumico Co.

52–4. Optical flats.

52–5. Monolight. Note crossed lines on the glass. These lines are projected onto the optical flat, providing reference lines for checking the straightness of the fringe lines.

Do All Co.

52–6. Interference bands (fringe lines).

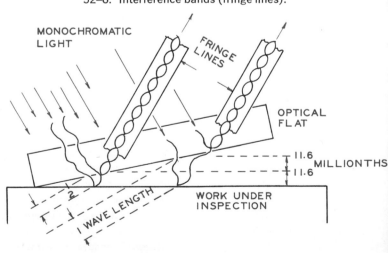

MONOCHROMATIC LIGHT

FRINGE LINES

OPTICAL FLAT

11.6
11.6 MILLIONTHS

2

1 WAVE LENGTH

WORK UNDER INSPECTION

Monochromatic light is preferred for most interferometry. 52–5. Colors of light vary with their wave lengths. White light consists of all visible wave lengths combined. Monochromatic light is of one color only. Monochromatic fringes are easier to see, to count, and to evaluate in terms of millionths of an inch (microinches) than white light. The light source used for practical shop work is helium, which has a wave length of 23.2 microinches.

Fundamentally, the functioning part of an optical flat is the surface facing the work. It is both transparent and capable of reflecting light. Therefore all light waves that strike the surface are in effect, split in two longitudinally. One part is reflected back by the surface of the flat. The other part passes through and is reflected back by the surface under inspection as illustrated. Whenever the reflected split portions of two light waves cross each other (interfere), they become visible and produce dark bands. 52–6 & 52–7. This happens whenever the distance between the reflecting surfaces is one-half of a wave length or multiples thereof.*

Each dark band is a measuring unit representing 11.6 millionths inch when fluorescent helium light is used. 52–8.

When the optical flat rests on the work under monochromatic light a thin, slightly sloping space (wedge) of air separates the surfaces. 52–9. The wedge is stable enough for band reading

* DoAll Company, "How to Be Your Own Bureau of Standards."

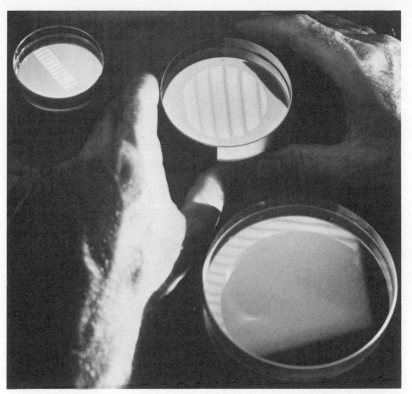

The Van Kevran Co.

52–7. Typical gage quality surfaces and one well-finished seal ring, all flat to about 2 millionths inch.

52–8. A 12″ test plate, wavy to about ½ band or 6 millionths inch.

The Van Kevran Co.

52–9. Shouldered shaft flat to 3 millionths inch, using optical flat with central hole to clear workpiece shank.

The Van Kevran Co.

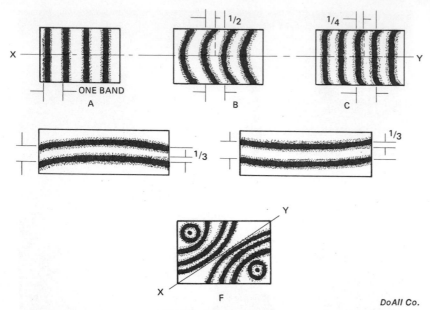

DoAll Co.

52–10. The extent of surface deviations from absolute flatness. (A) Wedge of 50 microinches will show four bands. If surfaces of both flat and work are perfect planes, the bands will appear straight and equidistant. (B) Surface is convex by ½; low along outer edge by 5.8 millionths inch. (C) Surface flat across center but low along outer edges by 2.9 microinches. (D) Surface is convex by ⅓ band. (⅓ of 11.6 equals 3.866.) Outer edges are low by 3.866 millionths inch. (E) Surface is concave by ⅓ band or 3.866 millionths of an inch. (F) Shows two points of contact which are high points on the surface. The center along line x-y is low by 4½ bands or 52.2 microinches.

52–11. Surface characteristics (ASA B 46.1) 1962 and symbols for indicating their maximum values.

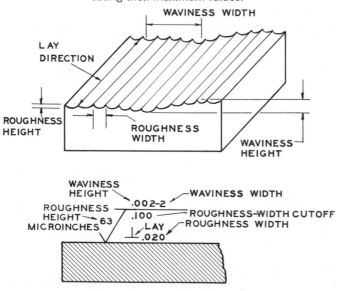

because of minute dust particles or lint.

If the air wedge is about 34.8 microinches higher on one side than the other, three bands will appear across the work surface, one band for each 11.6 microinches of elevation. In other words, the number of bands between two points on a surface can be used to determine the relative height difference in millionths of an inch between the flat and the surface by multiplying the number of bands between the points by .0000116″. 52–10.

If a work surface is not exactly flat but slightly cylindrical, the sloping space between the work and the optical flat would contain regions of uniform height, but they would not occur in straight lines. The interference pattern would therefore show curved bands.

When interpreting an interference band pattern, the surface of the flat is the reference surface. The flatness accuracy is within a few millionths of an inch across its diameter. It is the comparative height difference between the work and the reference plane that the bands reveal, and which can be interpreted.

SURFACE TEXTURE

The designer determines the type of surface to be produced on a given part. Standard symbols are used to indicate such surfaces. All machined surfaces have surface irregularities, including those which appear very smooth and flat. When viewed under a microscope, scratches and grooves in the form of peaks and valleys are noticeable. The surface texture is determined by such factors as width, height, and direction of surface irregularities.

In 1961, delegates of the United States, Great Britain, and Canada worked out an agreement on surface quality standards. In 1962 The American Standards Association approved these standards and they were designated in this country as American Standard (ASA B46.1-1962). 52-11.

Special measuring instruments have been devised to measure surface texture using the microinch (0.000001) as the unit of measurement. Visual comparison can be made with an established standard or microscopic comparison, light interference, and the measurement of magnified shadows cast by scratches on the surface.

The roughness of the surface may be checked with several types of instruments. The most widely used is an electrical type instrument employing a stylus which is passed over an irregular surface. The motion of the stylus is amplified and the average roughness is indicated in microinches. This instrument is known as a *profilometer*. 52-12.

Measurement by the profilometer is continuous, showing the variation in average roughness taken from a reference line, as in the drawing. 52-13.

The roughness height is expressed in microinches as a simple arithmetical average (AA) deviation, measured normal to the center line. NOTE: In former standards, the roughness height was expressed in microinches as the root mean average (RMS) deviation, measured normal to the center line.

Selecting a Finish

The quality of a surface is determined largely by the production method used to produce the surface. The range of surface finish may vary greatly with different production processes. In selecting the required surface finish for a particular part, the engineer bases his decision on past experience with similar parts, on field service data, or on engineering tests. The engineer's choice is based on such factors as size and function of the parts, type of loading, speed and direction of movement, operating conditions, physical characteristics of both materials in contact, type and amount of lubricant required, temperature, and possible stress reversals to which parts may be subjected. The range of machining operations may vary a great deal. Where a specific surface quality is required, the method which

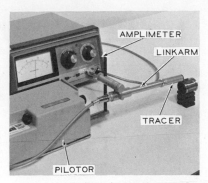

Bendix, Industrial Metrology Div.

52-12. Profilometer-amplifier shows arithmetical (AA) roughness height on a microinch meter as the tracer is moved along the workpiece.

will produce this surface *most economically* is selected.

Table 52, shown on page 222, gives the range of surface roughness produced by various production processes.

To secure quick measurements that are required by production methods, measuring devices that have a fixed shape or size are

52-13. The arithmetical average and rms values used in determining surface roughness.

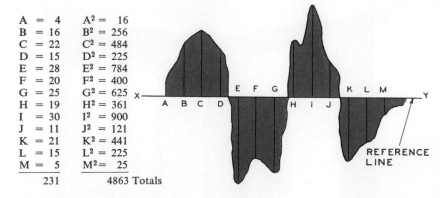

A = 4	A² = 16	
B = 16	B² = 256	
C = 22	C² = 484	
D = 15	D² = 225	
E = 28	E² = 784	
F = 20	F² = 400	
G = 25	G² = 625	
H = 19	H² = 361	
I = 30	I² = 900	
J = 11	J² = 121	
K = 21	K² = 441	
L = 15	L² = 225	
M = 5	M² = 25	
231	**4863** Totals	

$$\text{Arithmetical average} = \frac{231}{13} = 17.7 \text{ microinches}$$

$$\text{Root mean average} = \sqrt{\frac{4863}{13}} = 19.3 \text{ microinches rms}$$

Table 52. Surface Roughness Produced by Common Production Methods*

Process	2000	1000	500	250	125	63	32	16	8	4	2	1	0.5
Flame cutting													
Snagging													
Sawing													
Planing, shaping													
Drilling													
Chemical milling													
Electrical discharge machining													
Milling													
Broaching													
Reaming													
Boring, turning													
Barrel finishing													
Electrolytic grinding													
Roller burnishing													
Grinding													
Honing													
Polishing													
Lapping													
Superfinishing													
Sand casting													
Hot rolling													
Forging													
Permanent mold casting													
Investment casting													
Extruding													
Cold rolling, drawing													
Die casting													

KEY   ■■■■ AVERAGE APPLICATION

▨▨▨▨ LESS FREQUENT APPLICATION

The ranges shown above are typical of the process listed, expressed in profile   Higher or lower values may be obtained under special conditions.
MICROINCHES   * ASA B46.1—1962.

52–14. Surface finish comparator; contains reference scales for machined, grit blast, shot blast, and electrical discharge machined surface finishes.

Electroforming Div. of Heli-Coil Corp.

used. Use of such instruments cuts the inspection time to a minimum; in fact, much of this type of gaging can be done by the machine operators.

Checking Surface Texture

Surface quality can be checked in several ways, depending upon the type of equipment available to inspectors and machine tool operators. 52–14.

Comparison of surface qualities can be done by touch and sight. Standard specimens that have been previously checked with a surface measuring instrument may be used. A comparison can be made between the surface being checked and the specimen by dragging the finger-nail over both surfaces. When the feel is the same, the roughness (in microinches of height) is approximately the same. Also, with experience, the visual method quickly determines the approximate roughness value of a workpiece. Such methods can be used on parts that do not require close tolerances.

For best results in determining microinch roughness, comparison should always be of surfaces obtained with the *same machining process*. Each type of machining produces a different pattern of surface irregularities (tool marks). Two surfaces of the same microinch roughness produced by different machining processes (i.e., ground and turned) appear to differ in roughness because of the way light is reflected from surface irregularities. The brighter surface is not necessarily the smoother.

Profilometers and similar measuring instruments are advised

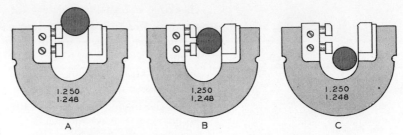

52–16(A). Parts checked in a limit gage: (A) Part is too large. (B) Part is satisfactory. (C) Part is undersize.

for short run jobs where fast production is not required.

GO AND NO-GO GAGES

A tolerance-limit gage is often referred to as a "go and no-go" gage. These gages are generally accepted as the most practical, accurate, and economical method of inspecting production tolerances. They check given dimensions by direct physical contact. They have two fixed parts, one to admit the dimension being checked and another to refuse the dimension.

Go and no-go (sometimes not-go) gages are built in wide variety of designs depending upon use. Snap gages, ring gages, and plug gages are the most common.

Snap Gages

The snap age is a limit gage available in several styles and sizes. 52–15. The one shown has one stationary anvil and two button anvils which are adjustable. In operation the outer button is set to the go size and the inner button to no-go.

Gage blocks can be used to set the size limits on a snap gage. 52–16 (A&B). The principle involved in testing cylindrical parts with a limit snap gage is shown in the drawing. The upper

Johnson Gage Co.

52–16(B). Indicating snap gage.

gaging point is the go point, while the lower is the no-go point. If the part passes through the go portion (A), the work is in tolerance. If it passes through both go and no-go (B), the work is smaller than the tolerance permits. If it does not pass through the go position (C), the work is larger than the tolerance permits. The reverse applies to inside measurements.

NOTE: *Thread* snap gages and ring gages are adjustable.

Ring Gages

Plain ring gages, taper ring gages, as well as thread ring gages, are commonly used for

52–15. Limit snap gage.

Automation and Measurement Div., Bendix Corp.

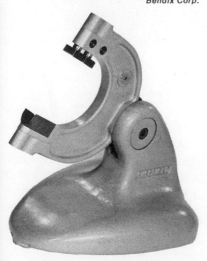

*Automation and Measurement Div.,
Bendix Corp.*

52–17. Plain ring gage.

*Automation and Measurement Div.,
Bendix Corp.*

52–18. Taper ring gage.

*Automation and Measurement Div.,
Bendix Corp.*

52–19. Plain cylindrical plug gage.

52–20. Plain cylindrical taper plug
gages with and without tang.

*Automation and Measurement Div.,
Bendix Corp.*

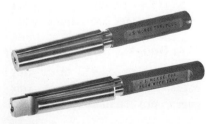

checking external diameters of
parts. 52–17.

Plain ring gages are in the
form of a cylindrical ring and
are used for checking external
diameters of straight round parts.
They are made in pairs and the
no-go ring is used to check the
minimum size limit while the go
ring, the maximum size limit. If
both rings pass over the workpiece, it is undersize. If neither
does, the workpiece is oversize.

Taper ring gages are used for
checking the diameter and the
amount of external cylindrical

taper on parts such as reamers,
drills, lathe centers, and other
tapered products. 52–18.

Plug Gages

Three types of plug gages
commonly used are: (1) plain
cylindrical, (2) cylindrical taper,
and (3) thread plug gages.

Plain cylindrical plug gages
are used for checking size limits
of straight cylindrical holes. 52–
19. The gage may be either the
single-end or double-end type.
The go and no-go are at opposite ends. The go end should
enter the hole with little or no
interference. The no-go gage
should not enter the hole.

Cylindrical taper plug gages
are used for checking the amount

52–21. Thread ring and plug gages.

The Van Kevran Co.

52–22. Thread snap gages.

Johnson Gage Co.

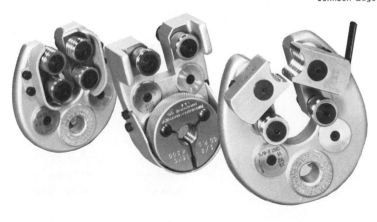

of taper and the size of tapered cylindrical holes, such as in drill sleeves and machine tool spindles. 52–20.

Thread Snap Gages

Three basic thread snap gages for attribute (non-indicating) are shown in the illustration: (1) The ring-snap, which employs segments for go and either rolls or segments for not-go, (2) the roll-snap which employs roll for both go and no-go, and (3) the ring roll-snap, which employs a single pair of rolls for no-go and a threaded ring gage for go. 52–22.

Thread Ring and Plug Gages

The accuracy of an external thread can be checked with a pair of thread ring gages. 52–21. The set includes a go and no-go gage. The go gage is used to check the pitch diameter, lead, flank angle, maximum pitch diameter, and the clearance at the minor diameter simultaneously.

Tapped holes can be checked with a thread plug gage. The illustrations shows a double-end gage with one end go and the other no-go. Both ring and plug thread gages are standardized, with size variations similar to plain ring and plug gages.

As said earlier snap and ring gages are of the adjustable type —can be locked in place with an adjusting screw.

DIAL INDICATOR

Dial indicators are among the most versatile and useful of all measuring instruments, for direct measurement work, checking a production run of parts, transferring heights, setting up ma-chines, inspecting and setting tools and machines, and many other applications. 52–23 (A).

A dial indicator is a comparison instrument showing minute deviations of unknown dimensions (or of a standard) which is usually arbitrarily set to zero on the dial. Dials are calibrated for continuous reading, 0 to 10, 0 to 50, 0 to 100, etc., and many models have count hands which indicate each revolution of the indicating hand. Dials are also calibrated for plus or minus readings in checking size, centering work, and wherever balanced readings are required. 52–23(B).

American Standard Gage Design governs several important dimensions on dial indicators, and provides uniform standards that meet the need for greater accuracy and more universal interchangeability of the dial indicators used on machine tools, jigs, and fixtures.

With the dial indicator it is possible to secure measurement of from one-thousandth to 50 millionth of an inch.

The contact point is attached to a spindle and rack, movement

Brown & Sharpe Mfg. Co.

52–23(A). Dial indicator.

52–23(B). Dial indicator in use.

Brown & Sharpe Mfg. Co.

of which is transmitted to a pinion and then through a train of gears to a hand, which sweeps the dial of the indicator.

The dial indicator has been incorporated in all types of special and standard gaging equipment, as well as in many machine tools. 52–24. Some gages are direct reading, while others serve as comparators showing plus or minus variations in size.

Some uses of the dial indicator are in comparators, on test and magnetic base indicators, dial bore gages (52–25), diameter gages, snap gages, internal groove gages, and many others.

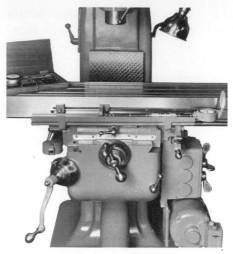

Index Machine Co.

52–24. Rod and indicator set in use on a horizontal milling machine.

52–25. Dial bore gage.

Unit 53.

Air and Electronic Gaging

The science of measurement—metrology—is often called the "keystone science" upon which all technological advances depend.

Not only are we measuring today in tenths and hundredths of thousandths of an inch, but also jobs calling for millionths are no longer a rarity. In the struggle to achieve close part tolerances, air and electronic gaging has become an important part of metrology.

AIR OR PNEUMATIC GAGING

Air gaging is the inspection tool that permits the measurement of many jobs faster, more conveniently, and more accurately than by other gaging methods. In measurement of all hole conditions, air gaging is unsurpassed for speed and accuracy, while in checking any dimensional characteristic, air gages offer sufficient magnification and reliability to measure tolerances well beyond the scope of mechanical gages.

Air gages effectively measure all common types of dimensions but are particularly suited to checking dimensional relationships. Some of these are taper, parallelism, squareness, bend, twist, and center distance.

In air gaging the proximity of a surface is measured by a jet of air directed toward it by a nozzle which never touches it. The restrictive effect as the surface

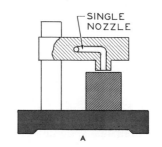

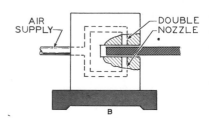

53–1. Nozzle elements: (A) single nozzle type and (B) double nozzle type.

approaches the nozzle has a well-defined relation to the clearance between the two.

Air gages may be classified as having *single-nozzle* and *multiple-nozzle* heads. 53–1. Multiple-

Federal Products Corp.

53–2. Air gage; represents the basic application of air gaging.

nozzle heads are the most widely used.

Air Plug

The most widely used type of air-gaging head is the air plug. The plug usually contains two opposing nozzles to measure internal diameters. A multiple-nozzle head need not be accu-rately centered within the hole it is gaging. Any decrease in the clearance to one nozzle will be compensated for by an increase in the clearance to another, pro-viding the nozzles have identical and linear flow characteristics.

One company manufactures a dimensional air gage that is basi-cally an air pressure type. This air gage has fixed magnification and a balanced air system. 53–2. A linear, calibrated scale gives graduations of definite known values. (See the illustration of the air system.)

To set up the gage, a master is placed on the measuring head (thus restricting the flow). The zero setting valve is then ad-

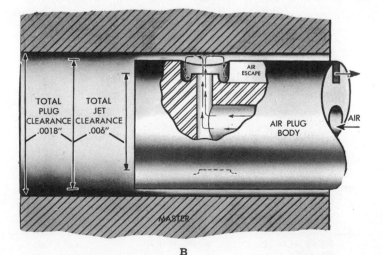

A

53–3. (A) Balanced system of air gaging. (B) Air plug; measuring jets are set deep into the plug body. (C) Air gages measure all common types of dimensions.

Federal Products Corp.

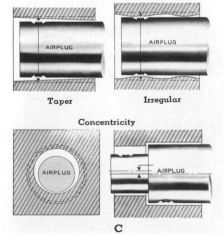

Plugs enter and gage holes of following types easier and faster.

Out-of-round

Taper   Irregular

Concentricity

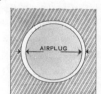

B

Automation and Measurement Div.,
Bendix Corp.

53–4. Pneumatic indicator used with a gaging stand for determining flatness, parallelism, and concentricity.

justed to equalize air pressure in the two channels. When this condition exists, the dial reads zero. No further adjustment is necessary. *Any deviation in the size of the workpiece* from the master size will change the pressure in the measuring leg and produce a change in the meter reading. 53–3 (Page 227).

53–5(A). Electronic comparator.

Automation and Measurement Div.,
Bendix Corp.

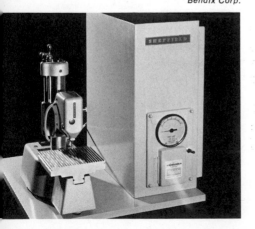

Contact Gaging

Not all air gaging is non-contact. Some gaging heads are equipped with a ball, plunger, lever, or blade which is located between the gaging nozzle and the workpiece. This type of gaging head is used to measure mouths of holes, very rough surfaces, very narrow protuberances, and porous surfaces. 53–4.

Advantages of Air Gaging

An air gage has many advantages over mechanical gages. An air gage can easily determine a size difference of 5 millionths of an inch. The non-contact characteristic of most air measuring units makes them particularly useful for checking soft, highly polished, thin-walled or otherwise delicate material.

Small gage heads and remote reading meters give air gages an advantage in measuring multiple dimensions.

Air gages are readily adaptable to measuring parts in the machine. Their small gage heads make most dimensions accessible and the indicating meter can be located to make it clearly visible. The stream of air tends to clean the measuring area from coolant

or oil, providing a clean measuring area. An expert inspector takes about 43 seconds to measure the inside diameter of a bore with a vernier caliper with an accuracy no closer than .001". of true size, while an *inexperienced* operator can check the same hole with an air plug and be accurate to 10 millionths of an inch in 4 seconds.

ELECTRONIC GAGING

Comparator-type electronic equipment is used in making setups, checking gage blocks, and production gaging and control. Sensitive gaging is needed even with large tolerances, to detect unfavorable trends before limits are exceeded. 53–5 (A&B).

In use, a gage head is positioned to the desired nominal work dimension or position, and a meter on an implifier shows how much the work deviates from nominal size or position.

Gage heads are available for every type of amplification, as regards both measurements and mounting. 53–6. They are used for checking diameter, thickness, height, length, concentricity of two or more diameters, flatness, straightness, and parallelism.

53–5(B). Principles of electronic gaging.
GAGE HEAD

Do All Co.

STANDARD

PART

REFERENCE PLANE   AMPLIFIER   METER

Electronic gaging equipment has to sense size differences as small as 1 millionth of an inch. It can amplify such measurements as much as 100,000 times. 53–7.

A typical electronic gaging system consists of a gaging head mounted on a height gage or comparator stand, plus an amplifier and indicator (sometimes combined). 53–8.

In any gaging system, the fewer the mechanical movements, the greater the reliability. A dial indicator contains a rack, pinion, and gear train. In contrast, an electronic gage head need only translate the change in length movement into an electrical signal which can be read on a meter. 53–9.

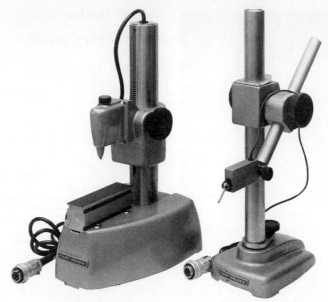

Taft-Pierce Mfg. Co.

53–6. Left: Electronic comparator stand. Right: Electronic height gage.

53–7. Transistorized amplifier.

Taft-Pierce Mfg. Co.

53–8. Electronic comparator.

Taper Micrometer Corp.

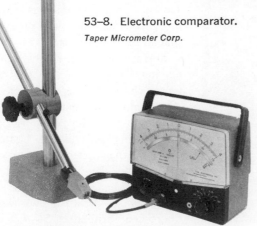

53–9. Electronic limit, no or no-go gage to be used with the electronic comparator.

Taper Micrometer Corp.

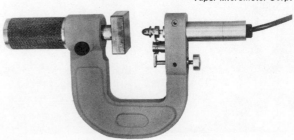

Unit 54.

Inspection and Quality Control

NONDESTRUCTIVE INSPECTION

The inspection and testing of parts has become very important in industry. 54–1. Equipment loads and operating speeds are being stepped up, so it is imperative that fatigue cracks and other flaws in parts be detected before they can result in equipment failure, expense, delay, and possible injury to operating personnel.

MAGNETIC PARTICLE TESTING

Modern inspection has become a manufacturing tool. It has been spurred on by advances in scientific, nondestructive testing.

Magnaflux and its sister process, Magnaflo, developed by the Magnaflux Corporation, are methods of nondestructive testing of magnetic materials, by magnetic particle inspection.

The Magnaflux-Magnaflo process covers practically the entire field of nondestructive testing of magnetic metals in any form.

By inducing a magnetic field within the part to be tested and applying a coating of magnetic particles, surface cracks are made visible, the cracks in effect forming new magnetic poles. A magnetic field is set up electrically within any part or piece of metal. 54–2. When fine particles of magnetic iron are blown (dry method) or flowed in liquid suspension (wet method) on the part, many of them are attracted, "cling" to the crack, and form a definite indication of its exact location, extent, and shape.

FLUORESCENT PENETRANT TESTING

Fluorescent penetrant testing is widely used to find pores, cracks, and crack-like defects in any magnetic solids.

The test's effectiveness is based upon a natural phenomenon—capillary action.

In operation the penetrant solution is applied to a part surface by dipping, spraying, or brushing. It does not "seep" into any defects that may be present. It is literally pulled into them by capillary action. Time is allowed for the penetrant to be drawn into all defects. The length of penetrating time varies with the material being inspected, the processes through which it has passed, and the type of defects expected. The time may be a few seconds or a few minutes. During this time, the part may be placed on a drain rack. 54–3.

Surface penetrant drains away, leaving the penetrant in the defects. The surface is rinsed clean with water and, before or after drying, a wet developer is applied. This acts like a blotter, drawing the penetrant back to the surface.

When inspected under black light, every defect glows with fluorescent brilliance. 54–4.

54–1. Mechanized fluorescent penetrant inspection system.

Howmet Corp., Austenal Microcast Div.

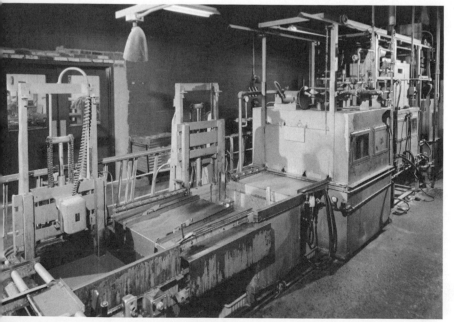

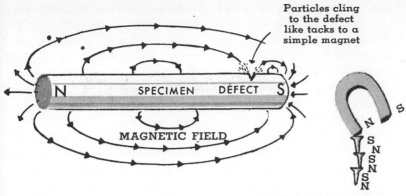

Particles cling
to the defect
like tacks to a
simple magnet

SPECIMEN   DEFECT

MAGNETIC FIELD

By inducing a magnetic field
within the part to be tested, and
applying a coating of magnetic
particles, surface cracks are
made visible, the cracks in effect
forming new magnetic poles.

Magnaflux Corp.

54–2. With the Magnaflux-Magnaglo process, a magnetic field is set up
with any part or piece of metal.

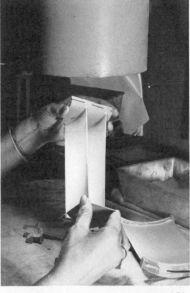

Howmet Corp., Austenal Div.

54–4. Inspection of turbine nozzles
under black light.

54–3. Fluorescent penetrant testing:
(A) Penetrant on the surface is drawn
into the crack by strong capillary
forces. (B) Water spray removes the
penetrant from the outer surface, but
not from cracks or pores. (C) Developer acts like a blotter, to draw the
penetrant out of the crack and hold it
on the surface. (D) Black light causes
the penetrant to glow in the darkened
area.

Magnaflux Corp.

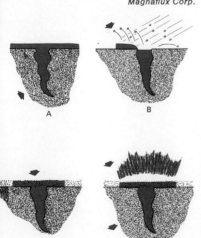

Numerous penetrants, emulsi-
fiers, and developers may be
used in many combinations, depending upon the nature of the
material being tested, type of defects looked for, degree of sensitivity desired, and other factors.
54–5.

ULTRASONIC TESTING

Ultrasonic testing utilizes the
resonant principle, responding to
mechanical resonant frequencies

provided by the test material.
54–6 (Page 232). Heavy-duty
electronic components generate
continuously varying frequencies,
fed to a crystal. Ultrasonic vibrations are emitted from this crystal
into the workpiece through a
couplant such as oil, glycerin, or
soap film. The mechanical resonant frequency of the workpiece
varies with its thickness. When
the constantly varying frequency
encounters this resonance, there

54–5. Inspection reveals cracks as glowing lines, porosity as spots.

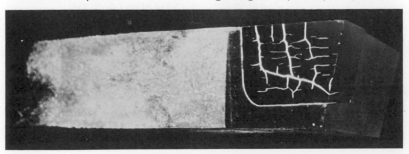

is an electrical charge within the crystal which is sensed by the instrument and displayed as a logarithmically spaced pattern of neon lights in a viewing window covering an arc of 108°.

One portable ultrasonic testing instrument accurately measures the thickness of a wide variety of products. To determine the thickness of a part, the operator selects the correct ranges, applies liquid couplant to the material to be measured, and positions the transducer. He then rotates a harmonic scale disc until division lines coincide most accurately with a flashing light pattern. A circular calibrated scale on the instrument control panel quickly gives the thickness of the workpiece.

PULSE ULTRASONICS

A beam of short ultrasonic pulses of energy "explores" in

54–6. Ultrasonic testing with a reflectoscope.

Mesta Machine Co.

depth the material to be tested. These pulses are generated electronically, then converted into ultrasonic waves by a piezoelectric (pressure-induced polarity) transducer. 54–7. The waves are transmitted into the workpiece either by contact or immersion through a liquid couplant.

The pulses are reflected from opposite walls or discontinuities in the workpiece. A crystal generates a signal on receiving them. A cathode ray tube measures the time lag between the initial signals and the returning ones and appears as pips on a CRT screen.

X-RAY AND GAMMA-RAY TESTING

X-ray is employed to photograph materials to determine the presence of hidden fissures, cracks, and other defects. 54–8. Welds have been inspected by X-ray for many years. However, costs can run very high per foot of weld inspected, and the area must be cleared of all personnel because of radiation hazards. This can mean production delays and excessive production costs. However, many products can be inspected by this method.

NOTE: Ultrasonic testing of welds is rapidly taking the place of X-ray testing.

FUNDAMENTALS OF QUALITY CONTROL

Most books and articles that deal with the specifics of quality control and reliability are long on statistics and analysis. This unit, therefore, endeavors to present the fundamentals of quality control in a more direct manner.

Inspection is conducted after the part has been produced. Inspection does not necessarily improve the quality of the product but does serve as a process that separates the acceptable parts from those that do not meet certain standards.

Quality control was greatly stimulated by World War II when high-production runs of low-tolerance parts posed an inspection problem and steps were taken to prevent product defects.

54–7. (A) Pulse ultrasonics. (B) Resonant wave ultrasonics.

Magnaflux Corp.

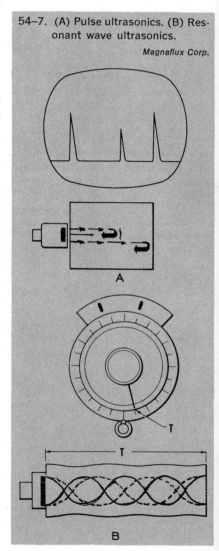

The purpose of modern quality control is to produce parts of high quality without the percentage of rejections that occur during inspection.

Methods of Controlling Quality

A successful quality control program can be based upon four things:

1. Monitoring the industrial process.
2. Control chart.
3. Control and measurement of process.
4. Sampling.

Monitoring the Industrial Process

In planning a product, a great deal of time is spent from the

54–8. Inspection with 1-million-volt X-ray unit.

Howmet Corp., Austenal Div.

concept stage to specifications for the product and construction of drawings. All this usually includes a great deal of research and development. Information acquired must include details concerning materials, part sizes, functions, and sometimes even color of the product.

After all this information is assembled, the management may have to make a decision as to whether to make certain parts or job them out to other plants for construction. No one plant is normally set up to make everything from jet engines to delicate gages and control instruments. Due to this fact, specific information regarding the construction of parts must be given the companies which are awarded contracts.

The prevention of defects must begin early in the production stage to eliminate costly "throwouts" at the inspection stage. 54–9. The diagram broadly traces the product from its early planning stage to the final testing of the part. A true monitoring system would have all details plotted with tests and inspections.

Control Chart Method

The control chart method makes use of statistics to predict future product quality. However, these statistics should be used as a valuable helping tool, not as a magic technique in solving quality control.

The first step that should be taken in laying out a chart is the gathering of well-founded data. The chart is developed with the thought that parts are to be in-

spected according to *variations that occur from desired dimensions,* so that the dimensions to be controlled can be evaluated on a continuous scale through measurable means.

It is possible to predict with some measure of accuracy what *won't* happen in the variation of a particular piece of equipment or process.

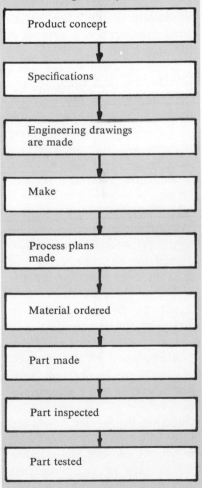

54–9. Chart showing a product from its early planning stage to final testing of the part.

Product concept

Specifications

Engineering drawings are made

Make

Process plans made

Material ordered

Part made

Part inspected

Part tested

If a surface grinder is designed to grind parts to a plus or minus 0.025", there is little use trying to grind parts to an accuracy of 0.001" with this machine. A prediction can be made that a large percentage of the parts won't be according to specifications. By compiling data based on all past experience on equipment and processes, a chart can be established for variations that occur in future products.

Control and Measurement

Controlling the process itself is important in quality management. If the process is controlled, the spoilage of parts can be reduced considerably. A process is a written-down, proved method of doing certain jobs the same accurate way each time.

In controlling a process, it is important to train workers to follow the process and at the same time measure their success (variation), so as to determine in advance how good the product will be.

An absolutely correct process is important. A specific method has to be adapted and rigidly adhered to. The equipment and tools must be adequate for the job and people must be properly trained to do the job. Each worker has to be identified with the task that he performs. Then, upon inspection of the product, the defects can be charged to the specific worker and a determination made as to the need for retraining of the worker or change in procedure. If all the variables are controlled, the process has more chance of being repeated successfully each time.

A good process control laboratory eliminates many problems.

Sampling Method for Quality Control

In quality control a combination of frequency charting and initial charting is favored today. In older inspection methods, parts were either "good" or "bad," according to whether or not they met specifications. It meant a 100% detail inspection of every part.

A sampling inspection is conducted by run-of-the-product to judge part quality so that the lot may be either accepted or rejected. This sampling inspection must be efficient, accurate, and economical.

There are several different sampling plans. In one typical plan, a sample of a predetermined number of parts is taken from a lot of adequate size. The number of rejected parts in the sample determines whether the lot will be acceptable or rejected. Sometimes it may become necessary to take two or more samples to make a decision.

In spite of all methods used to prevent product defects, some do occur. Good quality control determines how serious the descrepancy is, the cause, and who is responsible. After that, steps can be taken to assure that the defects do not occur again. The information gathered can be traced back to the source.

Controls and measurements must be checked and rechecked to make quality control effective. It must be remembered always that quality control is set up for the detection and prevention of product defects.

TOLERANCE AND ALLOWANCE

Tolerance is the amount a part may differ in size from the basic dimension and still be acceptable. The tolerance is the difference between the minimum and the maximum acceptable size limits for a given dimension.

It is necessary to add tolerance figures to a dimension so as to establish the degree of accuracy required in the part. The drawing for the part should give the size limits or tolerance, and parts which are to be interchangeable must be produced within certain size limits.

There are two type of tolerances, unilateral and bilateral. (1) A unilateral tolerance means that any variation is made in only one direction from the basic dimension. If the part calls for a dimension of $2.500 \pm \begin{smallmatrix} 0.005 \\ 0.000 \end{smallmatrix}$, which provides for a range of 0.005" in one direction, all parts in this range would then be acceptable. (2) A bilateral tolerance gives the basic size and the permissible variation in each direction. For example, 2.500" $\pm$ 0.005", means that the basic dimension of 2.500" may vary in either direction by 0.005".

Allowance is frequently confused with tolerance. However it has an altogether different meaning. Allowance is the minimum clearance space intended between mating parts necessary to secure a specific class fit.

The unilateral system is the most widely used by most manufacturing concerns. The reason is that it permits changing the tolerance while still retaining the same allowance or type of fit.

The Metric System of Measure

The metric system was developed in France during the last part of the 18th century. Most nations in Europe, Central, and South America adopted it for commercial use during the middle and last half of the 19th century. Following World War II the Soviet Union and China made the use of metric units mandatory. India and Japan followed in the 1950's. Britain began a ten-year conversion to the metric system in 1965, and within recent years, the remaining major nations of the British Commonwealth made commitments to metricate.

Use of the metric system in the United States was made legal but not mandatory by an act of Congress in 1866.

Several bills which would have made use of the metric system mandatory failed in Congress by very small margins during the first thirty years of this century.

In August, 1968, Congress passed a bill authorizing the Secretary of Commerce to conduct a program of investigation to determine the impact on this country of the worldwide use of metric units and to determine what action should be taken by the United States.

During the summer and fall of 1970, seven metric study conferences were held. At the conclusion of the three-year study, a report was submitted to Congress. The conclusion of the study was that in time the United States will join the rest of the world in the use of the metric system as the predominant common language of measurement.

ADOPTION OF THE METRIC SYSTEM

It will be to the advantage of the United States in all sectors of the economy to adopt metric units. Most scientific research is now conducted with metric units. The pharmaceutical industry is using metric units in the production and marketing of their products. Many hospitals have converted to the use of metric units for dispensing drugs and other uses. The United States Army, Coast Guard, and Geodetic Survey are using the system in some instances.

The complete change to metric units by industry will be costly. However, by using an orderly replacement of outdated equipment over a long period of time, the cost can be reduced. The adoption of the metric system by industry does not involve a complete change of industrial standards, since many ANSI and SAE standards are recognized as world standards by the ISO (International Organization for Standardization).

A number of large American corporations with overseas plants and markets have adopted the use of dual dimensioning (using both millimetres and inches) on new engineering drawings. This is a step toward the use of SI units (Système International d' Unités). One large tractor manufacturer now designs with metric modules of 1 and 0.5 millimetres.

ADVANTAGES OF THE METRIC SYSTEM

● There can be a savings made in teaching only the metric system in our elementary schools. As much as 25% of the time spent in teaching arithmetic could be saved by the elimination of most common fractions and complicated units of measure.

● The consumer/buyer would benefit since price comparison of packages would be simplified.

● The advantages of modular coordinated planning can be fully realized in architecture and building construction by use of the 100 millimetre basic module.

● American motor mechanics already own metric wrenches for work on imported vehicles. They have found them easier to use, since each wrench size is in whole numbers instead of fractions of inches.

● It is a fact that 90% of the world's people use the metric system; over 65% of all world production and trade is metric.

The metric system should be learned as a new and interesting language. One must learn to judge and think in metric units. However, during the period of changeover to metric, it will be necessary to make conversions. This can be done by multiplying the U.S. customary value by its equivalent value in metric units or by reference to dual-dimensioned monograms or conversion charts.

METRIC UNITS

The three main units—metre, liter, and gram—can be changed to more convenient sized units for specific purposes by means of several well known prefixes. Milli means 1/1000; centi means 1/100; deci means 1/10; and kilo means 1000. One merely learns the main units and the value of the most commonly used prefixes. The symbols for metric units are the same for single and plural amounts and are not followed by a period. Rates are usually shown by use of the slash, as in m/s.

DUAL DIMENSIONING*

Many manufacturing plants in the United States have been dimensioning their drawings to show decimal equivalents in place of fractions for some time. Some firms are also converting the decimal dimensions to millimetres and are showing both the English inch dimension as well as the metric. This system is known as "dual dimensioning."

Plants in the U.S.A. such as R.C.A., Westinghouse, International Harvester, Caterpillar Tractor, Deere & Company, and Clark Equipment have been using dual dimensioning for several years.

Dual Dimensioning Explained

The unit of measurement on all metric drawings is the millimetre (mm). Most firms that are using dual dimensioning on their present drawings show metric sizes above the dimension line and inch dimensions below. 55–1 and 55–2.

$$\frac{72 \pm 0.1mm}{2.835 \pm .004''}$$

Some plants use a slash (/) to separate the metric dimension from the inch.

$$72 \pm 0.1/2.835 \pm .004''$$

The metric equivalent should be shown first. The decimal sign (dot) for metric values is the

Table 55-A. Metric Units

Quantity	Unit	Symbol	Relationship of Units	
Length	millimetre	mm	1 mm	= 0.001 m
	centimetre	cm	1 cm	= 10 mm
	decimetre	dm	1 dm	= 10 cm
	metre	m	1 m	= 100 cm
	kilometre	km	1 km	= 1 000 m
Area	square centimetre	cm²	1 cm²	= 100 mm²
	square decimetre	dm²	1 dm²	= 100 cm²
	square metre	m²	1 m²	= 100 dm²
	are	a	1 a	= 100 m²
	hectare	ha	1 ha	= 100 a
	square kilometre	km²	1 km²	= 100 ha
Volume	cubic centimetre	cm³	1 cm³	= 0.0001 l
	milliliter	ml	1 ml	
	cubic decimetre	dm³	1 dm³	= 1 000 ml
	liter	l	1 l	
	cubic metre	m³	1 m³	= 1 000 l
Mass*	milligram	mg	1 mg	= 0.001 g
	gram	g	1 g	= 1 000 mg
	kilogram	kg	1 kg	= 1 000 g
	metric ton	t	1 t	= 1 000 kg

The underlined units in the above table are basic or derived units of the International System of Units (SI).

* Mass is a quantity or aggregate of matter, whereas weight is a force—earth's attraction for a given mass. Generally, however, we think of the term mass as a weight value.

55–1. A typical dual-dimensioned drawing.

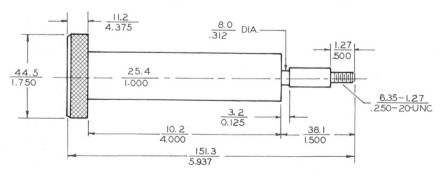

$$\frac{MILLIMETRE}{INCH} \text{ OR MILLIMETRE} / INCH$$

---

* Extracted from *U.S.A. Goes Metric*, Beloit Tool Corp., 1970.

same as now used for the inch decimal dimension.

You will note that the above examples show equal bilateral tolerancing ($\pm$). Unequal bilateral tolerances would be shown as follows:

$$\text{Metric} = 72 \begin{array}{c} + 0.08 \\ - 0.03 \end{array}$$

$$\text{Inch} = 2.835'' \begin{array}{c} + .003'' \\ - .001'' \end{array}$$

Unilateral tolerances are shown as follows:

$$\text{Metric} = 72 \begin{array}{c} + 0.1 \\ - 0 \end{array}$$

$$\text{Inch} = 2.835'' \begin{array}{c} + .004'' \\ - .000'' \end{array}$$

In the metric system, a decimal point is never used with a whole number. A zero "0" is used for metric dimensions of less than one millimeter which is placed to the left of the decimal point. For example, point 3 millimeter should be written 0.3 mm instead of just .3 mm. A comma is never used to show thousands. Use a space instead.

1,500 pieces is shown as 1 500. 8,000 rpm is shown as 8 000 rpm.

In the inch system, nonsignificant zeros are usually to the right of

55–2. Customary method of dimensioning a drawing using fractions. Both drawings are the same except B uses the metric system of dimensioning.

the decimal point so as to have the same number of digits in both the dimension and the tolerance.

$$2.8055'' \pm .0050''$$

In the metric system, nonsignificant zeros are not added to the right of the decimal point. This means the dimension and the tolerance may or may not have the same number of digits

Table 55-B. Metric Conversion Table*			
Millimetres	$\times$	.03937	= Inches
Millimetres	=	25.400	$\times$ Inches
Metres	$\times$	3.2809	= Feet
Metres	=	.3048	$\times$ Feet
Kilometres	$\times$	.621377	= Miles
Kilometres	=	1.6093	$\times$ Miles
Square centimetres	$\times$	.15500	= Square inches
Square centimetres	=	6.4515	$\times$ Square inches
Square metres	$\times$	10.76410	= Square feet
Square metres	=	.09290	$\times$ Square feet
Square kilometres	$\times$	247.1098	= Acres
Square kilometres	=	.00405	$\times$ Acres
Hectares	$\times$	2.471	= Acres
Hectares	=	.4047	$\times$ Acres
Cubic centimetres	$\times$	.061025	= Cubic inches
Cubic centimetres	=	16.3866	$\times$ Cubic inches
Cubic metres	$\times$	35.3156	= Cubic feet
Cubic metres	=	.02832	$\times$ Cubic feet
Cubic metres	$\times$	1.308	= Cubic yards
Cubic metres	=	.765	$\times$ Cubic yards
Liters	$\times$	61.023	= Cubic inches
Liters	=	.01639	$\times$ Cubic inches
Liters	$\times$	.26418	= U. S. gallons
Liters	=	3.7854	$\times$ U. S. gallons
Grams	$\times$	15.4324	= Grains
Grams	=	.0648	$\times$ Grains
Grams	$\times$	.03527	= Ounces, avoirdupois
Grams	=	28.3495	$\times$ Ounces, avoirdupois
Kilograms	$\times$	2.2046	= Pounds
Kilograms	=	.4536	$\times$ Pounds
Kilograms per square centimetre	$\times$	14.2231	= Pounds per square inch
Kilograms per square centimetre	=	.0703	$\times$ Pounds per square inch
Kilograms per cubic metre	$\times$	.06243	= Pounds per cubic foot
Kilograms per cubic metre	=	16.01890	$\times$ Pounds per cubic foot
Metric tons (1,000 kilograms)	$\times$	1.1023	= Tons (2,000 pounds)
Metric tons	=	.9072	$\times$ Tons (2,000 pounds)
Kilowatts	$\times$	1.3405	= Horse-power
Kilowatts	=	.746	$\times$ Horse-power
Calories	$\times$	3.9683	= B. T. units
Calories	=	.2520	$\times$ B. T. units

* L. S. Starrett Company

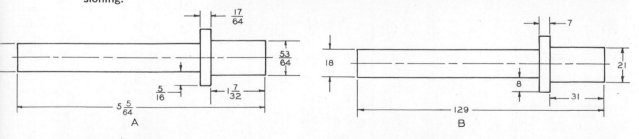

A   B

Table 55-C. Conversion Chart Inch/mm*

(In some parts of the world, the comma is used in place of the decimal point in the metric system. Note: this use of the comma in the millimetre dimensions throughout this chart.)

Drill No. or Letter		Inch	mm
		.001	0,0254
		.002	0,0508
		.003	0,0762
		.004	0,1016
		.005	0,1270
		.006	0,1524
		.007	0,1778
		.008	0,2032
		.009	0,2286
		.010	0,2540
		.011	0,2794
		.012	0,3048
80	.0135	.013	0,3302
79	.0145	.014	0,3556
		.015	0,3810
	1/64	.0156	0,3969
78		.016	0,4064
		.017	0,4318
77		.018	0,4572
		.019	0,4826
76		.020	0,5080
75		.021	0,5334
74	.0225	.022	0,5588
		.023	0,5842
73		.024	0,6096
72		.025	0,6350
71		.026	0,6604
		.027	0,6858
70		.028	0,7112
69	.0292	.029	0,7366
		.030	0,7620
68		.031	0,7874
	1/32	.0312	0,7937
67		.032	0,8128
66		.033	0,8382
		.034	0,8636
65		.035	0,8890
64		.036	0,9144
63		.037	0,9398
62		.038	0,9652
61		.039	0,9906
		.0394	1,0000
60		.040	1,0160
59		.041	1,0414
58		.042	1,0668
57		.043	1,0922
		.044	1,1176
		.045	1,1430
56	.0465	.046	1,1684
	3/64	.0469	1,1906
		.047	1,1938
		.048	1,2192
		.049	1,2446
		.050	1,2700
		.051	1,2954
55		.052	1,3208
		.053	1,3462
		.054	1,3716
54		.055	1,3970
		.056	1,4224
		.057	1,4478
		.058	1,4732
53	.0595	.059	1,4986
		.060	1,5240
		.061	1,5494
		.062	1,5748
	1/16	.0625	1,5875
		.063	1,6002
52	.0635	.064	1,6256
		.065	1,6510
		.066	1,6764
51		.067	1,7018
		.068	1,7272
		.069	1,7526
50		.070	1,7780
		.071	1,8034
		.072	1,8288
49		.073	1,8542
		.074	1,8796
		.075	1,9050
48		.076	1,9304
		.077	1,9558
47	.0785	.078	1,9812
	5/64	.0781	1,9844
		.0787	2,0000
		.079	2,0066
		.080	2,0320
46		.081	2,0574
45		.082	2,0828
		.083	2,1082
		.084	2,1336
		.085	2,1590
44		.086	2,1844
		.087	2,2098
		.088	2,2352
43		.089	2,2606
		.090	2,2860
		.091	2,3114
		.092	2,3368
42	.0935	.093	2,3622
	3/32	.0937	2,3812
		.094	2,3876
		.095	2,4130
41		.096	2,4384
		.097	2,4638
40		.098	2,4892
39	.0995	.099	2.5146
		.100	2.5400

Drill No. or Letter		Inch	mm
38	.1015	.101	2,5654
		.102	2,5908
		.103	2,6162
37		.104	2,6416
		.105	2,6670
36	.1065	.106	2,6924
		.107	2,7178
		.108	2,7432
		.109	2,7686
	7/64	.1094	2,7781
35		.110	2,7940
34		.111	2,8194
		.112	2,8448
33		.113	2,8702
		.114	2,8956
		.115	2,9210
32		.116	2,9464
		.117	2,9718
		.118	2,9972
		.1181	3,0000
		.119	3,0226
31		.120	3,0480
		.121	3,0734
		.122	3,0988
		.123	3,1242
		.124	3,1496
	1/8	.125	3,1750
		.126	3,2004
		.127	3,2258
30	.1285	.128	3,2512
		.129	3,2766
		.130	3,3020
		.131	3,3274
		.132	3,3528
		.133	3,3782
		.134	3,4036
		.135	3,4290
29		.136	3,4544
		.137	3,4798
		.138	3,5052
		.139	3,5306
28	.1405	.140	3,5560
	9/64	.1406	3,5719
		.141	3,5814
		.142	3,6068
		.143	3,6322
27		.144	3,6576
		.145	3,6830
		.146	3,7084
26		.147	3,7338
		.148	3,7592
25	.1495	.149	3,7846
		.150	3,8100
		.151	3,8354
24		.152	3,8608
		.153	3,8862
23		.154	3,9116
		.155	3,9370
		.156	3,9624
	5/32	.1562	3,9687
22		.157	3,9878
		.1575	4,0000
		.158	4,0132
21		.159	4,0386
		.160	4,0640
20		.161	4,0894
		.162	4,1148
		.163	4,1402
		.164	4,1656
		.165	4,1910
19		.166	4,2164
		.167	4,2418
		.168	4,2672
18	.1635	.169	4,2926
		.170	4,3180
		.171	4,3434
	11/64	.1719	4,3656
		.172	4,3688
17		.173	4,3942
		.174	4,4196
		.175	4,4450
		.176	4,4704
16		.177	4,4958
		.178	4,5212
		.179	4,5466
15		.180	4,5720
		.181	4,5974
14		.182	4,6228
		.183	4,6482
		.184	4,6736
13		.185	4,6990
		.186	4,7244
		.187	4,7498
	3/16	.1875	4,7625
		.188	4,7752
12		.189	4,8006
		.190	4,8260
11		.191	4,8514
		.192	4,8768
10	.1935	.193	4,9022
		.194	4,9276
		.195	4,9530
9		.196	4,9784
		.1969	5,0000
		.197	5,0038
		.198	5,0292
		.199	5,0546
8		.200	5,0800

Drill No. or Letter		Inch	mm
7		.201	5,1054
		.202	5,1308
		.203	5,1562
	13/64	.2031	5,1594
6		.204	5,1816
5	.2055	.205	5,2070
		.206	5,2324
		.207	5,2578
		.208	5,2832
4		.209	5,3086
		.210	5,3340
		.211	5,3594
		.212	5,3848
3		.213	5,4102
		.214	5,4356
		.215	5,4610
		.216	5,4864
		.217	5,5118
		.218	5,5372
	7/32	.2187	5,5562
		.219	5,5626
		.220	5,5880
2		.221	5,6134
		.222	5,6388
		.223	5,6642
		.224	5,6896
		.225	5,7150
		.226	5,7404
		.227	5,7658
1		.228	5,7912
		.229	5,8166
		.230	5,8420
		.231	5,8674
		.232	5,8928
		.233	5,9182
A		.234	5,9436
	15/64	.2344	5,9531
		.235	5,9690
		.236	5,9944
		.2362	6,0000
		.237	6,0198
B		.238	6,0452
		.239	6,0706
		.240	6,0960
		.241	6,1214
C		.242	6,1468
		.243	6,1722
		.244	6,1976
		.245	6,2230
D		.246	6,2484
		.247	6,2738
		.248	6,2992
		.249	6,3246
E	1/4	.250	6,3500
		.251	6,3754
		.252	6,4008
		.253	6,4262
		.254	6,4516
		.255	6,4770
		.256	6,5024
F		.257	6,5278
		.258	6,5532
		.259	6,5786
		.260	6,6040
G		.261	6,6294
		.262	6,6548
		.263	6,6802
		.264	6,7056
		.265	6,7310
	17/64	.2656	6,7469
H		.266	6,7564
		.267	6,7818
		.268	6,8072
		.269	6,8326
		.270	6,8580
		.271	6,8834
I		.272	6,9088
		.273	6,9342
		.274	6,9596
		.275	6,9850
		.2756	7,0000
		.276	7,0104
J		.277	7,0358
		.278	7,0612
		.279	7,0866
		.280	7,1120
K		.281	7,1374
	9/32	.2812	7,1437
		.282	7,1628
		.283	7,1882
		.284	7,2136
		.285	7,2390
		.286	7,2644
		.287	7,2898
		.288	7,3152
		.289	7,3406
L		.290	7,3660
		.291	7,3914
		.292	7,4168
		.293	7,4422
		.294	7,4676
M		.295	7,4930
		.296	7,5184
	19/64	.2969	7,5406
		.297	7,5438
		.298	7,5692
		.299	7,5946
		.300	7,6200

Drill No. or Letter		Inch	mm
		.301	7,6454
N		.302	7,6708
		.303	7,6962
		.304	7,7216
		.305	7,7470
		.306	7,7724
		.307	7,7978
		.308	7,8232
		.309	7,8486
		.310	7,8740
		.311	7,8994
		.312	7,9248
	5/16	.3125	7,9375
		.313	7,9502
		.314	7,9756
		.3150	8,0000
		.315	8,0010
O		.316	8,0264
		.317	8,0518
		.318	8,0772
		.319	8,1026
		.320	8,1280
		.321	8,1534
		.322	8,1788
P		.323	8,2042
		.324	8,2296
		.325	8,2550
		.326	8,2804
		.327	8,3058
		.328	8,3312
	21/64	.3281	8,3344
		.329	8,3566
		.330	8,3820
		.331	8,4074
Q		.332	8,4328
		.333	8,4582
		.334	8,4836
		.335	8,5090
		.336	8,5344
		.337	8,5598
		.338	8,5852
R		.339	8,6106
		.340	8,6360
		.341	8,6614
		.342	8,6868
		.343	8,7122
	11/32	.3437	8,7312
		.344	8,7376
		.345	8,7630
		.346	8,7884
		.347	8,8138
S		.348	8,8392
		.349	8,8646
		.350	8,8900
		.351	8,9154
		.352	8,9408
		.353	8,9662
		.354	8,9916
		.3543	9,0000
		.355	9,0170
		.356	9,0424
		.357	9,0678
T		.358	9,0932
		.359	9,1186
	23/64	.3594	9,1281
		.360	9,1440
		.361	9,1694
		.362	9,1948
		.363	9,2202
		.364	9,2456
		.365	9,2710
		.366	9,2964
		.367	9,3218
U		.368	9,3472
		.369	9,3726
		.370	9,3980
		.371	9,4234
		.372	9,4488
		.373	9,4742
		.374	9,4996
	3/8	.375	9,5250
		.376	9,5504
V		.377	9,5758
		.378	9,6012
		.379	9,6266
		.380	9,6520
		.381	9,6774
		.382	9,7028
		.383	9,7282
		.384	9,7536
		.385	9,7790
W		.386	9,8044
		.387	9,8298
		.388	9,8552
		.389	9,8806
		.390	9,9060
	25/64	.3906	9,9219
		.391	9,9314
		.392	9,9568
		.393	9,9822
		.3937	10,0000
		.394	10,0076
		.395	10,0330
		.396	10,0584
X		.397	10,0838
		.398	10,1092
		.399	10,1346
		.400	10,1600

Drill No. or Letter		Inch	mm
		.401	10,1854
		.402	10,2108
		.403	10,2362
Y		.404	10,2616
		.405	10,2870
		.406	10,3124
	13/32	.4062	10,3187
		.407	10,3378
		.408	10,3632
		.409	10,3886
		.410	10,4140
		.411	10,4394
		.412	10,4648
Z		.413	10,4902
		.414	10,5156
		.415	10,5410
		.416	10,5664
		.417	10,5918
		.418	10,6172
		.419	10,6426
		.420	10,6680
		.421	10,6934
	27/64	.4219	10,7156
		.422	10,7188
		.423	10,7442
		.424	10,7696
		.425	10,7950
		.426	10,8204
		.427	10,8458
		.428	10,8712
		.429	10,8966
		.430	10,9220
		.431	10,9474
		.432	10,9728
		.433	10,9982
		.4331	11,0000
		.434	11,0236
		.435	11,0490
		.436	11,0744
		.437	11,0998
	7/16	.4375	11,1125
		.438	11,1252
		.439	11,1506
		.440	11,1760
		.441	11,2014
		.442	11,2268
		.443	11,2522
		.444	11,2776
		.445	11,3030
		.446	11,3284
		.447	11,3538
		.448	11,3792
		.449	11,4046
		.450	11,4300
		.451	11,4554
		.452	11,4808
		.453	11,5062
	29/64	.4531	11,5094
		.454	11,5316
		.455	11,5570
		.456	11,5824
		.457	11,6078
		.458	11,6332
		.459	11,6586
		.460	11,6840
		.461	11,7094
		.462	11,7348
		.463	11,7602
		.464	11,7856
		.465	11,8110
		.466	11,8364
		.467	11,8618
		.468	11,8872
	15/32	.4687	11,9062
		.469	11,9126
		.470	11,9380
		.471	11.9634
		.472	11.9888
		.4724	12,0000
		.473	12,0142
		.474	12,0396
		.475	12,0650
		.476	12,0904
		.477	12,1158
		.478	12,1412
		.479	12,1666
		.480	12,1920
		.481	12,2174
		.482	12,2428
		.483	12,2682
		.484	12,2936
	31/64	.4844	12,3031
		.485	12,3190
		.486	12,3444
		.487	12,3698
		.488	12,3952
		.489	12,4206
		.490	12,4460
		.491	12,4714
		.492	12,4968
		.493	12,5222
		.494	12,5476
		.495	12,5730
		.496	12,5984
		.497	12,6238
		.498	12,6492
		.499	12,6746
	1/2	.500	12,7000

Table 55-C. Conversion Chart Inch/mm (Continued)

Fraction	Inch	mm
	.501	12,7254
	.502	12,7508
	.503	12,7762
	.504	12,8016
	.505	12,8270
	.506	12,8524
	.507	12,8778
	.508	12,9032
	.509	12,9286
	.510	12,9540
	.511	12,9794
	.5118	13,0000
	.512	13,0048
	.513	13,0302
	.514	13,0556
	.515	13,0810
33/64	.5156	13,0968
	.516	13,1064
	.517	13,1318
	.518	13,1572
	.519	13,1826
	.520	13,2080
	.521	13,2334
	.522	13,2588
	.523	13,2842
	.524	13,3096
	.525	13,3350
	.526	13,3604
	.527	13,3858
	.528	13,4112
	.529	13,4366
	.530	13,4620
	.531	13,4874
17/32	.5312	13,4937
	.532	13,5128
	.533	13,5382
	.534	13,5636
	.535	13,5890
	.536	13,6144
	.537	13,6398
	.538	13,6652
	.539	13,6906
	.540	13,7160
	.541	13,7414
	.542	13,7668
	.543	13,7922
	.544	13,8176
	.545	13,8430
	.546	13,8684
35/64	.5469	13,8906
	.547	13,8938
	.548	13,9192
	.549	13,9446
	.550	13,9700
	.551	13,9954
	.5512	14,0000
	.552	14,0208
	.553	14,0462
	.554	14,0716
	.555	14,0970
	.556	14,1224
	.557	14,1478
	.558	14,1732
	.559	14,1986
	.560	14,2240
	.561	14,2494
	.562	14,2748
9/16	.5625	14,2875
	.563	14,3002
	.564	14,3256
	.565	14,3510
	.566	14,3764
	.567	14,4018
	.568	14,4272
	.569	14,4526
	.570	14,4780
	.571	14,5034
	.572	14,5288
	.573	14,5542
	.574	14,5796
	.575	14,6050
	.576	14,6304
	.577	14,6558
	.578	14,6812
37/64	.5781	14,6844
	.579	14,7066
	.580	14,7320
	.581	14,7574
	.582	14,7828
	.583	14,8082
	.584	14,8336
	.585	14,8590
	.586	14,8844
	.587	14,9098
	.588	14,9352
	.589	14,9606
	.590	14,9860
	.5906	15,0000
	.591	15,0114
	.592	15,0368
	.593	15,0622
19/32	.5937	15,0812
	.594	15,0876
	.595	15,1130
	.596	15,1384
	.597	15,1638
	.598	15,1892
	.599	15,2146

Fraction	Inch	mm
	.600	15,2400
	.601	15,2654
	.602	15,2908
	.603	15,3162
	.604	15,3416
	.605	15,3670
	.606	15,3924
	.607	15,4178
	.608	15,4432
	.609	15,4686
39/64	.6094	15,4781
	.610	15,4940
	.611	15,5194
	.612	15,5448
	.613	15,5702
	.614	15,5956
	.615	15,6210
	.616	15,6464
	.617	15,6718
	.618	15,6972
	.619	15,7226
	.620	15,7480
	.621	15,7734
	.622	15,7988
	.623	15,8242
	.624	15,8496
5/8	.625	15,8750
	.626	15,9004
	.627	15,9258
	.628	15,9512
	.629	15,9766
	.6299	16,0000
	.630	16,0020
	.631	16,0274
	.632	16,0528
	.633	16,0782
	.634	16,1036
	.635	16,1290
	.636	16,1544
	.637	16,1798
	.638	16,2052
	.639	16,2306
	.640	16,2560
41/64	.6406	16,2719
	.641	16,2814
	.642	16,3068
	.643	16,3322
	.644	16,3576
	.645	16,3830
	.646	16,4084
	.647	16,4338
	.648	16,4592
	.649	16,4846
	.650	16,5100
	.651	16,5354
	.652	16,5608
	.653	16,5862
	.654	16,6116
	.655	16,6370
	.656	16,6624
21/32	.6562	16,6687
	.657	16,6878
	.658	16,7132
	.659	16,7386
	.660	16,7640
	.661	16,7894
	.662	16,8148
	.663	16,8402
	.664	16,8656
	.665	16,8910
	.666	16,9164
	.667	16,9418
	.668	16,9672
	.669	16,9926
	.6693	17,0000
	.670	17,0180
	.671	17,0434
43/64	.6719	17,0656
	.672	17,0688
	.673	17,0942
	.674	17,1196
	.675	17,1450
	.676	17,1704
	.677	17,1958
	.678	17,2212
	.679	17,2466
	.680	17,2720
	.681	17,2974
	.682	17,3228
	.683	17,3482
	.684	17,3736
	.685	17,3990
	.686	17,4244
	.687	17,4498
11/16	.6875	17,4625
	.688	17,4752
	.689	17,5006
	.690	17,5260
	.691	17,5514
	.692	17,5768
	.693	17,6022
	.694	17,6276
	.695	17,6530
	.696	17,6784
	.697	17,7038
	.698	17,7292
	.699	17,7546
	.700	17,7800

Fraction	Inch	mm
	.701	17,8054
	.702	17,8308
	.703	17,8562
45/64	.7031	17,8594
	.704	17,8816
	.705	17,9070
	.706	17,9324
	.707	17,9578
	.708	17,9832
	.7087	18,0000
	.709	18,0086
	.710	18,0340
	.711	18,0594
	.712	18,0848
	.713	18,1102
	.714	18,1356
	.715	18,1610
	.716	18,1864
	.717	18,2118
	.718	18,2372
23/32	.7187	18,2562
	.719	18,2626
	.720	18,2880
	.721	18,3134
	.722	18,3388
	.723	18,3642
	.724	18,3896
	.725	18,4150
	.726	18,4404
	.727	18,4658
	.728	18,4912
	.729	18,5166
	.730	18,5420
	.731	18,5674
	.732	18,5928
	.733	18,6182
	.734	18,6436
47/64	.7344	18,6532
	.735	18,6690
	.736	18,6944
	.737	18,7198
	.738	18,7452
	.739	18,7706
	.740	18,7960
	.741	18,8214
	.742	18,8468
	.743	18,8722
	.744	18,8976
	.745	18,9230
	.746	18,9484
	.747	18,9738
	.748	18,9992
	.7480	19,0000
	.749	19,0246
3/4	.750	19,0500
	.751	19,0754
	.752	19,1008
	.753	19,1262
	.754	19,1516
	.755	19,1770
	.756	19,2024
	.757	19,2278
	.758	19,2532
	.759	19,2786
	.760	19,3040
	.761	19,3294
	.762	19,3548
	.763	19,3802
	.764	19,4056
	.765	19,4310
49/64	.7656	19,4469
	.766	19,4564
	.767	19,4818
	.768	19,5072
	.769	19,5326
	.770	19,5580
	.771	19,5834
	.772	19,6088
	.773	19,6342
	.774	19,6596
	.775	19,6850
	.776	19,7104
	.777	19,7358
	.778	19,7612
	.779	19,7866
	.780	19,8120
	.781	19,8374
25/32	.7812	19,8433
	.782	19,8628
	.783	19,8882
	.784	19,9136
	.785	19,9390
	.786	19,9644
	.787	19,9898
	.7874	20,0000
	.788	20,0152
	.789	20,0406
	.790	20,0660
	.791	20,0914
	.792	20,1168
	.793	20,1422
	.794	20,1676
	.795	20,1930
	.796	20,2184
51/64	.7969	20,2402
	.797	20,2438
	.798	20,2692
	.799	20,2946

Fraction	Inch	mm
	.800	20,3200
	.801	20,3454
	.802	20,3708
	.803	20,3962
	.804	20,4216
	.805	20,4470
	.806	20,4724
	.807	20,4978
	.808	20,5232
	.809	20,5486
	.810	20,5740
	.811	20,5994
	.812	20,6248
13/16	.8125	20,6375
	.813	20,6502
	.814	20,6756
	.815	20,7010
	.816	20,7264
	.817	20,7518
	.818	20,7772
	.819	20,8026
	.820	20,8280
	.821	20,8534
	.822	20,8788
	.823	20,9042
	.824	20,9296
	.825	20,9550
	.826	20,9804
	.827	21,0058
	.8268	21,0000
	.828	21,0312
53/64	.8281	21,0344
	.829	21,0566
	.830	21,0820
	.831	21,1074
	.832	21,1328
	.833	21,1582
	.834	21,1836
	.835	21,2090
	.836	21,2344
	.837	21,2598
	.838	21,2852
	.839	21,3106
	.840	21,3360
	.841	21,3614
	.842	21,3868
	.843	21,4122
27/32	.8437	21,4312
	.844	21,4376
	.845	21,4630
	.846	21,4884
	.847	21,5138
	.848	21,5392
	.849	21,5646
	.850	21,5900
	.851	21,6154
	.852	21,6408
	.853	21,6662
	.854	21,6916
	.855	21,7170
	.856	21,7424
	.857	21,7678
	.858	21,7932
	.859	21,8186
55/64	.8594	21,8281
	.860	21,8440
	.861	21,8694
	.862	21,8948
	.863	21,9202
	.864	21,9456
	.865	21,9710
	.866	21,9964
	.8661	22,0000
	.867	22,0218
	.868	22,0472
	.869	22,0726
	.870	22,0980
	.871	22,1234
	.872	22,1488
	.873	22,1742
	.874	22,1996
7/8	.875	22,2250
	.876	22,2504
	.877	22,2758
	.878	22,3012
	.879	22,3266
	.880	22,3520
	.881	22,3774
	.882	22,4028
	.883	22,4282
	.884	22,4536
	.885	22,4790
	.886	22,5044
	.887	22,5298
	.888	22,5552
	.889	22,5806
	.890	22,6060
57/64	.8906	22,6219
	.891	22,6314
	.892	22,6568
	.893	22,6822
	.894	22,7076
	.895	22,7330
	.896	22,7584
	.897	22,7838
	.898	22,8092
	.899	22,8346
	.900	22,8600

Fraction	Inch	mm
	.901	22,8854
	.902	22,9108
	.903	22,9362
	.904	22,9616
	.905	22,9870
	.9055	23,0000
	.906	23,0124
29/32	.9062	23,0187
	.907	23,0378
	.908	23,0632
	.909	23,0886
	.910	23,1140
	.911	23,1394
	.912	23,1648
	.913	23,1902
	.914	23,2156
	.915	23,2410
	.916	23,2664
	.917	23,2918
	.918	23,3172
	.919	23,3426
	.920	23,3680
	.921	23,3934
59/64	.9219	23,4156
	.922	23,4188
	.923	23,4442
	.924	23,4696
	.925	23,4950
	.926	23,5204
	.927	23,5458
	.928	23,5712
	.929	23,5966
	.930	23,6220
	.931	23,6474
	.932	23,6728
	.933	23,6982
	.934	23,7236
	.935	23,7490
	.936	23,7744
	.937	23,7998
15/16	.9375	23,8125
	.938	23,8252
	.939	23,8506
	.940	23,8760
	.941	23,9014
	.942	23,9268
	.943	23,9522
	.944	23,9776
	.9449	24,0000
	.945	24,0030
	.946	24,0284
	.947	24,0538
	.948	24,0792
	.949	24,1046
	.950	24,1300
	.951	24,1554
	.952	24,1808
	.953	24,2062
61/64	.9531	24,2094
	.954	24,2316
	.955	24,2570
	.956	24,2824
	.957	24,3078
	.958	24,3332
	.959	24,3586
	.960	24,3840
	.961	24,4094
	.962	24,4348
	.963	24,4602
	.964	24,4856
	.965	24,5110
	.966	24,5364
	.967	24,5618
	.968	24,5872
31/32	.9687	24,6062
	.969	24,6126
	.970	24,6380
	.971	24,6634
	.972	24,6888
	.973	24,7142
	.974	24,7396
	.975	24,7650
	.976	24,7904
	.977	24,8158
	.978	24,8412
	.979	24,8666
	.980	24,8920
	.981	24,9174
	.982	24,9428
	.983	24,9682
	.984	24,9936
	.9843	25,0000
63/64	.9844	25,0031
	.985	25,0190
	.986	25,0444
	.987	25,0698
	.988	25,0952
	.989	25,1206
	.990	25,1460
	.991	25,1714
	.992	25,1968
	.993	25,2222
	.994	25,2476
	.995	25,2730
	.996	25,2984
	.997	25,3238
	.998	25,3492
	.999	25,3746
	1.000	25,4000

*Beloit Tool Corp.

after the decimal point (except for limit dimensions).

$$71.25 \pm 0.127$$

However, when showing limit dimensions in metric, and either the maximum or minimum dimensions have digits after the decimal point, the other value should have zeros added for uniformity.

$$\frac{18}{18.35} \text{ should be } \frac{18.00}{18.35}$$

When showing unequal or bilateral tolerances, both the plus and minus figures should have the same number of decimal places, adding zeros when necessary.

$$18 \begin{matrix} + 0.15 \\ - 0.1 \end{matrix} \text{ should be } 18 \begin{matrix} + 0.15 \\ - 0.10 \end{matrix}$$

The symbol "ϕ" designates a diametral value and should be shown on drawings either before or after the diametral dimension:

$$\phi \frac{25.4}{1.00} \text{ or } \frac{25.4}{1.00} \phi$$

Some machine tools made by American manufacturers can be changed from inch to metric operation by changing the feedback quantizers and making a simple electrical wiring change. Although a switch to change from one system to another is possible, the customers at this time do not feel that the additional cost is warranted. A recent U.S. Air Force study indicated that many machine tools can produce metric parts with little more than the adjustment of a dial, while others require only a minor modification. Since the inch is exactly 2.54 centimetres, it is possible to convert some inch-based machines to metric by using gears with 254 or 127 teeth.

Computers will play an important part in eliminating much of the work that would be involved in translating one measurement language to another. Many machine tools in use today are numerically controlled (controlled by tape). Guidance to metric dimensions needs only a change in the program. However, some types of machine tools will require major changes before they can use the metric system.

The N/C lathe shown here is sold as metric in Europe and with inch dimensioning in this country. 55–3. The change from one system to another is readily made prior to shipment.

Some companies that manufacture measuring tools in this country have available tools that are graduated in metric.

An example is this illustration of a thickness (feeler) gage, with the thickness of the leaves marked in metric sizes. 55–4.

One micrometer shown on this page is graduated in hundredths of a mm, 0 to 13 mm, (0 to ½ inch). 55–5(A).

One American tool company obtains its metric measuring tools for sale in this country from foreign manufacturers. The illustration shows a dual-dimensioned micrometer made in England. 55–5(B). This precision instrument is uniquely designed to provide the capabilities of two micrometers in one. Metric readings to 0.01 mm are in red and inch readings to .0004″ are in black on the actual instrument, eliminating the chance for confusion.

The rule shown here is 15 cm in length and graduated in ½ millimetres and 32nds on one side and on the reverse side in millimetres and 64ths. 55–6.

55–3. "Star" type, metrically arranged lathe that is sold to European companies.

Pratt and Whitney

This method of dual dimensioning a rule makes it possible for the machinist to learn the metric system more easily.

INDUSTRIAL CONVERSION TO THE METRIC SYSTEM*

The Caterpillar Tractor Company began converting to the metric system in the early 1950's when the company began selling sizable quantities of their products overseas. The part books and service information prepared for dealers and customers have listed equivalent metric measurements for inches, feet, gallons, quarts, etc.

This company is using a "soft" conversion. This means the physical size of the products will change little, if at all. No changes will be made from the use of U.S. engineering standards for thread sizes, sheet and plate thicknesses, bar diameters, etc. These standards will all remain the same.

New tooling and gages purchased for manufacturing new parts will have metric calibration. Inch-calibrated machine tools used on current designs will not be replaced until they wear out or become obsolete, according to Caterpillar's engineering department.

All machine tools can be placed in one of two categories: (1) those in which the measurement system of the machine determines the finished dimensions of the workpiece or (2) those in which the finished dimensions of the workpiece are determined by separate gaging equipment (the

dials or scales of the machine are used only for making adjustments).

The first type includes tool room jig borers, jig mills, precision horizontal bar machines, and most tape-controlled machines. If the measuring system of such a machine is in the inch system, the dimensional input to it must be in inches. For a number of years engineering drawings of metric piece parts will carry a chart of inch equivalents of the metric dimensions. This

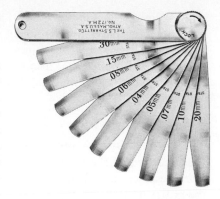

L. S. Starrett Co.

55–4. Thickness gage with leaf thicknesses in hundredths of a millimetre.

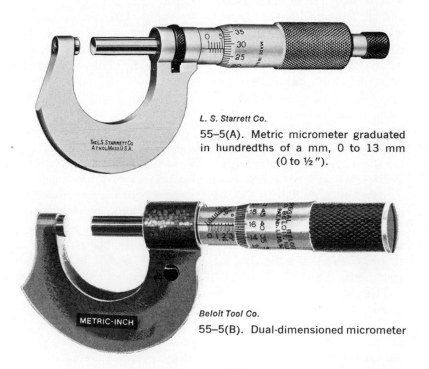

L. S. Starrett Co.

55–5(A). Metric micrometer graduated in hundredths of a mm, 0 to 13 mm (0 to ½ ").

Beloit Tool Co.

55–5(B). Dual-dimensioned micrometer

55–6. A 15-cm steel rule with graduations in metric and English measure.

L. S. Starrett Co.

* Victor Schellschmidt, Supervising Engineer of Planning in Manufacturing, Caterpillar Tractor Co.

will allow toolmaking and numerically-controlled (N/C) tape preparation on existing machines and will permit continued use of such machines used for production work.

Using Conversion Scales

The majority of production machines are of the second type. For these, setups are made with the aid of tool-setting gages, sample parts, tracer templates, or N/C tapes. A trial cut is taken, the piece part is measured with a separate gage or micrometer, and the amount of the required adjustment is determined. If a piece part is metric, the gage used will be metric. However, if a machine has inch calibration, the operator must convert the adjustment value into decimal inches. This does not involve converting piece part dimensions, but only the small adjustment values. Normally, this will be a few hundredths of a millimetre to be converted into thousandths of an inch. This conversion can be instantly done with the aid of a simple conversion scale like the one shown. 55–7.

This scale may be used to make quick—but not highly accurate—conversions from metric to inches. Numbers across the top are metric units; those across the bottom are inch units. Following is a list of conversions you can make with just these two scales.

- Centimetres to inches.
- Millimetres to tenths of an inch.
- Tenths of a millimetre to hundredths of an inch.
- Hundredths of a millimetre to thousandths of an inch.
- Thousandths of a millimetre to ten-thousandths of an inch.

This conversion list must be followed when using this scale.

Most conversions involve three steps:

- Step 1. Find the number you are converting and note its relationship to the other scale. It will usually fall between two numbers on the other scale, so write down the lower of those two numbers. This will be referred to as the *rough conversion*.
- Step 2. Consult the conversion list and express the rough conversion accordingly. (Remember that for metric numbers smaller than one, a zero is placed to the left of the decimal point.)
- Step 3. Refine by adding the desired number of decimal places to the rough conversion.

For example, suppose you want to convert 9 hundredths of a millimetre to some measurement in inches. Proceed as follows:

- Step 1. Note that 9 on the metric scale falls between 3 and 4 on the inch scale. Write down 3 (because it is lower).
- Step 2. The conversion list shows that hundredths of a millimetre convert to thousandths of an inch, so express the rough conversion accordingly—0.003.
- Step 3. Refine to 0.0035, because 9 on the metric scale falls roughly halfway between 3 and 4 on the inch scale.

The above procedure assumes that you are trying to achieve the greatest accuracy possible within the limitations of this method. Sometimes you may want to simplify. For instance, 13 millimetres might be simply converted to half an inch, since the 13 on the metric scale corresponds so closely with the 5 on the inch scale.

Conversions to inch units smaller than 1 might seem confusing at first, but they follow the rules given previously. For example, to convert 2 millimetres, first write down 0, because it is the digit lower than 1. Express it in tenths—.0—as the list shows. Then refine to about 0.075.

Examples given thus far have dealt with converting metric to inch units. The process works equally well in reverse. Thus 4 inches can be converted to about 10.2 centimetres by following the steps given earlier.

Figures larger than those shown on the scales can be converted by the use of simple ratios. Thus 18 millimetres would convert to about 0.7″. This is determined by simply doubling the conversion of 9 millimetres.

55–7. Conversion scale for machine adjustments. The metric units always appear above the line and inch units below the line on the conversion scale.

Caterpillar Tractor Co.

METRIC UNITS

INCH UNITS

Check Your Knowledge

1. Why is the rule a basic measuring tool?

2. Name some uses of a combination set.

3. Why is a solid square more exact than a combination set?

4. Describe the following: (A) firm-joint caliper, (B) spring-joint caliper, and (C) hermaphrodite.

5. What is the chief similarity between dividers and calipers?

6. What is a universal bevel protractor?

7. How many angles are read at each position of a vernier protractor?

8. What is a sine bar? Explain how it is used.

9. What is the typical range of a micrometer?

10. Explain the principal features of a micrometer.

11. Sketch the barrel of a 1" micrometer, reading 0.756.

12. How is higher amplification achieved on a micrometer?

13. What is the principal advantage of a vernier caliper?

14. Of what importance is the reference or support surface upon which height gages are used?

15. Give a brief description of how an optical comparator is used.

16. What is meant by measurement by comparison?

17. What is a toolmaker's microscope used for?

18. What are gage blocks?

19. When does the need for gage blocks become increasingly important?

20. What is a reference plane?

21. What reference surfaces are usually used for inspection purposes?

22. What is interferometry?

23. How are light waves used for measurement?

24. What is an optical flat?

25. How is surface texture determined?

26. What is generally accepted as the most practical, accurate, and economical method of inspecting productive tolerances?

27. What is inspected with no and no-go gages?

28. Why are thread gages made up as go and no-go?

29. Do dial indicators measure the length of parts? Explain.

30. Name some advantages of air gaging.

31. What is the chief unique feature of air gaging?

32. What is an electronic gage?

33. What are the main reasons for using electronic gages?

34. What are the advantages of each of the principal types of nondestructive testing?

35. What is magnetic particle testing?

36. Explain the fluorescent penetrant testing process.

37. Explain the principle of ultrasonic testing.

38. Specifically, what is meant by the term quality control?

39. What advantages does the metric system of measurement have over the customary system?

40. Name six basic units in the International Metric System.

41. What is meant by dual dimensioning?

References

Busch, Ted, *Fundamentals of Dimensional Metrology*, Albany, N.Y., Delmar Publishers, Inc., 1964.

DoAll Company, *How to Use a Surface Plate*, 1966.

DoAll Company, *Precision Measurement*, 1964.

Dodge, D. C., "Non-Destructive Testing," *Mechanical Engineering*, August, 1962.

Dwyer, John J. Jr., "Air and Electronic Gaging," *American Machinist*, Special Report No. 558, October 12, 1964.

Emery, Jackson K., "How to Measure Flatness," *American Machinist*, Special Report No. 591, August 29, 1966.

Heinhold, L. O., Jr., "Electric and Electronic Gages," *The Tool and Manufacturing Engineer*, February, 1967.

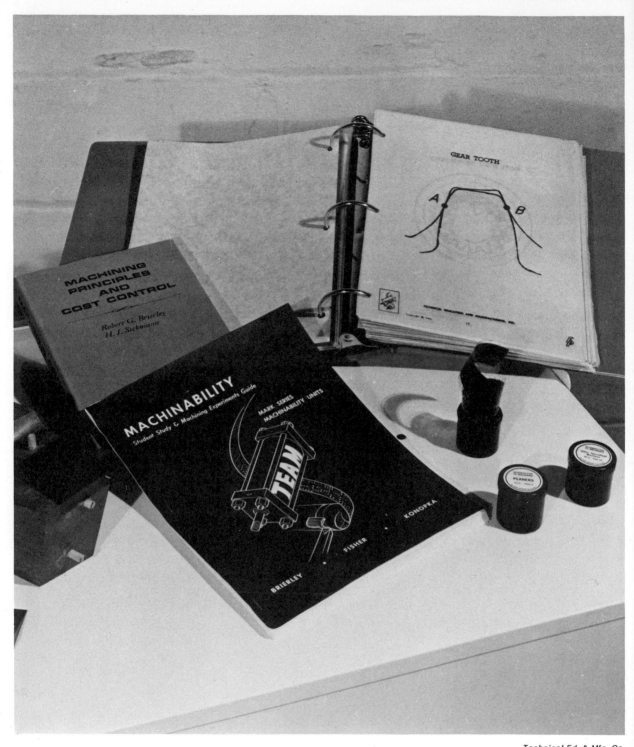

Many instructional materials can be found to help the student learn more about machining.

Section Ten

Changing the Shape of Metals
with Machine Tools

ONCEPTUALLY, all machine tools are basically alike, in that their purpose is to change the shape, finish, or size of a piece of material. No matter what kind of a machine tool it is, it accomplishes this by bringing some type of cutting edge, or edges, into contact with the material to be cut, when one or both are in motion.

There are three factors that determine the contour of the surface produced by any type of cutting action: (1) the line of the cut, (2) the path of consecutive cuts, and (3) the contour of the cut.

The two most essential factors are the line of cut and the path of consecutive cuts. These factors are determined by the motion applied to the tool and workpiece. The results that can be obtained on a particular machine tool are limited very largely by the types of motion it can apply. Regardless of how much machine tools seem to differ, the differences are fundamentally in the method in which motion is applied and controlled to produce the cutting action and the proper sequence of cuts.

Standard types of machine tools may be grouped in six basic classes:

1. Turning machines
2. Milling machines
3. Drilling and boring machines
4. Shapers and planers
5. Sawing and broaching machines
6. Grinding machines

The purpose of each of these machines is the same: to change the shape, size, or finish by removing material from the workpiece. The basic principle of each is the same: applying motion to either the workpiece or the tool while the two are in contact. *Differences:* The type of motion used is different with each machine, and also the way it is applied, and, in some instances, the structure of the tool used.

Turning machines: May differ from each other in many respects. However, the principles of operation are very much the same for all.

Turning machines in normal operations produce a cutting action by rotating the workpiece against the edge of the tool. The line of cut follows the circumference of a circle and the path of the cut is usually a straight path. The result is a surface that curves in one direction and follows a straight line in another direction, producing a form that is basically cylindrical. The turning machine or lathe is a highly adaptable machine tool. With proper adjustments and attachments, the lathe can do most any operation performed on other standard machine tools.

The milling machine: Provides cutting action by rotating the tool while the sequence of cuts is obtained by reciprocating the workpiece. The workpiece is moved in a straight line to obtain a sequence of cuts, so the surface produced will be straight in one direction. Since a multiple-edge tool is used, the surface will naturally conform to the contour of the cutting edges. It follows that the surface, though straight in one direction, may curve in another. A flat surface can be produced if the cutter has straight edges.

Drill press: The cutting action of a drill press is produced by a rotating multiple-edge cutting or boring tool. Consecutive cuts are obtained by advancing the tool downward in a perpendicular direction to the plane of the tool's rotation. The rotating tool produces circular holes in the workpiece. Reamers and boring tools can also be used to finish, enlarge, or taper holes that have already been produced.

The *shaper* and *planer:* Are very much alike in that reciprocating motion is applied to both the tool and workpiece. The basic difference between these two machines is that the planer's cutting action is obtained by reciprocating the workpiece fastened to the bed of the machine, and the sequence of cuts is obtained by reciprocating the tool to the right or left. The shaper's operation is just the reverse.

The surfaces produced by both of these machines will be straight in one direction, while in the other directon they will conform to the shape of the tool's cutting edge. The planer finds its usefulness on large work while the shaper is more efficient on parts having smaller surfaces.

Sawing machines: Are of various types, for taking straight or circular cuts. The power hacksaw uses a reciprocating motion for taking straight cuts. Circular saws have the same cutting action as milling cutters.

Band sawing machines are made to operate in either a horizontal or vertical position. Vertical band sawing machines can cut inside and outside shapes.

Broaching: Employs a tool with a series of teeth which is pulled or pushed over the surface of the workpiece. In some cases, the broach is reciprocated past the work; in others the tool is stationary and the workpiece is reciprocated.

Grinding machines: Are used to finish surfaces produced on other machines. Grinding machines differ from other types in that they use a tool with an abrasive surface which removes material in the form of tiny particles. Either the cutting action is generated by the rotating tool or the workpiece can be rotated. The workpiece can be reciprocated—or the head that rotates the tool reciprocates—to produce the sequence of cuts. In some operations a combination of these may be used. Since the motion producing consecutive cuts is flexible, a properly designed grinding wheel can be used on any metal surface.

Unit 56. Metal Cutting Tools and Cutting Fluids

Probably the most common of all cutting tools is the ordinary lathe tool. It is a single point tool with two cutting edges for side cutting and end cutting.

Orthogonal, single-point (or right angle) cutting will be discussed in this unit. 56–1. It is commonly known as *two-dimensional* cutting. The mechanics of orthogonal cutting is shown in A.

Such a cutting operation also has width as shown in B. The tool cutting edge is perpendicular to V, the cutting velocity vector. (A vector is a line that represents the size of some physical quantity and the direction in space in which this quantity acts.) The plane of any cross section taken through the cutting zone, perpendicular to the finished surface and parallel to the cutting velocity, is identical to the plane as shown in A.

In a lathe turning operation, the cutting velocity vector acts longitudinally to the workpiece, at the cutting tool. The magnitude or *scalor* value of this vector is generally expressed in surface feet per minute.

The velocity of the chip as it leaves the shear plane and the direction it takes in space, relative to the V, as it is deflected by the cutting edge of the tool, is the *chip velocity vector.*

CHIP FORMATION AND CUTTING ACTION

Two fundamental physical processes are involved in all types of metal cutting operations: (1) formation of chips and (2) movement of chips over the face of the tool.

As the cutting tool advances through the workpiece, the metal is sheared in a narrow plane starting at the cutting edge and proceeding at an oblique angle to the surface of the workpiece. Below this shear plane the micro-structure of the metal is undistorted and undeformed. However, above the shear plane the metal has been distorted by an internal-shearing process. (It is in this immediate area that the plastic flow characteristic of metal is important.)

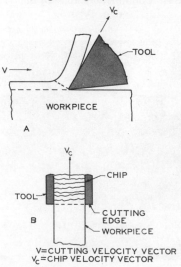

56–1. Diagram of chip formation using a single-point tool.

V=CUTTING VELOCITY VECTOR
V_c=CHIP VELOCITY VECTOR

56–2. Discontinuous segmental chip. Type 1.

56–3. Continuous chip without built-up edge. Type 2.

56–4. Continuous chip with built-up edge. Type 3.

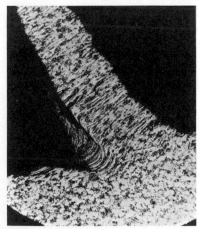

Upon the formation of the chip it tends to slide over the face of the tool and encounters frictional resistance. It is at this point that wear, friction, and lubrication are of major interest.

The chip formed may be one of three distinct types, depending on the type of material being machined and the condition under which it is formed. The three types are:

Type 1—discontinuous or segmental chip. 56–2.

Type 2—continuous chip without built-up edge. 56–3.

Type 3—continuous chip with built-up edge. 56–4.

The type 1 chip is formed when brittle materials are machined, or when certain ductile materials are cut at low speeds. In either case the metal cannot undergo the required amount of shear without rupturing. When machining such metals as cast iron and bronze, the chip consists of individual segments joined loosely to each other. The chip is more easily disposed of, and the finish of the workpiece is best, when pitch of the segments is small. NOTE: If the chip is formed from machining a ductile material, a poor surface finish and excessive tool wear is obtained.

The type 2 chip is formed when the metal is deformed continuously without rupture and flows smoothly over the face of the tool.

This is the ideal chip from the standpoint of quality of finish on the workpiece, temperature of the tool point, and power con-

sumption. The friction between the chip and tool is relatively low. The chip is obtained when machining ductile materials at speeds over 200 feet per minute, using carbide cutting tools, or by the use of effective cutting fluids on harder metals.

The type 3 chip is a continuous chip with built-up edge adjacent to the tool face. This chip is commonly formed in machining ductile material. Very high frictional resistance is encountered as the chip moves up the face of the tool. This results in a shearing away of the metal from the body of the chip and it remains on the face of the tool, producing a built-up edge. Surface finish is not as good as with the type 2 chip.

The chip formation is governed by several factors which include: (1) speed, (2) feed, (3) depth of cut, (4) rake angle, (5) type of metal being machined, and (6) cutting fluid. The finish is rough due to the fragments of built-up edge escaping from the workpiece.

OBTAINING A DESIRED SURFACE FINISH

The quality of surface finish depends a great deal on (1) the freedom with which the cutting tool moves across the workpiece face and (2) the type of chip produced.

The proper type of cutting fluid helps achieve a free moving tool. The proper cutting fluid permits the chip to move across the face of the tool with minimum interference.

The strain-hardenability characteristic of the metal being machined affects the surface finish.

All engineering metals will strain-harden upon being internally sheared or deformed. NOTE: The chip and the part near the surface of the metal being machined will be harder than the original metal.

TOOL SHAPES

In describing tool shapes, a *single-point tool* as applied to a lathe will be used as an example.

A tool is ground to a given form for two reasons: (1) to produce a cutting edge of a given contour located in a given position in relation to the tool's shank and (2) to produce a form that will permit the cutting edge to be fed into the workpiece so that it can cut efficiently. 56–5. The difference in form among tools is required by variations in the degree of *angle* to which the planes involved are ground and in the *radius* to which portions of the cutting edge may be rounded.*

Brief explanations of angles ground on a single-point tool are given below.

Side relief angle is ground back below the cutting edge. It is measured between the ground flank. The side relief angle permits free cutting by preventing the side flank from rubbing against the workpiece. 56–6.

End relief indicates that the nose of the tool has been ground back at an angle sloping down from the end cutting edge angle. End relief concentrates the thrust force exerted on the nose of

_____
* Shell Oil Company, Inc., "Changing the Shape of Metals With an Engine Lathe," 1946.

the tool in a small area adjacent to the end cutting edge.

Side cutting-edge angle is formed by the straight side cutting edge and a line representing the side of the tool shank before grinding. This angle may vary from 0 to 30° depending upon the type of material being machined. An angle of 15° is commonly used for rough turning, while one of 20° is used for general machining purposes.

End cutting-edge angle is formed when the plane at the end of a tool has been ground back at an angle sloping from the nose to the side of the shank, establishing the end angle in relation to the shank. An average

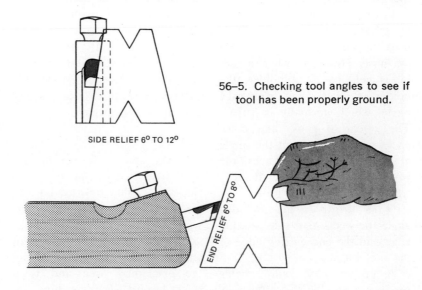

56–5. Checking tool angles to see if tool has been properly ground.

SIDE RELIEF 6° TO 12°

END RELIEF 6° TO 8°

56–6. Nomenclature of right-hand cutting tool.

angle of 15° to 30° can be used, depending upon the material being machined.

Side rake is formed by grinding the top of the tool back at an angle sloping from the side cutting edge. The extent of side rake influences the angle at which the chip leaves the workpiece as it is directed away from the side cutting edge.

Back rake angle is formed by grinding the top of the tool back at an angle sloping from the nose. However, when a tool bit is held by a toolholder, the holder establishes the back rake angle, which normally is 16½°. The extent of back rake influences to a great extent the angle at which the chip leaves the workpiece as it is directed away from the nose of the tool.

Nose angle is the included angle between the side cutting edge and the end cutting edge of the tool bit.

A proper nose radius helps produce a good surface finish. A too sharp-pointed tool has a tendency to groove the path of

the cut. On the other hand, a too large nose radius has a tendency to produce chatter. A radius of $\frac{1}{32}''$ to $\frac{1}{8}''$ is the most often used.

Most lathe cutting tools are ground by hand. The lip or cutting angle varies with the kind of material being cut. A keen cutting edge and good finish on the tool face will minimize the formation of a built-up edge and help secure a good finish on the workpiece. In sharpening high-speed, steel, cutter bits, it is good practice to stone the cutting edge after the cutting edge has been ground.

CHIP BREAKERS

Ductile materials can be cut more freely when relatively steep side-rake angles are used on single-point cutting tools. However, with steep angles, long continuous chips result. This type of chip is difficult to remove from the machining area and is a safety hazard to the machine operator. Also, because chip breakers produce short chips, they permit a better flow of cutting fluid to the tool point.

Three common types of chip breakers are shown. 56–7. The *gullet* type has a groove ground into the rake face of the tool. The *step* type has an offset also ground into the rake face of the tool.

The *screwed on* or clamp-type chip breaker has a block of cemented carbide screwed or clamped on the face of the tool. As the chip is formed, it hits the edge of the plate or block and breaks up into short pieces. However, the Carb-O-Lock principle has eliminated the need of

clamp-type toolholders. 56–8. One of the features of this type of tooling is its inexpensive disposable inserts, with easy indexible multiple edges and built-in chip control which deflects chips and forms an acceptable short helix or figure "9."

TOOL MATERIALS

A cutting tool can be made from a wide variety of materials, depending upon the many conditions imposed upon it.

The hardness of a tool must be greater than that of the material being machined throughout the temperature range to be encountered in the machining operation; yet the degree of hardness has to be controlled to avoid brittleness.

No one single tool material will satisfy all the desirable requirements. The relative importance of each property will vary according to: (1) nature of the finished product, (2) type of operation, (3) volume of production, (4) tool design details, (5) condition of tool, and (6) type of material being machined.

Cutting tool materials may be classified in different ways. One is by the main element, as: carbon steels, medium-alloy steels, high-speed steels, cast alloys, and cemented carbides. Of course iron is the main constituent of the first three.

Carbon Steels

Carbon steel tools have a limited use, as they are characterized by low hot hardness and poor hardenability. Carbon contents range from 0.8% to 1.3%. Tools of this type can be used for light work where tempera-

56–7. Types of chip breakers.

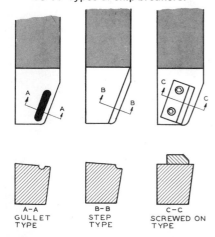

A–A
GULLET
TYPE

B–B
STEP
TYPE

C–C
SCREWED ON
TYPE

tures produced do not exceed 400°F.

MEDIUM-ALLOY STEELS

These steels are not satisfactory for operations where high temperatures are encountered, as in high production. In finishing operations, they can be used successfully.

High-Speed Steels

High-speed steel tools are characterized by superior wear resistance and hot hardness. Tools made of high-speed steel contain up to 18% tungsten and 51½% chromium as the principal alloying elements. Other alloying elements such as molybdenum and cobalt give special qualities. These cutters will retain keen cutting edges at temperatures up to 1100°F. Also, the proper cutting fluids can increase their life and improve use to a considerable extent.

Cast Alloys

A number of nonferrous alloys known as *stellites* have been developed for use as cutting tools. These alloys usually contain 2–4% carbon, 14–29% tungsten, 27–32% chromium, 40–50% cobalt. The tools must be used as cast and cannot be heat-treated. They are not affected by heat up to 1500°F. Although high-speed steel tools are somewhat harder than stellite up to 1000°F., above this temperature stellite retains hardness much better. Higher cutting speeds are actually obtainable with this type of tool than with high-speed steel tools.

The stellites, being cast, have a tendency to shatter under shock and must be well supported in the toolholder. They are tip brazed or welded to a shank of steel or as a removable bit in a special form of toolholder.

Cemented Carbides

Cemented carbide tools are known under trade names such as Carboloy, Kennametal, Vascoloy-Ramet, and Firthite. 56–9 (Page 252).

There are two general grades of metal-cutting cemented carbides in use:

1. The "C" grade. This grade is made up of tungsten carbide with cobalt as a binder. This grade is used in machining cast iron and nonferrous metals.

2. The "S" grade is made up of tungsten, titanium, and tantalum carbides with cobalt as a binder and is used on steels.

The cobalt content may vary from 3% to 16%. The larger the amount of cobalt, the tougher and more wear resistant becomes the tool. The "S" grades usually contain from 0% to 16% titanium carbide and 0% to 10% tantalum carbide. The mean grain size is important, as tools of identical chemical composition but of different grain size will have different properties. Coarser grain material is more shock resistant.

Cemented carbides have: (1) high hardness over a wide range of temperatures, (2) high thermal conductivity, (3) low thermal expansion, and (4) stiffness.

A

B

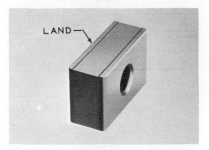

C

General Electric Co.

56–8. Carb-O-Lock design.
(A) "Hevi-Duty" tools are designed for use in heavy machining operations.
(B) Disposable cemented carbide insert and seat are set into toolholder on edge.
(C) Insert has chip control land on each cutting edge for better chip control.
(D) Negative rake tool adjusting insert.

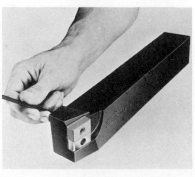

D

Table 56-A. Comparison of Cutting Speeds of High-Speed Steel and Carbide Tools*

Material	Rough	Finish	Rough	Finish
SAE 1020[a]	80–100	100–120	300–400	300–400
SAE 1050[a]	60–80	100	200	200
Stainless[a]	100–120	100–120	240–300	240–300
Gray cast iron	50–60	80–110	350–400	350–400
Semisteel[a]	40–50	69–90	250–300	250–300
Brass (85–5–5)	200–300	200–300	600–1000	600–1000
Bronze (80–10–10)	110–150	150–180	600	1000
Aluminum[b]	400	700	800	1000
Malleable iron[a]	80–110	110–130	250–300	350–400

[a] Water-soluble oil lubricant
[b] Kerosene lubricant
* Warner and Swasey Mfg. Co.

56–9. Patented toolholder and cemented carbides.

General Electric Co.

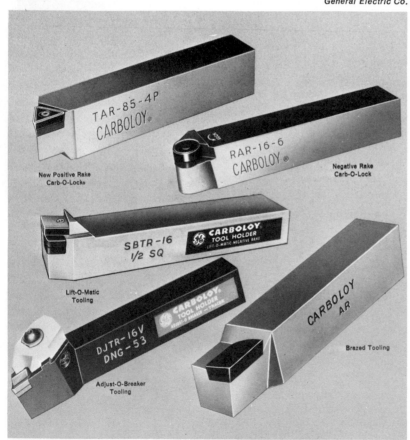

New Positive Rake Carb-O-Locks

Negative Rake Carb-O-Lock

Lift-O-Matic Tooling

Adjust-O-Breaker Tooling

Brazed Tooling

These tools should be used at much higher operating speeds than high-speed steel tools.

MACHINABILITY

"Machinability" is one of the most widely used terms in the machining industry but is the most difficult to define, as it has different meanings to different people at different times.

A part is said to have good machinability if it has a combination of characteristics, allowing for (1) better tool life, (2) better surface finish, (3) satisfactory chip formation and (4) low resistance to cutting force and power. 56–10. The relative importance of these factors depends on the equipment being used, nature of the operation, and the use of the finished part.

The machinability of a metal is governed by its hardness and ductility. Because metal machining problems are very complex, a wide range of machinability may be found in any type of

Table 56-B. Machinability Ratings of Steels*

	Group 1 Machinability Rating, 70 and Above	Group 2 Machinability Rating, 55–70	Group 3 Machinability Rating, Below 55
Carbon steels		C-1016, C-1020, C-1022, C-1025, C-1030, C-1035, C-1040, C-1045	C-1008, C-1010, C-1015, C-1050, C-1055, C-1060, C-1066, C-1070, C-1085, C-1095
Free machining steels	C-1109, C-1110, C-1111, B-1112, B-1113, C-1115, C-1117, C-1118, C-1132, C-1137	C-1141	
Molybdenum steels		A-4023, A-4027, A-4032, A-4037, A-4042, A-4130, A-4137, A-4615	A-4047, A-4063, A-4068, A-4140, A-4145, A-4150, A-4320, A-4340, A-4620, A-4640, A-4815, A-4820
Manganese steels			A-1320, A-1330, A-1335, A-1340
Nickel steels		A-2317	A-2330, A-2340, A-2345, A-2515
Nickel-Chromium steels		A-3120, A-3130	A-3135, A-3140, A-3145, A-3150, A-3240, E-3310
Chromium steels		A-5120, A-5140	A-5150, E-52100
Chromium-Vanadium steels			A-6120, A-6145, E-6150, A-6152
Silicon-Manganese steels			A-9260, A-9255, A-9315
Multiple alloy steels		NE-8024, 8124, 8233, 8245, 8339, 8620, 8624, 8630, 8640, 8645, 8720, 8730, 8739, 8740, 8745, 8817, 9415, 9420, 9425, 9440	NE-8442, 8447, 8650, 8744, 8750, 8949, 9430, 9440, 9450
Iron	Malleable, soft cast, cast steel	Medium cast	Hard cast
Stainless steels		303, 304, 308, 309, 310, 317, 416, 430, 51410, 30615 type 2	301, 302, 321, 347, 410, 414, 420, 430, 431, 440, 441, 446, 30705, 30805, 30905, 30915, 51210, 51310, 51335, 51710, 30615 type 1

*Texaco, Inc.
The machinability ratings are relative values based on a rating of 100% assigned to B-1112 steel when machined under normal conditions.

Group 4
Cast Iron

56–10. Machinability unit which provides instrumentation for learning to read the parameters in testing tool life, material cutting forces, and machining principles.

Technical Ed. & Mfg. Co.

steel. To put any steel into the best structural condition for easy machining operations may require special considerations based upon the type of steel, type of cutting operations, and degree of surface finish required. The grain size, structure, and the proportion of alloying elements are important factors for easy machining.

A soft material might be desirable for long tool life and power consumption but is not always the best type of material for a good surface finish. Annealing of the steel to a specified Brinell hardness might produce a steel with a structure that will produce the easiest machining characteristics but the surface finish might not meet the requirements. (Generally, a better finish is obtained if the steel is heat-treated to make it harder.)

By adding moderate amounts of sulphur and lead, a steel can be obtained that will be free cutting. Such a steel is known as free machining steel. NOTE: This type of treatment tends to weaken the structure of the metal and some strength is lost in the finished part.

TOOL FAILURE

There are many factors that can contribute to the failure of a cutting tool. Some of these factors may be classified as: (1) temperature failure, (2) fracture of the tool point, and (3) tool wear.

Temperature Failure

When the amount of heat generated at the cutting edge of the tool becomes excessive, the heat causes the tool to soften and failure occurs. Excessively high cutting speeds and heavy cuts will cause some types of tools to soften, with resulting wearing away and rupturing of the cutting edge. This type of failure occurs quite rapidly after reaching a certain point.

Fracture of Tool Point

Because of their high hardness, carbide tipped tools are mechanically brittle and weak. Cutting forces which are too great for a given tool result in causing small portions of the tip to break away; in some instances the whole tip may be destroyed. NOTE: Tool failures of this type are more likely to occur with multi-point tools, such as milling cutters, than with turning tools. Vibration and chatter, as when the tool or work is not properly supported, can cause tool point fracture.

Tool Wear

Tool wear can be attributed to two basic causes: (1) wear due to plowing or abrasive action of the carbides or other hard particles in the workpiece, (2) wear resulting from instantaneous "welds" that occur when the chip and finished surface slide over the tool face.

Such abrasive action may be regarded as secondary cutting, and the rate of wear depends upon the size and number of hard particles in the metal and the relative hardness of the tool and workpiece.

There are two types of welds that can cause wear, pressure welds and temperature welds. Pressure welds occur at temperatures below recrystallization temperature of the metal and temperature welds above.

Tool wear occurs in two regions, at the flank and the tool face. Flank wear extends from the cutting edge back along the clearance face. This type of wear can be controlled to a certain extent by increasing the rake and clearance angles along with a suitable cutting fluid.

When a tool has been in use for a period of time, wear will eventually become evident in two regions: (1) On the clearance face of the tool, which is known as "wear land." This type of wear extends from the cutting edge back along the clearance face. Its extent can be controlled by increasing the rake and clearance angles or by using the proper coolant. (2) Wear on the tool face begins some distance above the cutting edge. 56–11. This type of wear is known as *cratering*. It will weaken the cutting edge and eventually cause the edge to break off.

CUTTING SPEEDS AND FEEDS

No definite rule can be applied to cutting speeds for tools made of different materials.

Speeds

Speeds may vary according to:
1. Type of material being machined.
2. Amount of feed.
3. Depth of cut.
4. Finish desired.
5. Condition of machine.
6. Type of cutting tool.
7. Type of coolant used.

The following general rules for selecting cutting speeds may be followed:

1. High-speed tools may be operated at speeds approximately twice that of carbon-steel tools.

2. Cast-alloy cutting tools may be operated at 50% greater speed than high-speed tools.

3. Cemented-carbide cutting tools can be operated at cutting speeds from two to four times faster than high-speed tools using coolant.

4. Ceramic tools may be operated at approximately the same cutting speeds as cemented-carbide cutting tools.

In units on the lathe, shaper, drill press, and milling machines, recommendations will be given for cutting speeds to cover each.

Feed

Feed refers to the rate at which a cutting tool advances along or into the surface of the workpiece. On machines such as the lathe, the feed is expressed in inches per revolution.

CUTTING FLUIDS

A varying amount of the work performed in cutting operations is transformed into heat. A portion of the heat develops when the chip is formed on the workpiece and additional heat generates when the chip moves over the face of the tool. Because brittle materials form chips that usually break up into small pieces, very little heat is developed. A long curled chip produces a great deal of frictional heat. Machining hard and tough steels produces a higher amount of heat than machining softer materials, such as low-carbon steels or brass.

In order to produce long tool life, the temperature at the chip-tool interface should be kept as low as possible. In grinding operations it is important to keep the workpiece as cool as possible to prevent changes in surface hardness and any inaccuracies in dimensions. Cutting fluids can be very effective in keeping the workpiece at the proper temperature. The principal purpose of a cutting fluid is to: (1) cool the tool and workpiece, (2) lubricate the tool face, chip, and the built-up edge on the tool, (3) prevent welding of metal to the tool point and subsequent rough surfaces, and (4) produce a good finish.

CLASSIFICATION OF CUTTING FLUIDS

The basic differences between cutting fluids are the viscosity of the mineral oils used as a base and the chemical compounds added to this oil in order to achieve characteristics required for different cutting conditions.

All cutting fluids can be classified within two groups: (1) cutting oils and (2) water-soluble oil emulsions.

Broadly speaking, cutting oils are used where a large amount of tough metal is being removed per unit of time and demands cutting fluid with extreme pressure properties that will serve to: (1) prevent particles from welding to the tip of the tool, (2) provide good lubricating qualities, and (3) provide good cooling qualities. Generally, soluble oils are used where the cooling function is paramount and where the surface of the workpiece must be protected by a rust preventive fluid.

Cutting oils consist of one or more of the following ingredients in varying combinations: mineral oils, fatty oils or acids, sulfur, chlorine or phosphorus and other chemicals.

Water-soluble oils are composed of a mineral oil and an emulsifying base—the latter causing the formation of an oil-water emulsion when added to water.

The cooling function of present-day cutting oils is carried out by the mineral oil. The mineral oil acts as a lubricant but its principal value lies in its ability to carry away heat that occurs between the workpiece and the tool.

Fatty oils and acids give cutting oils extreme oiliness and also the property to spread and cling to metal surfaces. The fatty ingredients serve to reduce frictional heat, tool wear, and power consumption. They improve surface finish.

56–11. Tool wear takes place in two places: (1) on the flank wear, a small land is abraded away, and (2) on the face of the tool in the form of a small crater behind the tip.

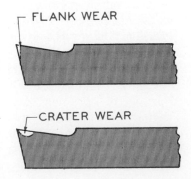

FLANK WEAR

CRATER WEAR

Sulfur, chlorine, and other chemicals provide anti-welding action by coating the tool and workpiece with a soaplike film, reducing the friction and heat which cause welding.

Soluble oils are used in an oil-water emulsion in proportions of one part oil to four to eighty parts of water. In this mixture the cooling action is provided almost entirely by the water. The mineral oil provides the necessary lubrication.

Mineral oils are generally used where a wide range of conditions are encountered in types of metal being cut, speeds, feeds, and depths of cut.

Transparent-Type Cutting Oil

The primary advantage of this type of oil is that the operator can observe the tool and workpiece through the transparent fluid, which makes the inspection of the part much easier. Other advantages are that it keeps shop operating conditions cleaner, with less handling of parts between operations, and reworking of parts to remove burrs is reduced.

A great many improvements have been made in cutting oils in recent years. For many years cutting oils have contained such additives as sulfur, chlorine, and others for the purpose of reducing frictional heat during the machining of steel or its alloys. These additives tend to darken oils. Highly compounded oils used in severe operations such as threading, tapping, and broaching were very dark in color. Transparent cutting oils,

with sufficient compounding, can handle most of the machining operations today.

These oils are classified as active and inactive types.

Active type oils contain active or corrosive sulfur in addition to ingredients such as fatty oils, sulfurized fatty oils, and/or sulfur and chlorine containing additives. NOTE: Because of their active nature, they cause discoloration of certain metals such as brass or copper.

Inactive type sulfurized fatty mineral oils contain chemicals so selected that they do not discolor copper or copper alloys. They come in several grades.

These oils will handle all types of machining operations on milder types of steel and non-ferrous metals. However, they do not possess the necessary properties for machining harder steels.

Classification of Water-Soluble Oils

Water is an efficient cooling medium. However, water cannot be used alone as a cutting fluid because of its rust-promoting characteristics and low lubricating value. Properties have to be added to water before it can even be used as a coolant. This is accomplished through the addition of soluble oil in a stable emulsion.

There are three classes of soluble oils: (1) transparent, (2) heavy-duty, and (3) opaque.

Transparent soluble oils contain a relatively high percentage of specially compounded soaps, which impart the high degree of

transparency to the cutting fluid which is desirable to see and gage an operation while the machine is running.

Heavy-duty soluble oils of high viscosity are used in denser concentrations than other classes of cutting oils. Mixed with water in proper proportions, they form a stable emulsion for many heavy cutting operations.

Opaque soluble oils are the most widely used of the soluble oils. They contain a smaller percentage of soaps than transparent oils but provide adequate cooling, lubricating, and rust preventing properties.

Selection of the Correct Cutting Fluid

Formerly, the selection of the proper type of cutting fluid was based on a trial-and-error method. The Special Research Committee of the American Society of Mechanical Engineers worked out a set of broad, general cutting fluid recommendations. These recommendations are based on the fact that there are two factors that control the selection of cutting fluid for a given machining operation, namely: (1) the machinability of the material to be machined and (2) the type of operation being performed—i.e., the severity of the operation as related to heat, friction, tool wear, etc. The committee rated all commonly used metals on the basis of their machinability under test conditions. AISI steel specification B–1112, cold drawn Bessemer steel, was given an arbitrary rating of 100%. Four classes or

Table 56-C. Type of Machining Operations According to Severity*

Severity	Type of Machining Operation
(Greatest) 1	Broaching; internal
2	Broaching; surface
2	Threading; pipe
3	Tapping; plain
3	Threading; plain
4	Gear shaving
4	Reaming; plain
4	Gear cutting
5	Drilling; deep
6	Milling; plain
6	Milling, multiple cutter
7	Boring; multiple head
7	Multiple-spindle, automatic screw machines and turret lathes; drilling, forming, turning, reaming, cutting-off, tapping, threading
8	High-speed, light feed, automatic, screw machines; drilling, forming, tapping, threading, turning, reaming, box milling, cutting off
9	Drilling
9	Planing; shaping
9	Turning; single-point tool, form tools
(Least) 10	Sawing (circular, hack) and grinding (plain, form; thread)

* Compiled from *Metals Handbook, Machinery Handbook,* and *AISI Steel Products Manual.*

groups of ferrous metals and two classes of nonferrous metals were then set up. Metals which are more difficult to machine have a machinability rating of less than 100%. Metals which machine more easily have a rating of more than 100%.

Machinability ratings are based on exact comparisons of various metals which are machined under conditions that are scientifically controlled.

The most common types of machine operations were rated according to the severity of the operation. The most severe operation was rated 1 and the least severe 10.

Check Your Knowledge

1. What is the fundamental purpose of a machine tool?

2. How is the cutting action obtained in a turning machine?

3. What type of surface is produced by a milling machine?

4. What is the most common type of cutting tool?

5. What is orthogonal cutting?

6. How does the cutting velocity vector act on a lathe turning tool?

7. How is the scalor value of this vector generally expressed?

8. What is meant by "chip velocity vector?"

9. What are the two fundamental physical processes involved in all types of metal cutting operations?

10. Name three types of chip formations.

11. Chip formation is governed by several factors. Name them.

12. Upon what factors does the surface finish produced depend?

13. Name two reasons for grinding a tool to a given shape.

14. What is the value of a nose radius on a cutting tool?

15. How does mounting a tool in a toolholder change the angles on the tool in relationship to the workpiece?

16. What are the advantages and limitations of carbide tipped tools?

17. Why are chip breakers formed on tools? What is their function?

18. Name three common types of chip breakers.

19. Is it possible to use a single tool material to satisfy all turning requirements? Explain.

20. How are cutting tools classified?

21. Name the main advantage of a high-speed steel tool over a like tool made of carbon steel.

22. Name three advantages of cemented carbide tools.

23. What is the machinability of a material based upon?

24. Name the main factor that affects the machinability of a metal.

25. What is a "free machining" steel?

26. What are some of the factors that can contribute to tool failure?

27. What effect does excessive heat have upon a tool?

28. What are the basic causes of tool wear?

29. Explain why the proper speeds and feeds are important in machining operations.

30. What characteristics should a good coolant have?

31. What are the basic differences in various cutting fluids?

32. Name two classifications of cutting fluids.

33. What is a water-soluble oil?

34. What is the purpose of adding sulfur, chlorine, and other chemicals to a cutting fluid?

35. Distinguish between active and inactive cutting oils.

References

Black, Paul H., *Theory of Metal Cutting,* New York, McGraw-Hill Book Co., 1961.

Hans, Ernst, *Physics of Metal Cutting,* The Cincinnati Milling Machine Co.

McGee, F. S., and Slay, G. S., *"A New Look at Tool Angles,"* American Machinist/Metalworking Manufacturing, October 2, 1961.

The Texas Company, *Cutting and Grinding,* 1959.

Trigger, Kenneth J., *"How Heat Affects Tool Wear,"* American Machinist, July 18, 1966.

Filing on the lathe.

Atlas Press Co.

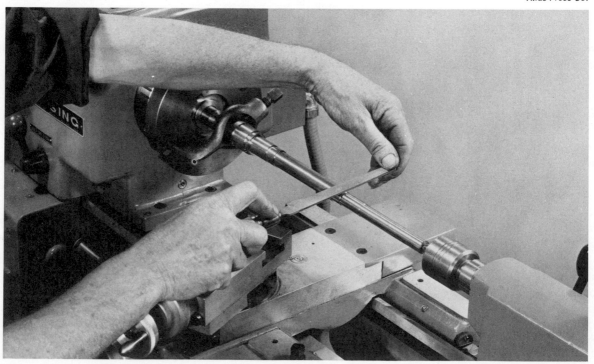

Section Eleven

Machining Metal With Turning Machines

THERE are many types of turning machines in use today, which are capable of producing a cylindrical form from metal. The oldest turning machine is the engine lathe. While all lathes are built to achieve a similar objective, in a similar manner, it is still necessary to have many different classes, types, and sizes.

Although the lathe is primarily adapted for cylindrical work using a single-point cutting tool to remove metal, as previously said, many other operations such as boring, threading, reaming, knurling, and even milling can be performed on the lathe.

Generally speaking, all turning machines can be classified into five major groups: (1) engine lathes, (2) turret lathes, (3)

Cincinnati Lathe and Tool Co.

screw machines, (4) boring mills, and (5) automatic lathes. In turn, each of these groups include two or more types. Many can be adapted to some form of numerical control.

Since the operating principles of all types of turning machines are somewhat the same, it is not possible to select a single fundamental principle for classifying each type.

The chart on page 261 shows one method of classifying turning machines.

Unit 57.	The Engine Lathe

Think of a lathe as being composed of *working units*. Each unit has a distinct function, and when all units are working together, the machine can be operated. The purpose of the various component parts is simply to make it possible to remove and shape metal by rotating the workpiece in contact with a cutting tool. 57–1.

To accomplish this, each part of the lathe is so designed as to assist in the performance of one or the other two important functions: (1) that of holding and rotating the workpiece and (2) that of holding and controlling the movement of the cutting tool.

All the parts located—or connected to mechanisms located—above the bed rails contribute to holding and rotating the workpiece. All parts which are located—or connected to mechanisms located—below the bed rails have to do with holding and controlling the motion of the cutting tool. 57–2.

HOLDING AND CONTROLLING DEVICES

The Headstock

The headstock houses and supports the spindle and its driving gears (or pulleys). 57–3 (Page 262). Where gears are employed.

57–1. Parts of an engine lathe.

R. K. LeBlond Machine Tool Co.

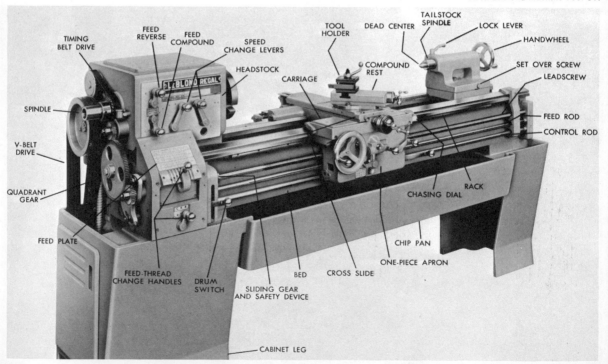

KINDS OF LATHES

General Purpose Lathes	Production Lathes	Guided-Path Lathes
	Hand-Fed	
Speed lathe	Hand-fed turret lathe	
Bench lathe	Second operation machine	
High-speed precision lathe	Hand-screw machine	
	Power-Fed But Manually Operated	
Power-fed basic lathe	Ram-type turret lathe	Tracer controlled lathe
Engine lathe	Saddle-type turret lathe	
Toolroom lathe	Precision chucking machine	
Gap lathe	Hand-screw machine	
Multicut lathe		
Facing lathe	**Automatic-Cycle**	
	Automatic turret lathe	Automatic tracer lathe
	1. Horizontal turret	Copying lathe
	2. Vertical turret	Duplicating lathe
	Single-spindle automatic	N/C lathe
	1. Bar machine	Cam controlled lathe
	2. Chucking machine	Single-point threader
	Automatic screw machine	
	1. Turret type	
	2. Sliding-head type	
	Multiple spindle automatic	
	1. Bar machine	
	2. Chucking machine	
	Vertical chucking machine	
	Boring mill	

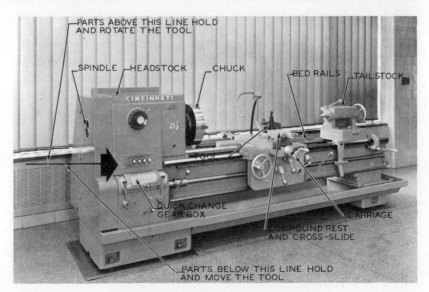

Cincinnati Lathe & Tool Co.

57–2. A lathe is composed of working units, each unit with a distinct function. When the various units are working together, lathe operations are made possible.

the headstock unit includes control levers for the proper speed selection. A built-in electric motor usually powers the spindle. The headstock is always located at the left-hand end of the machine.

The Spindle

The hollow spindle is built into the headstock. The nose on the spindle projects out from the headstock housing. The nose may be of the threaded type, a standard-key drive taper nose, or spindle nose of the cam-lock type. 57–4 & 57–5. The end of the spindle has an internal tapered hole into which tapered sleeves and centers can be placed.

WORKPIECE HOLDERS

Faceplate, Live Center, and Dog

These parts combine to drive and support the rotating workpiece at the headstock end between the lathe centers. The driving plate or faceplate is mounted on the spindle nose; the tail of the dog rides in the slot of the driving plate, turning the workpiece, 57–6 & 57–7. The live center fits in the tapered hole of the hollow spindle. 57–8.

Universal and Independent Chucks

Universal and independent (3-jaw and 4-jaw) chucks, are used to hold the workpiece while it is being machined. 57–9.

The jaws of a 3-jaw chuck can be simultaneously moved an equal distance toward or away from the center, by turning a chuck key.

R. K. LeBlond Machine Tool Co.
57–3. Headstock, showing gear assembly.

57–4. Threaded type spindle nose.

57–5. Standard key drive taper nose.
R. K. LeBlond Machine Tool Co.

South Bend Lathe Co.
57–6. Face or driving plates.

Armstrong Brothers Tool Co.
57–7. Safety lathe dog.

57–8. (A) Live center. (B) Dead center. (C) Drill pad for use with tailstock. Flat stock can be held against drill pad for drilling. (D) Round stock can be held in the V for machining.

57–9. Universal or 3-jaw chuck.

Because the 3-jaw chuck has one less jaw, it cannot grip the workpiece as tightly as a 4-jaw chuck. 57–10. This type of chuck is best used for holding round stock. Another advantage of a 4-jaw chuck is that the four jaws can be adjusted independently of each other. A workpiece that is either square, cylindrical, or of irregular contour can be held securely and centered accurately.

Collet Chucks

A draw-in collet chuck has a hollow, split, tapered head which can be adjusted to grip small-diameter bar stock and other small-diameter workpieces. 57–11. When the head is drawn into its closing sleeve, the workpiece is gripped on all sides, holding it in an on-center position. The entire assembly is hollow, thereby permitting long bar stock to be fed through. Different size collets are used with this assembly for different sizes and shapes. The gripping action is obtained by turning a handwheel attached to the threaded drawbar.

The Tailstock

The tailstock holds and adjusts the *dead center* which supports the right end of the workpiece. 57–12. It slides on the ways of the bed to any desired position. Taper shank drills and reamers can be mounted in the tailstock spindle when required.

Quick Change Gear Box

The quick change gear box, located below the headstock, is

57–10. Independent or 4-jaw chuck.

57–11. Draw-in collet chuck. This is the most accurate chuck for high-precision work. Insert shows a collet chuck which fits in collet sleeve for draw-in collet chuck.

57–12. Tailstock.

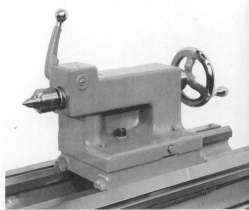

57–13. The lathe headstock with gear train and quick change gear box.

driven by the spindle through a train of gears. 57–13. The *lead screw* and *drive shaft* are rotated to move the carriage at a desired rate of travel on the bed. *Adjustable levers* can be set to obtain the proper speed controlling the carriage movement.

The Carriage

The carriage moves along the bed between the headstock and tailstock. 57–14. It supports the cross-slide on which the compound that holds the tool post is mounted. The carriage is moved by gears and controls housed in the apron. Carriage movement

57–14. Lathe carriage.

57–15. (A) Follow rest. (B) Steady rest.

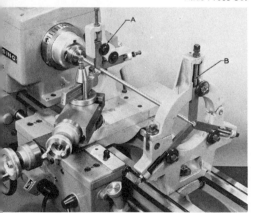

57–16. Taper attachment.

can be made by a *handwheel* or by a *power feed device* located on the apron.

Steady Rest and Follow Rest

These devices are detachable. They are used to support long slender, cylindrical workpieces when turning or threading, to prevent the material from bending. 57–15.

Taper Attachment

A taper attachment is an accessory that is attached to both the *cross slide* and *lathe bed*. 57–16. This attachment permits the machining of tapers without setting over (offsetting) the tailstock.

SIZES AND TYPES OF LATHES

Engine lathes vary in size from the small bench lathe to lathes that are capable of turning workpieces weighing thousands of pounds. 57–17. The size of an engine lathe is based upon (1) the diameter in inches of the largest piece of material

57–17. Bench lathe.

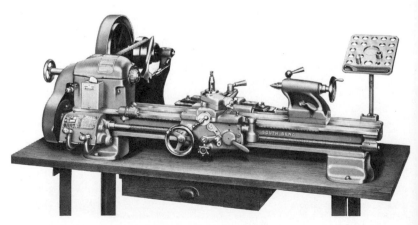

that can be revolved over the lathe bed and (2) the maximum distance between centers or the length of the bed as designated by some manufacturers. 57–18.

To meet the many demands of metal manufacturing industries, there are various types of lathes manufactured that have practically the same fundamental parts as the engine lathe. These are the speed lathe, bench lathe, toolroom lathe, duplicating lathe, production lathes, and special purpose lathes.

United Engineering and Foundry Co.

57–18. Giant lathe turning a 67″ x 166″, 108,000 pound backup roll.

LATHE CUTTING TOOLS

Most lathe tool bits are ground to cut in one direction only. The two most common types are referred to as right-cut and left-cut. The different types are described in the following paragraphs:

1. A *right-cut,* single-point tool is one which viewed from the point end with the face up, has the cutting edge on the right side, and cuts from the right to the left.

2. A *left-cut,* single-point tool is ground to cut from the left to the right.

3. A *round nose* cutting tool is a general-purpose tool. When ground flat on top it can be used for both *right and left* cuts, as a finishing tool.

4. A *cut-off* or parting tool cuts on the end only. The sides are ground back slightly. This tool is used for cutting off stock held in a chuck.

5. A *roughing* tool is used in taking heavy cuts to reduce the diameter to approximate size, leaving only enough material for the finishing cut. *The point is rounded very slightly.*

6. A *finishing* tool is used to take a final finishing cut. It has a keenly ground cutting edge. This tool is usually ground with a larger nose radius than a roughing tool.

7. *Side-facing* tools are used for finishing the ends of work smooth and square. A *right side-facing* tool is used to finish the end of a shaft held between centers or in a chuck.

8. A *threading* tool is ground to cut American National or Unified screw threads, to an included angle of 60°. It has a 3° to 5° side relief and about 8° front relief. The top of the tool has no back rake but may have a slight side rake.

Unit 58. Lathe Operations

As a concept in its basic form, turning consists of machining an external cylindrical surface with a single-point tool while the workpiece is rotating and with the tool moving parallel to the axis of the workpiece at a prescribed depth and speed, to remove the outer surface of the workpiece. 58–1(A&B). (Page 266).

As said previously, the simplest lathe not only can perform this operation but with only a few additional components can also perform operations such as taper turning, boring, drilling, reaming, and forming. 58–2 (A&B). Also, by the addition of certain accessories, a general-purpose lathe can be made into a machine that can turn out parts on a moderate production basis. 58–3. This can be accomplished by: (1) mounting certain tools in a turret so that reaming, drill-

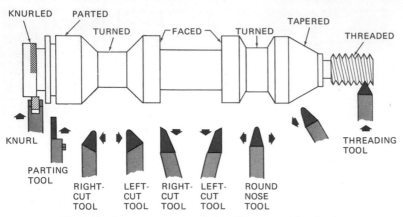

58–1(A). Common cuts made by different cutting tools.

Atlas Press Co.

58–1(B). Turning operation with a single-point tool.

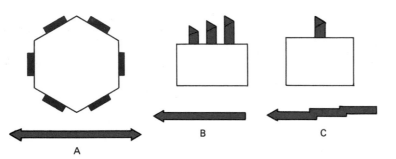

58–2(A). (A) Indexing tool principle. Tools mounted in turret provides quick indexing. (B) Massed tool principle. Permits tools to all cut at the same time. (C) Guided path principle. Permits one tool to do a series of cuts.

58–3. Massed tools held in tool block.

R. K. LeBlond Machine Tool Co.

58–2(B). Tools of different types can be mounted in this turret.

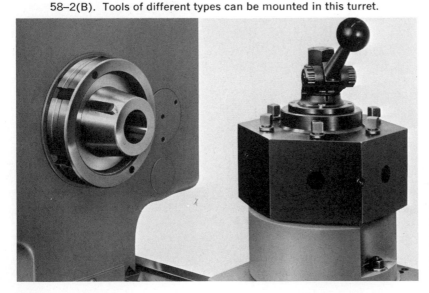

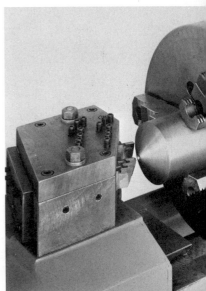

Table 58. American Standard Tapers (Morse)*

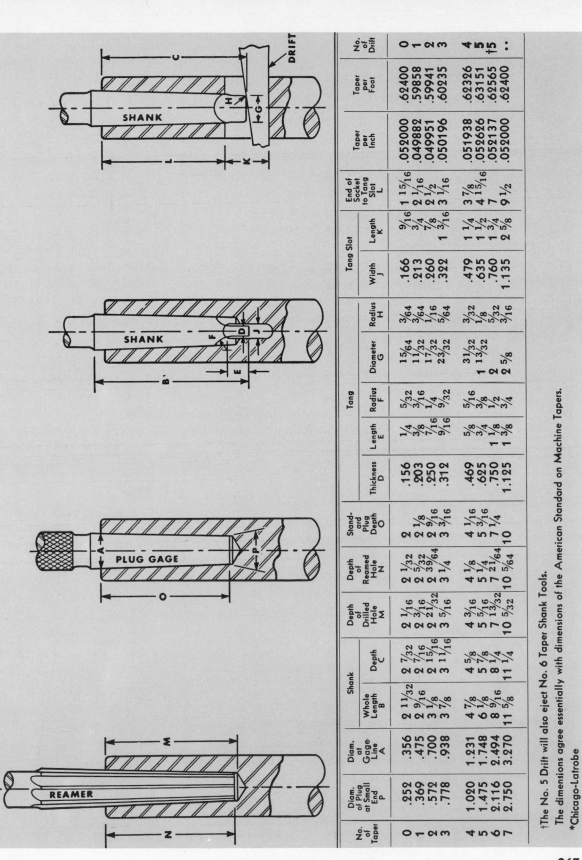

No. of Taper	Diam. of Plug at Small End P	Diam. at Gage Line A	Shank Whole Length B	Shank Depth C	Depth of Drilled Hole M	Depth of Reamed Hole N	Standard Plug Depth O	Thickness D	Tang Length E	Tang Radius F	Tang Diameter G	Tang Radius H	Tang Slot Width J	Tang Slot Length K	End of Socket to Tang Slot L	Taper per Inch	Taper per Foot	No. of Drift
0	.252	.356	2 11/32	2 7/32	2 1/16	2 1/32	2	.156	1/4	5/32	15/64	3/64	.166	9/16	1 15/16	.052000	.62400	0
1	.369	.475	2 9/16	2 7/16	2 3/16	2 3/32	2 1/8	.203	3/8	3/16	11/32	3/64	.213	3/4	2 1/16	.049882	.59858	1
2	.572	.700	3 1/8	2 15/16	2 21/32	2 39/64	2 9/16	.250	7/16	1/4	17/32	1/16	.260	7/8	2 1/2	.049951	.59941	2
3	.778	.938	3 7/8	3 11/16	3 5/16	3 1/4	3 3/16	.312	9/16	9/32	23/32	5/64	.322	1 3/16	3 1/16	.050196	.60235	3
4	1.020	1.231	4 7/8	4 5/8	4 3/16	4 1/8	4 1/16	.469	5/8	5/16	31/32	3/32	.479	1 1/4	3 7/8	.051938	.62326	4
5	1.475	1.748	6 1/8	5 7/8	5 5/16	5 1/4	5 3/16	.625	3/4	3/8	1 13/32	1/8	.635	1 1/2	4 15/16	.052626	.63151	5
6	2.116	2.494	8 9/16	8 1/4	7 13/32	7 21/64	7 1/4	.750	1 1/8	1/2	2	5/32	.760	1 3/4	7	.052137	.62565	†5
7	2.750	3.270	11 5/8	11 1/4	10 5/32	10 5/64	10	1.125	1 3/8	3/4	2 5/8	3/16	1.135	2 5/8	9 1/2	.052000	.62400	..

†The No. 5 Drift will also eject No. 6 Taper Shank Tools.

The dimensions agree essentially with dimensions of the American Standard on Machine Tapers.

*Chicago-Latrobe

267

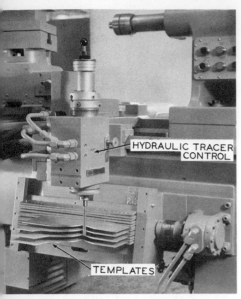

Cincinnati Milling Machine Co.,
Meta-Dynamics Div.

58–4. Two-dimensional tracer control permits hand-guided power movements or automatic tracing (when machine is in semiautomatic cycle) on a wide range of simple or complex contoured parts. Six successive passes can be made with a multiple-template attachment, semiautomatically.

58–5. A facing operation with part held in 3-jaw chuck.

Atlas Press Co.

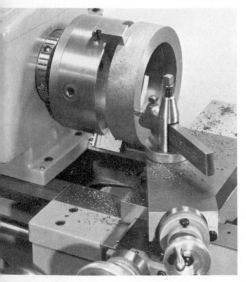

ing, etc., can be indexed into position quickly, (2) mounting several tools so that they all cut at the same time and finish the job at a single pass, and (3) making use of a template to guide one tool through a path which will machine all surfaces. 58–4.

FACTORS IN BASIC TURNING OPERATIONS

In any basic turning operation there are three primary factors: (1) cutting speed, (2) feed, and (3) depth of cut. Of course, there are other factors that are important, such as *type of material* being cut, *condition of machine,* and *type of tool* being used.

NOTE: Do not confuse cutting speed with rpm. *Cutting speed* refers to the workpiece and the spindle; *rpm* refers to the rotating speed of the spindle.

$$\text{rpm} = \frac{\text{cutting speed} \times 12}{\text{diameter} \times \pi}$$

Cutting Speed

To find the cutting speed, multiply the diameter of the work in inches by 3.1416. Multiply the product by the number of rpm of the headstock spindle. Divide this product by 12, to give the cutting speed in surface feet per minute.

$$CS = \frac{D \times 3.1416 \times \text{rpm}}{12} \text{ in sfm}$$

Feed

Feed refers to the rate at which the tool advances along its cutting path. The amount of feed is controlled through the use of the feeding and threading mechanisms. It is expressed in inches of tool advance per revolution of the spindle (ipr).

Depth of Cut

The depth of cut—the thickness of the metal removed from the workpiece—is expressed in inches. As a working rule, the diameter of the workpiece is reduced by two times the single depth of cut.

OPERATIONS

Facing

In getting stock ready for turning, one of the first operations is facing the ends. 58–5. This is done to produce a smooth, square end on the workpiece so

58–6. Setup for turning with a single-point tool. Part is held between centers.

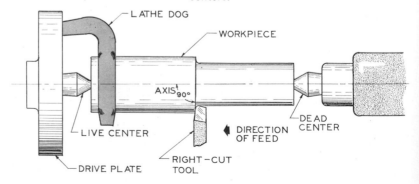

that uniform bearing for the centers may be obtained, and also to bring it to the desired length. The workpiece may be faced while held in a chuck or between centers. NOTE: In turning a workpiece between centers, the stock has to be provided with properly *countersunk holes.*

Plain Turning

The most common operation in lathe work is plain turning of cylindrical parts. 58–6. After the workpiece has been prepared for turning by drilling and countersinking holes in both ends in which the live and dead centers will fit, a dog is placed on one end and the workpiece placed between the centers. The workpiece is driven by the dog, the tail of which fits into a slot on the faceplate. The live center turns with the workpiece, while the dead center is stationary. NOTE: The dead center, held in the tailstock, must be lubricated to reduce friction. When a rotating tailstock center is used no lubrication is necessary.

The single-point tool may be of high-speed steel, cast alloy, or cemented carbide. 58–7. It is mounted in a toolholder held in a tool post. After the tool is adjusted for position and depth of cut, the automatic feed is engaged and feeding and cutting are done mechanically.

As noted earlier, turning cuts are generally of two types, roughing and finishing. 58–8. The roughing cut reduces the diameter of the workpiece to approximately $\frac{1}{32}''$ of the desired diameter. A finishing tool is then used to bring the diameter to the required size.

More than one roughing cut may have to be taken to bring the material to the required size for the finishing cut.

Taper Turning

Many machine elements have tapered surfaces that have been machined on the lathe. The shanks of twist drills, reamers, arbors, and end mills have tapered surfaces. These vary from short tapers turned by using the compound rest to long tapered surfaces that have been turned by the setover tailstock method or with the taper attachment.

Several different taper standards are in use:

1. Morse Standard tapers are used for lathe and drill press spindles. (See Table 58, page 267.) The taper is approximately .625″ per foot.

2. Brown and Sharpe tapers are used for milling machine spindles and milling cutter shanks with a taper of .5″ per foot.

3. Jarno tapers are used for some makes of lathes and milling machines. The taper is .6″ per foot.

4. The Sellers taper is used on equipment with a taper of .75″ per foot.

5. Taper pins are made with .25″ taper per foot for use in assembly work.

A variety of diameters are used in each of these standards. They are designated by numbers.

Methods

There are several methods of turning tapers in a lathe. 58–9 (Page 270).

The most common ones are: (1) by setting the tailstock over the desired amount; (2) by us-

Atlas Press Co.

58–7. A single-point tool mounted in a toolholder and held in a toolpost for turning. Round stock is held in a 3-jaw chuck.

58–8. Roughing cut being taken on an engine lathe. Heavy cut is made possible with a carbide tool.

Atlas Press Co.

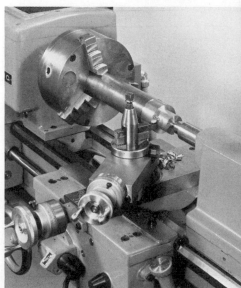

ing the taper attachment; (3) by setting the compound rest to the desired angle. Short tapers are machined by this method. 58–10.

Setting over the tailstock is a common method for turning tapers when the workpiece is sufficiently long.

Calculating Tapers In Inches Per Foot

Since taper attachments on lathes are usually graduated in degrees and the taper in inches per foot, it is frequently necessary to determine one of these factors.

The formula for finding the taper in inches per foot is as follows:

$$\text{tipf} = \frac{\text{large diameter — small diameter}}{\text{length of tapered portion (in.)} \times 12}$$

To find the amount of taper per inch (tpi) use the formula as given but do not multiply by 12.

Taper Turning By Setting Over the Tailstock

If a taper attachment is not available on the lathe, the top of the tailstock can be setover to turn the desired amount of taper. This method can be used when the taper is of sufficient length, as stated before.

The amount of setover from the center line of the lathe depends upon the tipf and the length of the workpiece.

To determine the amount of setover, divide the total inch length of the workpiece by 12 and multiply this quotient by one-half the amount of taper per foot.

$$\text{Setover} = \frac{\text{total length in inches}}{12} \times \frac{\text{taper per foot}}{2}$$

Tapers are generally given in inches per foot. For example if a Morse taper of .500″ per foot is to be machined on a piece of

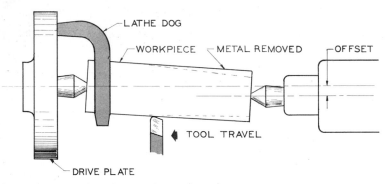

58–9. Turning a taper by offsetting the tailstock.

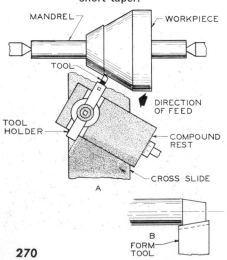

58–10. (A) Taper turning on an engine lathe using the compound rest. (B) Using a form tool to produce a short taper.

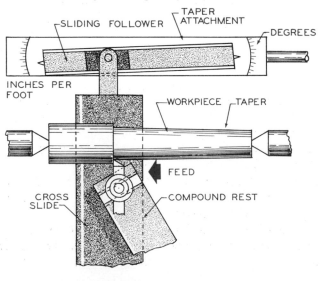

58–11. Taper turning using a taper attachment.

stock 12" long, the tailstock set-over would be .2500".

If the diameters at the ends of the taper are given, divide the total length of the workpiece by the length of the portion to be tapered; then multiply this quotient by one-half the difference of the two diameters.

$$\text{Setover} = \frac{\text{length of workpiece}}{\text{length of taper}} \times \frac{\text{large diam.} - \text{small diam.}}{2}$$

To find the angle at which to set the compound rest or taper attachment when the taper in inches per foot is known, divide the tipf by 24 and find the angle whose tangent produces this result. (Consult trigonometry tables.) The compound rest can be set at the desired angle and the taper machined by feeding the compound rest screw by hand.

The taper turning attachment offers many advantages. 58–11.

It is easily set up for turning tapers and the greatest accuracy is obtainable. One end of the guide bar is graduated in inches per foot and the other end in degrees of taper. The attachment is bolted to the back of the lathe. A guide bar controls the movement of the tool. As the carriage proceeds along the bed, a slide moves over the bar causing the tool to move in or out, according to the setting of the bar. The taper attachment permits the lathe centers to be kept in alignment.

Thread Chasing

Cutting threads on the engine lathe is usually done when only a few threads are to be cut or when special forms of threads are necessary. 58–12. For the operation, the lead screw is revolved at a desired ratio with the spindle of the lathe through a series of gears. Quick change gear boxes enable the operator to produce various pitches of threads, using control levers.

The cutting tool is ground to the shape required for the form of screw thread being cut. For cutting 60° V threads, a center gage is used for checking the angle when grinding the tool to shape.

In cutting a *right-hand exterior thread,* the compound is turned in the direction of the headstock and set at an angle of 29°. 58–13. The tool is set so its center line is at a right angle to the axis of the workpiece. This setting can be obtained by the use of the center gage as shown. 58–13(B). When the tool point fits uniformly into the V notch of the gage, the tool is at a 90° angle. 58–14 (Page 272). NOTE: The point of the tool should be at the same elevation as the center line of the workpiece.

In the *thread-cutting operation,* the lathe should be set at the correct ratio of feed to speed for the desired thread to be cut.

Next, the compound is adjusted so that the micrometer

58–12. Cutting threads on the engine lathe. On long slender workpieces a follow rest is used to support the workpiece.

Atlas Press Co.

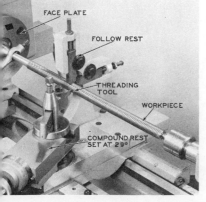

58–13. (A) Compound is turned in direction of the headstock and set at an angle of 29°. (B) Center gage is used to set the threading tool. (C) A thread chasing dial is used to save time when cutting long screw threads.

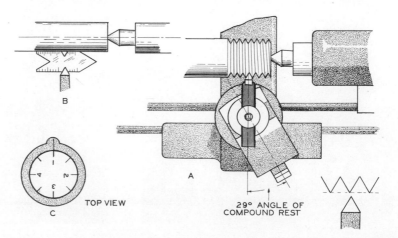

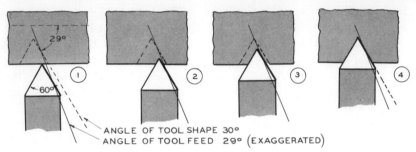

ANGLE OF TOOL SHAPE 30°
ANGLE OF TOOL FEED 29° (EXAGGERATED)

58–14. Any of 60° V-type thread forms may be produced by advancing the tool at a 29° angle. The illustration establishes the tool position in four stages in completion of a thread groove.

Thread Dial Indicator

Most modern lathes are equipped with a thread dial indicator, which saves time when cutting long screw threads. 58–15. The indicator is connected to the lead screw by a small worm gear. The face of the dial is numbered to indicate positions at which the half nuts may be engaged. When the lathe is set up for cutting screw threads, the thread dial indicates the relative position of the lead screw, spindle, and carriage of the lathe. This permits disengaging the half nuts from the lead screw at the end of the cut, returning the carriage quickly to the starting point by hand, and re-engaging the half nuts with the lead screw at a point which will assure that the tool follows exactly in the original cut. The position at which the half nut should be closed depends upon the pitch of thread, as follows:

dial on its collar is at zero. The tool is then brought into contact with the workpiece by adjusting the cross-slide and setting its micrometer dial to zero. All adjustments for depth of cut can be made from these settings.

It is common practice to use both the *cross-slide* and the *compound*. The tool is backed off the workpiece and the carriage is moved to where the tool is, at a point beyond the end of the workpiece. The cross-slide is then advanced until the micrometer dial reads the same as when the tool was touching the workpiece. Next, the compound is advanced .002″ to .003″ and a trial cut is taken. At the end of the cut, the cross-slide is backed off and the tool returned to its starting point. The cross-slide is then adjusted to its zero reading and the compound advanced a distance equal to the next cut. The operation is repeated until the proper depth of thread is obtained.

58–15. Thread chasing dial. The chasing dial indicates when the split-nut should be engaged with the lead screw to follow a previously cut groove.

Atlas Press Co.

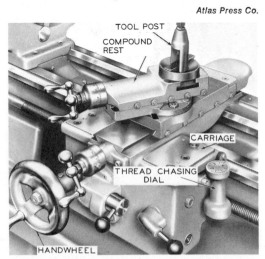

TOOL POST
COMPOUND REST
CARRIAGE
THREAD CHASING DIAL
HANDWHEEL

58–16. Boring on the lathe. Drilled or cored holes and recesses are bored with a boring tool.

Atlas Press Co.

CHUCK
WORKPIECE
BORING TOOL

- For all numbered threads, close half nuts upon any line on the dial.
- For odd-numbered threads, close half nuts on any numbered line.
- For threads involving half threads—any numbered line.
- For threads involving quarter threads—return to the original starting point before closing half nuts.

Boring

On the lathe, boring is an operation that enlarges a hole with a single-point tool. 58–16. Boring can be accomplished by either of two methods: (1) The workpiece is held in a chuck and the tool moves in a straight line. (2) The workpiece is fastened in a fixed position on the lathe carriage while the boring bar is turned between centers. When this method is employed, the tool must be reset to project a greater distance from the bar as each succeeding cut is taken, because no cross-slide movement is permissible.

Drilling on the Lathe

Most drilling operations on the lathe are accomplished with the workpiece held in a chuck, either in a fixed position in the tailstock spindle or a Jacob's chuck is held in the tailstock spindle. 58–17. In some instances, the drill is held and rotated in the headstock by a headstock chuck.

The drill is advanced into the revolving workpiece by turning the handwheel of the tailstock. The drill should be advanced slowly until the hole has reached its full diameter, to prevent the possibility of its "walking" to one side. If a large hole is to be drilled, a small lead hole is made first.

Reaming

Relatively small holes that must be trued, slightly enlarged, or provided with a smooth finish are usually reamed. With the workpiece held in a chuck, the tailstock can hold the reamer and control its rate of feed. 58–18. A taper-shanked reamer can be mounted in the tailstock spindle, or a straight-shank machine reamer is mounted in a drill chuck; or the reamer can be held by a tap wrench, one end of which is held against the tailstock center.

For finishing a hole, a fluted or shell reamer is used. The drilled hole should be not more than .010″ to .015″ under the finished hole. Slow spindle speed and feed are necessary in reaming.

58–18. Reaming on the lathe. The reamer is held in the tailstock spindle and fed into the workpiece by the tailstock handwheel.

Atlas Press Co.

58–17. Drilling with a taper shank drill held in the tailstock. The dog prevents drill from turning in the tailstock spindle.

R. K. LeBlond Machine Tool Co.

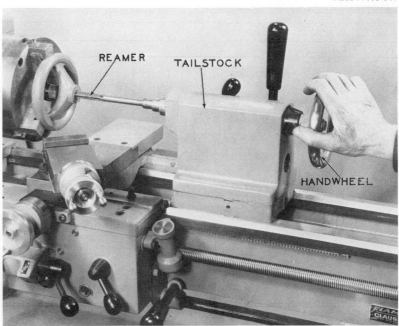

Unit 59. Turret Lathes

The modern turret lathe is an indexing-tool machine using a succession of tools that can be indexed, one after another, into cutting positions. 59–1(A).

The turret (indexible tool mount) is moved longitudinally, and the tools mounted in the six-faced or hexagon turret can be fed into the end of the workpiece. Most turret lathes have one or more cross-slides that move transversely to feed other tools into the side of the workpiece. These tools are mounted either on a toolblock or on another turret.

There are many different types of turret lathes, but they can be classified as *vertical* and *horizontal*.

VERTICAL TURRET LATHES

The vertical turret lathe is designed for turning heavy parts. It consists of a rotating table or chuck located in a horizontal position with the turret mounted on a cross-rail above the table. A side-head contains a square turret for holding the tools used in various operations. 59–1(B). Stops are provided for both the turret and side-head, arranged in such a manner that the length of cut is the same in each machining cycle. The turrets are indexed and locked in position by hand.

The side-head with the square turret can be fed by hand vertically, or power may be used for feeding or adjustment. The cross-rail cutting tools can be moved in two directions.

BAR AND CHUCKING MACHINES

Horizontal machines can be further classified as either bar or chucking machines according to the type of work they do. Basically, they are identical, the differences being their tooling. Bar machines are used for turning parts from bar stock or for machining forgings or castings that are of a size or shape similar to bar stock. Chucking machines are used for castings, forgings, and individual pieces of bar

59–1(B). Vertical turret lathe. Side-head contains a square turret for holding tools for different operations.

Bullard Co.

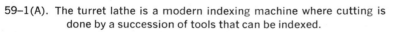

59–1(A). The turret lathe is a modern indexing machine where cutting is done by a succession of tools that can be indexed.

Atlas Press Co.

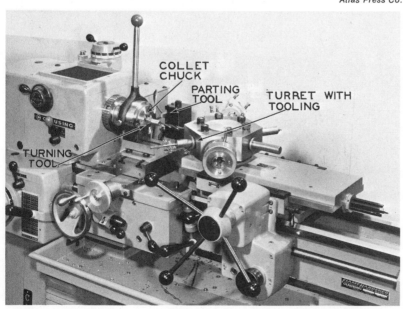

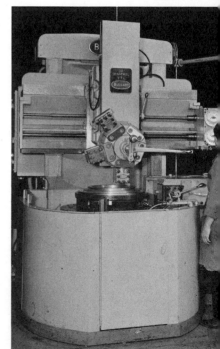

stock which can be held in chucks or fixtures.

There are some differences between bar and chucking tools. In *bar* work the toolholder is equipped with rolls which rigidly support the workpiece while the cutter is removing the metal. Bending and springing of the work is prevented. In *chucking* operations there is an overhang of chucking tools, which does not exist in bar work.

Ram and Saddle Types

Bar and chucking machines may be either of the ram- or saddle-type. Ram-type turret lathes have the turret mounted on a slide or ram which can be moved back and forth in a saddle which is *separately* clamped to the machine bed.

The ram-type turret lathe can be quickly and easily operated. 59–2. With this type of machine the hexagon turret can be moved backward and forward without having to move the entire saddle unit. This feature makes it best suited for bar work within its range and for chucking work where overhang of the ram can be kept short.

The saddle-type turret lathe has the turret mounted *directly* on a saddle. The saddle moves back and forth directly on the machine bed in unison with the apron. This type of turret lathe is suitable for longer and heavier chucking work which requires long turning or boring cuts. 59–3 (A&B) (Page 276).

In general, the ram-type machines are smaller than saddle-type lathes. Maximum swing ranges up to 22″ with a bar capacity up to 4½″.

Saddle-type machines have swings ranging from 16″ to 40″, with bar capacities from 2½″ to 6″.

As is evident, a significant difference between the two types of turret lathes is in the length of the hexagon turret travel. Because the turret base of the ram-type machine is clamped to the ways, the maximum turret travel is about 14″.

On the saddle-type machine, the whole turret support may have a longitudinal travel of 2½′ to 8′.

Turret Lathe Construction

Modern turret lathes are constructed with either electric heads, where a multiple speed motor is mounted directly on the spindle, or all-gear heads. Spindle speeds, with forward and reverse movements, are controlled by levers extending from the headstock.

Some machines are equipped with hydraulic speed selectors which make it possible for the operator to select and change spindle speeds quickly.

The cross-slide unit on modern turret lathes having greater than 1″ bar capacity is generally equipped with a universal type cross-slide which moves by hand or power in both directions and can be used for turning as well as facing, forming, or cutting off.

The cross-slide unit is made up of: (1) the square turret, (2) carriage, (3) cross-slide, and (4) the apron or gear box.

Two types of cross-slides are in common use: (1) the "side hung" type which is supported entirely on the front ways and a way located at the lower front side of the bed; (2) the "reach-over" type, which rides on both ways of the machine and is supported by the lower rail.

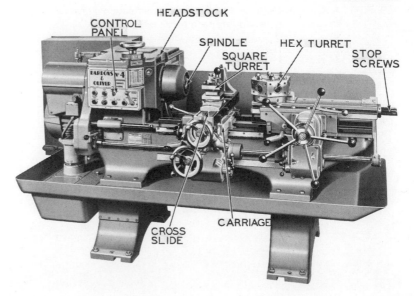

59–2. Ram-type turret lathe. On this type machine the turret is mounted on the ram which moves back and forth in a saddle clamped to the bed.

Bardons & Oliver

Type 1 provides greater swing over the cross-slide and is best for saddle-type machines where large diameter work is being machined.

A square turret can be quickly indexed and locked in position for the cut, and cuts to be taken, simultaneously with tools held on the hexagon turret.

The hexagon turret is the major tool handling part of the lathe.

On *hand-fed* machines, also, the turret is usually hexagonal— or it may be round in shape— and contains six tool stations. When the tool is in working position, its center is in line with the axis of the spindle.

Hand-fed lathes are the ram type. The turret is indexed automatically when the ram is moved to the fully retracted position. The same operation also indexes the stop drum to the next position. There are six stop screws, one for each turret station. These can be adjusted to stop the feed of each tool at the desired point.

For tripping the power cross-feed, feed trips are used.

All saddle-type machines have full power feed for both the cross-slide and turret. The larger ram-type machines have the power feed for the turret moving towards the headstock only; the operator retracts it manually. These machines also have *full power feed* to the cross-slides. 59–4.

When the saddle and larger ram-type machines have full power feed in four directions— the universal turret lathe—greater freedom is obtained in tooling setups.

Some saddle-type turret lathes are built with a cross-feeding turret, providing a feed in four directions to both the cross-slide and the turret.

TOOLING

The principal task on every turret lathe job is to tool up the machine and operate it so that the part may be made in the shortest possible time. There are four elements which make up the total production time for a job:

1. *Setup time* is the time that it takes to set and adjust all tools and cutters and arrange the work holding devices. When producing small quantity work, the best method of reducing setup time is by the use of universal tooling

Bardons & Oliver

59–3(A). Saddle-type turret lathe. On a saddle-type turret lathe the turret is mounted on a saddle which, together with its apron or gear box, moves back and forth directly on the bed.

59–3(B). A schematic-diagram showing the distinction between saddle-type and ram-type turret lathes.

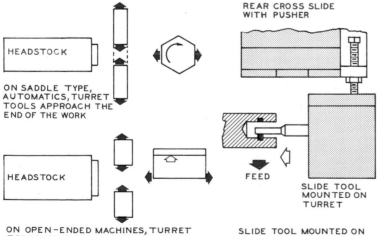

equipment and by keeping a permanent setup of tools on the machine.

2. *Work-handling time* is the time required to both load and remove the workpieces. Work-handling time can be kept to a minimum by the proper selection of chucks and fixtures which hold the work.

3. *Machine-handling time* can be considerably reduced by mounting all tools needed for a job on a turret so that each tool can be quickly indexed into cutting position. By so doing, efficiency and production are increased because the machine is cutting a greater percentage of the time available.

4. *Cutting time* is quite important in the high production of parts. Cutting time can be reduced by taking two or more cuts at the same time from one tool station (multiple cuts). Combine cuts by using the hexagon turret and cross-slide at the same time. Production time can be further reduced by increased feeds, which call for a rigid setup; by keeping overhang at a minimum, using rigid toolholders with high-speed tool bits; and by using overhead and center piloting on chuck work.

The illustration shows a basic hexagon-turret setup for a typical bar job such as the shaft shown. 59-5. This part is made from 2½″ diam. S.A.E. 3250 bar stock. Several changes in speed are made, so a ram-type universal machine of the all-gear head type is used.

The sequence of operations is given in the chart.

In short bar work of this type, the tooling should be arranged

Operation	Hexagon Turret	Square Turret
I	Feed to stock stop	Form to diameter (6)
II	Turn diameter (5)	Turn diameters (6) and (7)
III	Turn diameter (3)	Neck diameters (9) (7) (10)
IV	Face and chamfer (2)	
V	Center drill (1)	
VI	Support on center (1)	Turn diameter (4)
VII	Support on center	Neck diameter (8)
VIII	Thread diameter (3)	
IX		Cutoff and chamfer

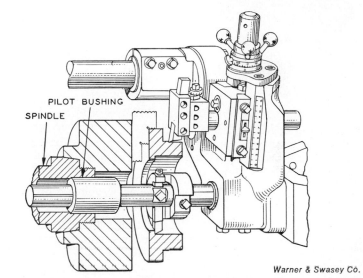

Warner & Swasey Co.

59-4. Multiple cuts should be made whenever possible. A boring cut can be combined with another cut. When a heavy boring cut is made, the boring bar should be supported on both ends.

59-5. Tooling setup for a shaft with twenty pieces in the lot.

Warner & Swasey Co.

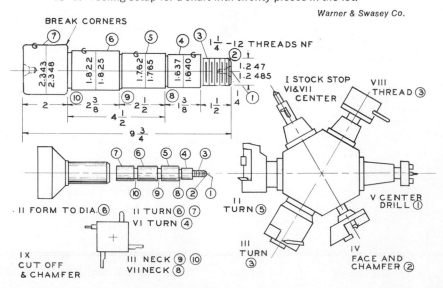

59–6. Bar or box turner combine in one unit a cutter holder and steady rest that travels with the cutter and supports the work.

59–7. Quick-acting slide tool. With this tool, boring, recessing, and back facing can be accomplished by simply changing the type of tool. Adjustment can be made quickly. Accuracy can be obtained with the micrometer adjusting screw.

BORING

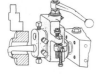

BACK FACING   RECESSING

so that cutters on the hexagon and square turret can be used at the same time without interfering with each other. By placing the square turret cutters in the right-hand corners the cuts can be combined. The setup is generally controlled by the number of pieces to be produced.

Tools and Attachments

In turning bar stock, collets and collet chucks are commonly used to hold the stock. Hand and power chucks of various types are used to hold individual pieces to be machined on turret lathes. Special fixtures are often used when holding irregular shapes.

Single-point tools of carbon tool steel, high-speed steel, Stellite, or carbide are used on turret lathes. These cutters are essentially of the same type used on engine lathes except that they are heavier.

Other tools consist of form tools, drills, reamers, taps, and dies.

Many devices are used for holding and adjusting cutting tools singly and in groups mounted on the hexagonal turret. Some of these devices are made for bar work, and others for chucking operations and, in some cases, for both.

Bar turners, sometimes called box or roller turners, are held on the hexagon turret. 59–6. They combine in one unit a holder for the cutter and steady rest that supports the work that travels with the cutter, permitting heavy cuts.

Stud boring bars and forged boring cutters are held in slide

59–8. Adjustable knee tool for bar work. This tool can be used for turning short diameters up to 1½″. Micrometer adjusting screw provides accuracy.

59–9. Drilling and turning tool turns the outside diameter of the stock and at the same time performs a drilling operation.

59–10. Combination stock stop and start drill for bar work.

COMBINATION STOCK STOP AND START DRILL

FEED

Warner & Swasey Co.

59–11. Reversible straight angle cutter holder for chucking work.

Brown & Sharpe Mfg. Co.

59–12. Pointing tool with "V" back rests.

59–13. Adjustable knurl holder. By loosening two screws, the adjusting screw, which screws into the bushing, and the swivel can be slid out easily as one unit, or quickly adjusted to the workpiece.

Brown & Sharpe Mfg. Co.

tools. Required adjustments can be made to size by means of a screw which has a graduated dial. This feature makes it possible to set the tool to any position desired, both accurately and quickly. 59–7. In addition to boring cuts, other operations, such as grooving, recessing, and back facing, can be accomplished by using this tool.

The *adjustable knee* tool can be used for turning, combined with drilling, boring, or centering. 59–8. This tool can be set up quickly and can be used on short pieces.

Drilling and turning tools perform two operations simultaneously. 59–9. They are fully adjustable, with the drill held by a bushing in an adjustable head. The turning blade is mounted in a blade holder, which is securely clamped to an arm protruding

from the side of the adjustable head.

The accuracy of a drilled hole is determined by its start in the work. *Starting drills* are always short and rigid in order to be able to stand up under heavy feeding pressure. 59–10. They produce a true cone in the metal so that the cutting edges of the second drill will have a clean, true start.

Reversible, adjustable-angle, cutter holders can be used in chucking operations. 59–11.

Pointing tools are used for pointing or facing the outer end of work requiring support. 59–12. Their blades, which cut tangentially, are set in the body and adjusted like box tool blades.

Adjustable *knurl holders* have a bushing arrangement which permits rapid adjustment or replacement of knurls. 59–13.

Unit 60. Automatic Cycle Lathes

The automatic lathe is distinguished from other lathes in a number of ways: (1) the way the tools are mounted, (2) the way they are fed into the work, (3) the arrangement about the work, and (4) the way the operation is done—in an automatic cycle.

Cutting tools are usually mounted in toolblocks carrying a number of individual single-point tools. Most of the cutting is done simultaneously.

The automatic lathe generally has two or more tool blocks, either mounted independently on a moving support such as the carriage or its own slide. Tool motion is synchronized; however, each tool can be set for its own travel path and distance.

One toolblock is mounted on the front of the lathe for turning operations—the movement being both longitudinally crosswise. The longitudinal feed is toward the headstock.

The other toolblock is located at the rear, to make forming, facing, and grooving cuts. All cutting tools remain in the machine during the entire machining operation.

Many different parts can be produced on automatic lathes. 60–1(A).

TWO AUTOMATIC LATHE TYPES

Automatic lathes can be placed in two broad general groups: (1) the type which supports the workpiece between centers, 60–1(B), and (2) the type that supports the work in a chuck, collet, or fixture. 60–2(A). Chucks are designed for fast loading and unloading; they may be operated pneumatically, hydraulically, or electrically.

The *between-center* automatic lathe can support long workpieces between centers, or it can hold shorter pieces at the spindle and be used for drilling and boring as well as turning and cross-feed operations.

The *automatic chucking* lathe does not have a tailstock and is used for operations that do not call for a two-ended support for the workpiece. 60–2(A).

Center-type machines use straight cam bars to transmit power to the cross-feed motions, while chucking machines seldom use cam control and generally use tracing attachments for curved and irregular shapes. Tailstock turrets on chucking machines can be indexed to several positions. 60–2(B).

AUTOMATIC SCREW MACHINES

Screw machines are so called because originally they were designed for machining screws and other small threaded parts.

The machines in this category may be single- or multiple-spindle types. Multiple-spindle machines are usually called multiple-spindle bar or chucking machines.

All types of screw machines—whether they be turret or sliding-headstock types—use time cycle control. This means that the total time for the production of a part is fixed in advance. The precise movement when each operation begins and ends is determined by cams, which also provide the driving force for all members. All cams on the machine rotate in unison, and the cycle is completed upon one revolution of the camshafts.

SINGLE-SPINDLE AUTOMATIC

The illustration shows a single-spindle, automatic, screw machine designed for bar work of small diameter and arranged so that it is completely automatic in operation. 60–3(A). Bar stock of various shapes is fed automatically through a hollow spindle against a bar stop and held during the operation by a collet. 60–3(B). The tools are mounted around a six-station turret which is in a vertical plane. The machine has a cross-slide which can

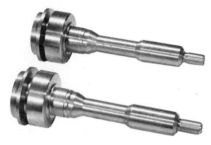

Sundstrand Machine Tool, Div. of Sundstrand Corp.

60–1(A). Part produced on an automatic lathe.

60–1(B). This automatic lathe has front, rear, and overhead carriages which face, chamfer, and form grooves in automobile clutch gears. Once parts are loaded, operation is completely automatic. Production rate is 153 parts per hour.

Sundstrand Machine Tool, Div. of Sundstrand Corp.

Warner & Swasey Co.

60–2(A). Single-spindle automatic chucking machine. This machine does not have a tailstock and is used for operations where the part has to be supported on one end only.

Brown & Sharpe Mfg. Co.

60–3(A). Single-spindle automatic turret-type screw machine. This machine is designed for bar work of small diameter and is completely automatic in operation.

60–2(B). Tailstock turret on chucking machine.

Pratt & Whitney Machine Tool

60–3(B). Close-up of end-working tools mounted on the turret which is mounted in a vertical plane and feeds toward the headstock. A variety of tools can be used in the turret. Operations such as countersinking, drilling, reaming, etc., can be done automatically on this machine.

Traub Strohm Corp.

carry tools on both front and rear. The turret indexes around a horizontal axis and is moved forward and backward on a slide which is controlled by a disc cam located at the right-hand end of the machine. 60–3(C). The cross-slide is controlled by two disc cams driven by the front drive shaft.

The front, rear, and right end of the machine are equipped with feed shafts for dog carriers, clutches, and cams that control operation.

Cams, clutches, levers, stops, and trip dogs are used to actuate and control the cutting tools without the attention of the operator. The stock is automatically fed and advanced the correct amount until the stock is used up. The control of the turret rotation, reverse spindle rotation to withdraw threading tools, and other operations are all done by self-acting mechanisms.

The camshaft usually rotates at a fixed rate of speed throughout the cycle. The cams that control the various motions are designed so that each motion starts and stops at a suitable time.

End-working tools are mounted on the turret which feeds toward the headstock.

All the common machining operations, such as drilling, reaming, turning, boring, and threading, can be done on these machines.

Many types of accessories can be used.

SWISS-TYPE AUTOMATIC

The Swiss-type automatic is a sliding-headstock type of lathe that works on an entirely different principle than the single-spindle automatic. 60–4(A&B). The work is fed longitudinally for turning operations, and cutting is done by a cross-slide tool arranged so that the tool is positioned in the path of the rotating

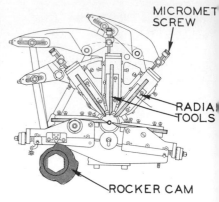

60–4(B). End view of Swiss-type screw machine showing tool-control mechanism and rocker cam.

George Gorton Machine Co.

workpiece. The workpiece is supported by a bushing which is held in a stationary support. The cutting is done in front of this bushing, which makes it possible to accurately machine long, slender workpieces.

Forming and cutting operations are performed by cross-feeding cuts. The headstock can

60–3(C). Turret-type screw machine has the turret mounted in vertical plane. Turret cam drives the turret through successive passes. The machine is provided with cams and dog carriers to control the machine motions.

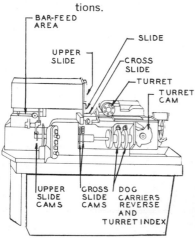

60–4(A). Swiss-type ⅜″ automatic bar machine. Five toolholders are mounted on the same support. The movement radially of the tools is straight in and out. See Fig. 60–4(B) for tool control mechanism and cam setup.

American Bechler Corp.

be controlled so as to dwell at any point while the cut is being made.

Five toolholders are mounted radially on the same support as the bushing. The movements of the tools are straight in and out. Curves, tapers, and other configurations can be machined by combining the motion of the cutting tool with the motion of the headstock.

By mounting accessories on the bed opposite the headstock, end-working operations such as drilling, boring, reaming, and threading can be accomplished.

Machines may vary in collet capacity from ³⁄₃₂″ to ½″, with a standard feed capacity of about 4″. Spindle speeds will range from 7,000 to 8,000 rpm.

The machines have a high degree of accuracy in precision work, such as producing small parts for watches and fine instruments.

MULTIPLE-SPINDLE AUTOMATICS

Multiple-spindle, automatic, simultaneous production cutting is made possible by the fact that these machines have a great deal more working space per tool than single-spindle automatics.

Multiple-spindle automatics may be equipped with four, five, six, or eight spindles. 60–5(A& B). The work is so arranged that each spindle is served by only one end-working tool and one cross-slide. Opposite each working spindle there is an end slide equipped with tools moving together and traveling the same distance. The cross-slide tools are usually individually mounted and are operated by individual

cams. The spindles carrying the barstock are held and rotated in an indexible stock reel. Machining takes place progressively at different tool positions until the final station is reached and the workpiece is completed. Since all cuts are made simultaneously, a finished part is produced every time the spindle indexes. The time consumed for completing one part is only equivalent to the

time taken during the longest operation plus non-cutting time.

The speed of the camshafts is increased during the non-cutting time for withdrawing the tools, spindle indexing, feeding the stock, and returning the tools into position for machining another part.

The cutting cycle is so arranged that all the tools start to feed at the same time. How-

Greenlee

60–5(A). Multiple-spindle automatic screw machine. This is a high-production machine capable of turning out a great number of screw machine products per hour.

60–5(B). Schematic of spindle arrangement for multiple-spindle automatic which shows spindle position where barstock is usually fed (shaded circle). Cut-off position is the one preceding the bar-feed position.

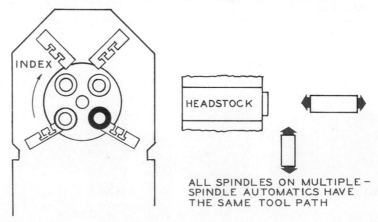

ALL SPINDLES ON MULTIPLE-SPINDLE AUTOMATICS HAVE THE SAME TOOL PATH

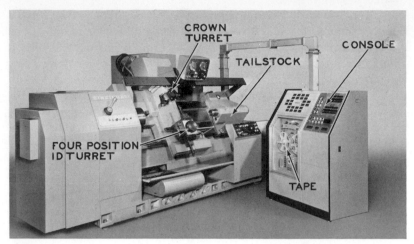

Cincinnati Milling Machine Co.

60–6. Numerically controlled turning center. This machine has two turrets, plus tailstock. Eight tools set in crown turret. Four-position ID turret with rapid toolchange system handles internal turning.

ever, on shorter cuts some of the tools will arrest cutting action as others cut at slower feed rates.

Standard cams of the disc or drum type can be used, depending upon the type of machine.

Multiple-spindle machines are made in a wide range of sizes not limited to bar stock but may be equipped with different types of chucks for holding individual workpieces. The machines are known as *chuckers*. They range from a 6″ swing to 15″, with power ratings from 7½ hp. to 75 hp.

Numerical Control Turning Center

The "Turning Center" shown in the illustration has been designed to produce workpieces of any configuration automatically, using numerical control (N/C). 60–6.

Shaft models are capable of all outside diameter turning operations, including profiling, necking, facing, rough turning, and threading. The machine remains permanently set up.

The unique design of the tool turret eliminates interference of tools with chuck, tailstock, or workpiece. The axis of the conical turret is tilted to make one edge of the cone perpendicular to the center line of the workpiece. Pre-set tools are mounted in slots around the periphery of the cone. The turret can be indexed through all eight of its positions without interference, and each tool point will index to the same precise point. Programming is exceptionally simple; you program the workpiece, not the tooling setup.

Universal models are designed to perform all internal machining operations—including boring, facing, grooving, profiling, threading, drilling, and reaming, as well as OD (outside diameter) operations. 60–7.

Expensive box turners and die chasers are not required. All tools use low-cost replaceable carbide inserts and the tools are pre-set off the machine in a simple setting gage.

VERTICAL BORING MILL

On this machine the workpiece rotates on a horizontal table. 60–8. The cutting tools, mounted on the adjustable-height crossrail, are held stationary except during feeding movements. The components of these machines duplicate the functions of various lathe components.

60–7. With five basic operations, almost any configuration can be made.

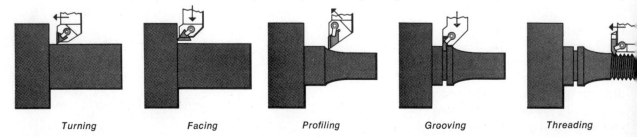

Turning   *Facing*   *Profiling*   *Grooving*   *Threading*

The main parts of the vertical boring mill are the *bed, housings, crossrail, heads,* and *arch.*

The table is rotated on bearings through a system of gearing. The boring mill shown here has a table diameter of 60″.

Infinitely variable feed rates are provided and may be changed without stopping the table. Turning a dial on the pendant increases or decreases feed while the tool is in the cut. All table feeds are geared to the table drive, thereby assuring constant chip load through the entire range.

A massive pentagon-shaped turret provides five tool positions and will accept a 3″ toolholder shank in each of the tool holes in the faces. The machine has a plain table, with or without steel body faceplate jaws, or with a 4-jaw independent chuck. All these units are interchangeable.

TRACER CONTROL LATHE

In the tracer control lathe, the tracing operation itself is automatic. 60–9. However, the operator has to position the tracing unit for each cut and has to return it to the starting position for the next cut.

A single-point tool is mounted on a slide that is connected to a tracing head. The slide and tracing head travel as a unit during the cutting operation. A sensitive *stylus* is located on the tracing head. This controls the source of power for the movement of the cross-slide which holds the cutting tool. The stylus is set so that it can follow the contours of a template, cutting the same contours on the workpiece.

Tracer systems can turn shapes that are difficult to machine on regular lathes. Other advantages are: (1) They can move the tool through a whole series of cuts, straight or contoured. (2) They use inexpensive single-point tools. (3) All parts produced are identical. (4) Complex parts can be inspected quickly. (5) Setup time is fast after the template is made.

The automatic tracer lathe shown here is an automatic copying lathe with 1 to 4 cut recycling The copying unit consists of a differential piston type hydraulic cylinder, the moving unit of which is integral with the tool block or blocks and a control

G .A. Gray Co.

60–8. Vertical boring mill, so named because the work rotates on a horizontal table. Cutting tools are stationary except for feed movements.

60–9. Automatic tracer lathe. This machine is an automatic copying machine.

H. E. S. Machine Tool, Inc.

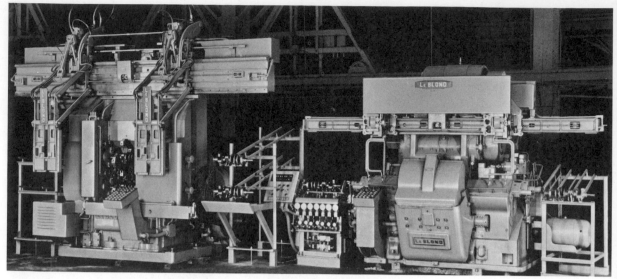

60–10. Crankshaft lathe. This center drive lathe is used to turn all line bearings, check the lobes of adjacent counterweights and turn the stub on flange ends. Both roughing and finishing are accomplished in the same cycle.

60–11. The automatic threading lathe can produce all types of threaded parts automatically.

valve linked to the tracer. "Piloting" consists of controlling the hydraulic feeds mechanically. This provides a constant feed per spindle revolution.

Programming is done by cut-out card wound on a drum which rotates relative to the longitudinal movement of the copying saddle. Every card has printed tracks, each of which corresponds to a function. The tracks are graduated to facilitate correct longitudinal positioning of the information in the cycle.

SPECIAL LATHES

Because lathes are widely used for many applications, highly specialized types have been developed.

For the automotive industry a lathe has been designed to machine crankshafts of forged steel, cast steel, or cast iron with 2, 3, 4, 6, or 8 throws. 60–10. These lathes are equipped for fully automatic cycles.

The automatic threading lathe shown here cuts left- and right-hand, single- and multi-start, internal and external, straight and tapered, Acme and buttressed, coarse and fine threads, to class 3 accuracy and better. 60–11. The single-point carbide tool with throwaway inserts maintains precision finish.

Simply setting a single block on vernier scale engages a single lathe lead cam at the desired position for all pitches from 4 to 24 tpi, using standard change gears.

Center drive contouring lathes are of massive construction. 60–12. The drive is located in the center of the machine. This machine has two square turrets located on the cross-slide as well as two carriages. Hexagon turrets are also located at the ends of the lathe. Each end of a part can be turned simultaneously on this lathe.

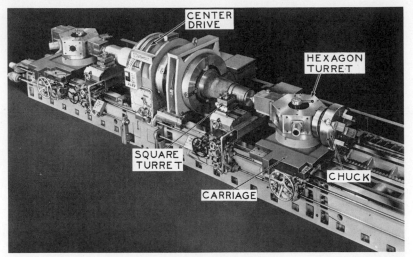

Gisholt Machine Co.

60–12. The center drive contouring lathe is provided with square and hexagon turrets with center drive.

Check Your Knowledge

1. Name three operations that can be performed on the engine lathe.

2. Name several types of production machines.

3. All lathe parts may be grouped into two major classifications. Name them.

4. What is the purpose of the following lathe parts: headstock, spindle, tailstock, lead screw, and quick change gear box?

5. How is the size of a lathe determined?

6. Name some types of lathes that have practically the same
fundamental parts as the engine lathe.

7. Describe the different types of single-point lathe tool bits.

8. Define cutting speed as it applies to lathe work.

9. In any basic turning operation, there are three primary factors. Name them.

10. Define feed.

11. What is the most common operation on the lathe?

12. Name four different types of taper systems.

13. Name three methods of cutting tapers on the engine lathe.

14. Describe a taper attachment.

15. Describe the method used in chasing threads on the lathe with a single-point tool.

16. How are turret lathes classified?

17. How does a turret lathe differ from an engine lathe?

18. Describe the difference between a ram and saddle-type turret lathe.

19. Why is "cutting time" important in the high production of parts?

20. What are "combined" and "multiple" cuts?

21. What is a governing factor in work-handling time?

22. What type of holding devices are used to hold stock in bar work?

23. What basic principle determines what type of tool should be selected for a certain job?

24. What type of work is done on a vertical turret lathe?

25. How is an automatic lathe distinguished from other lathes?

26. Describe a single-spindle automatic bar machine.

27. Describe a Swiss automatic. How does it differ from other automatic machines?

28. Compare a single-spindle automatic with a multiple-spindle automatic.

29. What special kind of work is done on a vertical boring mill?

30. Name some of the advantages of a tracer control lathe.

PROBLEMS

1. A bar of steel 3" in diameter is to be machined at 80 fpm. What spindle speed should be used?

2. Calculate the cutting speed in sfpm for a steel workpiece 2½" in diameter, revolving at 150 rpm in a lathe.

3. Calculate the amount of setover of the tailstock for turning a lathe center with a total length of stock 7", length of center 5⅛", length to be tapered 3⅞", with a No. 3 Morse taper of 0.602" per foot.

4. A taper 8" long has a large diameter of 2.0625" and a small diameter of 1.250". What should be the setting of the taper attachment in inches per foot to machine this taper?

5. Prepare an operation sheet for making a ⅝" x 4" hexagon head bolt on a turret lathe for 100 pieces.

6. What type of machine should be used for making ¼" x 1¼" hexagon head cap screws when quantities amount to 100 pieces; 25,000 pieces?

7. A rod 2" in diameter and turning at 150 rpm is to be cut off by a tool having a feed of 0.005" per revolution. What is the cutting time?

References

American Society for Metals, Metals Park, Ohio, *Metals Handbook,* 8th ed., "Machining," Vol. 3, 1967.

"Fundamentals of Turning," *American Machinist,* Special Report 567, 1965.

Johnson, Harold V., *General Industrial Machine Shop,* Peoria, Ill., Chas. A. Bennett Co., Inc., 1970.

The Warner and Swasey Company, Cleveland, Ohio, *Turret Lathe Operator's Manual,* 1940.

Boring workpiece held in chuck.

Clausing Div., Atlas Press Co.

Section Twelve

Producing Cylindrical Holes

HOLES in products can be produced by a variety of methods, by drilling, punching, coring, flame cutting, fly cutting, boring, ultrasonic and electric discharge machining, as well as by electron and laser machining. However, this section will be concerned chiefly with the drilling, boring, and reaming methods.

Hole production, though always important, formerly called for comparatively simple tools and equipment. Today hole production and finishing have become an exact science, in many instances calling for specialists with an extended knowledge of tools and machines.

Clausing Div., Atlas Press Co.

Most products today require holes for fasteners of various types.

A great many types of holes do not require extreme accuracy in their production. On the other hand, the production of interchangeable parts sometimes requires that the hole diameters and spacing between holes be held to limits of tolerance of plus or minus .0001″. Improvements in surface quality of holes have been made so that this quality is measured in microinches.

Drilling machines are most commonly used for the production of holes. The most common operations are: drilling, reaming, boring, counterboring, countersinking, and spotfacing.

Drills have been designed and engineered for almost every possible application so that the difference between one drill design and another is very small. Yet for production runs, it is important to use the correct drill designed for a particular operation.

Unit 61. Drills

Twist drills are by far the most commonly used. The illustration shows the accepted nomenclature for the different elements of a twist drill.

DRILL PARTS

Generally speaking, this drill has three principal parts: the point, the body, and the shank. 61–1. The point is the cone-shaped end which does the cutting. The body, which is the section between the point and the shank, has two grooves known as *flutes*. They provide a means of: (1) forming a suitable cutting edge or lip on the point of the drill, (2) providing a channel to carry the chips to the surface, and (3) providing a means for carrying the lubricant to the cutting edge. The *shank* is that part of the drill that fits into the spindle or chuck of the drill press. It varies in size and shape for the purpose for which it was designed.

The *point* has many construction features which must be carefully formed in relation to each other in order that the drill will cut efficiently and to size. The point as used here, is the entire cone-shaped surface of the cutting end of the drill.

The sharp edge at the extreme tip of the point is known as the *chisel edge*. The cutting action of the drill is done by the two *cutting lips*, or edges, which are formed by the intersection of the flutes and the cone-shaped point.

The section back of each cutting lip, called the *heel*, is relieved to form a cutting edge and prevent rubbing the material being drilled. The relieved portion is referred to as the *lip relief angle* and is one of the most important features of the point. When the drill is rotated under pressure, the two cutting lips shave metal off in chips and enable the drill to penetrate.

A narrow strip or *margin* at the end of each *land* (see drawing), running the entire length of the flutes, forms the full diameter of the body. Between the margin and the flute is a relieved portion which is known as *body clearance*. Body clearance reduces friction between the drill and the side of the hole and

Table 61-A. Suggested Lip Clearance Measured Across Margins*			
Drill Size	For General Purpose	For Hard and Tough Materials	For Soft and Free Machining Materials
No. 97 to 61	24°	20°	26°
No. 60 to 41	21°	18°	24°
No. 40 to 31	18°	16°	22°
⅛″ to ¼″	16°	14°	20°
F to 11⁄32″	14°	12°	18°
S to ½″	12°	10°	16°
33⁄64″ to ¾″	10°	8°	14°
49⁄64″ and larger	8°	7°	12°
* Chicago–Latrobe			

also allows lubricant to reach the point. This prevents the creation of excessive heat.

The angle between the flute and the axis of the drill is known as the *helix angle*. It affects the strength of the drill and the forming of chips.

The center column or backbone of the drill is known as the *web*. For added strength and rigidity the web is generally tapered from the point to the shank.

Lip Clearance

In order that the point may have effective cutting edges, the heel is relieved. This relief angle varies with the drill diameter and the material to be cut. See Table 61–A on page 290. If the lip-relief angle is too great, it weakens the cutting edge; if it is too small, there may not be sufficient clearance to allow the cutting edge to enter the work and the drill will split up the center. 61–2. The chisel edge angle generally should be about 120°–135°, but a few degrees less for smaller relief angles.

Lip Angle and Length

The two cutting lips of a drill must have exactly the same angle with the center line of the drill. 61–3. A difference in angles will cause one lip to take a larger cut and, consequently, put an unequal strain on the two cutting lips. If the cutting lips are unequal in length the chisel point will be off center even though the point angle may be uniform on both lips. 61–4. This condition will cause the drill to cut oversize. The effect of this condition is the same as though you put the axle of a wheel any place but the exact center of the wheel. Exception: Angle difference is sometimes purposely done to prevent binding in deep holes in material such as copper.

Drill Shanks

Drills may have either straight or tapered shanks. Tapered-shank drills are held in the tapered socket of the drilling machine while straight-shank drills are held in a drill chuck. Tapered-shank drills have a Morse taper of ⅝″ per foot and a tang

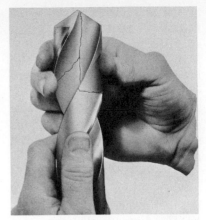

61–2. Drill splits up center due to insufficient lip clearance.

61–3. (A) A drill point without any lip clearance. Note that the corners of lip A and of heel B are in the same plane. (B) Proper lip clearance. Note how much lower the heel line B is than the cutting lip line A. This difference is the measure of the clearance.

Cleveland Twist Drill Co.

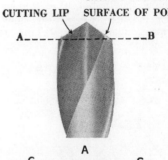

CUTTING LIP   SURFACE OF POINT

A — — — — — — — — — B

A

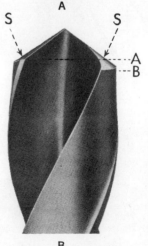

B

61–1. Parts of a twist drill.

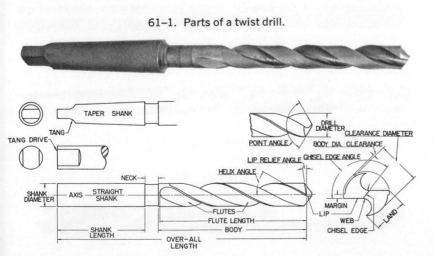

at the end of the taper which fits into a slot in the tapered spindle to prevent slipping. Many straight-shank drills also have a tang, 61–5, and are used with taper split sleeves. 61–6(A). The taper in the machine spindle should be free from burrs and scratches that may cause drill runout.

Tapered-shank drills can be removed from the spindle or sleeve with a drill drift. 61–6(B). NOTE: Fitted sockets are used to adapt tools having a different size of tapered shank than the tapered holes in the machine spindle.

DRILL SIZES

Drill sizes are indicated in four different ways:

1. Numerical—No. 80 to No. 1 (.0135″ to .228″).

2. Alphabetical—Letter A to letter Z (.234″ to .413″).

3. Fractional—$\frac{1}{64}$″ to 4″ and over by 64ths.

4. Drills are also available in fractional parts of a millimeter from .5 to $10.0^m/_m$ by $.1^m/_m$ and larger than $10.0^m/_m$ by $.5^m/_m$.

TYPES OF DRILLS

Many different drills may be used on drilling machines and other machine tools such as lathes, screw machines, turret lathes, jig borers, and special production machines. Each dif-ferent type is designed for a distinct application. As said, two general types are the straight-shank and the taper-shank drill. 61–7 & 61–9.

Some special types are here-with described:

Chipbreaker drills are de-signed to curl and break the chips in most materials where normally long, stringy chips are produced. 61–8.

Three- and four-fluted core drills are used for enlarging holes that have been previously cored or drilled. 61–10. Because of their use in cored holes in cast-

61–4. (A) Angles and lengths of cutting lips must be equal. (B) Lips are of equal length but have unequal angles. (C) Lips are of unequal length but have equal angles. (D) Lips are of unequal length and unequal angles.

Cleveland Twist Drill Co.

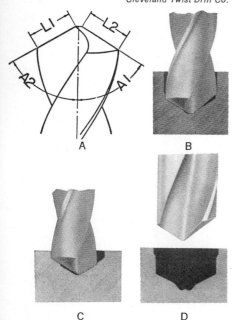

A

B

C

D

61–6. (A) Driver for straight-shank tanged drill. (B) Drill drift.

Cleveland Twist Drill Co.

Besly Products, Bendix Corp. Industrial Tools Div.

61–5. Straight-shank drill with tang.

A

B

Whitman & Barnes

61–7. Straight-shank drill.

Chicago Latrobe

61–8. Chipbreaker drill, pre-thinned.

61–9. Taper-shank drill.

Besly Products, Bendix Corp., Industrial Products Div.

ings, they are commonly called *core drills*. Their construction is such that the center portion will not cut. The amount of stock they remove is limited by the flute depth.

Coolant feeding or oil hole drills are designed for vertical heavy-duty drilling applications. 61–11. Coolants or lubricants are used in either mist or fluid form.

The gun drill is a simple, basic tool with three essential parts: tip, shank, and driver, usually constructed as one correctly aligned unit. 61–12.

The tip cuts the hole, maintains precision as it pilots the assembly through a straight hole, producing true high-finish walls.

The basic cutting angles may be varied for optimum results with the material to be drilled. 61–13.

The illustration shows the cutting angles. The tip is slightly larger than the shank, thus enabling the shank to rotate freely without contacting the hole wall. Oil is forced through the hole in the tip.

One end of the shank is attached to the driver, the other to the tip. The length may vary with the hole depth to be drilled, plus space for machine components. When securely fastened to the machine, the driver (and entire assembly) may revolve as it drills through a stationary workpiece; or the workpiece may revolve, with the drill remaining stationary.

A concentric hole through the driver's length permits oil to pass through to the shank and on through the tip.

National Twist Drill & Tool Co.

61–10. Three- and four-flute core drills.

National Twist Drill & Tool Co.

61–11. Taper-shank oil hole drill. Oil is fed under pressure to workpiece.

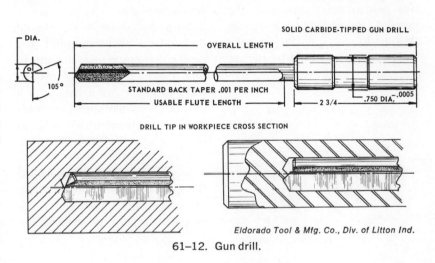

Eldorado Tool & Mfg. Co., Div. of Litton Ind.

61–12. Gun drill.

61–13. Nomenclature of gun drill nose.

Eldorado Tool & Mfg. Co., Div. of Litton Ind.

293

Gun drilling has become an essential machining technique. Gun drills are used on fast-run production jobs. They can hold diameter tolerances within a few thousandths inch.

Many types of holes can be produced by gun drilling methods, as shown. 61–14. Straight fluted drills are best suited for use in brass and other nonferrous metals.

Subland (two or more lands) drills are combination drills having separate margins for each of the two or more diameters, that extend the full length of the flutes. 61–15(A). The number of sublands is limited by the difference between the largest and the smallest cutting diameter.

Subland drills are used where it is desired to perform two or more operations in one pass of the tool. The two diameters or sublands may be ground so that they can be used both to drill and countersink for flathead machine screws, to drill and counterbore for socket head screws, or to drill a single or double radius to form a counterbored hole. 61–15(B).

These drills are used on high-production jobs.

Step drills—similar to subland drills—are recommended for production machining, to form in one operation a hole of two or more diameters, or a hole with a chamfer, counterbore, counterbore and chamfer, as well as other practical combinations involving angles or radii. 61–16.

Step drills are recommended for operations when subland drills are either too expensive or not practical because of small diameters, also when the difference between the diameters is too great. 61–17.

Spiral-Point Drills

Spiral-point drills offer many advantages not found on chisel-point drills. 61–18(A). The grinding of this drill has to be done on a grinding machine of special design.

In drilling a hole with a conventional drill, a center punch mark is required to start the drill. The spiral-point drill is

61–14. Types of holes that can be produced by gun drilling methods.

Eldorado Tool & Mfg. Co., Div. of Litton Ind.

PARTIAL HOLES   OVERLAP HOLES

BOLT CIRCLES & TUBE SHEETS

PLATENS—PARALLEL HOLES

STEP HOLES—CONCENTRIC

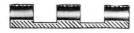

HINGES—INTERRUPTED HOLES

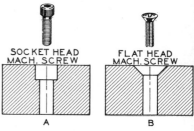

61–15(B). Subland drills can be used to drill two diameters simultaneously for (A) socket head machine screws and (B) flathead machine screws.

61–15(A). Subland drill.

Greenfield Tap & Die Corp.

61–16. Taper shank step drills.

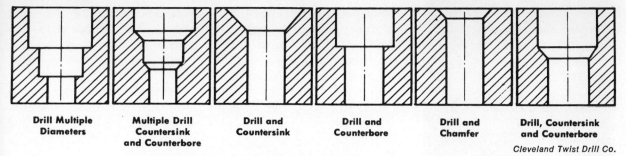

Drill Multiple Diameters | Multiple Drill Countersink and Counterbore | Drill and Countersink | Drill and Counterbore | Drill and Chamfer | Drill, Countersink and Counterbore

Cleveland Twist Drill Co.

61–17. Types of single operations possible with multiple-diameter drills.

ground so that it has a sharp point on the end, enabling the operator to start the drill accurately. 61–18(A). For production setups with chisel-point drills, drill bushings or jigs are necessary. In most instances, the spiral-point drill will start accurately and drill a hole without jigs or fixtures.

Most holes drilled with two-lipped drills are slightly oversize. With the spiral point, the average range of hole oversize is reduced 50%.

Spiral-point drills lend themselves to drilling operations on numerically controlled machines. The spiral point eliminates the need for hole-spotting (center punching or use of drill jigs and fixtures) operations.

Split-Point Drills

Split-point drills have a thinned web that serves to reduce end thrust. 61–19. This drill is commonly used for drilling tough work-hardening steels and super alloys. It produces accurate holes with a minimum amount of oversize.

BORING TOOLS AND BORING

Boring may be done on a variety of machines, such as vertical or horizontal boring mills, power fed drill presses, engine or turret lathes, milling machines, automatic boring machines, or jig borers.

When a very straight, accurate hole is required, a boring tool is generally used. Boring can be used to replace reamers when finishing holes to accurate size, or used to true up or enlarge drilled holes, to overcome eccentricity of the rough drilled hole, or to enlarge it to reaming size. The hole may be cored (made during the casting process by use of a green sand core). Boring can also be preliminary to a grinding operation performed on an internal grinding machine.

In all cases, a hole large enough to permit entry of the boring bar is a necessity. The boring head shown in the illustration is adjustable to 0.0005".

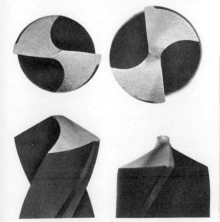

61–18(A). Comparison of a chisel-point drill (left) with a spiral-point drill (right).

Cincinnati Lathe & Tool Co.

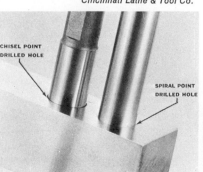

61–18(B). Comparison of hole roundness made by chisel-point drill and spiral-point drill.

Cincinnati Lathe & Tool Co.

CHISEL POINT DRILLED HOLE

SPIRAL POINT DRILLED HOLE

61–19. Split-point drill with thinned web to reduce end thrust.

National Twist Drill & Tool Co.

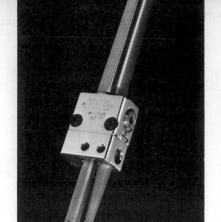

61–20. Adjustable boring head with micrometer adjustment.

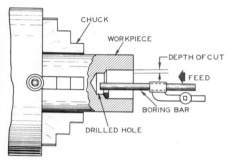

61–21. Boring with a single-point tool on the lathe.

61–22. Boring bar with Carboloy cemented carbide tips for doing a variety of boring operations.

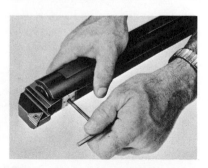

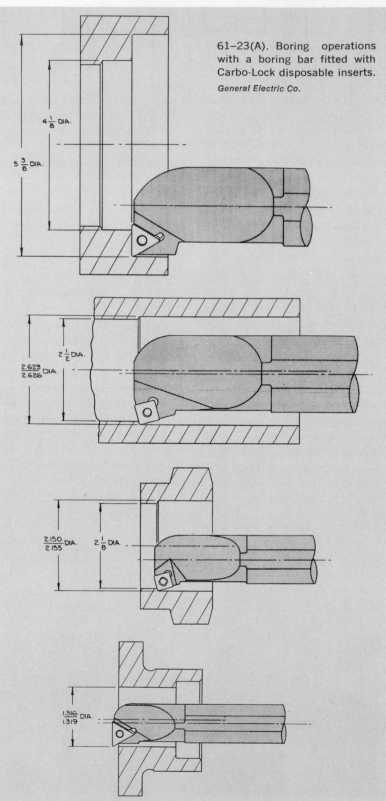

61–23(A). Boring operations with a boring bar fitted with Carbo-Lock disposable inserts.

61–20. This type is available in a wide range of sizes. Boring capacity may range from ¾" to 2" offset from center (hole capacity 4"). Similar types of boring heads are available with much larger boring capacity.

Boring tools are made in a wide variety of simple and compound designs. Many have micrometer or vernier adjustments.

Most boring operations use a single-point cutter inserted in a bar which can enter the hole. 61–21. Some boring bars use inserts of cemented carbide such as Carboloy. 61–22. These triangular inserts can be used for blind-hole boring, or boring to a square shoulder. The insert can be locked in place with a lock pin. The lock can be either tightened or loosened from the top or bottom, which makes insert indexing quick, easy, and accurate. 61–23(A).

Where tolerances are not too close, multiple-boring tools can be used advantageously.

Boring bars are of three basic types: (1) the stub bar, (2) the

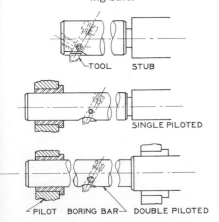

61–23(B). Three basic types of boring bars.

single-piloted bar, and (3) the multiple-piloted bar. 61–23(B).

Stub bars are used for boring short holes. The *single-piloted* bar is guided on its leading end as a prevention against its springing away from the work. The *multiple-piloted* bar is guided both ahead of and behind the cutter. NOTE: This bar ordinarily requires a floating or flexible driver.

The boring head may be equipped with either a tapered or straight shank.

COUNTERBORING, SPOTFACING, AND COUNTERSINKING

Counterboring, spotfacing, and countersinking can be performed on the drilling machine.

Counterboring is used to enlarge a hole to a given depth, as for a fillister head machine screw. The tool has a pilot which positions the counterbore in the hole. NOTE: Ordinarily, the pilot has a diameter about 0.0002" smaller than that of the drilled hole. Counterboring tools should be run at lower speeds than drills of corresponding diameter due to the shape of the tool and the large amount of cutting surface in contact with the work. 61–24(A&B).

Spotfacing is the process of smoothing off and squaring the surface of the workpiece around a hole to seat a washer, a nut, or a bolt. 61–25. This operation is similar to counterboring. Only a small amount of metal is removed around the top surface of the hole. A counterbore is often used, or a special spot-facing tool may be used.

Atlas Press Co.

61–24(B). Counterboring.

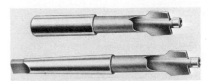

*Besly Products, Bendix Corp.,
Industrial Tools Div.*

61–24(A). Counterbores with straight shank and taper shanks for socket head cap screws.

61–25. Spotfacing.

Atlas Press Co.

Countersinking is for the purpose of enlarging the end of a hole to a conical form to receive a flat-head machine screw. 61–26(A). This tool has an included angle of 82° when used for this purpose. 61–26(B).

Countersinks for work turned on the lathe have an included angle of 60°. They are actually a combination center drill and countersink. 61–26(C).

Grinding the Drill

Most difficulties encountered in drilling arise from faulty grinding of either the point of the drill or the lip clearance. In grinding

61–26(A). High-speed single flute countersink.

61–26(B). Three-flute, carbide-tipped countersink.

61–26(C). Three types of combination drill and countersinks.

Threadwell Tap & Die Co.

a drill, three things have to be taken into consideration: (1) lip-relief or lip-clearance angle, (2) length and angle of the lips, and (3) location of the point and dead center in relation to the axis or center of the drill.

Point Angle

The proper point angle—as measured from the cutting edges through the axis of the drill—depends upon the material being drilled. 61–27. An included point angle of 118° as shown in Fig. A has been found satisfactory for the average class of work. In general it can be said that *the harder the material, the greater the point angle should be.* For example, an included point angle of 135° is recommended for manganese steel, while for wood fiber and similar materials, an included point angle of 80° is recommended. (See Figs. A, B, and C.)

Elimination of drill breakage depends to a very great extent upon the correct point grinding of the drill. It has been estimated that 90% of all drill breakage is caused by incorrect regrinding; for this reason, much emphasis should be placed upon the importance of this operation. 61–28.

Point grinding by hand requires a great deal of skill and care on the part of the operator; if skilled help is not available, the use of a point-grinding machine is recommended. 61–29. CAUTION:

Care should be taken during the regrinding operation that the drill is not allowed to get too hot. Also, it should never be cooled off in cold water, but

should be allowed to cool of its own accord. A sudden cooling is sure to result in a cracked drill.

Web Thinning

Owing to the fact that the web of a drill usually increases toward the shank, a web-thinning operation becomes necessary when the drill has been shortened by repeated grindings. 61–30. This operation is essential in order to minimize the pressure required to make the drill penetrate. Web thinning must be carried out equally on both sides of the web in order to assure that it will be centered. CAUTION: Care must also be taken that the point thinning is not carried out too far up the web, weakening the drill.

Drills of ⅛" diam. should have a web thickness of approximately 17%; ½" diam. drills

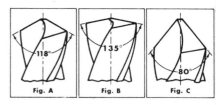

61–27. The proper point angle depends upon the material being drilled.

61–28. Incorrect point regrinding. (A) Unequal angles and length of lips unequal. (B) Unequal angles.

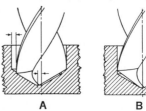

A   B

approximately 14%; 1" diam. drills 12%; over 1" diam., about 11%. A properly thinned web is shown.

Web thinning can best be accomplished on a special grinder, to obtain an accurate job. A tool-and-cutter grinder can also be used or the operation done freehand. However, it is difficult to obtain absolute accuracy by the freehand method.

Several different types of web thinning are in common use, as shown. 61–31(A). Again note: It is important that the job be done evenly, with some amount of stock removal from each cutting edge. The chip must form on the cutting edges and flow into the flute, and the shape of the thinning surface should not interfere with such chip flow.

Chip Formation in Drilling

Any drilling operation requires that the drill have the capability

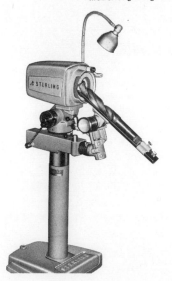

61–29. Drill pointing machine.

McDonough Mfg. Co.

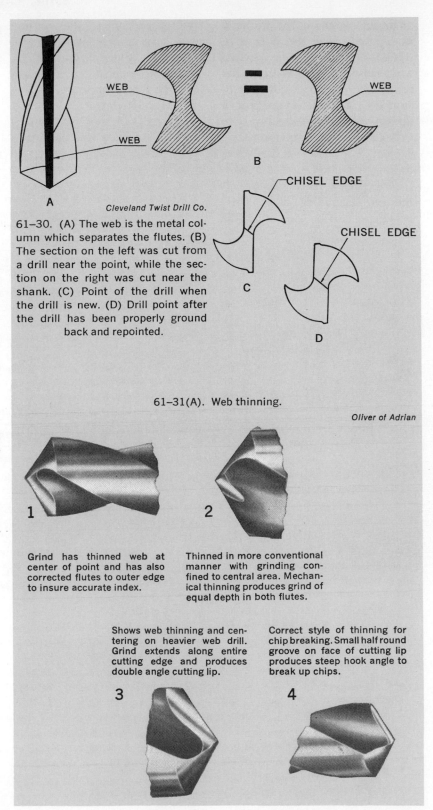

Cleveland Twist Drill Co.

61–30. (A) The web is the metal column which separates the flutes. (B) The section on the left was cut from a drill near the point, while the section on the right was cut near the shank. (C) Point of the drill when the drill is new. (D) Drill point after the drill has been properly ground back and repointed.

61–31(A). Web thinning.

Oliver of Adrian

1 Grind has thinned web at center of point and has also corrected flutes to outer edge to insure accurate index.

2 Thinned in more conventional manner with grinding confined to central area. Mechanical thinning produces grind of equal depth in both flutes.

3 Shows web thinning and centering on heavier web drill. Grind extends along entire cutting edge and produces double angle cutting lip.

4 Correct style of thinning for chip breaking. Small half round groove on face of cutting lip produces steep hook angle to break up chips.

of producing chips that are readily ejected from the hole. 61–31(B).

Because of the limited chip room in a drill, it is always desirable to have the chips broken up into relatively small pieces. Coiling of drill chips must be avoided, especially in deep hole drilling. 61–31(C). These coils tend to pack up in the flutes and prevent succeeding chips from coming out. This also stops the flow of coolant to the cutting edges, causing excessive heat and premature dulling of the tool.

The two main factors that affect chip formation are: (1) the ductility of the metal being drilled and (2) feed per revolution, or thickness of the chip. When drilling ductile material, the chips tend to bend and coil up as they are separated from the metal. The chips will tend to break up in less ductile materials, which is the desirable situation, and usually such materials can be drilled with standard drills. However, if this is not possible, chip breaker drills can be used in an effective manner. 61–31 (D).

Butterfield Div. of Litton Ind.

61–31(B). Chip produced with a chipbreaker drill.

61–31(C). An uncontrolled chip produced with a conventional drill. These coils tend to pack up the flutes and to prevent succeeding chips from coming out and also stop the flow of coolant to the cutting edges.

Butterfield Div. of Litton Ind.

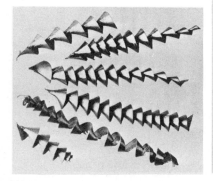

Table 61-B. Common Drill Troubles and Causes*	
Indications	Causes
Outer corners break down	Cutting speed too high. Hard spots in material. No cutting compound at drill point. Flutes clogged with chips.
Cutting edges chip.	Too much feed. Lip clearance too great.
Checks or cracks in cutting edges	Overheated or too quickly cooled while sharpening or drilling.
Margin chips.	Oversize jig bushing.
Drill breaks.	Point improperly ground. Feed too heavy. Spring or back lash in drill press, fixture, or work. Drill is dull. Flutes clogged with chips
Tang breaks.	Imperfect fit between taper shank and socket caused by dirt or chips, or burred or badly worn sockets.
Drill breaks when drilling brass or wood.	Flutes clogged with chips. Improper type drill.
Drill splits up center.	Lip clearance too small. Too much feed.
Drill will not enter work.	Drill is dull. Lip clearance too small. Too heavy a web.
Hole rough.	Point improperly ground or dull. No cutting compound at drill point. Improper cutting compound. Feed too great. Fixture not rigid.
Hole overside.	Unequal angle or length of the cutting edges—or both. Loose spindle.
Chip shape changes while drilling.	Drill becomes dull or cutting edges chipped.
Large chip coming out of one flute, small chip out of other flute.	Point improperly ground, one lip doing all the cutting.

* Cleveland Twist Drill Company.

Because of widely varying conditions, it is difficult to lay down hard and fast rules. Each job must be studied from the standpoint of chip formation.

SPEEDS AND FEEDS FOR DRILLS

The cutting speed for drilling operations is the peripheral speed of a point on the surface of the drill in contact with the workpiece. It is usually expressed in surface feet per minute. (sfm)

Because so many variables affect the results, no hard and fast rule for determining the exact cutting speed can be given. Several factors affect the choice of the best cutting speed: (1) kind of drill being used, (2) composition and hardness of material, (3) amount of feed, (4) condition of machine, and (5) use of coolant.

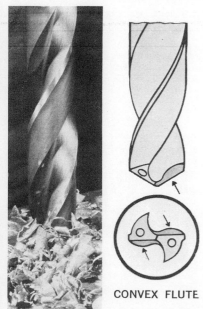

61–31(D). Chipbreaker drill.

Chicago-Latrobe Co.

CONVEX FLUTE

To find the rpm at which to run the drilling machine for a given cutting speed, use the following formula:

$$rpm = 3.8 \text{ x } \frac{sfm}{\text{Drill diam. in inches}}$$
$$sfm = .26 \text{ x rpm x drill diam. in inches}$$

Feed, as you know, is the distance the drill advances into the workpiece for each revolution. Although handbooks give surface

Table 61-C. Drill Speeds*	
Material to be Drilled	Recommended Speed in sfm
Alloy steel—300 to 400 Brinell	20–30
Aluminum and its alloys	200–300
Automotive steel forgings	40–50
Brass, bronze	150–300
Hard chilled cast iron	10–20
High-nickel steel or monel	30–50
High-tensile bronze	70–150
High-tensile steels (heat treated)	
35 to 40 Rockwell C	30–40
40 to 45 Rockwell C	25–35
45 to 50 Rockwell C	15–25
50 to 55 Rockwell C	7–15
Magnesium and its alloys	250–400
Malleable iron	80–90
Medium hard cast iron	50–100
Mild machinery steel, .2C to .3C	80–110
Plastics	100–300
Slate, stone, marble	15–25
Soft cast iron	75–125
Stainless steel	50
Steel, .4C to .5C	70–80
Tool steel, 1.2C	50–60
Titanium alloys	
Ti-75A (commercially pure)	50–60
RS-120	40–60
Ti-150A	40–50
Ti-140A	30–40
RC-130B	30–40
MST-6A1-4VA	20–35
MST-3A1-5CR	10–20
Wood	300–400

NOTE: Where carbon steel drills are applicable, decrease speeds from 40 to 50%.
* Chicago–Latrobe.

speeds and equivalent rpm for drills from $\frac{1}{16}''$ to $3''$, there are some reservations regarding feeds per revolution. As a general rule, the feed for a $\frac{1}{16}''$ drill should be about 0.0015″, with increases in close geometric ratio up to 0.013″ for a 1″ drill.

The speeds and feeds in the following tables apply to average working conditions and materials. They are recommended with due regard to conserving drills and avoiding excessive machine tool wear. Under many conditions, they may be considerably increased, while under others they are decreased. Of course, the liberal use of cooling compound will increase the life of tools.

DRILL JIGS AND FIXTURES

Drill jigs and fixtures are used to speed up production of drilled holes. They are largely associated with drilling machines and lathes, but some types are also used with shapers, milling machines, planers, and grinders.

Jigs, Vises

A jig is arranged so that the tool is guided to the workpiece by means of hardened bushings through which the drill passes and holds the workpiece in posi-

Table 61-D. Drill Feeds*	
Diameter of Drill, Inches	Feed per Revolution, Inches
Under $\frac{1}{8}$	.001 to .003
$\frac{1}{8}$ to $\frac{1}{4}$	.002 to .006
$\frac{1}{4}$ to $\frac{1}{2}$	.004 to .010
$\frac{1}{2}$ to 1	.007 to .015
1 and over	.015 to .025

* Chicago–Latrobe

tion. 61–32. This allows a considerable saving of time in drilling and allied operations such as reaming and boring.

When production is limited, fixtures and jigs can be quite simple in construction. 61–33. On the other hand, some drilling operations require more elaborate jigs and also locating and clamping methods for holding the workpiece. 61–34.

Vises and sometimes *V blocks* of various sizes can be used to hold cylindrical stock. 61–35(A). *Angle plates* can be fastened to

the machine table to hold workpieces to be drilled, while T bolts can be placed in slots on the table to hold work. 61–35(B).

Many other hold-down devices such as flat straps, U straps, gooseneck straps, and step blocks are used for special needs. 61–36.

Drill Chucks and Holders

Many drilling machines are equipped with Morse taper spindles. The drills are mounted directly in the spindle or by means of drill chucks, sockets, sleeves, or other holders that fit in the

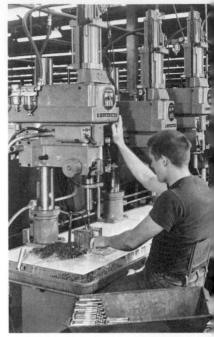

Atlas Press Co.

61–32. Drilling with a drill jig. The drill is guided to the workpiece through a drill bushing which locates the drill accurately.

61–33. Types of drill jigs: (A) hand operated, (B) air operated, and (C) foot treadle.

Heinrich Tools, Inc.

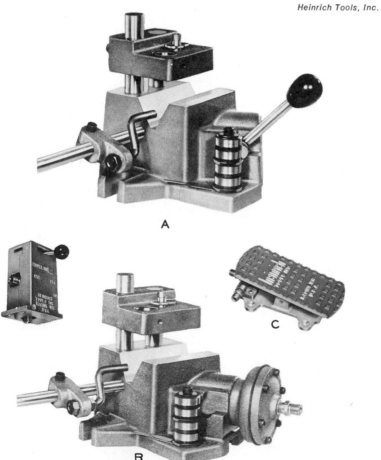

A

C

B

61–34. Drill fixture.

Atlas Press Co.

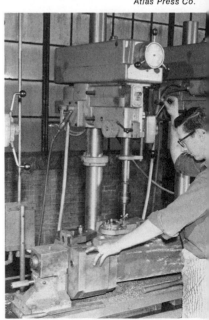

spindle. 61–37. Sleeves are used to build up the taper on the drill to fit the spindle. The tang on the drill fits into the sleeve or socket, and the drill can be removed from the socket or spindle with a drill drift. 61–38.

There are many different drill chucks in common use. Key-type and wrenchless hand-operated chucks hold straight-shank drills. 61–39. Hand-operated chucks are fast acting—can be opened or tightened by twisting a collar to lock the drill in place. *Quick change collets* permit tools to be taken off and put on the spindle of a drill press while the machine is running.

MULTIPLE-SPINDLE DRILL HEADS

A multiple-spindle drilling head may be mounted on the

R. K. LeBlond Machine Tool Co.

61–36. Gooseneck clamps being used to hold down workpiece being drilled.

61–35(A). Drill press vise.

61–35(B). Left: angle plate used to hold the workpiece during drilling. Right: a step block being used to hold work firmly while being drilled.

61–37. Sleeve or shell socket. Since a ½" drill with a No. 2 Morse taper shank will not fit a drill press spindle with a larger No. 3 hole, a sleeve or shell socket must be used.

61–38. A fitted socket is used to adapt drills having a different size tapered shank to the Morse taper holes in the drill press spindle.

61–39. Keyless drill chuck.

Golden Empire Corp.

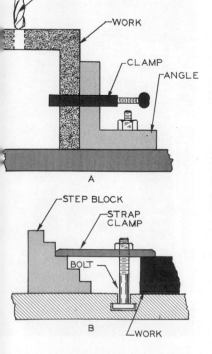

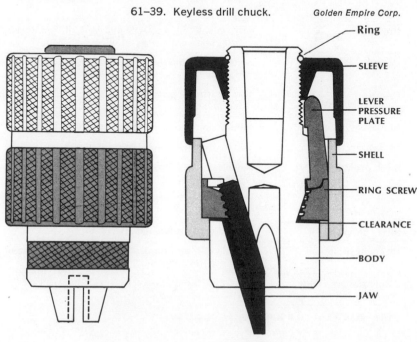

Ring

SLEEVE

LEVER PRESSURE PLATE

SHELL

RING SCREW

CLEARANCE

BODY

JAW

drill press spindle for drilling several holes at a time. 61–40. A jig or fixture is generally used in conjunction with a production drilling head. Horizontal drilling heads may also be used for drilling holes simultaneously in production operations.

CUTTING FLUIDS

Lubricants are important in extending the life of a drill and improving its cutting action. The ideal cutting medium is an oil that combines excellent lubricating qualities with equally good cooling qualities. Unfortunately, many of the best cutting lubricants do not possess good cooling properties. As previously noted, pure water is the best coolant available, yet it has virtually no lubricating properties.

Sulfurized oils have especially good lubricating qualities for machining steel, providing a superior finish.

Water-soluble oils have excellent cooling properties but do not provide the finish of sulfurized oils.

Straight mineral oils can be used on medium-heavy jobs but do not compare with sulfurized oils. The following list should be used as a suggestion only:

In production drilling machine work, the function of cooling the tool and workpiece becomes more important than that of lubricating. The amount of heat is so great that the life of the tool depends, to a large extent, upon the ability to carry away this heat at the same rate as it is generated. For that reason lubrication must often be subordinated to cooling. If, by means of the cutting fluid, the heat can be dissipated as fast as generated, overheating can be eliminated, and the only dulling action will then be that of abrasion. To obtain efficient cooling:

1. Direct as large a volume of coolant on the cutting edges of the drill as possible.

2. In vertical drilling of moderate-depth holes, direct a stream so as to fall onto the drill near the surface of the work.

3. In deep drilling, by raising the drill occasionally, the fluid

61–40. Multiple drilling head being used with a drill chuck in production operations.

Atlas Press Co.

Table 61-E. Lubricants Used in Drilling Operations*

Aluminum and its alloys:	Soluble oil; kerosene and lard oil compounds; light, nonviscous, neutral oil; kerosene and soluble oil mixtures.
Brass:	Dry, soluble oil; kerosene and lard oil compounds; light, nonviscous, neutral oil.
Copper:	Soluble oil; winter-strained lard oil; oleic acid compounds.
Cast iron:	Dry or with a jet of compressed air for a cooling medium.
Malleable iron:	Soluble oil or nonviscous, neutral oil.
Monel metal:	Soluble oil or sulfurized mineral oil.
Steel, ordinary:	Soluble oil; sulfurized oil; high extreme pressure valve mineral oil.
Steel, very hard and refractory:	Soluble oil; sulfurized oil; turpentine.
Steel, stainless:	Soluble oil or sulfurized mineral oil.
Wrought iron:	Soluble oil; sulfurized oil; high animal oil content, mineral oil compound.

Intermittent cooling of hardened steel should be avoided, as it may cause small checks or cracks.

* Cleveland Twist Drill Company.

can be directed into the hole ahead of the drill (skip drilling).

4. In horizontal drilling, the drill is usually directed horizontally along a flute so that some of it is forced down the flute toward the point.

5. In deep horizontal holes, it is often found advisable to use oil-feeding drills. Oil can be forced through the drill under pressure and is ejected next to the cutting edges.

To summarize, the best lubricants provide the following functions:

1. Drastically reduce friction between the tool and workpiece.

2. Dissipate heat and reduce friction.

3. Lubricate the chips, which aids in chip clearance.

4. Force chips back from the cutting edges and out the flute of oil-feeding drills.

5. Improve the finish of the work.

Unit 62.   Reaming

Reaming is a method of finishing and sizing holes that have been previously drilled or bored.

The material to be reamed has a great deal to do with the selection of the best type of reamer for the job. If the material is of the free cutting type, a reamer of fairly light construction can be selected. Hard, tough material requires a heavy reamer.

The terms applied to reamers are shown. 62–1. A great many standard types are available. The most common are: hand reamers, chucking reamers, shell reamers, adjustable reamers, expansion hand reamers, taper socket reamers, and taper pin reamers.

The *hand reamer* is made with both straight or spiral flutes. 62–2 (Page 306). This is a finishing tool used for the final sizing of holes. A starting taper is ground to provide easy entry of the reamer into the hole. Hand reaming is preferably done by guiding the tool in a fixture, as in hand tapping.

Chucking reamers are designed to provide efficient reaming in a wide range of materials. 62–3 (Page 306). They are commonly used in drill presses, turret lathes, and screw machines. They are regularly furnished with a 45° chamfer, are usually made of high-speed steel or have carbide cutting tips.

Rose chucking reamers have the lands ground cylindrically without radial relief. They have a back taper of approximately .005″ in the flute length to prevent binding in the reamed hole and are used primarily as roughing reamers. They can be used for finish reamers only on free

62–1. Terms applied to reamers.

Brown & Sharpe Mfg. Co.

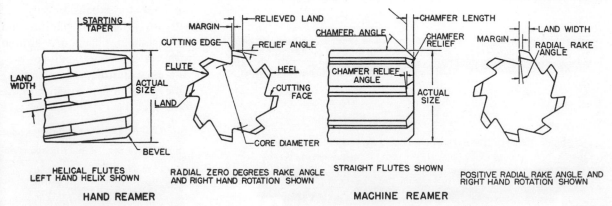

HAND REAMER — HELICAL FLUTES LEFT HAND HELIX SHOWN — RADIAL ZERO DEGREES RAKE ANGLE AND RIGHT HAND ROTATION SHOWN — MACHINE REAMER — STRAIGHT FLUTES SHOWN — POSITIVE RADIAL RAKE ANGLE AND RIGHT HAND ROTATION SHOWN

Union Twist Drill Co.

62–2. Hand reamer with spiral flutes and square shank.

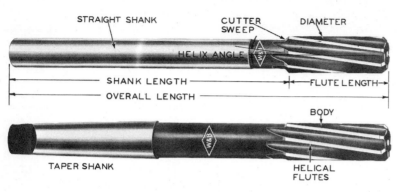

STRAIGHT SHANK   CUTTER SWEEP   DIAMETER

HELIX ANGLE

SHANK LENGTH — FLUTE LENGTH

OVERALL LENGTH

BODY

TAPER SHANK

HELICAL FLUTES

Whitman & Barnes

62–3. Spiral chucking reamer with helical flutes.

62–4(A). Shell reamer with helical flutes.

Cleveland Twist Drill Co.

62–4(B). Arbor for shell reamer.

62–5. Straight shank expansion chucking reamer.

62–6. Straight flute, right-hand cut, expansion, hand reamer.

Cleveland Twist Drill Co.

cutting steel and then only under the best conditions as to alignment and adequate flow of coolant.

Shell reamers are high-speed steel machine reamers. They are fluted almost their entire length and have a tapered hole (1/8″ per foot), the diameter being given at the large end. 62–4(A).

They are driven on an arbor which is tapered to fit the hole. 62–4(B). This tapered fit, coupled with slots in the reamer which engage lugs on the arbor, provides ample strength of drive. The large diameter of the arbor taper is slightly larger than the hole in the reamer, to allow space between the collar and the reamer. The space permits the reamer to be pried loose from the arbor without damaging either.

Adjustable reamers are production tools made in straight shank, taper shank, and shell styles. 62–5. They are designed for high-volume machine reaming operations. Blades can be expanded and reground many times before they are thrown away.

Expansion hand reamers are used to enlarge holes slightly to secure a desired fit. 62–6. They are made with an adjusting screw for expansion only and with an undersized pilot to aid in alignment. They are ground with an entering taper to provide easy starting. The following table gives limits to which these tools may be expanded:

Table 62-A. Reamer Expansion Limits

Size of Reamer	Limit of Expansion
1/4″ to 15/32″	+.006″
1/2″ to 31/32″	+.010″
1″ to 1 1/2″	+.012″

Table 62-B. Speeds, Feeds, and Stock Removal Allowances for High-Speed Steel and Carbide Tipped Machine Reamers*

Reamers will operate efficiently only when cutting evenly with all flutes at all times in properly drilled holes. The figures in this chart are based on this assumption. For best results, avoid holes that are rough with grooves at or beyond the finish diameter and holes that are crooked, bell-mouthed, oversized, or out of round. When holes to be reamed are not uniform or are out of line with the reamer, more stock must be allowed for removal. If conditions permit the use of carbide reamers, the speeds may often be increased over those recommended for high-speed steel reamers.

The 1/32" stock removal allowance for reaming the brass, bronze, and aluminum groups may be reduced to 1/64" drilling holes rather than cored holes. The cast iron groups do not include the alloyed cast irons, as these require 10% to 20% slower speeds.

MATERIAL TO BE REAMED

Diameter of Reamer Inches	Steel 120–200 Br. Low Carbon			Steel 200–300 Br. Low Carbon Alloy			Steel 300–400 Br. High Alloy			Cast Iron Soft 130 Br.			Cast Iron Medium 175 Br.		
	Speed, Feet Per Minute	Stock Removed Inside Diameter	Feed Per Revolution	Speed, Feet Per Minute	Stock Removed Inside Diameter	Feed Per Revolution	Speed, Feet Per Minute	Stock Removed Inside Diameter	Feed Per Revolution	Speed, Feet Per Minute	Stock Removed Inside Diameter	Feed Per Revolution	Speed, Feet Per Minute	Stock Removed Inside Diameter	Feed Per Revolution
1/4	75	1/64"	.005	60	1/64"	.004	25	1/64"	.004	100	1/64"	.006	85	1/64"	.006
3/8	75	1/64"	.007	60	1/64"	.007	25	1/64"	.006	100	1/64"	.008	85	1/64"	.008
1/2	90	1/32"	.008	70	1/32"	.008	30	1/32"	.007	120	1/32"	.010	95	1/32"	.010
5/8	90	1/32"	.010	70	1/32"	.010	30	1/32"	.008	120	1/32"	.012	95	1/32"	.012
3/4	90	1/32"	.012	70	1/32"	.012	30	1/32"	.010	120	1/32"	.015	85	1/32"	.015
7/8	90	1/32"	.013	70	1/32"	.013	30	1/32"	.010	120	1/32"	.017	95	1/32"	.017
1	90	1/32"	.015	70	1/32"	.015	30	1/32"	.012	120	1/32"	.020	95	1/32"	.020
1 1/4	90	1/32"	.020	70	1/32"	.015	30	1/32"	.012	120	1/32"	.020	95	1/32"	.020
1 1/2	90	1/32"	.020	70	1/32"	.015	30	1/32"	.012	120	1/32"	.020	95	1/32"	.020
1 3/4	90	1/32"	.020	70	1/32"	.015	30	1/32"	.012	120	1/32"	.020	95	1/32"	.020
2	90	1/32"	.020	70	1/32"	.015	30	1/32"	.012	120	1/32"	.020	95	1/32"	.020
2 1/2	90	3/64"	.020	70	3/64"	.015	30	3/64"	.012	120	3/64"	.020	95	3/64"	.020
3	90	3/64"	.020	70	3/64"	.015	30	3/64"	.012	120	3/64"	.020	95	3/64"	.020

Diameter of Reamer Inches	Cast Iron Hard 230 Br.			Brass and Bronze (Cast)			Malleable Iron (Cast)			Plastics			Aluminum Alloys (Cast)		
	Speed, Feet Per Minute	Stock Removed Inside Diameter	Feed Per Revolution	Speed, Feet Per Minute	Stock Removed Inside Diameter	Feed Per Revolution	Speed, Feet Per Minute	Stock Removed Inside Diameter	Feed Per Revolution	Speed, Feet Per Minute	Stock Removed Inside Diameter	Feed Per Revolution	Speed, Feet Per Minute	Stock Removed Inside Diameter	Feed Per Revolution
1/4	70	1/64"	.006	150	1/64"	.005	55	1/64"	.004	70	1/64"	.005	140	1/64"	.006
3/8	70	1/64"	.008	150	1/64"	.007	65	1/64"	.007	70	1/64"	.007	140	1/64"	.008
1/2	80	1/32"	.010	170	1/32"	.009	65	1/32"	.008	80	1/32"	.008	160	1/32"	.010
5/8	80	1/32"	.012	170	1/32"	.012	65	1/32"	.010	80	1/32"	.010	160	1/32"	.012
3/4	80	1/32"	.014	170	1/32"	.016	65	1/32"	.012	80	1/32"	.012	160	1/32"	.015
7/8	80	1/32"	.016	170	1/32"	.017	65	1/32"	.013	80	1/32"	.013	160	1/32"	.017
1	80	1/32"	.016	170	1/32"	.020	65	1/32"	.015	80	1/32"	.015	160	1/32"	.020
1 1/4	80	1/32"	.016	170	1/32"	.020	65	1/32"	.015	80	1/32"	.020	160	1/32"	.020
1 1/2	80	1/32"	.016	170	1/32"	.020	65	1/32"	.015	80	1/32"	.020	160	1/32"	.020
1 3/4	80	1/32"	.016	170	1/32"	.020	65	1/32"	.015	80	1/32"	.020	160	1/32"	.020
2	80	1/32"	.016	170	1/32"	.020	65	1/32"	.015	80	1/32"	.020	160	1/32"	.020
2 1/2	80	3/64"	.016	170	3/64"	.020	65	3/64"	.015	80	3/64"	.020	160	3/64"	.020
3	80	3/64"	.016	170	3/64"	.020	65	3/64"	.015	80	3/64"	.020	160	3/64"	.020

* Chicago-Latrobe.

307

Taper socket reamers are used for maintenance of holes for American Standard taper shanks. They are best for final finishing or for smoothing out nicks and burrs in machine spindles. 62–7.

Taper pin reamers have a taper of ¼″ per foot. 62–8. They are designed to ream holes into which standard taper pins will fit.

STOCK REMOVAL ALLOWANCE FOR REAMING

On many jobs the life of reamers is shortened because of insufficient amount of stock for the reamer to remove. The reason may be that the drill either is too near reamer size or is cutting too much oversize.

Many jobs are so set that only .015″ to .020″ is left for the reamer to remove. If this is true, the reamer must start to cut under very adverse conditions. Some holes may be drilled that are tapered or bell-mouthed due to lack of bushings or improperly pointed drills. The tendency of the reamer is to wedge in the hole rather than provide a cutting action. This can result in reamer wear or breakage.

Adequate stock removal allowances are important for best reaming results.

ALIGNMENT

To promote long reamer and bushing life and to produce straight, well-machined holes, it is essential that the spindle, reamer, bushing, and hole to be machined be in proper center line alignment. Misalignment between the bushing and spindle

Whitman & Barnes

62–7. Taper socket reamers: roughing reamer (top); finishing reamer (bottom).

Lavallee & Ide, Inc.

62–8. Taper pin reamer with spiral flutes and square shank.

can produce a worn bushing and a bell-mouthed hole.

REAMING SPEEDS AND FEEDS

Speeds and feeds for reaming may vary considerably depending in part on the material to be reamed, type of machine, and required finish and accuracy. In general, most machine reaming is done at about two-thirds the speed used for drilling the same material.

Feeds for reaming are usually much higher than those used for drilling, often running 200 to 300% of drill feeds. CAUTION: Too low a feed can result in excessive reamer wear. Too high a feed can reduce the accuracy of the hole and result in a poorer quality of finish.

Unit 63. Drilling Machines

PORTABLE DRILLS

Manually held electric portable drills are recommended only for operations that cannot be performed on drilling machines, especially in assembly work. 63–1. Portable drills are powered by small electric motors and contain chucks that will handle drills from ¹⁄₁₆″ to ¾″ in diameter. NOTE: When there is

a fire hazard from sparks, portable drills are powered by means of compressed air.

THE DRILL PRESS

The drill press is one of the most important machine tools in the industrial shop. The drilling machine can be used not only for drilling but also reaming, boring, counterboring, countersinking, and tapping. It can also be used in honing and lapping operations.

The size of the upright or sensitive drilling machine is determined by the diameter of the largest workpiece that can be drilled on center.

Sensitive Drilling Machine

This machine is hand fed, usually belt driven, for drilling small holes in light work. 63–2. The machine consists of a column which holds the motor, vertical spindle, and horizontal table. The feed is by means of a rack and pinion drive on the sleeve holding the rotating spindle.

Upright Drilling Machine

The upright drilling machine has a column rising from a base and carries a table for the workpiece and spindle head. This machine is heavier than the sensitive drill. Some types are equipped with belts and pulleys. Others have an all-gear drive for power. The machine shown in the illustration has an all-gear drive, with speeds as low as 60 rpm and as high as 2,880 rpm and capacities up to 1½" steel. 63–3. Auto-

matic power feed is available with hand reverse, foot reverse, or automatic reverse for tapping. The drill is carried in a tapered socket in the spindle, into which it seats itself to transmit power to make the cut.

Low speeds are ideal for spot facing, counterboring, reaming, large hole drilling, and tapping.

Gang Drilling Machine

The gang drilling machine is basically a series of single-spindle drilling heads mounted on a long table. 63–4. This machine is used for production work to perform a number of operations in sequence. Each head is equipped with a different tool to drill the part being machined as it moves from one station to the next. 63–5 (Page 310).

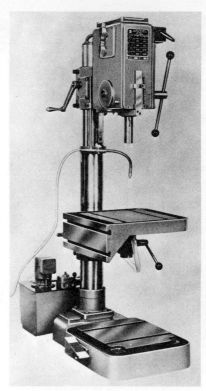

63–3. Upright drill press with direct gear drive. Has 1½" capacity in steel.

63–2. Sensitive-type drilling machine.

Atlas Press Co.

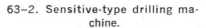
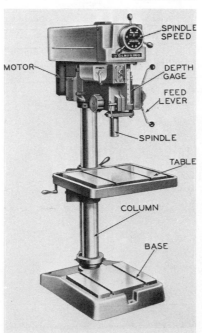

63–4. Gang drilling machine.

Cincinnati Bickford Machine Co.

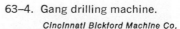
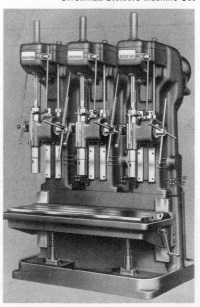

63–1. Portable power drill.

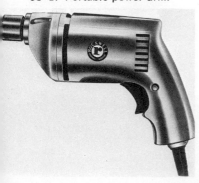

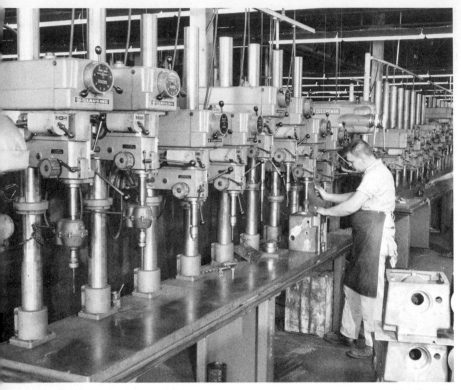

Atlas Press Co.

63–5. Gang drilling machine. Each head can be equipped with a different tool.

South Bend Lathe Co.

63–6. Multiple-spindle drilling and tapping machine.

63–7. Numerically controlled turret drilling machine used for boring, drilling, tapping, and milling operations.

Avey Machine Tool Co.

63–8(A). Sensitive radial drilling machine.

Fosdick Machine Tool Co.

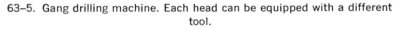

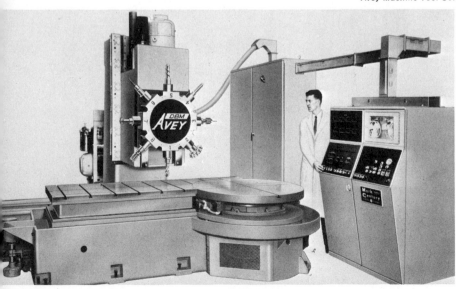

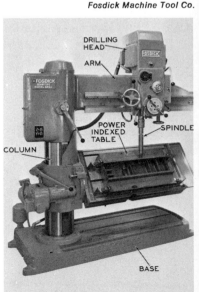

Production heads may be equipped with multiple drills so that several holes can be drilled simultaneously.

Multiple-Spindle Drilling Machine

Several types of multiple drill heads are available for different classes of work. 63–6. For long-run production, the most efficient type is the custom-designed, fixed-center head with each spindle geared to revolve the drill at the proper speed for the drill diameter. The majority of fixed-center drill heads are gear driven. Some types of adjustable-center heads use universal joints for more efficient control.

NOTE: Unless all holes are of equal diameter, or nearly so, the efficiency of the head is reduced to the maximum rpm of the drill with the largest diameter.

Drills in the head may be located at random, within the range of the drilling head and machine table. Drill jigs and fixtures are used in conjunction with this type of drilling. The drills are guided in bushings to maintain accurate hole location.

All drills should be kept sharp, as one dull drill in a cluster impairs the efficiency of all.

Machines of this type have been made with from 2 to more than 200 spindles and range from ½ hp to more than 100 hp.

Turret Drilling Machine

The turret drilling machine increases the production rate by eliminating the need for tool changes. 63–7. It is equipped with a multi-sided spindle turret having 6, 8, or 10 spindles. The turret may be indexed to the desired tool in the sequence desired.

Machines are available in a variety of sizes. One can take the place of several drilling machines. It performs all common drilling operations as well as tapping and other operations.

The machine has electrical controls for manual use as well as the tape-control system.

Radial Drilling Machine

Radial drilling machines are available in a variety of sizes and capacities. 63–8(A). Column diameters range up to 30″ or more with arm lengths of 14′. Drilling capacities for drills up to 5″ are possible.

The drilling head slides along a large radial arm to provide adjustment of the drilling distance from the column. The radial arm carries a drill head which can be moved over a large area and swung at angles necessary for angular drilling.

Large workpieces can be set on the base of the machine, which can also hold revolving fixtures and jigs for drilling. 63–8(B).

These machines are provided with a wide range of spindle speeds and automatic feeds.

Gun Drilling Machines

The choice of proper machines to be used with gun drilling or

63–8(B). Radial drilling machine. Part shown can be drilled on four sides with one setup.

Fosdick Machine Tool Co.

gun boring tools is of major concern in both manufacturing and machine shop operations. 63–9.

Gun drill machines may have one or many spindles with speeds ranging from 300 to 15,000 rpm.

Three types of spindles are used: (1) Way type: spindles that advance along a bar, a flat, or V-ways. (2) Quill type: such as drill press spindles. (3) Fixed spindle type: used where the work advances.

Spindles may be fix-mounted as to axial location, either stationary on the feed saddle, or they can be on a horizontal (X) and/or vertical (Y) slide for coordinate movement.

In some types of gun drilling machines, the gun drill is held stationary in the machine, while

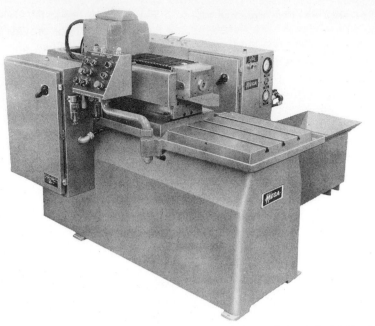

Eldorado Tool & Mfg. Co.,
Div. of Litton Ind.

63–9. Gun drilling machine.

63–10. Top: Typical gun drilling machine setups.

Eldorado Tool & Mfg. Co., Div. of Litton Ind.

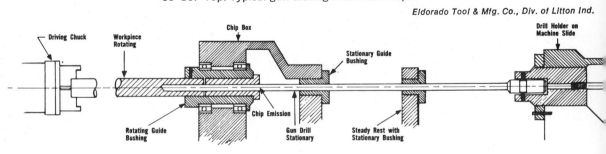

Normal machine set-up with rotating workpiece and stationary drill.

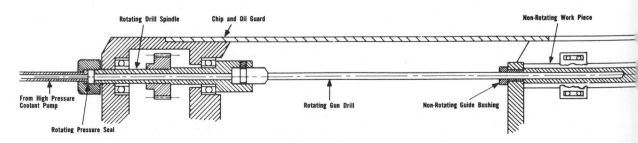

Machine set-up with stationary workpiece and rotating drill.

the workpiece rotates. 63–10. In this instance the cutting oil or coolant mix is forced under high pressure to the socket holding the gun drill and on to the tool's oil channel. In other machines the tool rotates and the work is stationary. A rotary union or gland is used, mounted either ahead or in back of the spindle, to introduce fluid into the coolant channel.

When the workpiece rotates, it is necessary to halt the spindle each time the work is loaded or unloaded.

The illustration shows a gun drilling machine in which all the elements are self-contained. The way type base, feed device, saddle, and chip box are integrated as one unit. The feed mechanism is arranged on a horizontal center plane of the spindle axis, and locked into the back of the chip box. All forces are concentrated on this center plane. This avoids misalignment caused by variations in cutting forces that result from having a feed mechanism below the ways of the machine, with the spindle axis above.

Some machines designed for horizontal gun drilling will drill holes up to 20″ in length or more.

Products such as crankshafts, camshafts, connecting rods, rifle barrels, and printing press rolls are drilled on these machines.

Transfer-Type Drilling Machines

In the automotive industry, there are many applications where workpieces index along a line between self-contained machining units.

These machines are frequently designated as automated because they transfer the workpiece from one station to the next, performing a series of operations such as finish boring, counterboring, facing, reaming, tapping, and others, until the part is completed. 63–11. They may have only two

63–11. Transfer machine. Aluminum automobile transmissions are produced at a rate of 124 parts per hour by this closed loop pallet-type machine. Operations performed are rough, semifinish and finish boring, counterboring, facing, reaming, tapping, and pressing a plain bearing.

Ex-Cell-O Corp.

or three stations or have a complex arrangement doing a great variety of operations, as illustrated.

The principal feature of transfer machines is that they are able to transfer between stations by means of a rail or conveyor. Sometimes the shape of the part makes this impossible, and it becomes necessary to provide a holding fixture or pallet (flat board or metal plate) on which the work is clamped.

The machine in the illustration uses a closed-loop numerical control system. In this system the instructions from the tape reader are sorted and acted on by a control unit in such a way that the servomotor moves the table the amount indicated on the tape.

BORING MACHINES

There are several types of drilling and boring machines in common use by industry. 63–12. They include (1) vertical boring

machines (61–13), (2) horizontal boring machines, and (3) jig boring machines. Many of the operations done on these machines can be done on others, such as the lathe or vertical and horizontal milling machines.

Horizontal Boring Machine

A horizontal boring machine can perform boring, drilling, and milling operations. Characteristically, the workpiece is held stationary while the tool revolves. The horizontal spindle supports and drives the cutting tool. It may be fed along its axis for boring and drilling, or can be clamped in a fixed position for milling. The direction of rotation is reversible for either right- or left-hand cutters and for tapping operations.

The headstock of the machine supports the spindle and spindle sleeve and also contains all spindle-drive and feed gearing. It

may be fed vertically or clamped in a fixed position.

Horizontal machines are primarily intended for large or heavy work, to assure their greatest efficiency and economy of application. 63–14.

The size is designated by the diameter of the spindle, which may range from 3″ to 14″.

With proper tooling and accessories, a series of operations can be performed in a single setup.

These machines, with their variety of operations, are ideally suited for numerical control.

Jig Boring Machines

Jig borers are constructed along two general lines: (1) the single-column and (2) the planer type. 63–15. These machines resemble vertical millers but in spite of the similarity, the small differences between them are of extreme importance.

63–13. Vertical numerically controlled drilling and boring machine.

Carlton Machine Tool Co.

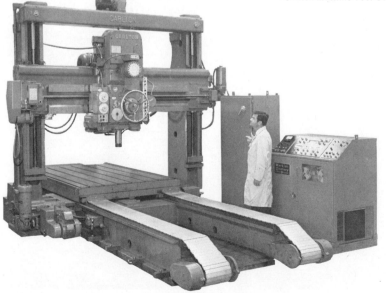

63–12. Horizontal production drilling machine.

Atlas Press Co.

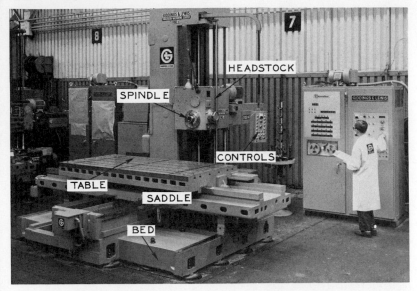

Giddings & Lewis Machine Tool Co.

63-14. Numerically controlled horizontal boring machine. The work is held stationary while the tool is revolved. Work is mounted on a table having longitudinal and crosswise movements.

The cutting tool rotates on a spindle which feeds along the vertical axis. The single-column machine accomplishes positioning by compound movement of the table. The planer-type machine provides movement through the table and cross-movement by transversing the head along the rail.

The jig borer's overall rigidity and mass serve to reduce errors caused by deflection, vibration, and temperature change, which is extremely important to precision work. The spindle is precise and rigid to provide accurate feeding along its axis. The positioning control is accurate to 0.0001″ for absolute spacing of holes. This accuracy is obtained

63-15. Precision jig borer. This machine resembles a vertical milling machine and is equipped with accurate measuring devices for controlling table movements.

Moore Special Tool Co., Inc.

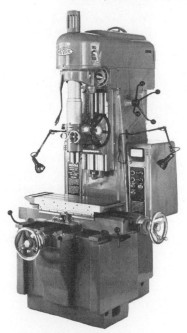

63-16. This double-end boring machine with two spindles at each end has flat and inverted V-way table construction and adjustable bridges.

Heald Machine Co.

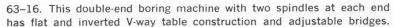

by one of three methods: (1) use of lead screws, (2) mechanical or electrical gaging, or (3) optical measuring.

Single-point tools assure maximum accuracy in hole geometry. Tools are usually held in a boring head. These can be of the offset variety.

Jig borers are used primarily in the production of dies, gages, and jigs. These machines, with their variety of operations, are ideally suited for numerical control.

Double-End Boring Machine

A double-end precision boring machine also makes use of single-point cutting tools. 63–16. The machines, if arranged with spindles on both ends, are capable of doing such work as boring, counterboring, grooving, and facing. Dimensional accuracy can be maintained to 0.0001″.

Check Your Knowledge

1. What operations can be performed on a drilling machine?

2. Name the three principal parts of a twist drill.

3. Name three functions of the flutes of a drill.

4. What is the recommended lip angle of drills used in general work?

5. What causes an oversize drilled hole?

6. What is the effect of insufficient lip clearance?

7. What is the effect of too much lip clearance?

8. Why is it important to have both cutting edges of a drill of equal length and angle?

9. What is the advantage of split-point drills?

10. What is the difference between boring and drilling?

11. Explain the terms counterboring, spot facing and countersinking.

12. In grinding a drill, three things have to be taken into consideration. What are they?

13. Name some important factors that influence the proper grinding of a drill.

14. What factors affect the choice of the best cutting speed?

15. What is the importance of drill jigs and fixtures in the production drilling of holes?

16. Define the meaning of feed as related to drilling operations.

17. Name three advantages of multiple-spindle drill heads.

18. What lubricants are best suited for drilling ordinary mild steel?

19. How are machine reamers classified?

20. How can you tell the difference between a hand reamer and a machine reamer?

21. What is the advantage of a rose reamer over a shell reamer?

22. Name four classes of drill presses.

23. What two types of feed mechanisms are used on drilling machines?

24. Describe an upright drilling machine and explain the purpose for which it is usually designed.

25. What are the advantages of a gang drilling machine?

26. What advantages do turret drilling machines have over other types?

27. Describe the gun drilling process.

28. Name the advantages of the transfer-type drilling machine.

29. Name three types of boring machines.

30. Give a description of a jig boring machine.

Problems

1. Calculate the diameter of a drill that has a cutting speed of 120 fpm at 320 rpm.

2. Calculate the approximate number of rpm to run a ⅜″ drill at a cutting speed of 280 fpm.

3. In drilling holes in mild steel, what would be the correct spindle speed for each of the following drills: ¼″, ⅜″, ½″, and ¾″?

4. Calculate the cutting speeds obtained from a 1⅛″ drill making the following rpm:

    (a) 170   (c) 407   (e) 102
    (b) 272   (d) 509

5. A 2″ hole is drilled in a workpiece with a drill revolving at the rate of 24 rpm. What is the cutting speed?

6. How many rpm must a 1½″ drill make in order to have a cutting speed of 30 fpm?

References

American Machinist's Handbook, New York, McGraw-Hill Book Co., 1955.

American Society of Tool and Manufacturing Engineers, *Tool Engineers Handbook,* 2nd ed., New York, McGraw-Hill Book Co., 1959.

Berg, R. T., "Fundamentals of Boring," *American Machinist,* June 25, 1964.

Oxford, C. J., "Mechanics of Drilling," *The Tool Engineer,* May, 1954.

Section Thirteen

Machining Metal with Shapers

and Planers

Rockford Machine Tool Co.

Unit 64.

The Shaper

One of the most common and useful machines found in the machine shop is the shaper.

The shaper is used primarily for machining flat surfaces with a single-point tool. However, many other operations such as cutting external and internal keyways, dovetails, T-slots, gear racks, grooves, and miscellaneous shapes can be machined on the shaper. Curved or irregular surfaces can also be machined on the shaper by skilled operators.

Shapers can be clasified according to their general design features as follows:

(A) Horizontal-plain or universal: (1) push-cut, (2) draw-cut.

(B) Vertical: (1) slotter, (2) keyseater.

(C) Special.

HORIZONTAL SHAPERS

There are two types of horizontal push-type shapers, (1) the mechanical crank type and (2) the hydraulic type.

Crank Shapers

In the crank shaper, circular motion may be changed to reciprocating motion by three different devices: (1) an eccentric, (2) a cam, and (3) a crank pin. The third method is standard. Forward and return strokes are transmitted to the ram by the circular motion of the crank gear or bull wheel, acting through the crank pin and rocker arm. 64–1(A&B).

Whether the bull wheel revolves fast or slowly is determined by the speed for which the machine has been set. As shown, the bull wheel carries a crank pin; as the wheel revolves, the crank pin describes a circular path and moves the rocker arm. The rocker arm pivots at its lower end on a hinge pin, and the upper end is connected to the shaper ram by a link attached to the clamp block. The slot in the rocker arm prevents the crank pin from locking the bull wheel and rocker arm together so that neither can move. The link which is connected to the clamp block makes it possible for the ram to travel horizontally back and forth. 64–2.

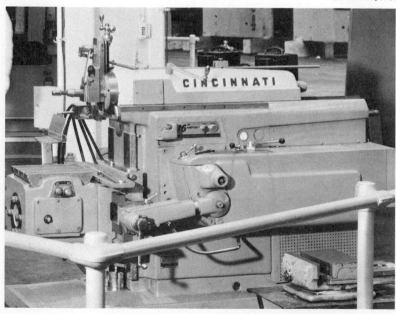

64–1(A). This crank shaper is mechanically driven, using a crankpin on the driving wheel to drive the ram.

Cincinnati, Inc.

64–1(B). Shaping a part on a crank shaper.

The ram of the shaper travels faster on the return stroke than on the forward cutting stroke. The principle is illustrated in the drawing. It takes about 1½ times as long for the ram to move forward on the cutting stroke as it does to make the "quick return."

The crank pin, designated as P^1, is in this position at the start of the cutting stroke and at the end of the return stroke. 64–3(A). When the shaper is in operation, the crank pin moves in a direction indicated by the arrow-arc, A, terminating at P^2. During this forward stroke, the sliding block has moved in the upper end of the rocker arm. Point P^2, therefore, also marks the beginning of the return crank pin stroke. 64–3(A).

The rotation of the crank pin reverses the direction of the rocker arm, causing the ram to begin its return stroke. The crank pin moves through the arc B until it reaches the original starting point P^1, ready for another forward stroke.

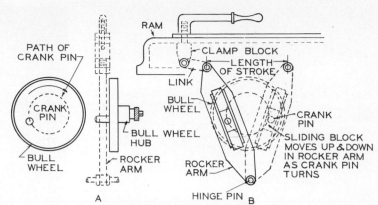

64–2. Drive of crank shaper. (A) Shows the path of the crankpin as the bull wheel revolves. (B) Shows the position of the rocker arm at each end of the stroke. The sliding block acts as a bearing for the crankpin in the long slot of the rocker arm.

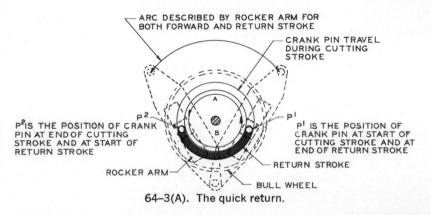

64–3(A). The quick return.

The Hydraulic Shaper

The hydraulic shaper is the same as the crank shaper in general appearance. 64–4. The fundamental difference is in the method used to drive the ram. In the hydraulic shaper, a flow of oil from a high-presure pump acts against a piston to move the ram. This gives the ram a smooth positive drive which prevents any backlash, common to the gear-driven shaper. It is possible to obtain a wider range of cutting speeds and feeds. The length of stroke and position of the ram may be adjusted without stop-ping the machine. The cutting speed can be adjusted by a single lever ranging from zero to maximum.

The table is equipped with a hydraulic feed across the line of tool travel. This takes place while the tool is clear of the workpiece.

The return stroke on the hydraulic shaper is approximately twice as fast as the forward cutting stroke.

VERTICAL SHAPER

The vertical shaper or slotter is equipped with a vertical ram which moves with a vertical reciprocating motion. 64–5. The drive mechanism is of the crank or gear type. The worktable may be revolved, permitting a variety of operations to be done on this machine. The circular feed of the table permits the machining of curved surfaces. 64–6.

A special vertical shaper used for cutting keyways in gears, pulleys, and other similar products is known as a *keyseater*.

DRAW-CUT SHAPER

In this shaper the cutting action of the tool is the opposite

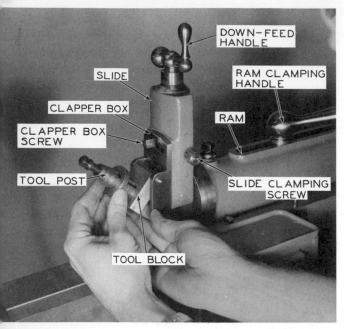

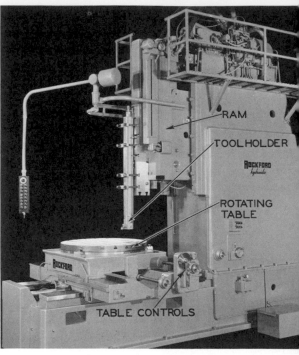

South Bend Lathe Works

64–3(B) Illustration showing the important parts of the toolhead of a crank shaper.

64–5. Hydraulic 36″ slotter.

64–4. Hydraulic ram shaper in operation.

Rockford Machine Tool Co.

64–6. Hydraulic slotter in operation. Ram moves in a vertical plane and tool cuts on the downstroke of the ram.

Rockford Machine Tool Co.

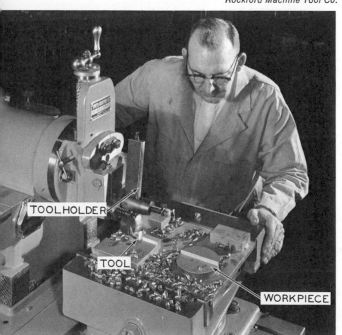

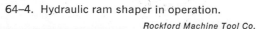

of the push-cut type. Horizontal draw-cut shapers are used where heavy cuts are necessary such as the machining of large die blocks. 64–7.

The draw-cut shaper permits a longer stroke than the push-cut type. An overarm support is provided for the ram, which permits the cutting force to act against the column so that the workpiece is forced against the adjustable back bearing or column face, reducing the strain against the cross rail and preventing vitbration and chatter.

Draw-cut shapers are made with strokes up to 72".

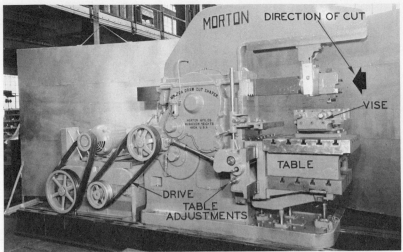

Morton Ind., Inc.

64–7. Draw-cut shaper. Cut is being made the opposite of a conventional shaper—toward the column.

Unit 65.   Shaper Tools

Shaper tools are single-point cutting tools, very similar to lathe cutting tools.

TYPES

Two basic types of tools are generally used in machining work on the shaper—tool bits and forged tools. 65–1 (Page 322). Tool bits are held in a toolholder, while forged tools are a heavy bar-type tool. Shaper tools can be made of high-speed steel, cast alloy, or cemented carbide. The high-speed tool bit has a greater impact toughness than tools made of cast alloy or cemented carbide.

The clearance angles and forms of shaper tools are of extreme importance. 65–2. Shaper tools should always be ground with the proper clearance on the side as well as the end of the tool. A side clearance of approximately 2° is commonly used. Various shapes of shaper tools are shown. Tool angles vary depending upon the material and particular job being done.

USING SHAPER TOOLS

The initial cut is usually a roughing cut, used to bring the work within a few thousandths of an inch of the finished dimensions. On steel, .010" to .015" should be left for finishing. On cast iron, the amount should be from .005" to .010".

The shaper tool sometimes has a tendency to chatter. This may be due to one of several things: (1) improper clamping and setting of the tool; (2) tool not ground properly; (3) improper clamping of the work; (4) improper adjustment of the machine; or (5) improper cutting speed.

SHAPER TOOLHOLDERS

The type of toolholder shown is commonly used to maintain the proper angle of tool to workpiece. 65–3. With this type, the tool bit may be rotated and held at different angles for a variety of cuts, which makes it possible to machine various corners. 65–4.

Lathe toolholders that hold the tool at a 16° to 20° angle generally do not work well on shapers. 65–5 (Page 322). Because it provides the tool with a steep back rake angle at the cutting edge, it can cause chatter during the cutting operation.

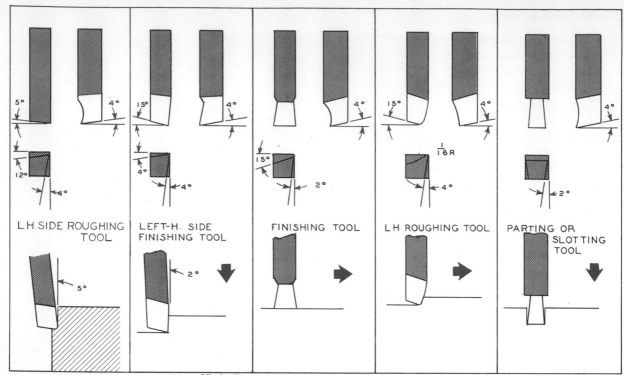

65–1. Tool shapes for machining mild steel.

L H SIDE ROUGHING TOOL

LEFT-H. SIDE FINISHING TOOL

FINISHING TOOL

L H ROUGHING TOOL

PARTING OR SLOTTING TOOL

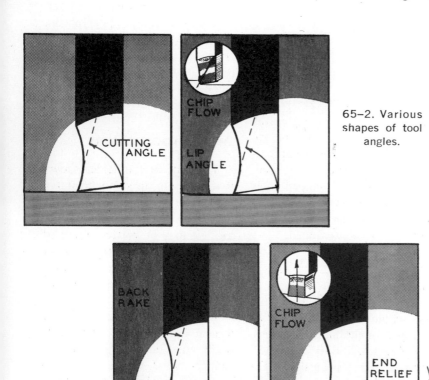

CUTTING ANGLE

CHIP FLOW

LIP ANGLE

BACK RAKE

CHIP FLOW

END RELIEF

65–2. Various shapes of tool angles.

65–3. Adjustable shaper toolholder. Tool is adjusted by loosening the nut and swiveling the tool to the desired angle.

Armstrong Bros. Tool Co.

NUT

TOOL

An *extension* shaper tool can be used for machining the inside of holes for internal machining operations such as shown. 65–6.

Holding the Workpiece

The workpiece must be held securely and solidly while it is being machined, in order to obtain accurate results. It is equally important that the workpiece not spring out of shape during the cut. It has to be supported properly or efforts at proper tool grinding and careful shaper operation are a total loss.

Most work done on the shaper is held in a vise. 65–7 & 65–9. Seating the workpiece properly is important. When doing this: (1) clamping surfaces should be free of burrs and nicks; (2) the workpiece should be tapped with a soft hammer to seat it properly in the vise; and (3) rough castings should be shimmed to get ample support.

Vise jaws are commonly set in alignment with the stroke of the ram or with the cross-feed of the table. The workpiece should be clamped with its true side against the solid jaw of the vise. A wedge (sometimes called a hold-down) can be used on the opposite side of the workpiece against the movable jaw. 65–8.

Workpieces may also be bolted with clamps directly on the table in a variety of ways. 65–11 (Page 324). Thin work can be held in

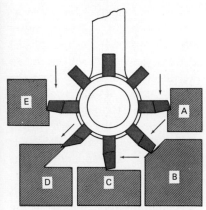

65–4. Shaper toolholder at various angles. Swivel head of adjustable toolholder can be turned in several positions: (A) vertical cut; (B) angular cut; (C) horizontal cut; (D) angular dovetail cut; and (E) vertical cut.

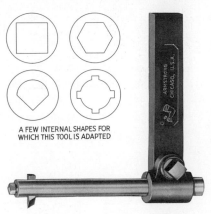

A FEW INTERNAL SHAPES FOR WHICH THIS TOOL IS ADAPTED

Armstrong Bros. Tool Co.

65–6. Extension shaper toolholder.

65–5. Lathe toolholders do not work well on the shaper.

Cincinnati, Inc.

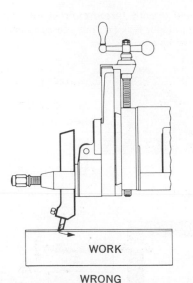

WORK

WRONG

LATHE TOOL USED FOR SHAPING WILL DIG INTO WORK

WORK

RIGHT

GOOSENECK TOOL WILL SWING OUT OF WORK

65–7. Shaper vise.

65–8. Hold-downs or wedges used to hold workpieces in vise.

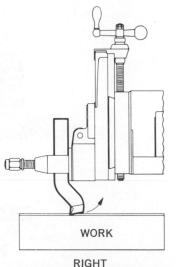

8°

WEDGE

WORKPIECE

WEDGE

PARALLELS

MOVABLE JAW

FIXED JAW

UNEVEN SURFACE

DRILL ROD

MACHINED SURFACE

South Bend Lathe Works

65–9. Clamping the workpiece in the shaper vise. Note that the hold-down is against the movable jaw.

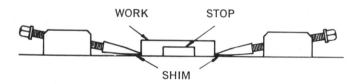

WORK   STOP

SHIM

HOLDING THIN WORK WITH TOE DOGS

Cincinnati, Inc.

65–10. Holding work with toe dogs.

place with toe dogs (65–10) and other workpieces can be mounted on angle plates. 65–12.

When mounting work on the table, a solid, square, dial indicator, or surface gage can be used to align the workpiece in the setup. 65–13.

The tool should be set vertically so that it will swing away from the work if it slips. 65–14. The clapper box should be set so that its top slants away from the cutting edge of the tool, permitting the tool to clear the workpiece on the return stroke of the ram. The cutting edge is also protected from undue wear by these precautions. 65–14.

A rigid setup can be obtained by clamping the tool with the smallest possible overhang. 65–15.

SHAPER OPERATIONS

Most shaper work consists of machining a flat surface held in

65–11. Right and wrong methods of clamping the workpiece to the table of the shaper.

Cincinnati, Inc.

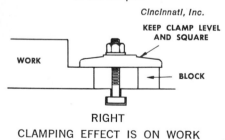

KEEP CLAMP LEVEL AND SQUARE

WORK

BLOCK

RIGHT
CLAMPING EFFECT IS ON WORK

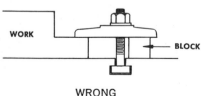

WORK

BLOCK

WRONG
CLAMPING EFFECT IS ON BLOCK

65–12. Top: Workpiece mounted directly to the table clamps and blocks. Bottom: Angle plate and planer jack holding and supporting the workpiece.

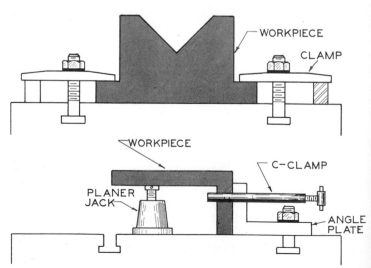

WORKPIECE

CLAMP

WORKPIECE

PLANER JACK

C-CLAMP

ANGLE PLATE

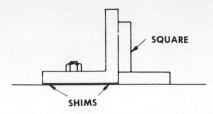

SHIMS

SQUARE

SQUARING UP ANGLE FOR SHAPING

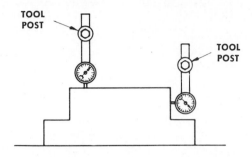

TOOL POST

TOOL POST

USING DIAL INDICATOR FOR SETTING WORK LEVEL AND PARALLEL

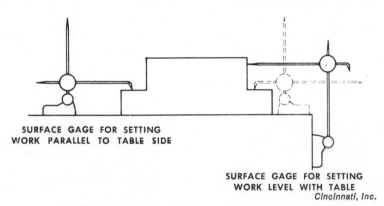

SURFACE GAGE FOR SETTING
WORK PARALLEL TO TABLE SIDE

SURFACE GAGE FOR SETTING
WORK LEVEL WITH TABLE

Cincinnati, Inc.

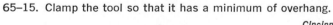
65–13. Aligning the workpiece on the shaper table.

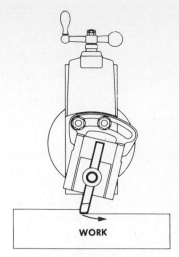

WORK

WRONG
TOOL WILL DIG INTO WORK

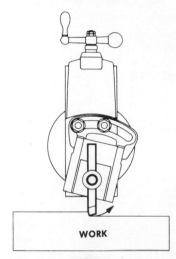

WORK

RIGHT
TOOL WILL SWING OUT OF WORK

Cincinnati, Inc.

65–14. Set the tool vertically so that
it will swing away from the workpiece
if it slips.

65–15. Clamp the tool so that it has a minimum of overhang.

Cincinnati, Inc.

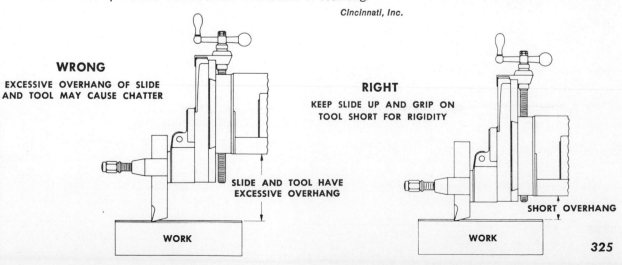

WRONG
EXCESSIVE OVERHANG OF SLIDE
AND TOOL MAY CAUSE CHATTER

SLIDE AND TOOL HAVE
EXCESSIVE OVERHANG

WORK

RIGHT
KEEP SLIDE UP AND GRIP ON
TOOL SHORT FOR RIGIDITY

SHORT OVERHANG

WORK

a vise or mounted directly on the table. A good finish depends upon several factors: (1) shape of the tool; (2) speed; (3) depth of cut; (4) the rate of feed; (5) the type of material being machined; and (6) the condition of the machine.

To review the operations that can be performed on the shaper, these are: (1) making horizontal cuts; (2) squaring stock; (3) making vertical and angular cuts; (4) using index centers to machine splines; (5) cutting keyways and stop cuts; and (6) planing irregular surfaces. 65–16, 65–17, & 65–18.

SHAPER SPEEDS AND FEEDS

When set for any particular speed, a shaper will make a constant number of strokes regardless of the stroke length. The speed rate of a crank shaper is based on the number of strokes made by the ram during 1 minute of operation. Thus the operator must change the rate to achieve good results with different conditions.

On modern shapers, speed changes are made by levers that are convenient to the operator. An *index plate* indicates which gears to engage.

Cutting Speed

Since cutting speed is the distance per minute that the cutting tool moves over the workpiece, adjustment depends upon the following factors: (1) kind of material to be cut; (2) amount of material to be removed at each cut; (3) type of material in the cutting tool; and (4) condition of the machine.

Table 65 gives the recommended cutting speeds for shaping.

Because the cut is intermittent, computation of cutting speed requires a little more figuring than finding the cutting speed of the lathe or drill press.

Table 65. Cutting Speeds (fpm) for Shaping	
Tool—High-Speed Steel	
Brass	200
Mild machine steel	80–100
Tool steel	50–60
Cast iron, soft	60–70
Tool—Carbon Steel	
Tool steel	25
Cast iron, soft	30
Mild machine steel	40
Brass	100

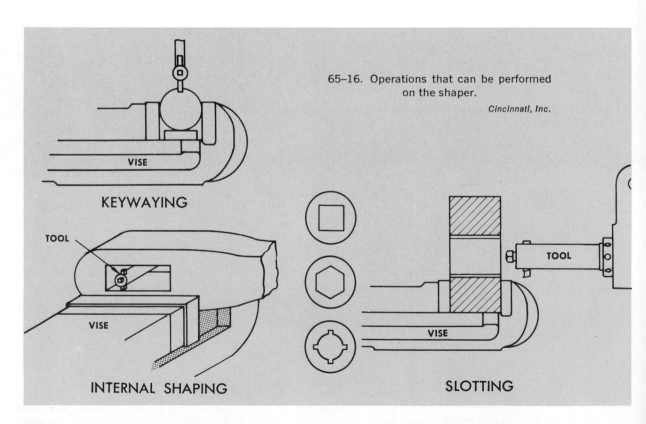

65–16. Operations that can be performed on the shaper.

Cincinnati, Inc.

VISE

KEYWAYING

TOOL

VISE

INTERNAL SHAPING

TOOL

VISE

SLOTTING

The cutting speed for the shaper is stated as the rate of tool travel as it makes a given number of strokes of a given length in 1 minute, and the ratio of cutting stroke time to return stroke time. Most shapers take about 1½ times as long to make the cutting stroke as to make the return stroke. The ratio is 2:3. The sum of these figures is 5;

therefore the return stroke requires $\frac{2}{5}$ of the cycle time, and the cutting stroke requires $\frac{3}{5}$ of the cycle time. One cutting stroke and one return stroke would make one complete cycle ($\frac{5}{5}$).

Given the length of the stroke in inches and the number of strokes per minute, their product is the number of inches cut during 1 minute of the shaper's operation. Since the cutting speed is always given in fpm, this must be multiplied by 12 to reduce to inches.

The actual cutting time is $\frac{3}{5}$ of the total time. Since *distance divided by time equals rate,* divide the distance in feet by $\frac{3}{5}$ (multiply by $\frac{5}{3}$). The resulting answer will be the cutting speed. NOTE: It will be easier to mul-

tiply by .14 than to multiply every time first by 12 and then by $\frac{5}{3}$ ($\frac{1}{12} \times \frac{5}{3}$) = 0.14 approximately.

The formula for figuring the cutting speed would then be $CS = 0.14 \times N \times L$.

Where

CS = cutting speed in fpm
N = strokes per minute
L = length of stroke

Feed

The feed can be hand or power. However, when vertical surfaces are machined, the feed is controlled by the crank handle on the tool head.

The amount of feed is based upon: (1) depth of cut, (2) condition of machine, (3) cutting speed, and (4) finish desired.

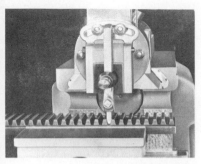

Cincinnati, Inc.

65–17. Machining a rack on a shaper.

65–18. Machining a spline using a shaper index center.

Cincinnati, Inc.

Unit 66.   Planers

Planing is used primarily for producing horizontal, vertical, or inclined flat surfaces. The action of a planer is different from that of work done on the shaper in that the workpiece is reciprocated past stationary single-point tools.

Planers are capable of handling large and heavy workpieces. Such pieces are reciprocated at relatively slow speeds and the crossrail is provided with several tool heads so that simultaneous cuts can be made at each movement of the table. A combination

of tools can be mounted in each tool head and can be moved in and out of position so that cuts can be made during both directions of table movement.

PLANER DRIVES

Planers are provided with a variety of drives: (1) gear drive, (2) hydraulic drive, (3) belt drive, (4) screw drive, (5) crank drive, and (6) variable-speed motor drive. Plate or edge planers are generally operated by the screw drive. Small planers generally employ the crank drive.

Hydraulic table drives eliminate the need for gearing and variable-speed electrical equipment. They provide for infinitely adjustable table speeds on both strokes, with very smooth operation. However, hydraulic drives are limited to the smaller types of planer because it is difficult to control the long piston strokes and the compressibility of hydraulic fluids when heavy cuts are being made.

Geared drives employ reversing motors. The table is driven by means of a gear engaging a rack on the underside of the table.

PLANER SIZES AND CAPACITIES

The size of a planer is designated according to the size of the largest work that the table will accommodate. For example, a 36″ × 36″ × 10′ planer will accommodate work of these

66–1. Planer tools: (A) left-cut tool, (B) shear-cut tool, (C) for finishing cast iron, (D) and (E) for finishing square or angular corners.

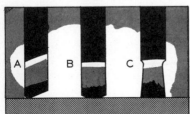

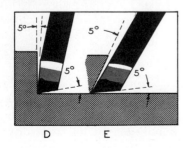

dimensions as its minimum capacity. This factor of accommodation is determined by the distance between the uprights, the distance between the platen and the crossrail at its highest position, and the maximum stroke length.

In capacity, planers rank among the largest machines in both power and size. Open-side planers may range in size from 36″ × 8′ to 96″ × 60′. Double-housing planers range from 30″ × 30″ × 8′, up to 120″ × 120″ × 60′.

PLANER TOOLS AND ACCESSORIES

The same types of tools are used on both the planer and shaper—generally single-point removable bits held in toolholders. 66–1. The toolholders are designed with the bit secured near the center line of the pivot point so that with the tip of the cutter bit back, the tendency of the tool to dig in is lessened.

Cutter bits can be made of high-speed steel, cast alloys, or bits with carbide inserts. The carbide tools are generally used for finishing cuts.

The angles on the cutting bits are quite similar to those on shaper tools.

Accessories and attachments consist of various types of work-holding devices. Since most workpieces which are to be machined on the planer are usually large, heavy, and sometimes irregular, it is important that they be securely fastened to the table. NOTE: Care has to be taken that deflection does not occur when mounting the workpiece on the table. Planer tables are pro-

vided with T-slots and holes that can be used with bolts and clamps for mounting the workpiece.

Stops can be used at each end of the workpiece to prevent slipping during the planing operation. Table jacks are frequently used to support overhanging sections. Small work can be held in planer vises while being machined. 66–2.

Sometimes a number of parts are lined up in a row on the planer table and all machined at the same time. This operation is commonly known as "multiple" or "gang" machining.

TYPES OF PLANERS

Planers can be classified as: (A) double-housing, (B) open-side, (C) pit-type, and (D) edge or plate.

Double-Housing Planer

The double-housing planer is a large machine tool with a long heavy bed on which the table reciprocates. The bed of the planer is twice the length of the table. The upright housing is located near the center on the sides of the base and supports the crossrail on which the tools are mounted and fed across the workpiece. The tools can be fed

66–2. Planer vise with round swivel base.

Skinner Chuck Co.

manually or by power vertically or crosswise. The toolhead consists of a saddle, swivel plate, slide, clapper box, and tool clamp. The tool can be swiveled on its saddle so that angular cuts can be made.

Open-Side Planer

This planer has a housing on one side only to which the cross-rail is mounted. 66–3. It permits the machining of wide work-pieces with a great deal or over-hang. Jobs can be done on this machine that could not be handled on a double-housing planer because one side of the double-housing planer would not permit the passage of the workpiece.

The setup of jobs on an open-side planer is often far more simple than on the conventional planer.

Pit-Type Planer

This planer differs from other types in that the table remains stationary and the tool reciprocates on the columns and cross-rail. It is massive in construction and suitable for large heavy work. Two ram-type tools heads are mounted on the crossrail and permit cutting in both directions. Feeds on these planers are automatic and reversible.

Plate or Edge Planer

Plate or edge planers are special planers used to machine the edges of heavy steel plates. 66–4. The plate is mounted and clamped on the bed, and the tool reciprocates while the work is held stationary. The drive is of the screw drive type, and cutting takes place during both directions of the table travel.

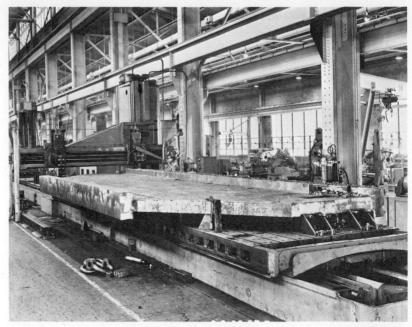

Cincinnati, Inc.

66–3. Open-side planer machining a bed to be used on a large mechanical press brake.

66–4. Plate or edge planer. Close-up view of the tool being used to shape the tongue to be used on a press brake.

Cincinnati, Inc.

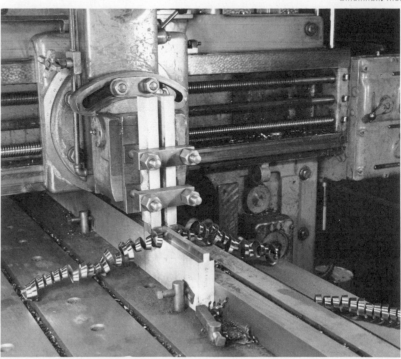

Check Your Knowledge

1. Explain the difference between the crank shaper and the hydraulic shaper.

2. What is a draw-cut shaper?

3. What are the common kinds of shaper drives?

4. Describe a vertical shaper. What type of work is done on this shaper?

5. What are hold-downs and what purpose do they serve?

6. What can cause chatter during the cutting operation on the shaper?

7. What is the amount of feed based upon?

8. What advantage does an open-side planer have over a double-housing planer?

9. How does a shaper differ from a planer?

10. Describe the typical forms of planer drives.

11. Name and describe the principal types of planers.

12. How is work held in a planer?

13. What are the advantages of a divided-table planer?

Problems

1. What is the cutting speed for a block of tool steel 6" long if the number of strokes per minute is 60?

2. For what number of spm should the shaper be run to machine a piece of steel, if the cutting speed is 60 fpm and the stroke is adjusted for 5"?

3. Find the cutting speed of a shaper making 30 rpm with a reverse of 2:1 if the length of stroke is 14".

4. Find the time required for taking a complete cut on a plate 2' x 3', if the cutting speed is 30 fpm, the return is 4 to 1 and the feed ⅛". The clearance at each end is 3".

5. How long will it take to finish one face of a casting 2'6" x 4'0" if the planer has a forward stroke of 20 fpm, a return of 3 to 1, a roughing feed of ⅛" and a finishing feed of 1⁄16". Allow 3" at each end for the tool to clear.

6. With a return of 2:1 and a speed of 27 rpm, what is the cutting speed of a crank shaper if the length of stroke is 15"?

References

American Society of Tool and Manufacturing Engineers, *Tool Engineers Handbook,* 2nd ed., New York, McGraw-Hill Book Co., 1959.

Johnson, Harold V., *General Industrial Machine Shop,* Peoria, Ill., Chas. A. Bennett Co., Inc., 1970.

McCarthy, Willard J., and Smith, Robert E., *Machine Tool Technology,* Bloomington, Ill., McKnight & McKnight Publishing Co., 1968.

Murphy, J. J., "The Shaper as a Manufacturing Tool," *Machinery,* June, 1959.

Section Fourteen

Machining Metal with Milling Machines

MILLING can be defined as the process of producing surfaces by the use of rotary cutters having single or multiple teeth. The workpiece can be held on the machine table by a variety of methods and fed to the rotating cutter by movement of the machine table. In some instances the workpiece and cutter may move in a definite relation to each other, depending upon the operation being performed and the type of milling machine being used.

Gorton Machine Corp.

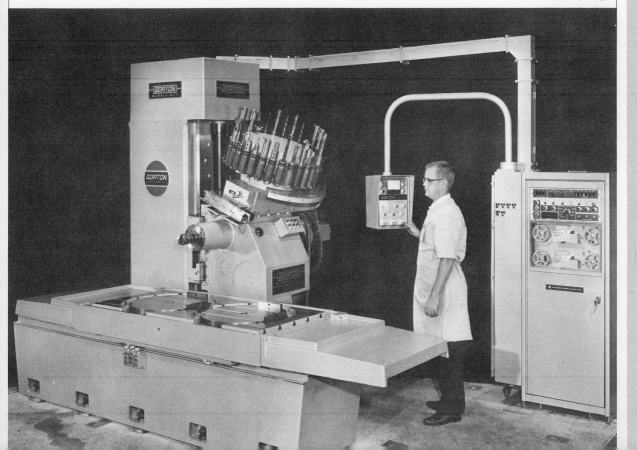

The milling machine can be used for a variety of operations, such as: drilling, boring, slotting, producing flat or irregular surfaces, making of gears, and even thread cutting.

A high productivity rate can be obtained with the milling machine. For this reason, it is used by industry for mass-production work.

Unit 67.

Classification of Milling Machines

There are many different milling machines in use today. They are made in a great variety of sizes and types. Milling machines are generally classified as:

A. Column and knee type: (1) hand miller, (2) plain milling machine, (3) universal milling machine, (4) ram-type universal.

B. Planer milling machine.

C. Fixed bed manufacturing type.

D. Special types: (1) rotary table machines, (2) planetary machines, (3) duplicating, (4) pantograph, (5) profiling, (6) machining center.

GENERAL TYPES

Hand milling machines may be of the column and knee type or constructed with a table mounted on a fixed bed. This type of machine is intended for small work only. The hand feed operates by means of levers or a hand screw for work such as slotting and cutting grooves and keyways. The machine is provided with a horizontal spindle with speeds of 75 to 4,000 rpm (4 ranges). The worktable has longitudinal and vertical feeds as well as a cross-feed. A machine of this type can be used for production work if provided with stops and specially designed fixtures where parts can be rapidly loaded and unloaded. 67–1.

PLAIN HORIZONTAL MILLING MACHINE

These column and knee type machines have a horizontal spindle which is at right angles to the column face. 67–2. This spindle is hollow and tapered internally to receive the cutter arbors which can be mounted in it. The other end of the arbor is supported by an overarm. The overarm and other supports that are sometimes used give rigid support to the arbor, providing rigidity to the cutter during milling operations. The table, supported on guideways in the saddle located on the knee, is adjustable transversely. The table has a machined surface provided with T-slots on which the workpiece can be clamped. A vise or fixture can also be clamped to the table for holding workpieces. Either hand or power operation can be used to move the table. Most modern milling machines are equipped with power traverse to move the table rapidly into horizontal, crosswise, or vertical position. Spindle speeds, as well as table feeds, are easily changed. All adjustments of the knee, saddle, and table are controlled by lead screws and have micrometer adjustment at the handwheel.

UNIVERSAL MILLING MACHINE

The universal milling machine is very similar in appearance to

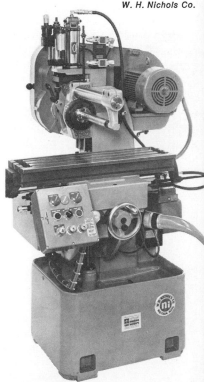

67–1. Production milling center is used for keyseating, keyway cutting, pocket milling, facing, plunging, fluting, slotting, and many other milling operations. All types of cutters can be used with this machine.

W. H. Nichols Co.

the plain horizontal machine. 67–3. In addition to the three movements of the plain milling machine, the universal machine table can be swiveled on a swivel block about the center of the universal saddle. This provides feeding movement which is at an angle to the axis of the spindle. An angular movement of 45° on either side of the normal position can be obtained, making it possible to mill spirals such as on drills, milling cutters, reamers, and cams.

Automatic cycle arrangements can be provided for these machines, to control the feed and table traverse.

RAM-TYPE MILLING MACHINE

This is a new concept in milling machine versatility, combining three-way milling—horizontal, vertical, and angular—with jig boring. 67–4 (Page 334).

This machine has an adjustable cutter head with full 90° calibrated swivel scale and positive lock which permits instant changeover from the vertical, to angular, to horizontal milling without changing the work setup. A drive motor powers the spindle. The cutting force in the machine is against the side of the ram for maximum stability and freedom from vibration.

Index Machine & Tool Co.

67–2. Plain horizontal milling machine: (1) coolant, (2) saddle handwheel, (3) table, (4) table handwheel, (5) arbor, (6) overarm, (7) vertical feed handcrank, and (8) knee.

Greaves Machine Tool Div. of J. A. Fay & Egan Co.

67–3. Universal milling machine: (1) spindle, (2) overarm, (3) table, (4) table swivels here, (5) vertical feed handcrank, (6) crossfeed handwheel, (7) elevation screw, (8) table traverse handwheel, (9) outer arbor support, and (10) speed change levers.

VERTICAL MILLING MACHINE

A vertical milling machine has the same table movements as a horizontal machine. It is called a vertical milling machine because the spindle is located vertically and at right angles to the top of the table. The head may be swiveled for angular or bevel milling operations. 67–5(A&B).

Vertical milling machines use end-milling cutters of various types and sizes depending upon the kinds of operations to be performed. These operations consist of milling horizontal surfaces, angular surfaces, milling grooves, keyways, T-slots, and dovetails. 67–6.

Vertical milling machines can also be used for drilling and boring operations where it is necessary to space a number of holes

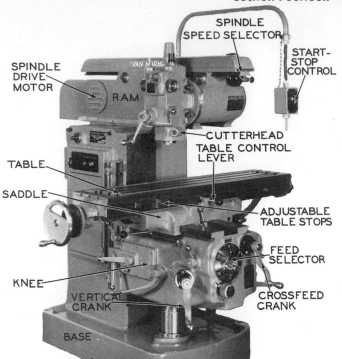

Van Norman Machine Co.

67–4. The ram-type milling machine.

67–5(A). Vertical milling machine showing rapid traverse to table suspended from saddle.

Index Machine & Tool Co.

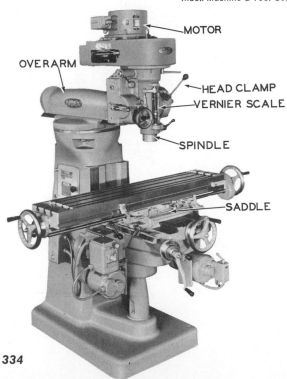

67–5(B). Combination horizontal and vertical milling machine: (1) varible speed motor, (2) horizontal spindle, (3) power feed unit—horizontal and vertical, (4) handwheel, (5) knee and saddle, (6) vertical spindle, (7) adjustable overarm, and (8) arbor support.

Index Machine & Tool Co.

accurately. 67–7. In this type of operation, dial gages, vernier scales, precision measuring pins, and rods can be used advantageously for producing precision holes.

FIXED-BED MILLING MACHINE

Fixed-bed milling machines have a bed that consists of a heavy casting which supports the table. The table is limited to horizontal movement, and the vertical adjustment is made in the spindle head. The transverse adjustment is confined to the spindle quill. This adjustment range is approximately 2½" to 3". Some machines are provided with more than one head. Single-spindle, bed-type machines are known as simplex milling machines, while machines having two to three spindles are known

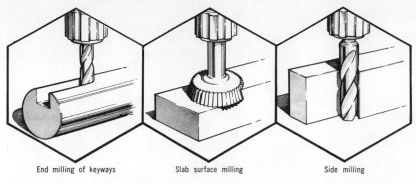

End milling of keyways   Slab surface milling   Side milling

Famco Machine Co.

67–6. Some milling operations that can be performed on a vertical milling machine.

as duplex and triplex machines respectively. The duplex and triplex machines permit the machining of two and three surfaces at the same time.

The machine shown is known as a rise-and-fall machine and is of the hydraulic type. 67–8. The rise-and-fall feature is built into

the machine to raise or lower the cutter spindle to perform certain work. The operation is automatic and is synchronized with the automatic traverse table movement. This feature permits the machining of surfaces located in different planes quickly and economically.

67–7. Vertical mill equipped with optical measuring equipment. This system is a unique measuring and positioning device which brings accurate measuring directly to the machine tool.

Index Machine & Tool Co.

67–8. Hydraulic rise-and-fall milling machine is useful for many milling operations. The rise-and-fall feature raises or lowers the cutter spindle hydraulically.

Kent Owens Machine Co., Div. of Ex-Cell-o Corp.

OPTICAL
MEASURING
AND
POSITIONING
DEVICE

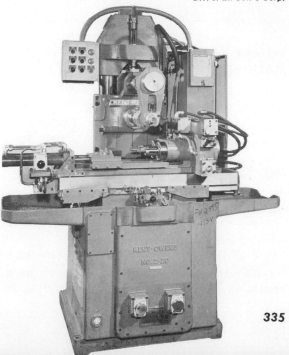

335

INGERSOLL

PLANER-TYPE MILLING MACHINE

The planer-type milling machine resembles a planer in appearance. 67–9. It has a rotary cutter and a variable table-feeding movement.

The machine is used for machining large parts with the table and the workpiece fed as a unit against one or several milling cutters. The cutter spindle carrier can be moved in a vertical or transverse motion. On this machine, the part can be machined to dimensions in a single pass, while a planer would require several passes to complete the operation.

United Engineering & Foundry Co.
67–9. A 15½′ planer-type milling machine.

Unit 68. Special Milling Machines

ROTARY TABLE MILLING MACHINE

The rotary table milling machine is a production machine that is equipped with a horizontal rotary table. 68–1. The workpiece is mounted directly on the table or held in fixtures for machining. The machine is equipped with vertical spindles, and the table rotates past these spindles where roughing and finishing operations can be performed in succession. The operation is continuous; the

operator can load and unload this machine without stopping it. This production machine is limited to flat surfaces.

PROFILING MACHINE

These comprise a variety of machines such as die sinkers, duplicators, profiling, and pantograph machines. They are similar to vertical milling machines in their general construction. 68-2.

The illustration shows what is known as a 2-30 Tracemaster, which is an automatic electro-

hydraulic servo-tracer mill. 68–3. This machine operates at a 1-to-1 ratio of master to part, and its hydraulic servo system requires approximately 6 ounces of operator pressure to cause movement of the machine slides (about the same effort as power steering on an automobile). This machine is extremely versatile and finds widespread usage in all types of profiling and 3-dimensional duplicating, ranging from aerospace to automotive. The workpiece illustration is of a large, two-cavity metal pattern for an automobile differential housing.

An illustration is shown of the Auto-Trace-Master, which is an automatic, tracer-controlled, milling machine with which the operator does not have to be present for operation. 68–4.

68–1. Rotary table milling machine.

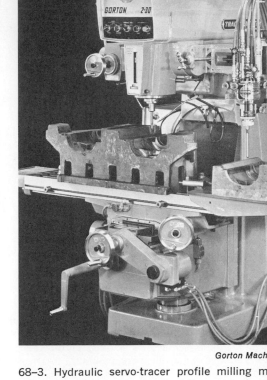

68–3. Hydraulic servo-tracer profile milling machine, Model 2-30. Every movement of the manually operated stylus is precisely duplicated on the workpiece, maintaining a true, constant 1-to-1 relationship.

68–2. High-speed vertical milling machine with fully automatic 2-dimensional and manual 3-dimensional tracing system.

68–4. Automatic tracer controlled milling machine. This machine can be operated as a duplicator or as a profiler as applications demand.

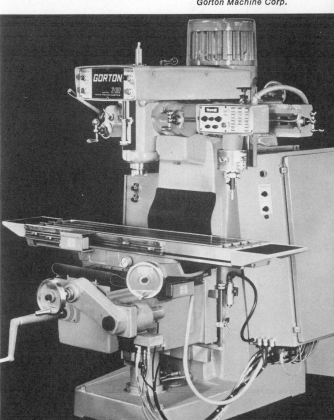

Gorton Machine Corp.

68–5. Numerically controlled, 2-axis and 3-axis, continuous path, contour, milling machine. As a 3-axis model, the machine is capable of producing full 3-dimensional dies, molds, prototype parts, and aerospace components.

68–6. This manually operated engraving-duplicating machine can be utilized to produce 3-dimensional dies, molds, and tooling, as well as finished parts.

Gorton Machine Corp.

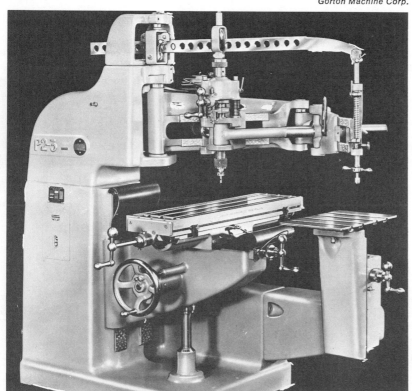

This machine is built in two versions, one an automatic, two-dimensional profiling machine for production work and the second an automatic profiler and rise-and-fall die-sinking machine. The control is very similar to a numerically controlled contouring system—with the exception that the control is sensing a 2- or 3-dimensional master.

Fig. 68–5 illustrates a 2-axis and 3-axis continuous path milling machine. This machine operates from standard 1″, 8-channel punch tape and its application ranges from ordinance components to the contour milling of dies and molds.

PANTOGRAPH ENGRAVING MACHINE

Pantograph engraving machines work at a ratio, utilizing enlarged masters, and are basic machines in the die casting and plastic mold field. 68–6. The range of 2-dimensional and 3-dimensional machine applications is extremely wide, extending from jewelry dies to medical research.

These machines can be used to produce a workpiece of the desired shape by tracing a master. Knee and column construction is used to position the workpiece, which remains stationary throughout the cutting cycle. The tracing stylus is usually operated manually by light finger pressure on the tracer stylus. This pressure is transmitted to the servo system of the machine, which provides the necessary power to cause the movement of the tool. The size relation between the master and the workpiece is variable, from 1-to-1 to a reduction as great as 40-to-1 on some machines.

AUTO-SCAN MILLING MACHINE

This type of milling machine automatically machines parts of irregular shapes and contours directly from line drawing templates by use of an optical scanning control system which keeps tool travel constant to maintain optimum machining action, regardless of the complexity of the part contour. 68–7. The machine has a common table for template and workpiece which assures absolute accuracy of longitudinal travel. The precision micrometer side-offset compensator on the

68–7. Auto-Scan milling machine. Automatic milling is done by optical line-tracing control.

Van Norman Machine Co.

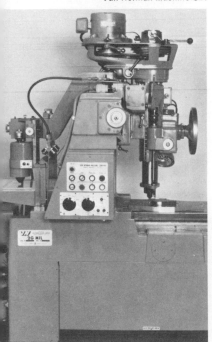

tracing head serves to provide simplified compensation for tool wear, allows milling of male and female parts from the same template drawing, and permits the selection of various tool sizes without changing the template.

Prototype machining of parts may be done automatically from ink or pencil drawings, and point-to-point programming can be accomplished by setting the line scanning system to stop automatically at cross lines.

Unit 69.

Milling Machine Attachments and Holding Devices

The usefulness of milling machines is greatly extended by the availability of numerous attachments. Since some of these do only one particular thing, they are, in the strictest sense, attachments. Many others, however, are so designed that a number of operations can be performed through their use.

VISES

The vise is the most common device used in milling operations. 69–1. Most often used is the *adjustable swivel vise*. This can be fitted into a base which is graduated in degrees on the full circle, permitting the jaws to be set at any angle.

69–1. Adjustable-swivel, milling machine vise.

Wilton Tool Div. of Wilton Corp.

The cam-lock vise is built to hold pieces for machining duplicate parts where fast clamping is desired. 69–2 (Page 340).

An *adjustable tilting vise* is another example of a superior vise for holding workpieces. 69–3 (Page 340). The vise proper can be tilted and locked in place for angular milling.

THE INDEXING OR DIVIDING HEAD

This is most commonly used to obtain exact spacing of numbers of divisions upon the periphery (circumference) of workpieces, such as fluting taps and reamers, cutting teeth of gears and ratchets, milling the sides of nuts or heads of bolts, and a multitude of other operations. 69–4 (Page 340).

Direct Indexing

Direct indexing is done by means of a plate on the front of the spindle of the head. For direct indexing, the worm must be disconnected from its gear so that the spindle will rotate freely. In direct indexing the plate rotates with the spindle. This plate

69–2. Cam-lock vise.

has a circle of equally spaced holes, usually 24 or some other number divisible by 4. For direct indexing the worm gear is disengaged and the plunger is drawn back; then the plate is rotated through the number of spaces desired.

Simple Indexing

Simple indexing is accomplished by means of a worm wheel attached to the spindle of the index head and moved through a worm which is keyed to a shaft to which a crank is attached. 69–5. One complete revolution of the crank causes any one tooth on the worm gear to make a complete revolution. Forty turns of the crank are required to turn the spindle one full revolution. On some heads only five turns are needed.

An index plate is mounted on the dividing head beneath the crank. The plate contains a number of holes which are laid out in concentric circles and equally spaced in each circle. The crank handle contains a plunger pin, which is adjustable, to engage the holes of any circle. This permits the crank to be turned any fractional part of a circle. The entire spindle assembly may be moved from a horizontal to a vertical position. The index plate is stationary, and when the plunger is inserted in a hole the crank is locked in place. Movable sector arms, located on the plate, eliminate the need for counting spaces when the crank is turned between cuts. Two complete turns of the worm will rotate the spindle $\frac{2}{40}$ or $\frac{1}{20}$ of a turn. By means of whole turns of the crank, indexing for all numbers from 1 to 40 which are factors of 40 can be done.

Suppose it is required that a reamer be cut with five equally spaced teeth. If 40 turns of the index crank make a full revolution of the workpiece, then $\frac{1}{5}$ of 40 turns—or 8 turns—after each cut will space the reamer for five teeth.

$$\text{Number of turns} = \frac{40}{N}$$

In the above formula, 40 represents the number of crank turns required to rotate the workpiece one complete turn; N represents the number of equal divisions

69–3. Adjustable-angle milling machine vise.

Brown & Sharpe Mfg. Co.

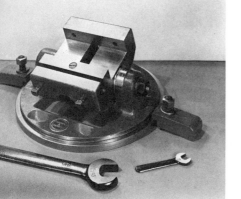

69–4. Dividing head with footstock.

Nichols-Morris Corp.

into which the workpiece is to be divided.

In indexing for 6 equal spaces: 40 divided by 6 equals $6\frac{2}{3}$ turns of the index crank handle to each division. No plate contains so few holes as 6. Multiplying by the common multiplier 6, we have $\frac{2}{3} \times \frac{6}{6} = {}^{12}\!/_{18}$. Hence, for one division of the workpiece, the index crank pin is placed in the 18-hole circle, the crank is given 6 complete revolutions, and then is moved ahead 12 additional holes. These additional holes, representing the fractional part of a turn, will lie in the space between the sector arms. As $^{14}\!/_{21}$ is a multiple of the original fraction $\frac{2}{3}$, 14 holes in the 21-hole circle might be used in place of 12 in the 18-hole circle.

The spaces count, not the holes. The hole in which the

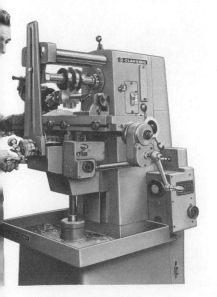

69–5. Simple indexing on a horizontal milling machine.

Atlas Press Co.

plunger pin has been placed is not counted. The number of spaces on the index circle, indicating the fractional part of a turn, is included between the beveled edges of the sector arms.

When it is desired to divide the circumference in degrees or parts of degrees, it can often be done by *plain indexing*. One complete turn of the crank produces $\frac{1}{40}$ of a turn of the workpiece, or $^{360}\!/_{40}=9°$. Following this method:

2 holes in the 18-hole
   circle = 1°
2 holes in the 27-hole
   circle = $\frac{2}{3}$°
1 hole in the 18-hole
   circle = $\frac{1}{2}$°
1 hole in the 27-hole
   circle = $\frac{1}{3}$°

Other odd fractional parts of a degree can easily be found by dividing the number of holes in any given circle into 9°. Note that $\frac{1}{4}$° cannot be obtained this way.

Differential Indexing

Differential indexing is used when the standard dividing plates do not provide a circle of holes containing the required number of holes necessary for simple indexing. 69–6. With the change gears and three index plates furnished with the headstock, it is possible to index all numbers from 1 to 382; in addition, many other divisions beyond 382 can be indexed.

In this type of indexing, the index crank is moved in the same circle of holes, and the operation is like that of plain indexing. The headstock spindle and index plate are connected by

a train of gearing, and the stop pin at the back of the plate is thrown out. As the index crank is turned, the spindle is rotated through the worm and wheel, and the plate moves either in the same or opposite direction to that of the crank. The total movement of the crank at every indexing is, therefore, equal to its movement relative to the plate—*plus* the movement of the plate when the plate revolves in the same direction as the crank, or *minus* the movement of the plate when the plate revolves in the opposite direction to the crank.

Spiral Milling

Spiral milling is done by rotating the workpiece as the cut is being taken, using connecting gears from the lead screw of the table to the handle spindle of the dividing head. By using different combinations of change gears, the ratio of the longitudinal movement of the table to the rotary movement of the workpiece can be varied. NOTE: The

69–6. Headstock geared for differential indexing.

Brown & Sharpe Mfg. Co.

Brown & Sharpe Mfg. Co.

69–7. Rotary milling, using rotary attachment with power feed. This is used on a variety of circular milling operations, such as circular T-slots, segment outlines, and on tool-and-die-making jobs.

spiral cut on milling machines is designated in terms of *inches to one turn,* rather than in *turns,* or *threads per inch;* thus, a spiral is said to be *8″ of lead.*

The table feed screw has four threads to the inch, and forty turns of the worm make one turn of the headstock spindle. If change gears of equal diameter are used, the workpiece will make one complete turn; the lead would be 10″. The ratio for computing these gears is:

$$\frac{\text{Product of driven gears}}{\text{Product of driving gears}} = \frac{\text{Lead of required spiral}}{10}$$

ROTARY ATTACHMENTS

There are two types of rotary attachments: the hand-feed type and the power-feed type. Both can be used on plain, universal, or vertical milling machines.

Both attachments are graduated on the circumference of tables. 69–7. Graduations read to half degrees, and both have adjustable dials on the worm shaft, reading to five minutes and two minutes of arc respectively. The power drive type is driven from the feed drive of the machine. Circular milling such as for making circular T-slots, segment outlines, splining, slotting, or irregular form milling can be done on these attachments.

Brown & Sharpe Mfg. Co.

69–8. This vertical milling attachment is used on a wide range of work such as end milling, T-slot cutting, drilling, boring, and face milling.

VERTICAL MILLING ATTACHMENTS

Vertical milling attachments are used for a wide range of milling work such as end milling, drilling, boring, and face milling. 69–8. They can be used on a horizontal milling machine if a separate vertical milling machine is not available.

The slotting attachment, mounted on a horizontal mill, is used largely in toolmaking. 69–9. It consists of a tool slide that is driven from the machine spindle by an adjustable crank that allows the stroke to be set for different lengths. The attachment can be set at any angle between 0 and 90°, either side of the center line.

69–9. A slotting attachment is used largely in toolmaking, such as in forming box tools for screw machines, making templates, splining keyways and slotting.

Brown & Sharpe Mfg. Co.

Unit 70.   Milling Cutters

The common types of milling cutters may be classified as: 1. Arbor cutters: plain, side, staggered tooth, metal-slitting saw, angular, inserted tooth, and form. 2. Shank cutters: End mills—solid, shell, T-slot, Woodruff key seat, and fly cutter. 70–1.

ARBOR CUTTERS

Plain Milling Cutters

Plain milling cutters are cylindrical with teeth on the periphery only. 70–2(A) (Page 244). (The periphery of a milling cutter is the imaginary cylindrical surface enveloping the outer ends of the peripheral teeth and determining the diameter of the cutter.) These cutters are used primarily for milling flat surfaces. However, they can be combined with cutters of other types to produce surfaces with various forms. The teeth may be either straight or helical, depending upon the width of the cutter. (Plain milling cutters with helix angles of 45° to 60° and higher are called helical cutters.) 70–2(B).

Side Milling Cutters

Side milling cutters are quite similar to plain cutters. However, they also have teeth on one or both sides. 70–3. In milling operations where two cutters are placed side by side, they have teeth on only one side. The teeth can be straight, helical, or staggered as shown. 70–4.

Staggered Tooth Milling Cutter

Staggered tooth milling cutters are narrow cylindrical cutters having staggered teeth and with alternate teeth having opposite helix angles. These cutters are ground to cut only on the periphery, but each tooth has a chip clearance ground on the protruding side. These cutters have a free cutting action which makes them useful in milling deep slots.

Metal-Slitting Saws

Metal-slitting saws are designed for cutoff operations and for cutting narrow slots. 70–5. The sides are slightly tapered toward the hole to prevent binding. Like other milling cutters, they can be plain or made with side teeth or with staggered teeth.

Angular Milling Cutters

Angular milling cutters are used for operations such as: cutting V-grooves, notches, dovetails, flutes on milling cutters, and reamer teeth. Single-angle cutters have one angular surface while double-angle cutters are provided with V-shaped teeth. These cutters, with equal conical angles on both faces, are made with an included angle of 45°, 60°, or 90°. 70–6(A&B).

Inserted Tooth Milling Cutters

Inserted tooth milling cutters have teeth made of Stellite, cemented carbides, or ceramics. 70–7(A&B). Cutter body materials depend upon the type, size, and design of the cutter. Solid milling cutters have tips brazed to a less-expensive material. Inserted tooth cutters are usually used in face milling operations with sizes ranging from 6″ diam. or over.

Form-Relieved Cutters

These cutters are used for machining surfaces that require an irregular outline. They are available in concave and convex styles, corner rounding cutters, gear cutters, formed tooth cutters, thread milling cutters and special formed cutters. 70–8, 70–9, 70–10 & 70–11 (Page 245).

SHANK CUTTERS

End Mills

End milling cutters have teeth on the end face as well as the periphery. 70–12. They are made in two distinct styles, the solid end mill and the shell end type.

70–1. An assortment of different types of milling cutters.

Brown & Sharpe Mfg. Co.

Brown & Sharpe Mfg. Co.

70–2(B). Plain milling cutter with helical teeth.

Barber-Colman Co.

70–2(A). Plain milling cutters.

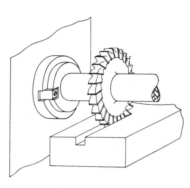

Standard Tool Co.

70–3. Side milling cutter.

Standard Tool Co.

70–4. Staggered tooth milling cutter.

70–5. Slitting saw.

Brown & Sharpe Mfg. Co.

70–7(A). Carbide tipped cutters.

Brown & Sharpe Mfg. Co.

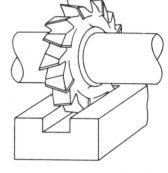

70–6(A). A 60° angular cutter with threaded hole.

70–6(B). Double-angle cutter.

Barber-Colman Co.

70–10. Gear cutter.

Kennametal, Inc.

70–7(B). Four typical face cutters of a modern design concept. Note the location of the indexible inserts in a nest which is itself a replaceable part. This insures the greatest possible accuracy of insert location while permitting complete protection of the body in the event of accident or misuse.

DoAll Co.

70–11. Thread milling cutter.

Standard Tool Co.

70–8. Concave cutter.

70–12. End milling cutters: (A) multi-flute ball end mill, (B) multiple-flute single end cutter, and (C) double end mill.

Brown & Sharpe Mfg. Co.

70–9. Corner rounding cutters.

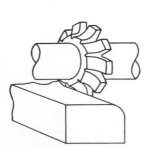

The solid end mill is a single piece of metal with teeth and shank as an integral part. Except for the shell type, all end mills have either a straight shank or a taper shank, which is mounted into the spindle of the machine for driving the cutter. Various adapters are available for securing end mills to the machine spindle. Slotting or two-lipped end mills can be used for machining slots, keyways, pockets, etc., where ordinary arbor milling cutters cannot be used. Many end mills have carbide teeth making increased production possible. 70–13.

A two-flute end mill (which comes under the solid type) can be fed into the workpiece like a drill. 70–14. There are two cutting edges on the circumference with the end teeth cut to the center.

Multi-flute end mills can be run at the same speed and feed as comparable two-lipped end mills, but have a longer cutting life and will produce a better finish.

Shell End Mills

These are made to be mounted on a short arbor. They have end and peripheral teeth. 70–15(A&B). The use of shell end mills is generally more economical than the use of large solid end mills. They are cheaper to replace when broken or worn out. Cutters of this type are intended for slabbing or surfacing cuts, either face or end-milling operations. Shell end mills are made with right-hand cut, right-hand helix, or with left-hand cut, left-hand helix.

T-Slot Cutters

T-slot cutters are a special type of end mill having either straight or tapered shanks and designed for cutting T-slots in machine tables and similar applications. 70–16(A&B). NOTE: In producing a T-slot, a groove for the narrow portion of the slot is first machined with an end mill or side mill and then finished with the T-slot cutter.

Woodruff Key Seat Cutters

These cutters are of special design for cutting key seats for Woodruff keys (which have the shape of a half circle). These are available in all sizes and are of two types, end mill and arbor cutters. 70–17. The end mill is

Brown & Sharpe Mfg. Co.

70–13. Carbide tipped end mills. Top —taper shank with straight flutes. Bottom—straight shank, two flute.

70–14. A two-flute end mill can be fed into the workpiece in much the same manner as a drill.

Atlas Press Co.

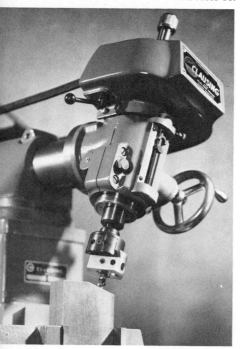

70–15(A). Shell end mill.

Brown & Sharpe Mfg. Co.

70–15(B). Milling operation with shell end mill mounted on a horizontal milling machine.

available in diameters from ¼″ to 1½″; the arbor type, in diameters from 2⅛″ to 3½″.

Fly Cutters

A fly cutter consists of one or more single-point tool bits mounted in a bar of some type which can be attached to the spindle of the milling machine. 70–18. Its principle in operation is quite like that of a boring tool. Set screws are used to hold the tool bit in place. This type of tool is used for special applications.

ARBORS, COLLETS, AND ADAPTERS

Arbors are used for mounting the milling cutter and are inserted and held in the spindle by a draw-bolt or a special quick-change adapter. 70–19.

Shell end-mill arbors may fit into the spindle or spindle of the vertical attachment. These devices permit face milling which can be done either vertically or horizontally.

Collet adapters are used for mounting straight shank end mills, drills, and tapered shank

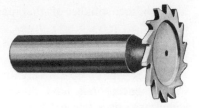

70–17. Narrow width Woodruff cutter.

Atlas Press Co.

70–18. A fly cutter consists of a single-point tool.

70–16(A). T-slot cutter with taper shank and carbide tipped teeth.

70–16(B). Milling a T-slot on a vertical milling machine.

Atlas Press Co.

70–19. Arbors, collets, and adapters used on milling machines to accommodate the various types of cutters used in milling operations.

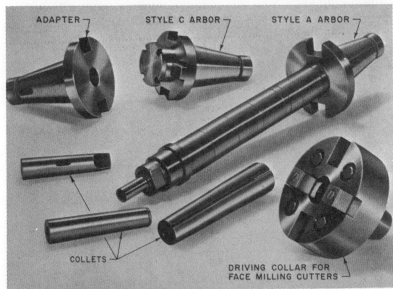

ADAPTER STYLE C ARBOR STYLE A ARBOR

COLLETS

DRIVING COLLAR FOR FACE MILLING CUTTERS

tools in the spindle of the machine.

CUTTER TEETH

Cutters with comparatively few widely spaced teeth have distinct advantages over fine-toothed cutters.

A *coarse-toothed cutter* with few widely spaced teeth has the ability to remove a maximum amount of metal, without distressing the cutter or overloading the machine. These cutters have a free cutting action, largely due to the fact that a smaller amount of cutting is required to remove a given amount of metal. Other advantages are: (1) The rake and increased spiral of the teeth gives a shearing action. (2) Wide spacing decreases the tendency of the cutter to slide over the surface. (3) Less friction is created, resulting in cooler teeth and consequently decreasing the necessity of regrinding operations. (4) There is decreased power consumption. (5) Increased production is possible. 70–20.

Positive radial rake angles of 10° to 15° are used on high-speed steel cutters. These angles serve in machining most materials and give good cutting ability to the cutter without sacrificing strength of the cutter. In milling softer materials, a greater rake angle can be provided to improve cutting ability.

Negative rake angles are provided on carbide-tipped cutters for high-speed milling operations. Since the angles are both radial and axial, tool life can be increased by increasing the lip angle. For softer steels, a negative rake angle of 5° to 10° is generally provided on plain milling cutters with teeth on the periphery. This angle is normally increased when medium-carbon and alloy steels are being machined. 70–21.

Clearance angles are kept on the small side to avoid weakening the cutting edge of the tooth. With a minimum amount of material in back of the tooth, the strength of the tooth is diminished. Clearance angles of 3° to 5° are generally used on cutters over 3″ in diameter. This is increased on smaller diameter cut-

70–20. Cutter and end mill nomenclature.

Brown & Sharpe Mfg. Co.

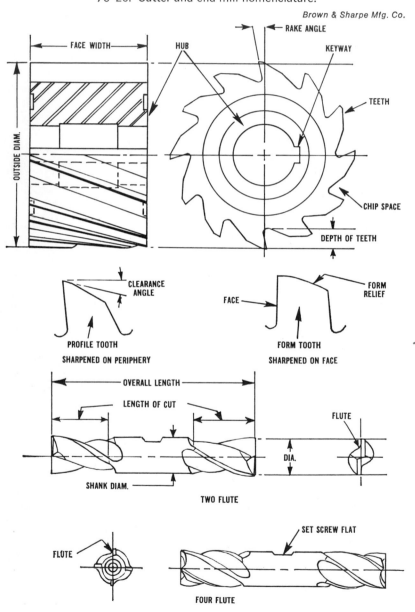

ters to prevent the teeth from a rubbing instead of a cutting action.

The type of material being machined affects clearance angles. If *cast iron* is being machined, 4° to 7° might be used; *nonferrous* materials require clearance angles of 10° to 12°. The *land* on a cutter can be from $\frac{1}{32}''$ to $\frac{1}{16}''$ in width, with a secondary clearance back of the land.

SPEEDS AND FEEDS

Cutting speed as applied to milling can be defined as circumferential speed of the milling cutter expressed in surface feet per minute (sfpm). It is the distance which the periphery of a milling cutter tooth travels in one minute.

The revolutions (rpm) refers to the number of revolutions that the cutter makes in one minute. A small milling cutter must rotate at a higher rpm to cut at the given cutting speed of a larger cutter. A small cutter is more efficient because it travels a shorter distance. 71–11(C). Cutting speed is expressed in the following equations:

$$CS = \frac{\pi \times DN}{12}$$

Where D = diameter of cutter in inches

N = rpm

If the number of spindle revolutions is unknown, the following formula can be used:

$$N = \frac{12\,CS}{\pi\,D}$$

Where N = rpm

CS = cutting speed

The determination of the correct cutting speed is a matter of experience. There are a number of factors to be considered, such

as: (1) the material being cut, (2) cutter material, (3) use of coolants, (4) depth of cut, (5) finish required, (6) type of cutter, and (7) rate of feed.

FEED

Feed is expressed in *inches per minute* because this is the setting that must be made on the machine. However, the basis for all feed rates is the *feed per tooth,* which is a figure that does not change with different cutter sizes or different numbers of teeth in the cutter. NOTE: Most larger milling machines have a

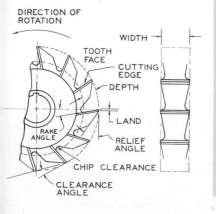

70–21. Milling cutter elements.

DIRECTION OF ROTATION

WIDTH
TOOTH FACE
CUTTING EDGE
DEPTH
LAND
RAKE ANGLE
RELIEF ANGLE
CHIP CLEARANCE
CLEARANCE ANGLE

Table 70. Basic Recommendations for Milling Cutter Surface Footage†

The attached table contains basic recommendations for milling cutter surface feet per minute for various common materials within a Brinell hardness range. The range of surface feet per minute is in relation to the Brinell range of the material.

Cutter type, holding device, condition of equipment, horsepower, and finish requirements will have considerable effect on the use of these recommendations.

These figures do not take into consideration feed or horsepower, as each type of milling operation would cause variation to these recommendations.

While no exact figures can be given applying to all operating conditions and grades of materials, it is possible to indicate the general principles applying to the setting of speeds and feeds for initial setups. The figures in the following tables represent recommended speeds and feeds.

SPEEDS

Material	Brn. Range	H.S.S. Cutter S.F.M. Range	Cast Alloy Cutter S.F.M. Range	Carbide Cutter S.F.M. Range
Aluminum	100—150	1000—550	2000—1100	4000—2200
Brass	100—175	650—250	1300— 500	2600—1000
Low-Carbon Steel	100—200	325—100	650— 200	1300— 400
Free-Cutting Steel	150—200	250—150	500— 300	1000— 600
Alloy Steel	150—250	175— 70	350— 140	700— 280
Alloy Steel	250—350	70— 40	140— 80	280— 160
Cast Iron	125—175	100— 60	200— 120	400— 240
Cast Iron	175—200	60— 45	120— 90	240— 180
Cast Iron	200—225	45— 40	90— 80	180— 160
Cast Iron	225—250	40— 35	80— 70	160— 140

Reduce Speeds for: hard materials; abrasive materials; deep cuts; high alloy content. Increase Speeds for: soft materials; better finishes; light cuts; frail work pieces and setups; fine pitch thread milling.

†Browne & Sharpe Mfg. Co.

feeding mechanism which can be set in inches per minute and is independent of the spindle rpm.

After selecting a starting feed from a table, the feed rate can be calculated based on the following formula:

$$F = R \times T \times rpm$$

Where F = feed rate in inches per minute

R = feed per revolutions of tooth per revolution

T = number of teeth

FEEDS

The following table of suggested feeds should prove of value in setting up initial jobs:

Type of Cut	Starting Feed per Tooth, Inches
Face Milling	.008
Straddle Milling	.008
Channel or Slit Milling	.008
Slab Milling	.007
End Milling or Profiling	*.004
Sawing	.003
Thread Milling	.002

* For end mills smaller than ½ inch diameter, feeds per tooth must be much lower than the figure given.

† *Brown & Sharpe Mfg. Co.*

3. Proper selection of speeds and feeds.
4. Condition of machine.
5. Type of cutter.
6. Type of material being machined.

In *face milling* the milled surface, resulting from the combined action of cutting edges located on the periphery and the face of the cutter, is generally at a right angle to the cutter axis. 71–3(A). (See illustration.) The milled surface is flat, with no relation to the contour of the teeth, except when milling to a shoulder. A combination of errors in manufacture, use, and maintenance of face milling cutters will affect the geometry of the surface of the part being milled.

Face milling can be done on milling machines with horizontal or vertical spindles. 71–3(B). The cutter is usually mounted on an adapter inserted in the spindle of the machine. Some face mills have a shank which is part of the cutter. In face milling, both the bottom and peripheral cutting edges do the cutting. This type of machining operation pro-

---

Unit 71. Milling Operations

Milling operations can be classified in two broad categories: peripheral and face milling.

In *peripheral milling* the milled surface is generated by teeth located on the periphery of the

71–1. Peripheral milling. The operation in this illustration is slab milling with a helical milling cutter.

Atlas Press Co.

cutter body. 71–1. As when milling with a helical mill, the surface is generally in a plane parallel to the cutter axis. Milling operations with form relieved (curved tooth outline) and formed profile (irregular shape) are included in this class. 71–2. The cross section of the milled surface corresponds to the outline or contour of the milling cutter or combination of cutters used. The surface produced may vary from a flat surface (as in slab milling) to a formed surface. (See illustration.)

This type of operation is performed on horizontal milling machines. The quality of the work produced is governed by several factors:

1. Geometry of the machining process.
2. Plastic flow of the metal being milled.

71–2. An example of peripheral milling.

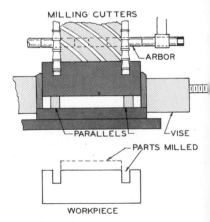

duces a flat surface. (See illustration.)

METHODS OF MILLING

In peripheral milling, the workpiece can be fed either with or against the direction of cutter rotation. In face milling, however, characteristics of the two methods are usually combined, since the feeding motion is generally partly with and partly against the direction of cutter rotation. The two methods are known as up milling and down milling.

Up Milling

In up milling, the cutter rotates against the direction of feed as the workpiece advances toward it from the side where the teeth are moving upward. The separating forces produced between cutter and workpiece oppose the motion of work. 71–4 (A&B) (Page 352).

In up milling, since the cutter teeth come up from the bottom of the cut, the chip is very thin at the beginning where the tooth first contacts the workpiece. 71–5. Gradually, the chip increases in thickness, reaching its maximum thickness where the tooth leaves the workpiece (C). Theoretically, the chip should form at the center, but due to the resistance of the material to penetration, the cutting action is delayed somewhat and cutting starts slightly ahead of the center. The cutter slides over the workpiece to be machined until sufficient pressure has been built up to force it to bite into the surface of the workpiece to produce a chip.

In up milling, the milled surface consists of a number of

Giddings & Lewis Machine Tool Co.

71–3(A). A face milling operation being performed on a numerically controlled horizontal milling and boring machine.

71–3(B). A modern shear angle cutter in operation showing the clean efficient cutting action. This cutter has a combination negative/positive geometry.

Kennametal, Inc.

elemental surfaces which are generated during the early stages of the engagement of the tooth with the workpiece. 71–6(A). At this point, while the chip thickness is small, the cutting edge of the tooth is covered with a film of cutting fluid. The surface is usually smooth and free from fragments of a built-up edge.

As the cutting action continues through the workpiece, the built-up edge will eventually form, but its presence will be noticed at some distance from the point first contacted by the workpiece. 71–6(B). At the feed per tooth normally employed, this part of the surface is re-

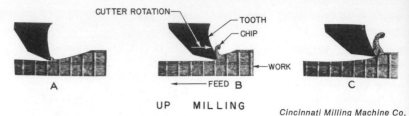

UP MILLING

Cincinnati Milling Machine Co.

71–5. Chip formation in up milling.

71–4. (A) Conventional, or up milling, and (B) climb, or down milling.

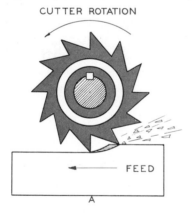

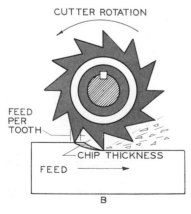

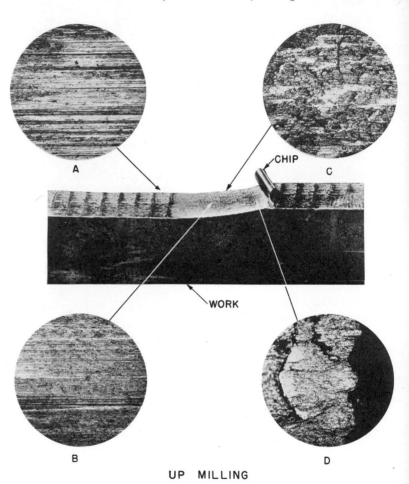

UP MILLING

Cincinnati Milling Machine Co.

71–6. Change in quality of milled surface along tooth path in up milling.

71–7. Chip formation in down milling.

Cincinnati Milling Machine Co.

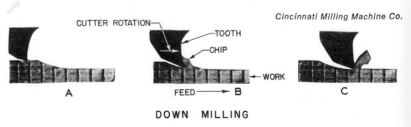

DOWN MILLING

moved by the tooth following. 71–6(C). Good quality surface finish is generally obtained on the workpiece. 71–6(D).

In some instances, the quality of surface finish will be affected by chips falling on the machined surface and are dragged under by the teeth on their engagement with the workpiece. This condition will produce scratches or blemishes on the machined surface. A cutting fluid will wash away these chips and prevent them from adhering to the cutter.

Down Milling

If down milling is used, all looseness must be eliminated in the table feed screw, as the motion of the cutter tends to pull the workpiece into the cutter. The machine must be designed with special features, adapting it to down milling (sometimes known as climb milling) if this type of milling is to be used.

In down milling, the maximum chip thickness is obtained close to the point where the tooth contacts the workpiece. 71–7. No built-up pressure is developed in down milling, and, therefore, no heavy burr (a protruding, ragged metal edge) forms on the surface of the metal.

In down milling, the portion of the tooth contact with the workpiece shows a very good finish. 71–8. But an element of the final milled surface is produced at the end of the tooth travel when the built-up edge is completely developed. This could mean that the finish of the final surface might be of poorer quality than produced by up milling. However, this is not always true,

especially when milled surfaces of different types of materials are compared. 71–9 (Page 354).

Plain or Slab Milling

One of the simplest operations that can be performed on the horizontal milling machine is plain or "slab" milling. 71–10. This operation consists of machining a plain, flat, horizontal surface with cylindrical milling cutters which have lengths usually greater than their diameters. *Helical* cutters usually produce a better surface in this type of operation than cutters with straight teeth.

The part to be milled is securely mounted in a vise or directly to the table. 71–11(A&B). Many jobs can be milled to size in one cut; but if a very large amount of material is to be removed, a roughing cut followed by a finishing cut is sometimes necessary.

The cutter diameter should be as small as possible, but still large enough to prevent any interference when the cut is being made. It takes less time to take

71–8. Change in quality of milled surface along tooth path in down milling.

Cincinnati Milling Machine Co.

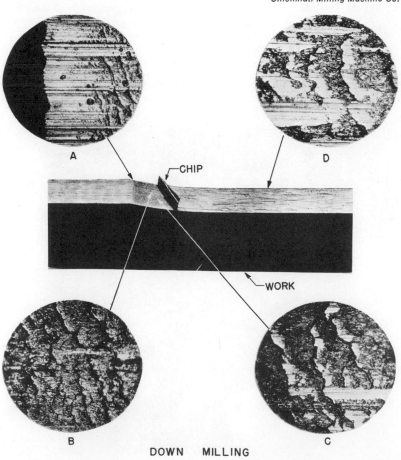

DOWN   MILLING

UP   MILLING

SAE 3115   STAINLESS STEEL   DURALUMIN   BRASS

DOWN   MILLING

Cincinnati Milling Machine Co.

71–9. Surface quality obtained in up milling and down milling in S.A.E. 3115 steel,
"Rezistal" stainless steel, duralumin, and brass.

71–10. Plain or slab milling using a helical cutter.

Index Machine & Tool Co.

a cut across a surface with a small-diameter cutter than a large-diameter cutter. See Fig. 71–11(C) on the next page.

Side Milling and Straddle Milling

Side milling operations are used to machine a vertical surface on the side of the workpiece using a side milling cutter. 71–12. This operation can be performed for squaring an end of the workpiece and also on an inner surface.

Straddle milling is quite similar to the above operation except that it is performed with two half-side milling cutters. 71–13. They are spaced on the arbor a definite distance apart, using spacing collars and shims. Two or more parallel surfaces

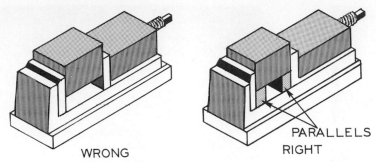

WRONG

PARALLELS
RIGHT

71–11(A). In order to hold the work securely in the vise for milling operations, parallels should be used under the workpiece.

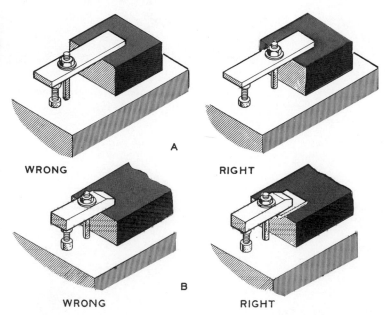

A

WRONG

RIGHT

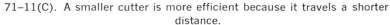

WRONG

RIGHT

B

WRONG

RIGHT

U.S. Burke Machine Tool Co.

71–11(B). A—If a clamp stud is incorrectly placed, holding power is dissipated. Placing the stud close to the workpiece permits the clamp to exert holding power. B—By using a shim, the workpiece will be protected and the clamping force will spread over a large area.

71–11(C). A smaller cutter is more efficient because it travels a shorter distance.

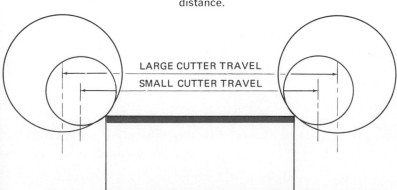

LARGE CUTTER TRAVEL
SMALL CUTTER TRAVEL

71–12. Side milling operation using a staggered tooth side milling cutter on a vertical surface.

71–13. Straddle milling. Interlocking cutters are used in the center of the setup. The outside cutters must be spaced to the exact distance to get the desired results.

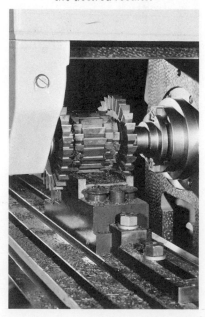

355

71–14. Gang milling. Notice coarse tooth cutter being used.

Atlas Press Co.

71–15. Milling a slot on a vertical milling machine.

71–16. End mill mounted in horizontal mill for milling slots in workpiece.

Cincinnati Milling Machine Co.

71–17. A boring operation being performed on a vertical mill.

Atlas Press Co.

can be machined at the same time in this manner. Common operations performed with straddle mills include milling parallel surfaces to some specific width or length and milling square or hexagon heads on bolts. Either right- or left-hand side milling cutters are used in straddle milling.

Slotting and Cutting Off

Metal-slitting saws are used for cutting off stock and milling narrow slots. Operations are performed with saws that have teeth on the periphery or with saws having alternating side teeth with side chip clearance. The latter type of cutter gives a smoother finish on the sides of the slots than is possible with the plain type.

Form Milling

Form milling is the machining of irregular contours with formed cutters. Besides the regular convex and concave shapes, many special shaped cutters can be used for this operation.

Gang Milling

Gang milling consists of machining surfaces by means of two or more cutters mounted on an arbor. 71–14. Sometimes a combination of cutters may be used for plain milling and side milling at the same time.

For one of the most common operations, helical cutters are mounted on the arbor to machine a surface. In this case cutters with opposed spirals are used, with each cutter counter-acting the thrust caused by the shearing action of the teeth of the other cutter.

Vertical Milling

Milling operations can be done with end mills on either vertical or horizontal milling machines. 71–15. On horizontal machines, the end mills are mounted in adapters. 71–16. Vertical milling attachments that can be mounted on horizontal milling machines also are used for end-mill operations.

Operations that can be performed with the described set-ups consist of milling horizontal surfaces, vertical surfaces, angular surfaces, grooves, shoulders, keyways, slots, T-slots, dovetails, and many similar operations. 71–17.

Check Your Knowledge

1. Name several different types of milling machines.

2. Explain the distinguishing difference between the plain and universal milling machines.

3. What are the distinguishing features about vertical milling machines?

4. What operations can be performed on a profiling machine?

5. What is the most common workpiece holding device used on a milling machine?

6. State the rule or formula which may be used to determine the number of turns of the index crank required to move the workpiece through one division of any number of equally spaced divisions in a circle.

7. Describe an index head.

8. Explain how the sector is used on a dividing head.

9. Explain how direct indexing is accomplished with a dividing head.

10. Describe spiral milling.

11. Sketch a plain milling cutter and indicate the clearance angle, face angle, tooth face, land, and tooth depth.

12. What are some of the advantages of inserted tooth milling cutters?

13. What are the advantages of a coarse-tooth milling cutter over a fine-tooth cutter?

14. Define the meaning of cutting speed as applied to milling.

15. What factor must be considered for determining the cutting speed?

16. Define feed as applied to milling operations.

17. Milling operations can be classified into two broad categories. Name them.

18. What are the governing factors in peripheral milling?

19. Explain the difference between up milling and down milling.

20. What feature must be provided on machines used for down milling?

21. Describe the operation of straddle milling.

Problems

1. Calculate the rpm of a 3"-diam. cutter which is to cut at 95 fpm.

2. *Calculate the rpm of a ⅞"-diam. end mill which is to cut at 70 sfpm.*

3. *Calculate the approximate cutting speed for a 1½"-diam. end mill which is operating at 165 rpm.*

4. *Determine the rate of feed in inches per minute for machining low-carbon steel at 60 fpm, 90 rpm, using a plain milling cutter 2½" in diameter, with 8 teeth, and with .004" feed per tooth.*

5. *Give the direct indexing for cutting a milling cutter with 8 teeth.*

6. *Using simple indexing, index for 120 divisions.*

7. *How many numbers from 225 to 240 can be indexed by simple indexing?*

8. *What indexing is necessary for cutting a gear with 16 teeth; 17 teeth; 21 teeth?*

9. *A certain dividing head in common use has three index plates, with the following circles of holes:*

First plate; 15, 16, 17, 18, 19, 20.

Second plate; 21, 23, 27, 29, 31, 33.

Third plate; 37, 39, 41, 43, 47, 49.

What indexing is required for cutting a gear with 24 teeth; 35 teeth?

References

American Society of Tool and Manufacturing Engineers, *Tool Engineers Handbook,* 2nd ed., New York, McGraw-Hill Book Co., 1959.

Brown and Sharpe Manufacturing Company, *Practical Treatise on Milling and Milling Machines,* 1947.

Cincinnati Milling Machine Company, *A Treatise on Milling and Milling Machines,* 3rd ed., 1951.

"Fundamentals of HSS Cutting Tools," *American Machinist,* Special Report No. 549, April 13, 1964.

Horizontal boring, drilling, and milling machine.

Mesta Machine Co.

Section Fifteen

Sawing and Filing

1. Reciprocating: power hacksaw.

2. Band saw: horizontal, vertical cutoff, and friction.

3. Circular saw: cold saw, steel friction disc, and abrasive disc.

Unit 72.

Sawing

There have been many sweeping changes and advances made in the last decade in the development of metal sawing equipment —new methods, machines, and materials have replaced old. High-speed band saw blades, the profile saw, heavy feed power hacksaws, and blades made from newer materials have made it possible for industry to increase production in metal cutting.

HAND SAWING

Metal that is too small and limited in production to be cut in a machine economically can be placed in a vise and cut to size with a hand hacksaw. 72–1. In the selection of hand hacksaw blades, choosing the right blade for a particular job is important. There are three things to consider: (1) type of steel (regular or high-speed); (2) type of blade

(all hard or flexible back); and (3) pitch (number of teeth per inch). The blades can range from 8″ to 12″ in length, held in a hacksaw frame. The tooth pitch can vary from 14 to 32 teeth per inch, with the average around 18 tpi (teeth per inch).

In selecting the correct pitch, remember that at least two teeth should be engaged in the material at all times. A fine tooth for small or thin sections and a coarse tooth for larger sections is the general rule. Also, soft, easily machined metals require a coarse tooth because larger spaces are needed to carry away the larger chips and prevent clogging. 72–2.

POWER SAW BLADES

Metal cutting saw blades for power sawing are made in straight, circular, and continuous shapes, depending upon the type of machine on which they are to be used.

SAWING MACHINE TYPES

Metal sawing machines are generally classified as;

RECIPROCATING SAWING MACHINES—HACKSAWS

Reciprocating power hacksaws are used primarily for cutting to length metal of various sizes, kinds, and shapes. 72–3. These sawing machines vary in design, from light-duty, crank-driven machines to large, heavy-duty machines that are hydraulically driven. Actual cutting takes place in only one direction and the saw blade is lifted slightly on the return stroke, saving wear on the saw teeth.

On the lighter reciprocating machines, the saw is fed into the workpiece by gravity, through the weight of the saw frame and blade. The saw frame is usually lowered a fixed amount on each stroke. Some machines are designed with faster return strokes for the saw blade.

The larger machines usually employ a hydraulic feed mechanism which provides a pressure feed that can be controlled by the operator. Many larger machines are equipped with automatic bar feed and discharge

72–1. Hand hacksawing.

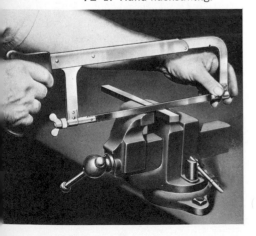

72–2. Pitch selection.

Henry G. Thompson & Son Co.

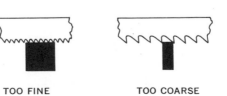

TOO FINE   TOO COARSE   O. K.

72–3. Reciprocating power hacksaw.

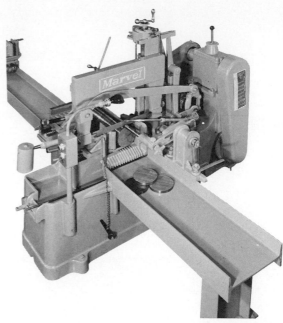

72–4. Hacksawing machine with automatic bar feed, cutting stock to size.

track. 72–4. The stock is fed automatically to the correct length, is clamped, and the stock cut off. The saw is then raised to its original position, the vise is opened, and the cycle is repeated.

Considerable care has to be taken in setting up the work and clamping workpieces in the vise in order to secure efficient operation. 72–5.

Hacksawing is not a rapid method of cutting off stock. However, the machines are easy to operate and require very little maintenance.

Power Hacksaw Blades

Power hacksaw blades vary in length from 12″ to 32″ and from 0.050″ to 0.125″ in thickness. Production economy demands that blades be as short as the

workpiece and machine size will permit. The blade must be wide and thick enough to withstand the necessary feed pressures and to provide the rigidity needed to resist flexing and vibration. 72–6

72–5. Work setup for power hacksawing.

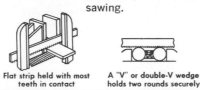

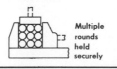

Flat strip held with most teeth in contact

A "V" or double-V wedge holds two rounds securely

Multiple rounds held securely

wedges

A "V" wedge holds two rounds securely

WRONG
Teeth strike sharp edge

RIGHT POSITION
Several teeth contact work

(Page 362). Shorter, heavier blades are more rigid, stand more pressure, resist breakage, and assure straighter cuts.

In selecting a blade with the proper pitch (number of teeth per inch) the following general principles should be observed:

1. At least two teeth should be engaged in the material to be cut at all times.

2. Large sections require coarse teeth to provide ample chip clearance.

3. Small or thin-wall sections require fine teeth.

4. Soft, easily machined metals require slightly coarser teeth to provide chip clearance.

Feed Selection

Note these general principles when determining the correct feeds for particular jobs:

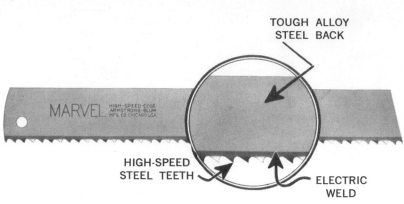

TOUGH ALLOY
STEEL BACK

MARVEL HIGH-SPEED-EDGE
ARMSTRONG-BLUM
MFG. CO CHICAGO USA

HIGH-SPEED
STEEL TEETH

ELECTRIC
WELD

72–6. High-speed edge hacksaw blade.

TYPE OF MATERIAL	PITCH (Teeth per Inch)		SPEED	FEED	
	Material 2″ and Under	Material Over 2″	Strokes per Minute	Inches per Stroke	Pounds Pressure
Aluminum, Alloy	6	3	100–150	.003–.012	60
Pure	6	3	100–135	.003–.012	60
Brass					
Free Machining	6–10	3–6	120–150	.003–.012	60
Hard	6–10	6	100–135	.003–.006	60
Tubing	10–14	10–14	120–150	.003–.006	60
Bronze					
Commercial	6–10	3–6	90–120	.003–.006	120
Manganese	6–10	6	60–90	.003–.006	60
Copper	6–10	3–6	90–120	.006–.009	120
High Density Alloys					
A286, Discalloy	4	3	50–75	.006–.009	300–400
Hastelloy					
Titanium					
Iron, Cast	6–10	4–6	90–120	.009–.012	120
Malleable	6–10	6	90	.006–.009	125
Pipe	10–14	10–14	90–120	.003–.009	60–100
Magnesium	6	3–4	120–150	.009–.015	80
Nickel Alloy					
Inconel	6–10	3–6	50–80	.003–.009	125
Monel	6–10	3–6	60–90	.003–.009	100–150
Nickel	6–10	3–6	60–90	.003–.009	100–150
Nickel Silver	6–10	6	60	.003–.009	150
Steel, Alloy	6–10	3–6	60–120	.003–.009	100–150
Carbon Tool	6–10	6	60–90	.003–.009	120
Cold Rolled	6	3–6	100–135	.006–.012	125
Hot Rolled	6	3–6	100–135	.006–.012	125
High Speed	6–10	6	60–90	.003–.006	120
Machinery	6–10	3–6	100–135	.006–.009	150
Pipe and Tubing	10–14	6–14	90–135	.006–.009	50–100
Stainless	6–10	3–6	60–90	.003–.009	100–150
Structural	6–10	6–10	90–135	.003–.006	120
Tool	6–10	6	60–90	.003–.009	120

Table 72-A. Recommended Pitch Cutting Speeds and Feeds for Power Hacksawing*

* Henry G. Thompson & Son Co.

1. Moderate feed pressures must be used when straight, accurate cutting is desired. 72–7.

2. Excessive feed pressures cause the machine to vibrate or chatter.

3. A free-cut, curled chip indicates ideal feed pressure for fastest cutting with longest blade life. Coolant is recommended when sawing ferrous metals (except cast iron) and most nonferrous metals.

The most common type of saw blade is the straight or regular tooth design with zero rake. 72–8. The undercut tooth is used for large and coarse pitch blades.

Tooth set refers to the manner in which the saw teeth are offset from the center line. 72–9. Tooth set permits the saw to make a cut which is wider than the thickness of the back portion of the blade and prevents the saw blade from binding in the slot, reducing heat from friction.

Raker set is recommended for general purpose shop cutting on cut-off, contour, and die work, using vertical band sawing machines. Teeth are set alternate right, left, followed by straight.

A *wave, or wavy, set* consists of an alternate arrangement of several teeth set to right and several teeth set to left. Wave set is suited for cutting solids, angles, pipe, and tubing.

Hook teeth with a positive rake give a smooth, shear cut, with less feed pressure required.

Skip tooth saw blades are designed for high-speed cutting of nonferrous metals, plastics, special compositions, and wood. These teeth have ample gullet capacity.

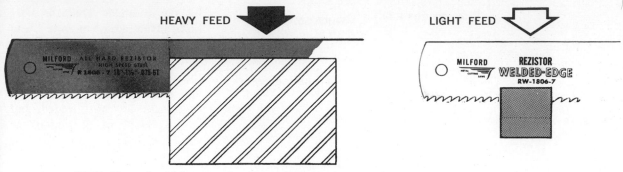

HEAVY FEED   LIGHT FEED

72–7. Heavy feed pressure should be applied to large workpieces and hard materials, light pressure to small workpieces and soft materials.

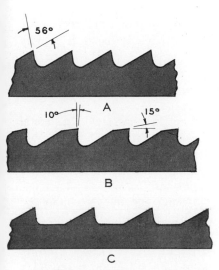

72–8. Tooth construction for hacksaw blades: (A) straight tooth, (B) undercut tooth, and (C) skip tooth.

72–9. Types of tooth set for metal-cutting saw blades.

L. S. Starrett Co.

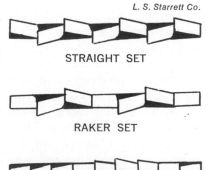

STRAIGHT SET

RAKER SET

WAVE SET

CIRCULAR SAWING MACHINES

Circular saws are used on machines commonly known as cold sawing machines.

Workpieces are clamped in a vise or fixture, one or more pieces at a time. The circular blade is mounted on a power driven arbor and rotated through the cut. 72–10.

Some machines are mounted on a carriage and have a hand feed. Other types of machines are hydraulically operated and are capable of sawing stock up to 8″ in diameter with close length tolerances of 0.003″.

The cold saw leaves a smooth, accurate surface finish similar to milling and provides a fast method for cutting off. High production can be obtained with these machines.

Circular Saw Blades

Circular metal saws may be solid, similar to slitting saws used on milling machines, may carry segments, each with several

72–10. Automatic circular cold sawing machine.

Motch & Merryweather Machinery Co.

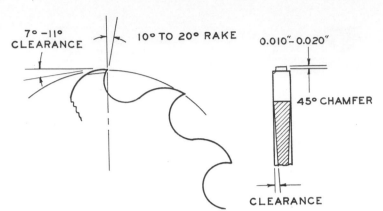

72–11(A). Tooth construction for circular saws.

Simonds Saw and Steel Co.

72–11(B). Circular metal-cutting saws.

72–11(C). Slotted segmental circular saw.

Simonds Saw and Steel Co.

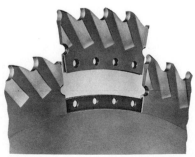

teeth, or have inserted teeth. Saws with segmental or inserted teeth have the disc made of less-expensive steel while the teeth may be of high-speed steel or tungsten carbide. 72–11(A). Segmental blades have segments mounted around the periphery of the disc.

Inserted teeth are usually used on large circular saws with each tooth as a separate piece fastened to the blade and held in place by brazing, or fastened with wedges or screws. 72–11(B&C). Both inserted and segmental type blades are economical due to the fact that the teeth can be replaced when worn.

A coolant is recommended for all circular sawing operations except cast iron.

FRICTION SAWING WITH STEEL DISCS

Friction sawing differs from all other metal sawing techniques because it is not actually a cutting operation, but rather a burning process similar to torch cutting. It is much faster than conventional sawing. Very hard materials, normally impossible to saw, are cut rapidly and easily

by this method. There is very little blade drag, so bulky and irregular shapes can be easily cut. In this type of machining, the disc is rotated at speeds of approximately 20,000 fpm. Cutting teeth are not needed, but various kinds of projections or small indentations along the saw edge may be used.

The high speed of the disc rubbing against the material generates a large amount of heat by friction. As the heat is generated to a certain point and the tensile strength of the metal is rapidly lowered to a point where the temperature increases, the material loses strength and is wiped away.

The hardness of the metal does not limit friction cutting but the structure of the metal and its melting point characteristics are important.

Nonferrous metals cannot be cut by this method because only those metals which lose sufficient strength below their melting point can be friction sawed. One of the requirements of friction sawing is that the grain structure of the metal should not break down before the metal reaches the proper temperature.

ABRASIVE SAWING

Abrasive discs are also used for cutting off stock. An abrasive disc is a thin, flexible grinding wheel. The disc is mounted on a machine that can be adapted for either wet or dry cutting. *Dry cutting* is done at speeds of approximately 16,000 sfpm, using resinoid-bonded wheels. 72–12. In the dry cutting process, the high wheel speed causes the metal to heat rapidly, softening it for easy metal removal. Solids up to 2" in diameter or 3½" tubing can be cut by this method.

Rubber bonded wheels are employed for *wet cutting,* operating around 8,000 sfpm. The surface speed is kept at this figure so that coolant can be used to prevent the overheating of the material. Since abrasive grains in the wheel provide the cutting action, no softening of the material is obtained by this process.

BAND SAWING MACHINES

Modern band sawing covers a wide field of operations includ-

ing cut-off, straight sawing, and contour ("profile") sawing. Both rough shaping and semifinishing are possible with almost all ferrous and nonferrous materials.

Most band saw machines fall into one of three general classifications: (1) horizontal machines for cut-off sawing; (2) vertical machines for straight or profile sawing at conventional speeds; and (3) vertical machine for nonferrous cutting and/or friction cutting. 72–13.

Horizontal band saws for high-speed cutting-off operations, using endless high-speed band saw

Allison-Campebll Div. of American Chain & Cable Co., Inc.

72–12. Dry abrasive cutting machine.

72–13. Horizontal band sawing machine.

FEED CONTROL AND GAUGE
BLADE SELECTOR CHART
SPEED CONTROL
TACHOMETER
CARBIDE BACK ROLLER GUIDES
CARBIDE SIDE GUIDES
HYDRAULIC BLADE TENSION CYLINDER
AUTOMATIC BAR FEED
HYDRAULIC CYLINDERS FOR VISE CLAMPING
OUTBOARD VISE
HYDRAULIC TANK

WORK AREA LIGHT
SAW CONTROL
HEIGHT SELECTOR
COOLANT CONTROL
START AND STOP PUSH BUTTONS
CAM-ACTION LOCK-ON GUIDE ARM
CALIBRATED WORK STOP
CHIP SCREEN
SECOND RECEIVING TABLE
FIRST RECEIVING TABLE
COOLANT TANK

DoAll Co.

72–14. Horizontal production type heavy-duty band sawing machine with a capacity of 12″ x 16″.

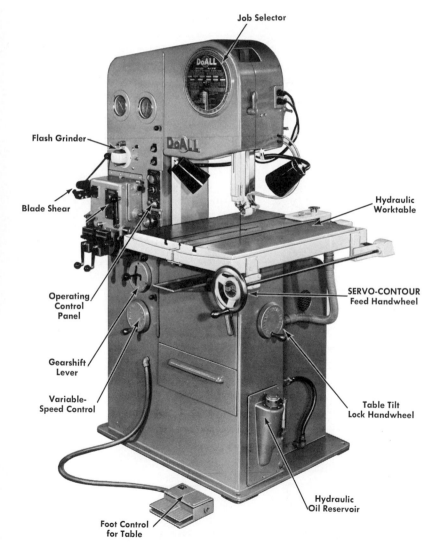

Job Selector

Flash Grinder

Blade Shear

Operating
Control
Panel

Gearshift
Lever

Variable-
Speed Control

Foot Control
for Table

Hydraulic
Oil Reservoir

Table Tilt
Lock Handwheel

SERVO-CONTOUR
Feed Handwheel

Hydraulic
Worktable

blades represent a new production cut-off method.

The horizontal band saw machine produces a narrower kerf, resulting in reduced chip losses, fast efficient cutting with low per-cut costs, and smooth accurate cutting. However, due to the high feeding pressures required for fast cutting, the slightest inaccuracy in tooth set can cause the blade to drift off the cutting line.

The illustration shows an automatic shuttle-feed type of horizontal band sawing machine that is ideal for slugging to supply blanks for chuckers. 72–14. The hydraulically actuated shuttle-feed vise has a 0 to 24″ stroke. The machine can be operated manually for single cuts or, if equipped with a counter, set to cycle automatically to cut a predetermined number of blanks. A servo-controlled micrometer indexing reduces setup time and assures exact repeatability of index length on an automatic saw.

Vertical Band Sawing Machines

Contour or profile sawing is a fast, accurate method of producing intricate contours in a variety of metals. 72–15. With the proper blade selection, radii as small as $\frac{1}{16}$″ can be cut, and either external or internal contours can be sawed. Where *internal contours* are involved, it is first necessary to drill a hole within the contour area to admit the saw blade. The blade is cut, threaded through the hole, and

DoAll Co.

72–15. Standard-duty vertical band sawing machine.

then rewelded. 72–16 (Page 368). Machines have a built-in butt welder for this purpose.

Vertical band sawing machines are available with either fixed or variable speeds. The variable-speed feature permits easy adaptation to operating conditions as well as to the characteristics of materials.

Some sawing machines are equipped with a speed indicator (tachometer) which gives the speed the blade is traveling in fpm.

Proper cutting speed is an important factor in band machining. If the machine is operated too fast for the type of material being cut, the teeth are not allowed sufficient time to dig into the material. As a result, they merely rub over the work, creating friction and dulling the edge of the teeth.

Blades for profile sawing are always *raker set* because this type of tooth provides the necessary side clearance. The proper *width of blade* to be used depends upon the smallest radius to be cut.

In addition to high-speed steel bands, abrasive and diamond edge bands are used to cut the hardest steels and brittle or abrasive materials.

The *tooth shape* of band saw blades is practically the same as for hacksaw blades. Manufacturers' recommendations should be followed for the proper selection of blades for different materials. 72–17. Table 72-B.

Special blades for *friction cutting* are available for this type of sawing, which is much faster than conventional sawing methods. Very hard materials, which could not normally be cut by conventional methods can be cut by this process.

Vertical Band Machining Operations

For the suitable gage of metal, the band machine offers many advantages. Unlike other machine tools, it cuts directly to a layout line and removes material in sections instead of in chips, re-

Table 72-B. Recommended Speeds for Band Machining Common Metals*

AISI Type	Description	Average Recommended Saw Speeds in F.P.M.	
		Carbon Steel Blades	High-Speed Steel Blades
Group I—Easily Machinable			
1010–1035	Straight-Carbon Steels	150–175	300
1040–1050	Medium-Carbon Steels	100–150	200
1108–1130	Free cutting Low-Carbon Steels	150–175	300
1137–1150	Free cutting Medium-Carbon Steels	100–150	250
Group II—Moderately Difficult to Machine			
1065–1095	High-Carbon Steels	80–125	150
1320–1345	Manganese Steels	70–125	200
2317–2517	Nickel Steels	75–100	175
3115–3315	Nickel-Chrome Steels	50–100	200
4017–4068	Moly Steels	75–135	200
4130–4150	Chrome-Moly Steels	50–100	225
4317–4340	Nickel-Chrome Moly Steels	50–100	200
4608–4820	Nickel-Moly Steels	50–100	200
5045–5160	Chromium Steels	40–100	200
50100–52100	Carbon-Chrome Steels	50–125	150
6117–6152	Chrome-Vanadium Steels	40–100	175
8615–8750	Moly Steels	50–90	175
9255–9262	Silicon Steels	50–125	150
9310–9850	Nickel-Chrome Moly Steels	50–80	175
A-2, O-1, O-2, O-6	Tool & Die Steels	70–125	175
H-2, H-4	Hot Work Tool Steels	50–125	150
S-1, S-5	Shock Resisting Tool Steels	50–125	150
Group III—Machined with Difficulty			
2515	5% Nickel Steel	50–80	100
T-1, T-2	High-Speed Steel	50–80	100
T-4, T-5	High-Speed Steel	50–80	100
T-6, T-8, T-15	High-Speed Steel	50–80	75
M-1, M-2	High-Speed Steel	40–80	100
M-3, M-10	High-Speed Steel	35–75	90
D-2, D-3	Die Steel	60–90	100
D-7	Die Steel	50	75
308, 309, 310	Stainless Steel	50–90	75
314, 316, 317	Stainless Steel	50–90	75
330, 420, 430, 446	Stainless Steel	50–90	75
446	Stainless Steel	50–90	75
302, 304, 321, 347, 440	Stainless Steel	50–90	100
303, 420F, 430F, 440F	Free Machining Stainless Steel	60–100	150

* Henry G. Thompson & Son Co.

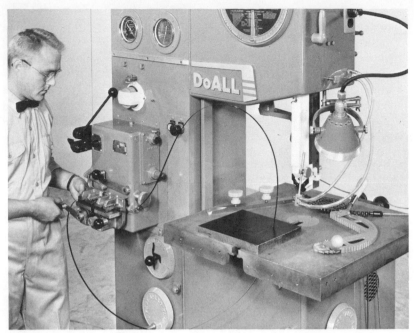

72–16. Blade is cut, threaded through hole, and rewelded.

Precision blade has 0-deg. rake angle and smooth radius gullet. Produces excellent finish.

Buttress blade is designed to accommodate maximum chip load, longer flex life and good surface finish.

Claw Tooth blade is similar to Buttress blade, but has a 10 deg. positive rake angle which provides for faster cutting.

DoAll Co.

72–17. Types of blades used on band sawing machines.

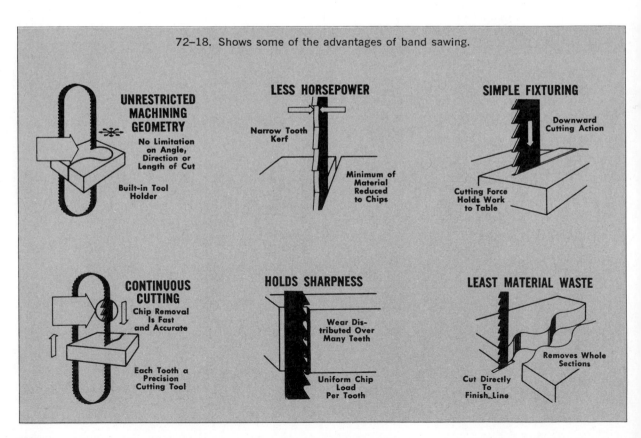

72–18. Shows some of the advantages of band sawing.

UNRESTRICTED MACHINING GEOMETRY
No Limitation on Angle, Direction or Length of Cut
Built-in Tool Holder

LESS HORSEPOWER
Narrow Tooth Kerf
Minimum of Material Reduced to Chips

SIMPLE FIXTURING
Downward Cutting Action
Cutting Force Holds Work to Table

CONTINUOUS CUTTING
Chip Removal Is Fast and Accurate
Each Tooth a Precision Cutting Tool

HOLDS SHARPNESS
Wear Distributed Over Many Teeth
Uniform Chip Load Per Tooth

LEAST MATERIAL WASTE
Removes Whole Sections
Cut Directly To Finish Line

sulting in savings in time and material.

The cutting tool on a vertical band machine actually is an endless band of single-point cutting tools. It cuts continuously and fast. Wear spreads over all teeth to extend tool life, and there is no wasted motion as on a reciprocating hacksawing machine.

The thin band tool, a fraction of an inch thick, saves more material and takes less horsepower to overcome material resistance than do the larger, wider cutting tools on other machines.

A significant advantage of band machining is its *unrestricted geometry*. There is no limit to the length, angle, contour, or radius that can be cut. 72–18.

The constant downward force of the band saw holds the workpiece to the table, making it simple to hold fixture work for production runs. Making a setup or changeover is fast, operation is easy, and cost per cut is low.

The Contour-matic machine differs from fixed table models in four principal respects:

1. Hydraulically powered worktables feed work into the saw band at a constant, preset rate.

2. Built-in recirculating cutting fluid system provides fluid to cool and lubricate the saw band teeth.

3. Greater horsepower makes possible maximum depth of saw tooth penetration and faster band saw speed.

4. Greater rigidity and strength fully utilize the added horsepower and withstand the increased band tension needed to produce fast and accurate cuts.

These band machines can do work that just cannot be done by any other method.

The illustrations show some applications possible with band machining. 72–19. The band machine's narrow kerf and loading ease can cut costs in half on many slotting, splitting, ripping, notching, turning, and facing operations; in machining contours, angles, and grinding reliefs; and in sawing a blanking punch and die from one piece of metal. 72–20, 71–21 & 72–22. Adaptability is limited mostly by man's resourcefulness in utilizing proper workholding and supporting devices.

DoAll Co.

72–20. Splitting high-carbon, high-chrome tool steel cylinders on a Contour-matic band machine.

72–19. Magnifying lens and work-holding jaw—two aids for precision band sawing.

DoAll Co.

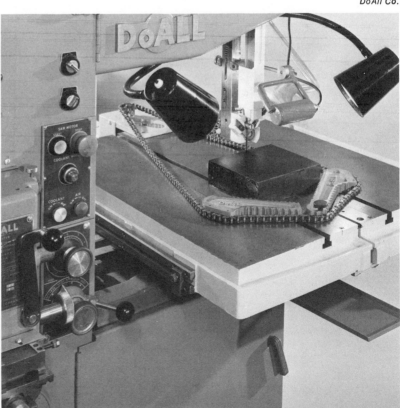

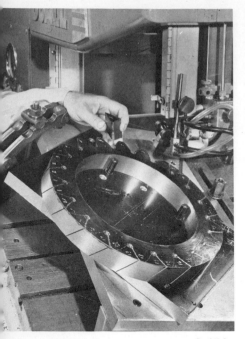

72–21. Angle cuts made on a Contour-matic band machine.

72–22. Die shapes being sawed in the development of auto fender skirts from a solid piece of 4140 steel 9″ thick.

Unit 73.   Filing

Filing may be done by hand or on filing machines. Hand filing requires great skill to produce the required surface.

FILE CLASSIFICATION

Files have three distinguishing features: (1) length, (2) kind or name, and (3) cut. 73–1.

The length of a file is the distance between its heel and the point.

Kind of file refers to the shapes or styles of files. These are divided, according to their cross sections, into three general geometrical classes: quadrangular, triangular, and circular. There are also many miscellaneous shapes.

File cuts are called, with reference to the character of the teeth, either: (1) single, (2) double, (3) rasp, or (4) curved. 73–2. The coarseness of the teeth may be classified as: coarse, bastard, second cut, and smooth cut.

Single-cut files have rows of teeth extending across the width of the file at a 65° to 85° angle. *Double-cut* files have two series of parallel teeth across the width of the file. Both series of teeth are cut at an angle of 40° to 45°.

The *rasp cut* is a series of individual teeth produced by a

73–1. Parts of a file.

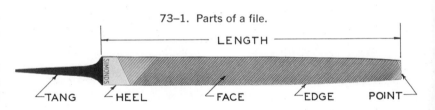

TANG   HEEL   FACE   EDGE   POINT

sharp, punchlike, cutting chisel. The *curved cut* has file teeth which are made in a curved contour across the file blank.

There are hundreds of shapes, cuts, and sizes of files. This is because there are hundreds of special filing needs, each of which can be best satisfied by using the right file for the job.

DIE-FILING MACHINES

While accurate filing can be accomplished by hand filing by

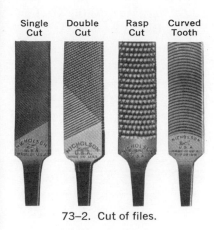

| Single Cut | Double Cut | Rasp Cut | Curved Tooth |

73-2. Cut of files.

73-3. Die-filing machine.

a skilled workman, it is a slow and laborious process. Die-filing machines have provided an accurate, easy method of filing. 73–3.

They operate at 300 to 500 spm, with the filing operation taking place on the down stroke. A short length file made for this type of filing is fastened below a horizontal table to a clamping device. The upper end of the file is fastened and supported by a roller guide. The cutting is done on the downward stroke, which serves to hold the workpiece to the table. Angles can easily be filed by tilting the table.

BAND FILING MACHINES

Both filing and polishing can be done on contour sawing machines. A special file band is substituted for the metal cutting band saw blade. The file band is made of straight file segments approximately 3" long mounted on a flexible band. Provisions are made at both ends so that the ends may be locked together to form one continuous band. The band file runs over the two wheels of the vertical sawing machine, the blade passing over the wheels. Where the file passes through the table, the file is supported above and below by a grooved guide.

For internal filing, the band can be passed through an opening in the workpiece, snapped back together, and the filing operation be done. 73–4. Filing speeds range from 50 to 250 sfpm. The cuts and shapes of files used for this purpose are the same as for standard commercial files.

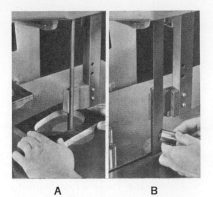

| A | B |

73–4. (A) Band filing is a fast and accurate way to finish die castings; (B) band polishing operation.

DISC-FILING MACHINES

The disc-filing machines combines the qualities of both the die-filing and the band machine. The disc files provide a continuous filing action. This machine is used primarily for external filing of surfaces. The workpiece is placed on the table, which can be tilted if necessary, and is held against the rotating discs.

Check Your Knowledge

1. List the various types of power sawing machines and describe each.

2. What three things should be considered in the proper selection of hand hacksaw blades?

3. What type of feed mechanism is employed on the larger hacksawing machines?

4. Why is tooth spacing important in sawing thin materials?

5. What general principles should be followed in selecting a blade with the proper pitch?

6. What type of feed pressure should be used when straight and accurate cutting is desired?

7. What is the advantage of inserted teeth in circular saws?

8. Describe friction sawing. What are some of its advantages?

9. Why cannot nonferrous metals be successfully cut by friction sawing?

10. What type of saw is used in the friction sawing process?

11. What is abrasive sawing?

12. Name three classifications of band sawing machines.

13. Explain the difference between horizontal and vertical band sawing machines.

14. How is internal sawing done on a vertical band saw?

15. Name three distinguishing features of files.

16. Name the cuts of files.

17. Why should a file with coarse tooth spacing be used for soft materials?

18. What are some of the advantages of a band sawing machine?

19. Describe a die-filing machine.

Problems

1. A piece of cold-rolled steel ⅝″ thick is to be cut on a horizontal band saw having a 14 pitch blade and operating at 100 sfpm. The average metal removal per tooth is 0.0001″. How long will it take to cut through three pieces of the same thickness?

2. Using a 14″ high-speed steel saw blade with 12 tpi, to cut a 4″ cold-rolled steel bar, with the saw operating at 70 spm and having a feed rate of 0.010″ per stroke, calculate the cutting time.

References

American Society for Metals, *Metals Handbook,* 8th ed., "Machining," Vol. 3, 1967.

American Society of Tool and Manufacturing Engineers, *Tool Engineers Handbook,* 2nd ed., 1959.

Black, P. H., *Theory of Metal Cutting,* New York, McGraw-Hill Book Co., 1961.

Habicht, F. H., *Modern Machine Tools,* Princeton, N.J., D. Van Nostrand Co., Inc., 1963.

Section Sixteen

Broaching

Unit 74.

Classification

Broaching consists of forcing, by either pushing or pulling, a special tool across or through a piece of metal, forming a shaped surface quickly and accurately. The broach has a series of teeth which progressively increase in size from the starting end so that each tooth takes a cut across the part to be formed. Broaching is an exceptionally rapid and accurate method for cutting an accurate, good quality finish. The process is also a good way to produce a large quantity of duplicate parts.

There are two major classifications given to broaching: *internal* and *surface*. An example of internal broaching is the addition of a hole, usually other than round, in a part through which a round hole has been formed by drilling. 74–1. Keyways, internal gears, splines, and square holes are some examples.

Surfaces externally shaped by this process are numerous. External surfaces are often generated by broaching instead of milling because of the increased speed and accuracy of the broaching process.

Broaching machines may be either *vertical* or *horizontal* in design. Such factors as size of the part, quantity required, size of broach, and type of broaching desired governs the type of machine to be used. Vertical type machines with the broach supported on a proper slide can be used in surface broaching. Pull- and push-type internal machines are also vertical. Horizontal machines are made only to pull the broaching tool.

Power is supplied to the broach by either mechanical or pneumatic/hydraulic means, although hydraulic is the most common means because of the control flexibility and smooth application.

The workpiece on broaching machines is held by a rigid holding fixture. A means for supplying cutting fluid to the broach is provided as an aid to smooth cutting.

BROACHING TOOLS

The principal parts, shape, and arrangement of teeth of a broach are shown. Each of the long broaching tool's teeth removes only a small portion of the metal along the entire cut. 74–2. The first teeth of the broach are the *cutting teeth* and the last few are the *finishing teeth*. The short end next to the finish teeth is the *rear pilot*. Like threads, broaches also have pitch to the teeth, which is the distance from a point on one tooth to the corresponding point on an adjacent tooth. The pitch is controlled by three factors: (1) length of broach, (2) chip thickness, and (3) kind of material being machined.

Each broaching tooth is a wide single-point cutting tool which is arranged somewhat like saw teeth with a "step," which determines the depth of cut of each tooth. 74–3. It will be noted from the illustration that the top portion of the tooth, called the land, is given slight clearance which ranges from 1/2° to 4° or about 25% of the pitch. The finishing teeth have an angle of 0 to 1 1/2°. The rake angle is ground from 0 to 20° depending upon the type of material being cut. For most steels this angle will vary from 12° to 15° and increase for softer materials. Too large rake and clearance angles have a tendency to shorten the life of the broaching tool. The fillet at the bottom of the tool

74–1. Holes of any shape may be broached.

National Broach & Machine Co.

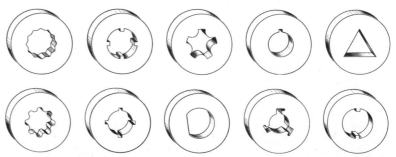

strengthens the tooth and curls the chip as it comes from the material being machined.

TYPES OF BROACHES

Broaches are production tools adapted for a single operation. Broaching combines both roughing and finishing cuts in a single operation and removes stock to precision limits quickly and economically.

For many years broaching was an internal operation only, used primarily for cutting keyways in pulleys or gears, with broaches pushed through a hole with a hand arbor press. 74–4. This type of broaching is still done today on a production basis with either hand or hydraulically operated presses.

A variation of internal broaching is obtained by rotating the broach as it is pulled through the workpiece, making it possible to machine helical internal splines or rifle gun barrels in one pass.

External broaching of various types is standard practice today for engine blocks. Typical broached parts include gears, gear shift levers, hinges, axle parts, connecting rods, steering gear levers, bearings, rifle and cannon barrels, pump bodies, pistol frames, and many other products. 74–5 (Page 376).

Broached holes may be started in holes that have been cored, punched, forged, drilled, bored, or reamed. The broaching process can produce parts with a very fine finish, with no other finishing operation necessary.

A

B

The duMont Corp.

74–4. Broaching a keyway in a gear on a hand-operated arbor press.

74–2. Typical internal round broach.

National Broach & Machine Co.

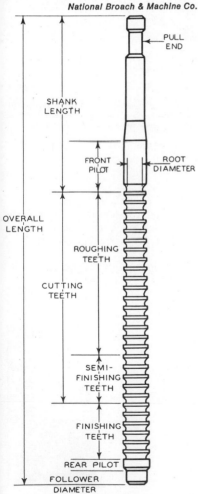

PULL END

SHANK LENGTH

FRONT PILOT

ROOT DIAMETER

OVERALL LENGTH

ROUGHING TEETH

CUTTING TEETH

SEMI-FINISHING TEETH

FINISHING TEETH

REAR PILOT

FOLLOWER DIAMETER

74–3. Standard terminology for broach teeth.

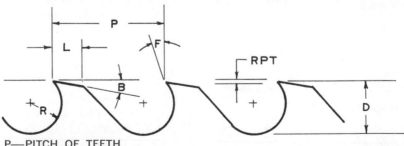

P—PITCH OF TEETH
D—DEPTH OF TEETH
L—LAND BEHIND CUTTING EDGE
R—RADIUS AT BOTTOM OF TOOTH
F—FACE ANGLE
B—BACKOFF ANGLE
RPT—RISE PER TOOTH—CHIP LOAD

Illinois Tool & Instrument, Div. of Illinois Tool Works, Inc.
74–6. Push-type serration broach.

Broaching tools, in a wide variety of shapes and sizes, may be generally classified as to:

1. Method of operation—pull or push broaches.

2. Type of operation—external or internal.

3. Type of construction—solid built-up, progressive, circular, inserted teeth, etc.

4. Function—round hole, keyway, spline rifling, burnishing, and special shapes.

The construction of a broach is governed by the method of operation. Push broaches (74–6) are short due to their type of operation, while pull broaches (74–7) can be made longer and can ordinarily remove as much material as several push broaches due to their method of operation and length. The majority of internal broaching operations is done with pull broaches because they are capable of taking longer and heavier cuts than the push type. 74–7.

Keyway broaches are used for cutting keyways and slots in gears and pulleys. 74–8. They are generally of the push type.

Progressive surface broaches, used on castings and forgings, have one or more rows of teeth,

Illinois Tool & Instrument, Div. of Illinois Tool Works, Inc.
74–7. Pull-type broach.

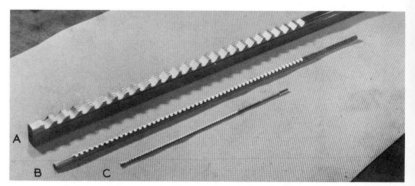

Illinois Tool & Instrument, Div. of Illinois Tool Works, Inc.
74–8. (A) and (C) Conventional keyway broaches. (B) Round body and single keyway broach.

74–5. Several broached products.

narrower than the surface to be broached. 74–9. The rows are arranged at an angle with the longitudinal axis of the broach so that the full width is machined in one pass of the broach. NOTE: Each tooth cuts full depth but only a small part of the width.

The "double jump" broach has been developed for material with a hard scale. 74–10. Teeth are arranged to cut below the scale, with the initial cut being quite heavy to prevent dulling the teeth.

The circular broach is used on special broaching machines for

74–9. External broaching with vertical-surface broaching machine, using a progressive type broach.

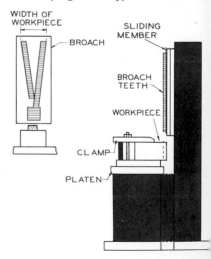

machining straight or curved surfaces. 74–11.

Inserted tooth and built-up broaches are constructed to provide: (1) support for the cutting edge that is tougher and more shock resistant than edge material, (2) limited size adjustment to compensate for sharpening, (3) replacement of the teeth, (4) for reduction in the cost of construction.

Burnishing broaches, or burnishing sections on regular broaches, are used to produce a smooth burnished finish. The teeth have no cutting action. Their burnishing action provides a dense, compacted, smooth surface.

Some broaches are made with removable shells. The broach consists of a main body broach, or roughing broach, and the removable shell for the finishing operation. The shell is located in the rear of the roughing broach and held in place by a lock-nut. These sections can easily be replaced when worn or broken.

Surface broaches are designed for flat surfaces and are mounted on a sliding or stationary member of a broaching machine. 74–12. They are made with either straight or angular teeth slanted 5° to 20° from the perpendicular to the direction of broach travel. With the angular teeth, vibration is reduced and a smoother surface is obtained. The action is similar to a helical milling cutter.

Broaching of irregular or intricate shapes is possible with specially designed broaches.

Broaching fixtures are used for the same purposes as holding devices on machine tools. Fixtures

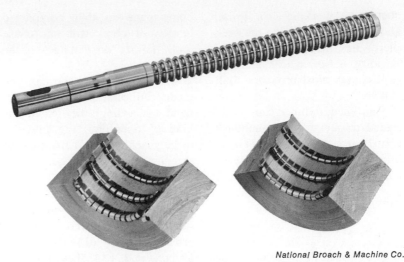

National Broach & Machine Co.

74–10. Double Jump broach developed for broaching cored or pierced holes when hard abrasive scale is encountered. Chip formation shown.

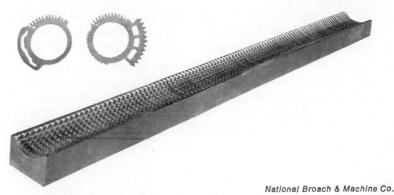

National Broach & Machine Co.

74–11. Gear sector broach.

74–12. Internal contour surface broaches with holders.

National Broach & Machine Co.

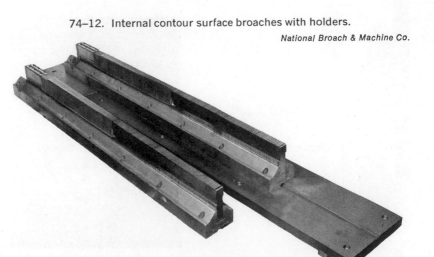

377

clamp the workpiece or broach and also serve to locate the workpiece in the proper position. Rigidity is so critical that lack of it causes most broaching difficulties.

Simplified fixtures can be designed to reduce work handling, eliminate time loss between broaching strokes, and provide automatic discharge of the work.

BROACH DESIGN

Length of Cut

The broach designer must provide adequate strength, enough cutting capacity, and sufficient carrying capacity. 74–13. The pull broach must be strong enough so that it won't be pulled apart and the push type broach must be strong enough so that it won't buckle. Both types must have enough teeth and proper

chip space so that compacted masses of chips will not cause tooth failure or damage to the workpiece.

Before the broach can be made, information must be on hand regarding the particular kind of operation, the material to be machined, and the type of machine on which the broach will be used.

The length of a broach is determined by: (1) the amount of stock to be removed from the broached part, (2) the length of cut, and (3) the allowable chip thickness for the material to be machined.

The length of cut, with other factors, determines tooth spacing; allowable chip thickness determines the number of teeth required. Length of the cutting portion of the tool is arrived at by the number of teeth needed

multiplied by the tooth spacing. The lengths of pull shank and rear pilot are added to make the total length.

The feed of a broach is fixed, while the speed is controlled by the design of the broaching machine.

Too heavy a cut taken with a broaching tool will overload it, causing failure of the broach. Too light a cut can damage the cutting edges, causing a rubbing rather than a cutting action.

Sound broach design practice dictates that, in the roughing section of the broach, the step per tooth should not exceed 30% of the total chip area. The cut per tooth in free machining steel varies from .003″ to .005″ for surface or external broaching. For internal broach design, these figures vary somewhat, since the chip formed must be contained in an area somewhat smaller than the diameter cutting.

The pitch, or space between the cutting teeth of a broach, determines the length of cut and chip thickness, based upon the material being broached. It affects the construction and strength of the tool and the allowable chip space.

The basic formula for pitch is:

$$\text{Pitch} = .35\sqrt{\text{length of cut}}$$

Since pitch is a function of the length of cut it also dictates the number of teeth that are engaged in a part at any one instance. With this fact in mind, the force requirements necessary for a broaching operation can be developed from the following formula:

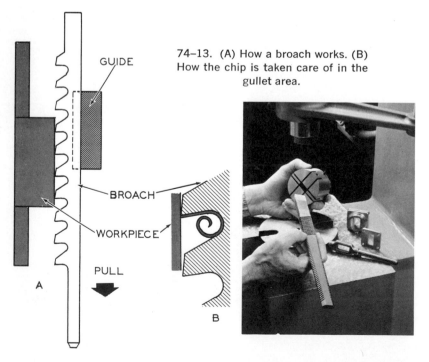

74–13. (A) How a broach works. (B) How the chip is taken care of in the gullet area.

GUIDE

BROACH

WORKPIECE

PULL

A

B

$F = N \times I \times K$

in which F = total force in pounds

N = number of teeth engaged

I = total width of cut in inches

K = empirical value in pounds representing the chip per tooth for material being machined

Empirical values for pounds of force required for one linear inch of tooth engagement in free machining steel are as follows:

Table 74-A. Empirical Values for Lbs. of Force

Chips per Tooth	K-pounds
0.0005	400
0.001	650
0.002	1,000
0.003	1,200
0.004	1,400
0.005	1,700

The chip space or gullet between each two teeth must hold all the metal removed by one tooth throughout the stroke. Gullet design in a broaching tool is of extreme importance. Gullet design should have several characteristics: (1) face angle, (2) two radii, (3) a cross-sectional area, and (4) a surface finish. A compromise must be reached between the ideal contour and the limits of the cross-sectional area for holding and curling chips.

Since the entire chip, as cut from the work, must be freely contained within the tooth gullet, size of the tooth gullet area, and, as a result, the spacing of the teeth, is established by the size of the chip area.

The Face Angle

Another element of broach design which affects surface finish and tool life is the face angle. It is an important factor in determining chip clearance for any given material. The face angle varies with the type of material being broached, its hardness, toughness, and ductility. The angle generally increases with the ductility of the metal, and for steel decreases slightly with hardness. A brittle metal, such as cast iron and brass, is cut more effectively by teeth with smaller face angles. Typical face angles for various materials are:

Table 74-B. Typical Face Angles of Broaches

Hard steel	8° to 12°
Soft steel	12° to 20°
Cast iron	6° to 8°
Aluminum	10°+
Titanium	18°

Land and Clearance Angle

On the cutting teeth of a broach, the entire land is usually relieved by a clearance or back-off angle, the value of which depends upon the type of material being cut. These angles are held to a minimum in order to minimize loss of size of the broach diameter when a broach is resharpened. Backoff angles on finishing teeth are generally half the angle used on roughing teeth.

Part of the land of finishing teeth is straight and is graduated in length from the first finishing tooth to the last, which prolongs the life of the broach.

For free machining steel, the clearance angle of the roughing teeth will vary between 2° and 3°; for cast iron, between 3° and 5°; for brass and bronze 1°.

Cutting Action of a Broach-Chip Area

The cutting action of a broach resembles that of any single-point tool. The difference is in disposal of the chips which occurs during the cutting action.

In ordinary machining operations with such machine tools as the lathe and milling machine, the chips are removed almost as soon as they are formed. 74–14. However, chips created by a broaching operation are confined in the chip space for the entire length of cut. It is for this reason that sufficient chip space must be provided in broach design.

The pitch of the broach teeth limits chip space and the diam-

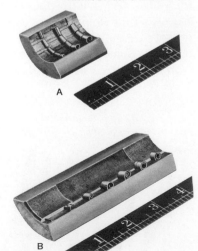

74–14. (A) Progressive chip formation showing the necessity for chip breakers. (B) Chip formation as broach teeth progress through the workpiece.

National Broach & Machine Co.

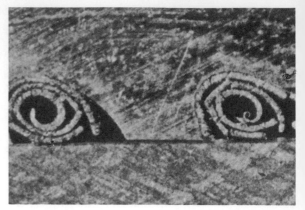

National Broach & Machine Co.

74–15. (A) A relatively heavy chip is not restricted, will coil as shown. (B) Indicates the effect of insufficient gullet space.

eter of the broach. A broach cannot cut more metal than chip space allows without placing a considerable amount of strain on the broach.

The cutting action of the teeth tends to roll the chips into a coil. The length of a chip developed by a broach tooth is always equal to the length of cut in the workpiece. 74–15. This fixed chip length and the chip load per tooth establish a chip area that cannot be changed without redesigning the broach. Too small a chip space will tend to wedge the coil in the chip space and the chip will not drop out of the gullet at the end of the cut. Some types of chips, such as cast iron and brass,

74–16. Typical pull ends.

National Broach & Machine Co.

break up easily, while those of steel and malleable iron tend to form a continuous, curled watch-spring form.

The final size of the chip curl can be affected by: (1) length of cut, (2) hardness of material, (3) chemical nature, and (4) metallurgical structure.

In all cases, tooth design must permit unimpeded flow of the chip from the cutting edge. Chip flow is substantially normal to the cutting edge, so any requirement involving cutting tool surfaces at an angle to each other cannot generally be satisfied with the same broach tooth.

For most effective operation, broaches must be designed for a single type of material and under specific working conditions.

Chip breakers serve to break up the chip into segments that work out of the chip space more easily, and also counteract the foreshortening and widening of the chip in a confined cut such as produced by round internal broaches. Spline, keyway, and surface broaches are usually provided with chip breakers.

Pilots

Pilots are used to guide the broach in its cutting stroke. The front pilot on an internal broach extends completely through the workpiece. It serves not only as a guide but also acts as a safety gage to prevent overloading the first tooth.

The rear pilot supports the part as the last finishing teeth are passing through it. If the rear pilot is omitted, or if it is made too small in diameter, it will allow the workpiece to cock on the rear end of the broach and can cause a bell-mouthed hole in the finished part.

74–17. Key type puller used in broaching keyways.

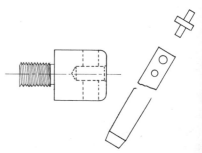

Illinois Tool & Instrument, Div. of Illinois Tool Works, Inc.

74–18. Face sharpening a round broach.

Broach Puller

A broach puller is a coupling —automatic or manually operated—which is easily connected to or disconnected from the broach shank.

Unlike other types of cutting tools used in machining operations, the internal broach must be disconnected from its power source after each piece is broached. Then it must be removed, a new part threaded over the broach, and the tool reconnected to the power ram. NOTE: The only exceptions are in keyway broaching.

There are several types of pullers in common use: (1) key-type, (2) pin-type, (3) threaded, (4) automatic pin-type, (5) automatic rectangular-shank, (6) automatic round-shank, and (7) flat-type. 74–16.

The *key-type* puller is a slotted puller with a key. 74–17. The broach shank enters the puller head and a key is passed through slots.

The *pin-type* puller has a round hole offset from center instead of a slot. It is used where the entering hole of the part is small or the broach shank is too small for the slot.

The *threaded* puller is used to fasten a keyway broach to the ram. It consists of a bushing threaded internally at one end to fit the broach and externally at the other end to fit the ram.

Automatic pin-type pullers are used for shanks ½″ or less in diameter. The cross pin slides in a slanting slot in the housing. A plunger on the face of the housing moves the pin when it strikes the reducing bushing.

Automatic rectangular-shank pullers are used on keyway broaches. *Automatic round-shank* pullers are used for high production of round, splined, or specially formed holes. *Flat-type* pullers are very similar to the pin-type.

SHARPENING BROACH TOOLS

The customary practice in sharpening broach tools is to sharpen the teeth on the face angle. 74–18. Careful attention is required to duplicate the gullet radius to the form provided by the manufacturer. 74–19.

Too large a radius may change the face angle. Too small a radius can result in chips sticking in the gullet and accumulating, resulting in tooth breakage. 74–20.

74–19. The right and wrong method of sharpening a broach.

National Broach & Machine Co.

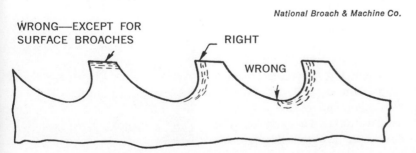

WRONG—EXCEPT FOR SURFACE BROACHES

RIGHT

WRONG

74–20. In sharpening a broach, the plane of the wheel is set at a greater angle than that of the face angle of the tooth in order to produce the correct face angle.

National Broach & Machine Co.

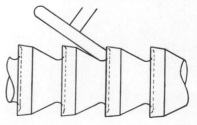

The following rules should be followed in broach sharpening:

1. Allow the wheel to spark out at the end of the feed stroke.

2. In sharpening sections of a surface broach, dress only the face angle surface and gullet radius, using the grinding wheel.

3. On internal broaches use smaller diameter wheels with the wheel spindle axis inclined from the normal face angle.

4. For surface broach sections, top sharpening is commonly applied to permit use of automatic grinding equipment and to remove craters that develop in the cutting edges of the broach as a result of cutting parts containing abrasive material.

holes to be broached and power applied to automatically pull the broach through the part. 75–3(B).

In *large volume* production, arrangements for rapid loading and unloading are made when one or more tools are used. The machines can be equipped with a shuttle table for rapid loading and unloading.

The illustration shows a latitudinous shuttle table which for convenience of loading and unloading moves to one side of the broaching station and thus is clear of the broaching tool and broach retriever interference with any overhead crane facility.

Upon pressing the dual push buttons to start the machine cycle, the shuttle table moves along to bring the part directly under the broaching tool, which then lowers automatically. The pull shank passes through the workpiece into the automatic 4-jaw broach puller mounted to the

Unit 75. Broaching Machines

Broaching can be done on a small scale with the use of a hand or hydraulically operated arbor press, mostly for internal push broaching, such as hole sizing and keyway cutting. Hand and hydraulic presses are simple and inexpensive yet, as shown, can be used in a variety of internal broaching operations. 75–1. Broaches are available individually or in sets for use on arbor presses. They include keyway, keyseating, hexagon, round, square, and special shape broaches. 75–2.

Broaching machines may be classified as:

VERTICAL MACHINES	HORIZONTAL MACHINES
Broaching presses (push broaching)	Pull
Pull-down	Surface
Pull-up	Continuous
Surface	Rotary

VERTICAL PULL-DOWN MACHINES

Vertical pull-down machines are generally used for internal broaching operations. 75–3(A).

The lower end of the broach is fastened to a pulling mechanism in the base of the machine. The other end of the broach is held by an upper carriage. The broach is lowered through the

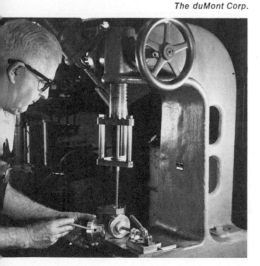

75–1. Broaching a square hole transversely through a brass winch cap.

The duMont Corp.

75–2. A ram adapter in which standard round broach has been inserted.

The duMont Corp.

main slide pull bracket beneath the machine platen.

The main slide starts its downward travel, closing the puller, and the broach is pulled through the barrel. When the end of the broach is below the top of the platen, the shuttle table moves sideways. The main slide and retriever automatically return the broach to its position above the platen.

VERTICAL PULL-UP MACHINES

On these machines the pulling ram is above the worktable and the broach-handling mechanism is below. 75–4 (Page 384). In operation, the broach is lowered and the workpiece placed over the broach pilot. The broach is raised until it engages the puller

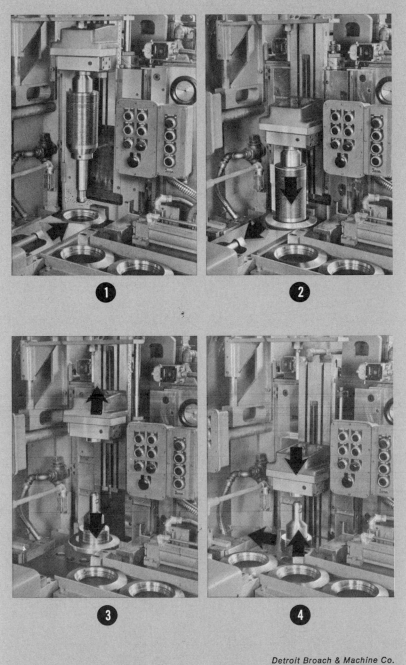

75–3(A). Vertical pull-down broaching machine. Axle ring gear is being sized and broach bored.

Detroit Broach & Machine Co.

Detroit Broach & Machine Co.

75–3(B). (1) Part is automatically shuttled into position. Broach is suspended from handling slide, ready for broaching cycle. (2) Tool handling slide is lowered, engaging broach in automatic puller on main slide bracket. (3) Broach continues through work, disengaging from detent in upper tool handling bracket. (4) Part has automatically ejected and broach is returning to be engaged in retriever in upper tool handling bracket.

75–4. Vertical pull-up broaching machine.

head. As the broach is raised, the workpiece comes to rest against the underside of the table and is held there until the broaching operation is completed. The workpiece then falls free and is deflected into a container. This highly productive machine may have as many as eight rams.

VERTICAL SURFACE BROACHING

In vertical surface broaching the vertical single-ram broaching machine has a ram that carries the broach downward for the cut and then returns to top position. 75–5. The table in front of the ram slide carries the fixture holding the workpiece and is moving into machining position just before the ram descends, and is withdrawn for unloading and loading as the ram returns to top position.

A double-ram machine has two ram and fixture sets side by side. One ram descends with its fixture in cutting position. At the same time the other returns while its fixture is unloaded and loaded making for a continuous operation.

HORIZONTAL PULL BROACHING MACHINE

In a horizontal pull broaching machine the broach is pulled by a drawhead actuated by a hydraulic piston and cylinder. These machines are used mostly for internal broaching but can be used for some types of surface broaching.

A horizontal pull broaching machine offers convenient access to any part of the machine. The lifting of heavy broaches is avoided and a long stroke is possible. However, a machine of this type takes up more floor space than a vertical machine.

HORIZONTAL SURFACE BROACHING MACHINES

These machines are made in a variety of types and sizes. The broaches are mounted on heavy, ram-driven slides. The broach is pulled over the top surface of the workpiece, which is held in a fixture. In one sequence of operations, this machine can: automatically load two parts, clamp, tilt fixture up, broach, tilt fixture down, unclamp, and automatically unload two parts. 75–6. Parts are automatically handled by power and free-turning conveyors and transfer bars from

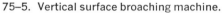

75–5. Vertical surface broaching machine.

one end of the machine to the other.

The illustration shows a V-8 engine block on which the cylinder bank faces have been rough and finish broached. 75–7. Broaching speed for this operation is 120 feet per minute, with a production rate of 280 parts per hour.

CONTINUOUS BROACHING MACHINES

Continuous broaching machines are used for surface broaching of parts that require repetitive cutting, such as gear teeth. 75–8. The machine shown broaches external gear teeth with tools arranged on a chain. One gear tooth on two parts is broached with each revolution of the machine chain. Two automatic indexing fixtures are mounted in a series to the machine frame, with broach inserts mounted to carriers on the machine chain. The gear blanks are manually loaded, unloaded, and clamped. After the machine is

Detroit Broach & Machine Co.

75–6. A 30-ton, 180"-stroke, horizontal, hydraulic-surface, broaching machine.

started, it cycles automatically until all gear teeth are cut. Part adapters are required for variations in parts and number of gear teeth to be broached.

Eleven broach holders are required to mount broaches to the carriers which are mounted to the machine chain.

ROTARY BROACHING MACHINES

These are continuous-production machines with broaches attached around a central column. The work is mounted on fixtures on a rotary table and circled past the broaching stations. For some work the fixture is pro-

75–7. Broaching operation being done on an engine block.

Detroit Broach & Machine Co.

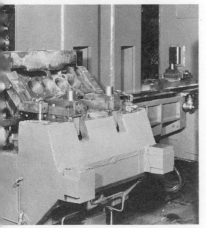

75–8. Continuous broaching machine with tools on a chain.

Detroit Broach & Machine Co.

GEAR

BROACH

CHAIN

vided with a clamp so that the operator can quickly load and unload the workpieces. The broaches are made in short sections for easy sharpening and adjustment. The machines are limited to surface broaching of small parts.

POT TYPE BROACHING MACHINES

Pot type broaching, the *simultaneous* external broaching of the outside periphery of a workpiece, is accomplished by pushing the workpiece through a pot arrangement containing the tools. 75–9. The tool arrangement is an inversion of internal broach design. Separate cutting tools can be mounted in a holder or designed as integral details in

National Broach & Machine Co.

75–9. Vertical pot broaching machine used to pot broach angular splines.

75–10. A 15-ton, 42"-stroke, vertical, universal, pot-broaching machine.

Detroit Broach & Machine Co.

75–11. One-piece pot broach for broaching 86-tooth external helical gear.

National Broach & Machine Co.

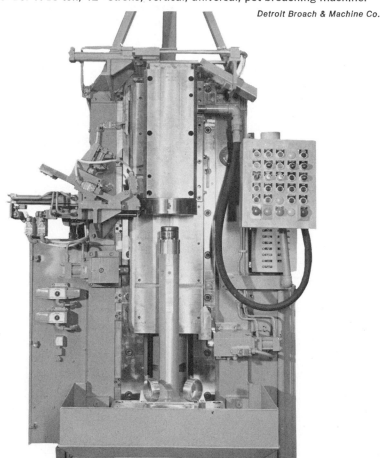

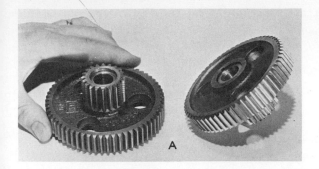
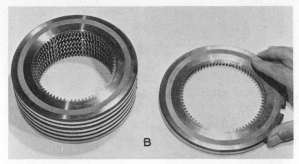

National Broach & Machine Co.
Landis Tool Co.

75–12. (A) The pot-broached cast iron gears with 61 teeth on the larger diameter are produced simultaneously from solid metal in a single pass of the pot-broaching tool. (B) The full-form finishing rings from the pot-broach assembly for a 72-tooth gear.

which each detail is equivalent of a broach tooth or short series of teeth. 75–10.

The teeth on running gears require the ultimate in finish and accuracy. Instead of completing the pot broaching of all of the teeth at one time by a tool made up of an assembly of generating rings of successively larger tooth lengths, a full-form finishing section (patented) has been added at the end of the tool. 75–11.

This avoids the fine parallel generating lines on the tooth surface produced by conventional generating methods.

In its first application, the full-form finishing pot broach is applied to produce cast iron gears in a 15-second machining cycle. 75–12. The gears produced are 61 and 72-tooth, 16 pitch, 20-deg. pressure angle gears about 1″ wide and with 3.896″ and 4.584″ outside diameters.

The pot broaching tool for the gears has 11 full-form finishing rings at the rear of a series of generating rings. All of the rings are hardened and ground high speed steel.

Check Your Knowledge

1. What is meant by broaching?

2. What are the two main classifications given to broaching?

3. Describe a hole broach and name its principal elements.

4. Name the factors that control the pitch of teeth in a broach.

5. How are broaching tools classified?

6. What are some of the advantages of inserted-tooth and built-up broaches?

7. What are broaching fixtures? What are they used for?

8. What determines the proper length of a broach?

9. What is pitch as applied to a broaching tool?

10. What is the function of burnishing teeth on broaches?

11. Why is gullet design of extreme importance in broach design?

12. Compare the cutting action of a broaching tool with that of other cutting tools used on milling machines and lathes.

13. What is a puller? Describe its use.

14. What are some of the factors that affect chip space in a broaching tool?

15. Why must the teeth of internal broaches be sharpened by grinding only their faces?

16. What is the essential difference between an arbor press and a broaching press?

17. Classify broaching machines according to their methods of operation.

18. What advantage does a vertical pull-down machine have over a vertical pull-up machine?

19. Explain how continuous broaching machines function.

20. Describe a horizontal surface broaching machine.

Problems

1. The roughing section of a broach is to remove 0.120″ from a steel surface 10″ long and 3″ wide. Each tool takes a 0.006″-deep cut. How long should the roughing section be?

2. A flat, solid surface broach has a tooth step of 0.001″. If a surface 8″ long is to be ma-

chined, what is the minimum cross-sectional area which must be provided in the chip gullet between adjacent teeth?

3. If a 10″ cut is to be taken on a piece of material with a broaching tool, determine the pitch and number of teeth in contact with the work.

4. A keyway broach removes 0.004″ per tooth and has a tooth pitch of 1.2″. If the broaching speed is 30 ipm, how long will it take to cut a keyway ¼″ deep?

References

Black, P. H., *Theory of Metal Cutting,* New York, McGraw-Hill Book Co., 1961.

Habicht, F. H., *Modern Machine Tools,* Princeton, N.J., D. Van Nostrand Co., Inc., 1963.

Kamischke, R. L., *Broaching and Broach Design,* Technical Paper, American Society of Tool and Manufacturing Engineers, 1960.

National Broach and Machine Company, Detroit, Mich., *Broaching Practice,* 1953.

So that no damage will be inflicted to the many cutting edges, a rack like this one can be used for storing broaches.

Illinois Tool & Instrument, Div. of Illinois Tool Works, Inc.

Section Seventeen

Grinding and Grinding Machines

GRINDING is one of the most important machining operations in industry today. The grinding process is used when other types of operations are not practical. In the heat treatment of steel parts, distortion is quite common and grinding is a means of bringing these parts to their required accurate dimensions.

ADVANTAGES

Some of the important advantages of grinding are:

1. Grinding can be done with very light pressure, making it possible to machine delicate or thin parts.

Landis Tool Co.

2. The grinder can be readily applied to such surfaces as scale on castings and forgings, which can be destructive to other types of cutting tools.

3. The magnetic chuck can hold the workpiece without the interference from fixtures of conventional holding devices that are ordinarily used to hold parts to be machined on other types of machine tools.

4. The grinding process cannot only be used to finish surfaces that have been formed on other machine tools, but high-powered grinders can take over stock removal which not too long ago was reserved for cutter-type machine tools.

5. Many different types of surfaces can be produced by grinding, such as flat, cylindrical, formed, and internal.

6. Only a small amount of stock needs to be left on the workpiece for grinding.

7. Work can be performed to very close tolerances and fine finishes by grinding.

8. Cost of wheels can be lower than for some types of cutting tools.

9. Sharpening costs can be eliminated.

10. Fixture costs are small because most parts can be held on a magnetic table.

11. Part handling and loading of magnetic chucks are fast and easy.

12. Heavy stock removal and final finishing can often be accomplished in one setup.

Unit 76. Abrasives

An abrasive can be defined as any hard, sharp material that wears away another material when moved in pressure contact.

The ability of a mineral grain or particle to penetrate the material being ground depends to a large extent upon: (1) the hardness and shape of the abrasive and (2) the ability of the abrasive to resist breakdown under the stresses of the grinding operation.

The abrasive grain with the most effective abrading qualities has a polygon shape, with each side a sharp-edged wedge. The cubical and spherical shapes are used when heavy grinding pressures are employed because they do not fracture as readily as other shapes. On operations employing light pressures, these shapes tend to polish rather than remove a great deal of material from the part being machined.

For centuries the only abrasives used in any quantity were prepared from sandstone. Early grinding wheels were made from natural abrasives such as emery and corundum. With the development of harder metals and alloys, particularly steel, came the need for harder and more efficient abrasives. The use of natural abrasive in the manufacture of grinding wheels today is almost negligible. The materials are not suitable for high-speed grinding work.

MANUFACTURED ABRASIVES

In 1891, Edward G. Acheson, an electrical engineer, built a small, crude electric furnace and from a mixture of clay and powdered coke produced a small amount of bright crystals of small size. These very hard crystals proved to be a new substance, silicon carbide—SiC. The material was first used to polish precious stones but proved too costly. Eventually a process was developed to produce silicon carbide commercially.

Another engineer, by the name of Charles B. Jacobs, employed by an electrochemical company in New Jersey, set out to make synthetic corundum. As a source of aluminum oxide, he used bauxite and fused it electrically into a material similar to emery and corundum, but harder. He found that this material could be produced in uniform grade of high purity (93 to 94% aluminum oxide). Approximately 75%

of all grinding wheels today contain an aluminum oxide abrasive.

In 1955 man-made diamonds were successfully produced, which led to the development of diamond grinding wheels, widely used today for grinding carbides, ceramics, glass, stone, and even some tool steels.

Silicon Carbide

Silicon carbide is manufactured by the chemical interaction of sand and carbon at extremely high temperatures in an electric furnace. 76–1. These common materials react with one another to form the silicon carbide crystals used in a large variety of abrasive and refractory products.

The mixture of sand and coke is built up around a carbon electrical conductor, and then walled around with uncemented brick. Sawdust is added to the mixture to make it porous, permitting the escape of carbon monoxide which is formed during the process. When an electric current is passed through the carbon conductor, the heat produced is high enough to cause a chemical reaction between the sand and coke. The resulting product consists of a core of silicon carbide crystals surrounded by unconverted raw material.

Aluminum Oxide Abrasive

In 1899 Charles B. Jacobs invented a process for making crystalline alumina or manufactured corundum in the electric furnace by the fusion of bauxite. Bauxite is a claylike substance, originally formed by the leaching action of sea water on granite. Bauxite is a prime source of alu-minum and the most plentiful of minerals.

Bauxite consists of aluminum oxide, AL_2O_3, combined with water and containing varying amounts of other impurities.

Aluminum abrasives are made in an electric-arc furnace, consisting of a cylindrical sheet steel shell supported on a carbon base. 76–2(A). The shell has no lining. A continuous spray of water, played upon the shell during the process, chills the adjoining layer of the furnace charge, forming an effective lining.

Suspended in the furnace are two carbon electrodes of opposite polarity. The current forms an arc from one electrode to the mass, passing through it, and then arcs back to the other electrode. The resulting temperature of 3700° F. melts the bauxite, and the impurities settle to the bottom of the furnace.

Carborundum Co.

76–1. Typical silicon carbide grain.

76–2(A). Typical aluminum oxide grain.

Carborundum Co.

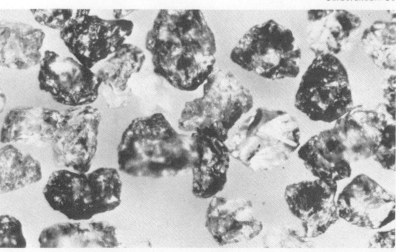

Grain Sizes

Aluminum oxide emerges from the furnaces in massive pigs. Silicon carbide emerges in crystalline masses. 76–2(B).

To be used commercially, the abrasives must be refined and reduced to standard sizes before they are manufactured into wheels.

The abrasives are crushed and screened; that is, they are passed through screens containing meshes of standard sizes. These sizes are determined by the number of meshes to the linear inch through which the grains will pass. For instance, a grain that will pass through a screen having 8 mesh openings per linear inch is called

Table 76-A. Commercial Grain Sizes					
Very coarse	Coarse	Medium	Fine	Very fine	Flour sizes
4	12	30	70	150	280
6	14	36	80	180	320
8	16	46	90	220	400
10	20	50	100	240	500
	24	60	120		600

an 8-grit size and measures roughly ⅛″ across. A 20-grit size is one that will pass through the next smaller 24-mesh screen.

These grit sizes are classified as very coarse, coarse, medium, fine, very fine, and flour sizes.

The screening method is used only for 220-grit grains or larger. The smaller sizes are separated by hydraulic flotation and sedimentation processes.

Structure

Structure refers to the pores, which are air spaces or voids between the abrasive grains and posts of bond in which they are imbedded. 76–2(C).

The size and number of pores are dependent upon the spacing of the grains throughout the wheel body.

Two wheels may contain the same number of pores. In one the pores may be large and few in number, while in the other

they may be small and many in number. In the first wheel, the grain spacing is wide and in the second wheel the grain spacing is more dense. With a different structure, one wheel will cut faster on the same materials.

Grinding Wheels

An abrasive wheel is made up of two principal components, the abrasive grains and the bond which cements the grains together. Abrasive wheels are manufactured in sizes and grades to suit many purposes, with their quality and structure controlled by careful choice of grain size and kind, type of bond, and the proportions of bond and grain. The bond must be strong enough to stand the stresses on a rapidly rotating wheel. 76–3. The bond must hold the grains firmly and yet must be of open enough structure not to interfere with cutting.

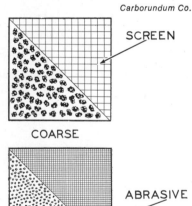

76–2(B). Grain sizes. Grains are crushed and passed through screens.

Carborundum Co.

SCREEN

ABRASIVE

COARSE

MEDIUM

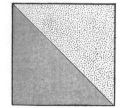

FINE

76–2(C) Grain structure.

Carborundum Co.

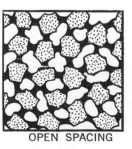

OPEN SPACING

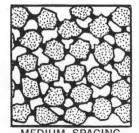

MEDIUM SPACING

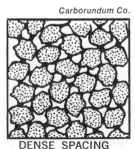

DENSE SPACING

Vitrified abrasive wheels, used for two thirds of grinding operations, are made by mixing abrasive grains with ceramic materials such as clay, feldspar, and flint, molding the mixture to shape, and burning it in a kiln to a temperature of 1270° C.

Abrasive wheels which require toughness and elasticity are bonded with rubber and synthetic resins.

For finishing the very hardest materials, such as sintered carbide, bonded diamond abrasive wheels have been developed. Diamond abrasive grain may be bonded with metal, synthetic resins, and other materials.

GRINDING WHEEL SHAPES

The United States Department of Commerce and the Grinding Wheel Institute in cooperation with the principal manufacturers of grinding machines have established nine standard grinding wheel shapes and have standardized the dimensional sizes in which these sizes are obtainable. 76–4. Manufacturers also make a great number of special grinding wheel shapes. These wheel shapes can be used in less frequent or for specialized grinding operations.

Table 76-B. Letters Which Represent the Method of Designating Various Dimensions of Standard Wheel Shapes

D	=	Overall diameter	M =	Large diameter of bevel
E	=	Center or back thickness	P =	Diameter of recess
F	=	Depth of recess	R =	Radius of corners
G	=	Depth of recess	T =	Overall thickness
H	=	Hole	U =	Width of edge
J	=	Diameter of outside flat	W =	Wall thickness at grinding face
K	=	Diameter of inside flat		

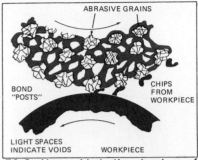

76–3. How voids in the structure of a grinding wheel assist in clearing chips from the wheel face, thus eliminating "loading."

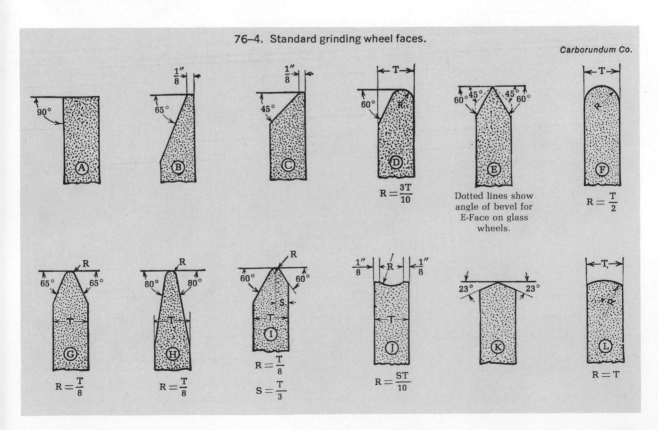

76–4. Standard grinding wheel faces.

Carborundum Co.

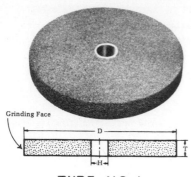

Grinding Face

TYPE NO. I
STRAIGHT

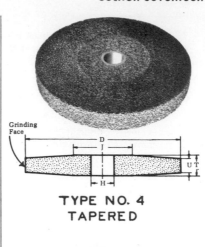

Grinding Face

TYPE NO. 4
TAPERED

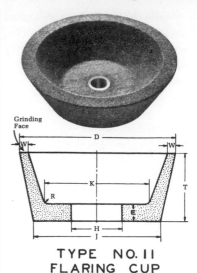

Grinding Face

TYPE NO. 11
FLARING CUP

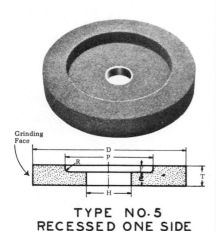

Grinding Face

TYPE NO. 5
RECESSED ONE SIDE

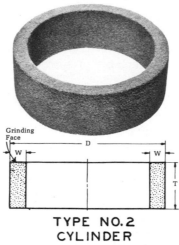

Grinding Face

TYPE NO. 2
CYLINDER

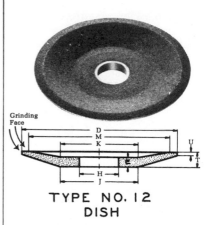

Grinding Face

TYPE NO. 12
DISH

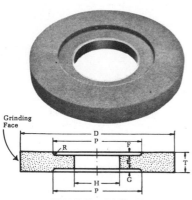

Grinding Face

TYPE NO. 7
RECESSED BOTH SIDES

Carborundum Co.

76–5. Straight wheel types for cylindrical grinding, internal and tool grinding, off-hand grinding, and snagging.

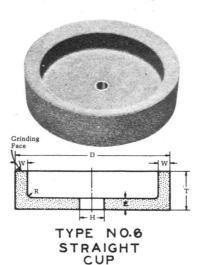

Grinding Face

TYPE NO.6
STRAIGHT CUP

Carborundum Co.

76–6. Wheel types used for surface grinding.

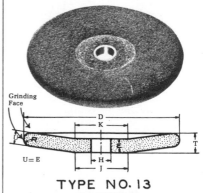

Grinding Face

TYPE NO.13
SAUCER

Carborundum Co.

76–7. Types 11 and 12 are used for toolroom grinding. Type 13 is used for sharpening saws.

Straight wheel type No.'s 1, 5, 7 are standards for cylindrical grinding, internal grinding, tool grinding, off-hand grinding, and snagging. 76–5. *Type No. 4* is a *tapered wheel type* having a taper on both sides and used principally in snagging operations. *Wheel type No. 2* is used for *surface grinding* on both horizontal and vertical spindle machines, with grinding performed on the face wall of the wheel. 76–6. *Type No. 6* is a *straight wheel used for surface grinding* on horizontal or vertical spindle machines. *Type No. 11* is a *flaring cup wheel* used for grinding in the toolroom. It has either a plain or beveled face. *Type No. 12* is a *disc wheel* for toolroom grinding. The thinness of the wheel permits getting into narrow places. 76–7. *Type No. 13* is a *saucer wheel* used for resharpening saws.

GRINDING WHEEL FUNCTIONS

In general, three fundamental functions of grinding wheels are basic to all grinding operations: (1) to generate size, (2) to generate surface, and (3) to remove stock. 76–8(A).

Sizing involves the removal of sufficient material to bring the material being ground within close tolerance of size established for the work.

On cylindrical pieces grinding wheels are used to generate size of formed parts. On flat pieces the wheel may be used to grind either a flat surface or a formed surface. A variety of holes may also be machined with proper grinding wheels. These holes may

be either straight, tapered, or formed and open or blind.

In generating a *surface* the operation may or may not involve achieving precision limits or close tolerances. Steel sheets may have a high polish but not necessarily be held to close limits while parts like gage blocks may

have a smooth finish combined with extremely close tolerances.

In some cases roughing and finishing operations can be performed with the same wheel by changing the rate of stock removal. However, one type of grinding wheel—as to grit, grade, and bond—cannot be required to

76–8(A). Generating size.

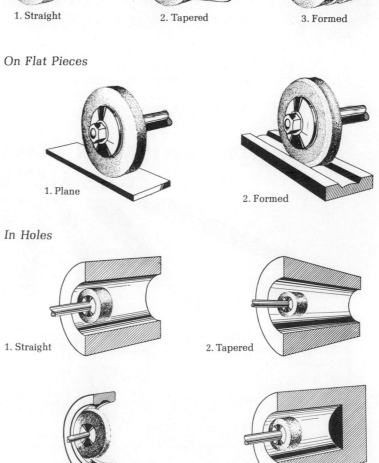

Carborundum Co.

On Cylindrical Pieces

1. Straight   2. Tapered   3. Formed

On Flat Pieces

1. Plane   2. Formed

In Holes

1. Straight   2. Tapered

3. Formed   4. Blind

perform too many different functions at maximum efficiency.

In the selection of a wheel to perform a certain function, the following guidelines may be used:

● To remove stock: Soft wheel grades can remove stock more rapidly than hard wheel grades. Use coarse grit.

● To generate size: (1) Fine grit sizes do a better job of sizing than coarse grit sizes. (2) Hard wheel grades maintain piece size better because wheel wear is less.

● To produce surface finishes: (1) Fine grit sizes produce the best finishes. (2) Hard wheel grades do not produce the best finishes. High wheel pressures are built up between the workpiece and wheel.

GRINDING WHEEL MARKINGS

Since 1944 a standard system for marking wheels has been used by wheel manufacturers. 76–8(B). Each marking consists of the following:
1. Abrasive type
2. Grain size
3. Grade
4. Structure
5. Bond type
6. Bond modification symbol

Manufactured abrasives fall into two distinct groups: the aluminum oxide group and the silicon carbide group. To designate a particular type of either aluminum oxide or silicon carbide abrasive, the manufacturer may use his own symbol or bond designation as a prefix.

The *grain size* is indicated by a number, usually from 10 (coarse) to 600 (fine). Sometimes it is necessary to indicate a *special grain combination*. The wheel maker may then use an additional symbol appended to the regular grain size. Example: 364 (36 grit, No. 4 combination).

The *grade* is indicated by a letter in the alphabet, ranging from A (soft) to Z (hard) in all bonds or manufacturing processes.

The *structure* or *grain spacing* is generally indicated by a number from 1 to 12.

76–8(B). Structure numbers are not always shown in marking. Nevertheless, such products may be made to a definite structure.

Norton Co.

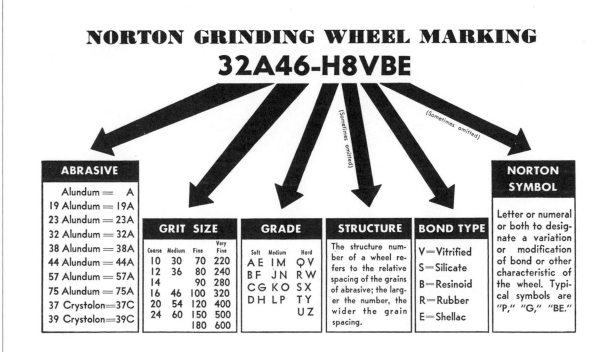

NORTON GRINDING WHEEL MARKING
32A46-H8VBE

ABRASIVE

Alundum =	A
19 Alundum =	19A
23 Alundum =	23A
32 Alundum =	32A
38 Alundum =	38A
44 Alundum =	44A
57 Alundum =	57A
75 Alundum =	75A
37 Crystolon =	37C
39 Crystolon =	39C

GRIT SIZE

Coarse	Medium	Fine	Very Fine
10	30	70	220
12	36	80	240
14		90	280
16	46	100	320
20	54	120	400
24	60	150	500
		180	600

GRADE

Soft	Medium	Hard
A E	I M	Q V
B F	J N	R W
C G	K O	S X
D H	L P	T Y
		U Z

STRUCTURE

The structure number of a wheel refers to the relative spacing of the grains of abrasive; the larger the number, the wider the grain spacing.

BOND TYPE

V = Vitrified
S = Silicate
B = Resinoid
R = Rubber
E = Shellac

NORTON SYMBOL

Letter or numeral or both to designate a variation or modification of bond or other characteristic of the wheel. Typical symbols are "P," "G," "BE."

(Sometimes omitted)

The bond or process is designated in the following manner:

V = Vitrified   E = Shellac
B = Resinoid   S = Silicate
R = Rubber

GRINDING WHEEL SELECTION

In the selection of a grinding wheel for a given operation, several other factors are important.

Information has to be available as to the nature and properties of the material to be ground. Aluminum oxide is generally best suited for grinding high-carbon steel and steel alloys, while silicon carbide wheels are more efficient for grinding cast iron and nonferrous metals.

Fine grit should be used when grinding hard or brittle materials. Soft, ductile, and easily penetrated metals can be ground successfully with coarse grit wheels.

In selecting a wheel to grind very hard, dense materials, relatively soft grade wheels are usually best. The harder materials resist penetration of abrasive grains and cause dulling of the wheel, while a softer wheel enables dull, worn grains to break away and expose new, sharp grains.

In rough grinding operations, a coarse grit will remove stock rapidly. When close tolerances and high finishes are required, it is best to select a wheel with fine grit size.

Fast cutting and commercial finishes require vitrified bonded wheels and, if a high finish is required a resinoid, rubber, or shellac bond should be used, depending upon the density of the material to be ground.

If a wheel is to be run at speeds of not over 6,500 rpm, a vitrified wheel is a proper selection. Any speed over this figure requires a resinoid bonded wheel.

Wheels have the safe operating speed shown on the wheel tag or blotter; these speeds should be carefully observed.

A good general rule is to select a coarse grit wheel when grinding a large area of contact. A fine grit should be selected when the area of contact is small.

COATED ABRASIVES

A coated abrasive consists of a flexible-type backing upon which is glued a coating of abrasive grains. 76–9. This backing may consist of paper, cloth, vulcanized fiber, or a combination of these materials. The adhesives may be hide glues or various types of resins. For abrasives used, see earlier discussion.

Abrasive minerals are selected for their hardness, toughness, heat resistance, particle shape, and size.

The hardness and shape of the abrasive control its ability to penetrate the workpiece. A mineral particle has to be tough in order to resist breakdown under grinding operations.

In the manufacturing process of coated abrasives, the backing is run through a machine consisting of a *printer, adhesive coater,* and *abrasive dispenser.* Although the equipment may vary, the general pattern and sequences of manufacture are practically the same.

Production of Coated Abrasives

The desired type of backing is selected and run through the printing press, where the back is imprinted with the necessary identifications. From the printer the backing moves to receive the application of adhesive bond in an amount carefully regulated according to the particle size of the mineral to be bonded. The grains are then applied by either of two methods: (1) mechanical

76–9. Coated abrasive belt used for polishing.

Rotor Tool Co.

or (2) electrostatic. The application can be systematically varied from an open coat to a very dense mass of grains.

Machines using coated abrasive belts are designed for all types of grinding operations. 76–10. There are manually operated machines, where the work is fed to the machine by hand; semi-automatic machines which control the positioning and cut but still require the work to be brought to the fixture or conveyor by hand; and fully automatic machines.

Coated abrasive machines may also be classified by the type of coated abrasive they employ: belt, disc, drum, cover, sheet, roll, or some special shape.

Most machines use either belt or discs. In belt machines the abrasive belt passes around a contact wheel and idler, and grinding or polishing is done against the contact wheel. On disc grinders the abrasive paper or cloth is fastened to metal discs.

The belt's ability to remove stock rapidly, produce fine finishes, plus make very fast and cool cuts has led to a rapid development of belt machines, many of which are semi- or fully automatic. Belts can be made in any length, and in widths of from 1/8″ to 88″. Applications range from such gentle operations as removing hulls from peanuts to removing excess weld metal from heavy products.

Coated abrasive discs, ranking second in importance to belts in volume usage, are made of aluminum oxide grain with tough fiber backing. Grit ranges from 16 through 80. Discs are used on pneumatic or electric, portable or flexible shaft grinders. They remove rust and die marks on sheet metal, grind or smooth welds, and also prepare various surfaces for finish coats.

76–10. View of a straight-line belt polishing machine. This machine has increased production capacity 3.7 times at the Singer Manufacturing Company.

3M

Table 76-C. Table of Comparative Grit Sizes*—Approximate Comparison of Numbers				
Durite® Metalite®	Adalox® Garnet	Flint	Emery cloth	Emery polishing paper
Extra fine 600 500 400 360 320	400(10/0) 320(9/0)			4/0 3/0 2/0 0 1/2
Very fine 280 240 220	280(8/0) 240(7/0) 220(6/0)	Extra fine		1 1-G 2
Fine 180 150 120	180(5/0) 150(4/0) 120(3/0)	Fine	Fine	3
Medium 100 80 60	100(2/0) 80(0) 60(1/2)	Medium	Medium Coarse	
Coarse 50 40	50(1) 40(1½)	Coarse		
Very coarse 36 30 24	36(2) 30(2½) 24(3)	Extra coarse	Very coarse	
Extra coarse 20 16 12	20(3½) 16(4)			

* Table prepared by Behr-Manning Division of the Norton Company. Metalite and Adalox are made from aluminum oxide manufactured abrasives. Durite is made from silicon carbide manufactured abrasives.

Grinding Machines

Grinding machines are designed to machine metal parts with an abrasive wheel to very close tolerances and produce high-quality finishes. With the aid of these machines, parts of the same size, shape, and finish can be produced in quantity.

The grinding operation itself depends upon the abrasive or cutting qualities of the grinding wheel. As is true of all grinding wheels each abrasive in the wheel is a very minute sharp cutting tool. As the grinding wheel revolves, it removes a small chip from the workpiece.

Grinding machines may be classified as:

Surface grinder: (1) Planer type (reciprocating table)—horizontal spindle, vertical spindle and (2) Rotary type (table revolves)—horizontal spindle, vertical spindle. 77–2(A) (Page 400).

Cylindrical grinder: (1) center type, (2) centerless, (3) chucking, (4) toolpost, and (5) crankshaft and special.

Internal grinder: (1) chucking, (2) centerless, and (3) planetary.

Tool grinder: (1) universal and (2) special.

Special grinder: (1) swing frame, (2) offhand, (3) portable, and (4) flexible shaft.

SURFACE GRINDING*

Surface grinding is a term used to describe the grinding of flat surfaces. However, there are a few exceptions such as grinding

---

* The Norton Company, *The A B C of Surface Grinding*.

convex or concave surfaces on rotary table machines and form grinding on reciprocating table machines, using the periphery of the wheel trued to the desired angle, radius, or contour.

Many parts that were formerly machined on milling machines and shapers are now done on large, high-powered surface grinders. 77–1.

Reciprocating Table Surface Grinders

The *horizontal spindle, reciprocating table, surface grinder,* using the periphery of a straight wheel, is one of the most common surface grinders. These machines are built in a wide range of sizes for flat grinding. The size of a surface grinder is determined by the size of the surface that can be ground. Thus a 6″ x 18″ machine has a working area at least 6″ x 18″, a traverse table movement of 6″, and a longitudinal table travel of slightly more than 18″.

77–1. High-powered, horizontal-spindle surface grinder.

Mattison Machine Works

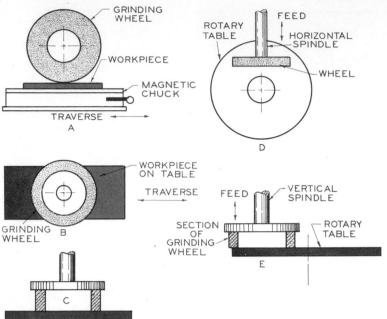

77–2(A). Common types of surface grinding machines: (A) horizontal spindle—reciprocating table, (B) vertical (top view of machine) spindle—reciprocating table (C) bottom view of (B), (D) horizontal spindle—rotating table, and (E) vertical spindle—rotating table.

Grinders are available with either hand feed, power feed, or both. 77–2(B). The power feed for both cross-feed or longitudinal feed may be either a mechanical-type or a hydraulically operated feed mechanism. 77–3. The grinding wheel may be fed in a vertical direction with a hand-wheel generally graduated in 0.0002″ for accurate adjustment. Both the transverse and longitudinal movements can be controlled by limit dogs.

In the majority of surface grinding operations, the work-piece is held on a *magnetic chuck,* which is fast to apply, easy to use, and will hold a large number of small pieces in place for grinding. 77–4. Only magnetic materials can be held by direct contact. However, parts

77–2(B). Hand-feed surface grinder.

Clausing-Covel

77–3. Hydraulic type surface grinder.

Clausing-Covel

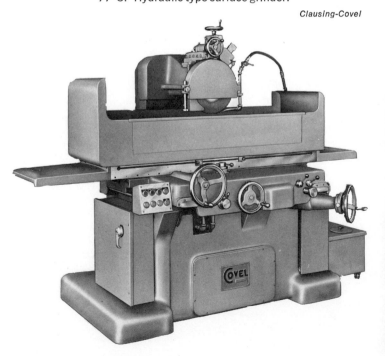

may be held in fixtures such as V-blocks, angle plates, or a vise fastened to the table. The chucks get their holding power through direct current, which energizes the electromagnets. There are two types of magnetic chucks in common use: (1) the electromagnetic (77–5) and (2) permanent magnetic types. Special alloy magnets are used in permanent magnetic chucks; the chuck is so constructed that the magnets can be rotated manually to bring the magnetic field within range of the faceplate. 77–6.

Rotary Table
Surface Grinders

Horizontal rotary table machines, using the periphery of a straight wheel, are not used to a great extent. These machines are limited in the types of work that can be done on them and are usually constructed in small sizes.

Vertical spindle rotary table machines, using cylinder wheels or segments, are built with from one to five spindles mounted on a central column. 77–7 (Page 402). Large productive vertical spindle surface grinders for handling large work have been developed with rotary magnetic chucks up to 108″ in diameter and equipped with 54″ segment wheels driven by 100 hp motors. These machines are used for grinding, so that roughing and finishing cuts can be taken on large parts with only one pass through the machines.

FACE GRINDERS

These are large, horizontal spindle, reciprocating table machines. The workpieces are mounted on a vertical table and ground with cylinder wheels or segments. The machines may either be the traveling wheel or traveling table type.

O. S. Walker Co.

77–5. Electromagnetic chuck.

CYLINDRICAL GRINDERS

Cylindrical grinders work the outside diameters of cylindrical pieces.

Typical cylindrical pieces ground on their outside diameters can be: (1) round metal bar stock, (2) tapered spindles, (3) parts having two or more diameters, and (4) complicated shapes such as crankshafts. 77–8.

There are two types of grinding operations where the workpiece is held between fixed

77–4. Workpiece held in fixture on a permanent magnetic chuck.

O. S. Walker Co.

77–6. Permanent magnetic chuck.

O. S. Walker Co.

remove another layer of metal. The principle resembles machining on an engine lathe.

Traverse grinding is employed when the workpiece is longer than the maximum width of the wheel.

Plunge grinding is a mass-production method accomplished by using a wheel that is as wide as the surface to be ground. 77–10. The wheel is fed into the revolving workpiece which is mounted between centers and does not reciprocate past the wheel. The infeed is continuous rather than intermittent.

Because this type of grinding lends itself to automatic operation, some machines are arranged with more than one grinding wheel for plunge grinding several diameters at the same time.

In plain cylindrical grinding, the workpiece is mounted between headstock and tailstock centers. The grinder is designed to give three movements: (1) rotating the workpiece on its axis between centers, (2) reciprocating the workpiece horizontally in front of the grinding wheel (traverse movement), and

Mattison Machine Works

77–7. Vertical spindle rotary surface grinder.

77–8. Examples of cylindrical grinding: (A) ordinary pieces of round metal bar stock, (B) tapered spindles, (C) pieces having two or more diameters, and (D) complicated shapes.

Carborundum Co.

centers: (1) traverse and (2) plunge grinding. 77–9. In *traverse* grinding, the work table reciprocates past the grinding wheel. As the workpiece passes, the wheel removes a fixed amount of metal (infeed) from the diameter. At the end of the pass, the wheel is advanced another increment of distance to

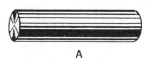

A

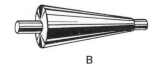

B

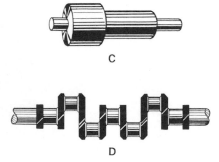

C

D

77–9. Machine and work movements in center-type grinding.

Carborundum Co.

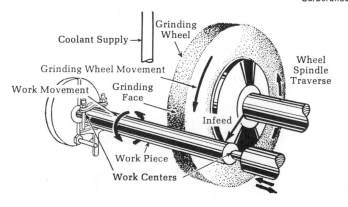

(3) moving the workpiece into and away from the workpiece—infeed.

All these movements can be combined and controlled accurately. The base of the machine supports the parts mounted on it. The table moves on machine ways and, located in the rear of the machine, is a column on which the wheel spindle, power unit, and grinding wheel are mounted. 77–11.

The headstock and footstock are mounted on the table. The table can be reciprocated manually or by a hydraulic drive mechanism. The speed of the table can be varied and the length of the movement controlled by means of trip dogs which can be adjusted to desired positions.

The headstock is mounted on the left end of the table and driven by a motor. Drive of the workpiece can be accomplished by the workpiece fastened with a dog on one end or held in a chuck.

The footstock is quite similar to the one used on an engine lathe. The dead center in the footstock spindle supports the workpiece.

The grinding wheel is mounted on a spindle which is driven by an electric motor. In the plain cylindrical grinder, the wheelhead is mounted on a cross-slide at right angles to the ways of the table. The wheel is fed toward the revolving workpiece by hand or automatically.

UNIVERSAL GRINDERS

The universal grinding machine is designed to perform a wide variety of grinding operations. 77–12. The machine is constructed to perform both external and internal grinding operations. These operations include the grinding of straight surfaces, ta-

Landis Tool Oo.

77–11. 10" x 36", type R, plain hydraulic, cylindrical grinding machine.

77–12. Universal grinder.

Heald Machine Co.

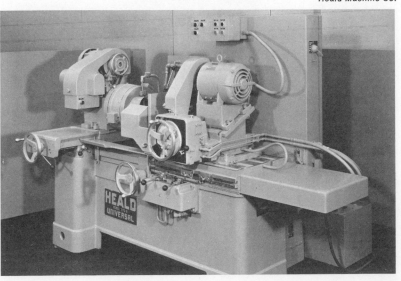

77–10. Plunge grinding.

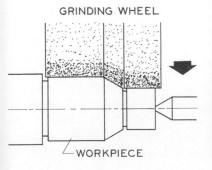

GRINDING WHEEL

WORKPIECE

Landis Tool Co.

77–13. A 14″ x 36″, type R, universal grinding machine. Headstock is swiveled for grinding a tapered workpiece.

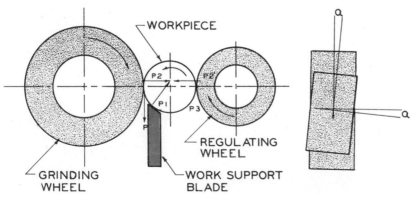

Landis Tool Co.

77–14. Two No. 12R centerless grinders arranged with a work loader and tooled for through-feed grinding the OD of bearing races.

77–15. Schematic diagram of centerless grinding.

pered surfaces, shoulders, and facework. Tool and cutter grinding can also be done. On these machines the headstock and the wheelhead can be swiveled about a vertical axis, which permits the grinding of tapers of all angles. 77–13. Most universal grinders have dual spindles on the wheelhead. One spindle is equipped for internal grinding and the second spindle for external grinding. By swiveling or tilting the wheelhead, either spindle can be put to the proper use.

CENTERLESS GRINDING

Centerless grinding is accomplished by grinding cylindrical surfaces without rotating the workpiece between fixed centers. 77–14. The workpiece is supported between three fundamental components: (1) the grinding wheel, (2) the regulating wheel, and (3) the work blade.

In the illustration the grinding wheel at the left does the actual grinding while the work support blade positions the workpiece for grinding. 77–15. The regulating wheel has three functions: namely, (1) govern the speed of workpiece rotation, (2) govern sizing of the workpiece, and (3) govern the rate of workpiece travel through the grinder in throughfeed grinding.

The grinding and regulating wheels rotate in the same direction, while the workpiece operates in the opposite direction (counterclockwise). This produces a "climb cut" operation.

"The grinding wheel, when in contact with the workpiece, attempts to rotate it at the same surface speed as the wheel by a force equal to P. P1 is the resisting force normal to the bearing surface on the work blade. The horizontal component, P2, of this resisting force is that exerted on the workpiece by the feed wheel. The product of this horizontal force and the coefficient of friction of the regulating wheel on the workpiece is the braking force, P3, of the regulating wheel which prevents the wheel from rotating at the grinding wheel's peripheral speed. This force, therefore, must be greater than the force exerted on the workpiece by the grinding wheel to prevent 'spinners.' Thus, it is evident that the angle on the workpiece support blade governs the horizontal force component between the workpiece and the regulating wheel."*

The position of the workpiece in relation to the two wheels should be such that the center of the workpiece does not fall on the center line of the wheels.

The three principal classes of centerless grinding are: (1) throughfeed, (2) infeed, and (3) endfeed. 77–16(A&B).

Throughfeed grinding is done by passing the workpiece between the grinding wheel and the regulating wheel. The actual movement of the workpiece past the face of the grinding wheel is imparted by tilting the regulating wheel at a slight angle about a horizontal axis from 0° to 7° to 10° relative to the axis of the grinding wheel spindle.

The infeed method is used on work which has a shoulder, head, or some portion larger than the

ground diameter. This method corresponds to plunge cut or form grinding.

The endfeed method is used primarily on taper work. Either the grinding or regulating wheel (or both) is dressed to the desired taper.

INTERNAL GRINDERS

Internal grinders work internal surfaces or holes (inside diameters).

This application is extensive. Range of types of parts and hole sizes are only limited by the capacity of the machine. Various

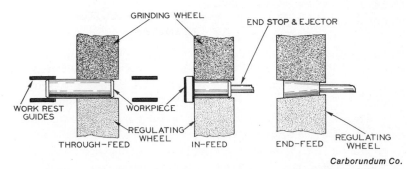

77–16(A). Schematic sketch of various types of centerless grinding.

Carborundum Co.

77–16(B). Sketches show applications of centerless grinding operations.

Carborundum Co.

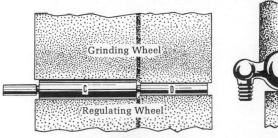

Multiple diameter centerless grinding.

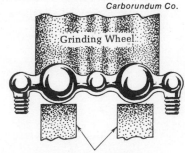

Regulating Wheels

Centerless profile (formed) grinding.

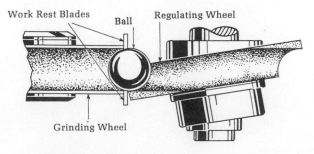

Spherical centerless grinding.

* The Norton Company, *Lectures on Grinding.*

types of grinders have been developed so that internal grinding can be performed efficiently on a wide range of hole sizes.

Types of Internal Grinders

There are three types of internal grinding machines:

1. The workpiece is held in a chuck and rotated. The chuck is mounted on the spindle of the workhead. 77–17. The revolving wheel spindle moves in and out of the hole during the operation. Straight or tapered holes may be ground.

2. The workpiece is rotated by the outside diameter between rolls. The outside diameter of the workpiece generates a path for grinding the inside diameter, and this diameter is ground concentric to the outside diameter. 77–18.

3. The workpiece is held stationary, mounted on the table of the machine, and travels to and from the wheel, which not only rotates on its axis but travels in a circular path of the desired diameter. This machine is sometimes called a *planetary* type grinder. It is used only for bore grinding of heavy or irregular shaped work which is difficult to rotate.

TOOL AND CUTTER GRINDERS

The grinding of all types of cutting tools is highly important. 77–19. Machines for grinding cutters vary from simple types designed for sharpening single-point tools to universal tool and cutter machines for sharpening multitooth cutters.

Cutter grinders may be divided into general classifications, depending upon the design of the cutter and the method used to sharpen it. They can be classified in the following manner:

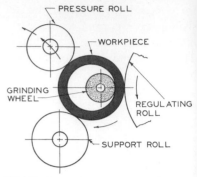

77–18. Centerless internal grinding.

1. Cutters having teeth which must be sharpened on the periphery or sides, such as slab milling cutters, side mills, keyway cutters, face mills, end mills, and machine reamers. 77–20.

2. Formed cutters, such as gear cutters, convex and concave cutters, and special formed cutters. 77–21.

Although tool and cutter grinding machines are essentially designed for sharpening cutters, they can also be used for cylindrical, surface, internal, and taper grinding.

77–17. Internal grinder. Note that controls are all located at the front of the machine, convenient to the operator.

Heald Machine Co.

77–19. Tool and cutter grinder.

Clausing-Covel

HEADSTOCK
CUTTER
TOOTH REST
CUP WHEEL
WHEELHEAD

R. K. LeBlond Machine Tool Co.

77–20. Face mill being sharpened on a tool and cutter grinder.

Moore Special Tool Co.

77–22. Precision jig grinder for toolroom and production grinding.

JIG GRINDERS

A jig grinder somewhat resembles in appearance a jig borer. This grinder has an infinite selection of grinding speeds from 6,500 to 175,000 rpm and is used for toolroom and production grinding. Accuracies of plus or minus 0.0001″ can be obtained. 77–22.

77–21. Formed cutter being sharpened on a tool and cutter grinder.

R. K. LeBlond Machine Tool Co.

Unit 78. Electrochemical Grinding

Electrochemical or electrolytic grinding is a process used for metal removed by an electrochemical decomposition of the work material aided by the cutting action of an abrasive (mechanical). 78–1 (Page 408).

In the electrochemical process, a metal bonded wheel is used as the cathode(—) and the workpiece is electrically connected to a DC power source and used as the anode(+). 78–2. The DC current from the power supply unit passes through the electrolyte between the wheel and the workpiece and electrochemically attacks the workpiece.

An abrasive wheel continuously removes an electrically resistant film which would otherwise remain on the workpiece and stop the electrochemical action.

Electrochemical grinding (ECG) is done without burr or heat or metallurgical damage. 78–3. NOTE: A great deal more power is required to remove a given amount of material by this method than in conventional grinding.

The electrolyte has two primary functions: (1) to pass high current from the workpiece to the wheel and (2) to combine

407

chemically with the workpiece material. These functions require that the electrolyte completely fill the gap area. It is necessary that a continuous controlled supply of filtered electrolyte be distributed evenly over the cutting area.

Power supplies generally range from 50 to 3,000 ampere DC capacities. The power supply must be able to provide constant voltage under varying load conditions.

Two abrasives are commonly used in electrolytic wheels: diamond and aluminum oxide. Diamond wheels are used when machining tungsten carbide, and aluminum oxide wheels are used when machining other materials.

The electrochemical machine must be a good quality machine

tool with adequate corrosion protection, a good electrolyte system, and a variety of speeds and feeds.

There are several facets of the grinding operation which offer definite advantages over conventional methods:

1. There is a savings in wheel costs. Since 90% of metal removal is accomplished by electrochemical action and only 10% by abrasive action, there is considerable reduction in wheel wear.

2. Trueing of the wheel is done less frequently due to low wheel breakdown.

3. High production rates are obtained when machining hard materials such as cemented carbides or Stellite.

78–2. Diagram of the electrolytic grinding process.

Cincinnati Milling Machine Co.

4. Cutters ground by this method generally have increased life due to the elimination of the rough edges that are obtained in conventional tool grinding operations.

5. Freedom from workpiece distortion is due to the "cold machining" characteristic of this type of grinding.

A comparison of three processes, electric discharge machining, electrochemical machining, and electrochemical grinding, is shown. 78–4.

78–1. Electrochemical grinding machine.

Hammond Machinery Builders

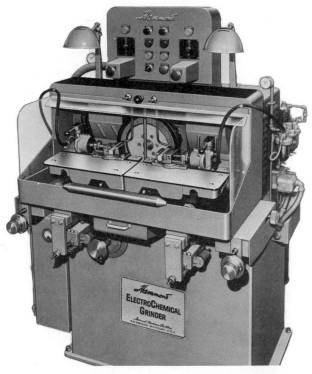

78–3. Grinding being performed by an operator on an electrochemical machine.

Hammond Machinery Builders

THE THREE PROCESSES

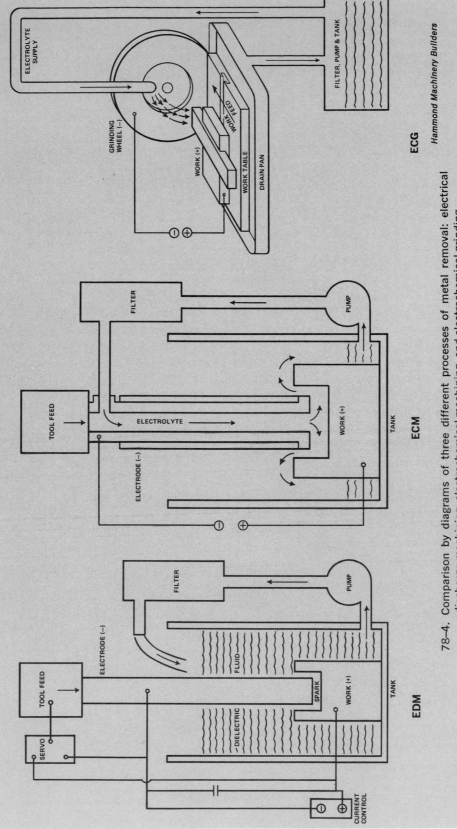

78–4. Comparison by diagrams of three different processes of metal removal: electrical discharge machining, electrochemical machining, and electrochemical grinding.

Hammond Machinery Builders

<table>
<tr><td>

Unit 79.   Abrasive Machining

</td></tr>
</table>

In the past, grinding has been considered to be a finishing process with tolerance the primary objective. It is now applied to large surface production work.

Remember, all cutting tool machining is a chip-making process because it produces sizable metal chips while forming the workpiece to shape.

With abrasive machining, the chips are not unlike those made by milling cutters, except for minute size. 79–1.

An abrasive wheel consists of millions of small, sharp edges which actually produce chips; hence, the concept of heavier stock removal with abrasives is similar in principle to other conventional chip-making operations.

The abrasive wheel, as applied to heavy stock removal, is ac-tually a self-sharpening, throw-away tool.

Replacing milling cutters with abrasive wheels is currently done in machining large, flat work-pieces when heavy stock removal —as much as ½″—is done on specially built surface grinders. 79–2.

The expanded use of abrasives into the area of heavier stock removal will in most cases involve an extension of grinding methods already being done for conventional operations.

Abrasive machining has two main advantages: (1) it de-creases the productive time of metal removal operations and (2) it tends to improve the quality of the finished product as compared to other conventional machining operations, because good results are easier to achieve.

Other advantages include:

1. Smaller amounts of excess stock are required on castings and carbon steel because abrasive wheels can cut through scale as readily as through the solid metal beneath.

2. Both light and heavy cuts can be made on the same wheel.

3. Expensive fixtures and tooling are eliminated because magnetic chucks and pieces of scrap metal can be used to hold the workpieces in position.

4. Setup time is shorter, which cuts labor costs.

5. Due to the fact that the wheel is a self-sharpening tool, there is no need for "down time" in changing tools for sharpening.

6. Secondary operations for finishing are not necessary.

7. Parts can be economically machined from the solid after the material has been hardened, providing a more accurately finished product, free from distortion.

79–2. A typical machine designed for abrasive machining. This is a heavy duty vertical surface grinding machine.

Norton Co.

79–1. Magnified view of actual chips produced by an abrasive wheel.

Norton Co.

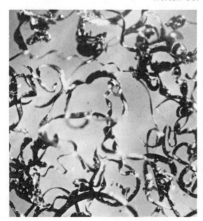

Compared to internal grinding and lapping, honing is a relatively new and completely different stock removal process. In its early development, honing was considered a finishing or polishing operation. Today, however, technological improvements have also made it one of the major stock removal processes.

HONING

Honing is a low-surface-speed, metal-shearing operation wherewith stock is removed simultaneously by thousands of solidly held abrasive grains spaced over the full area of a rigid abrasive stone. Because of the relatively large area in contact with the workpiece and the low pressure used, honing eliminates bore distortion, heat checks, fractured metal, and other surface damages.

However, internal grinding requires high surface speeds and generates heavy localized pressure, resulting in high chip root temperatures at the contact line between the abrasive wheel and workpiece. Also "crowding" the grinding wheel can cause spindle deflection and vibration which produce bore geometry errors and chatter marks.

Honing stones are self-sharpening because abrasive grains dislodge when they become dull, allowing sharp "new" grains to contact the work surface. 80–1.

The honing operation produces geometrically perfect bores with a cross-hatched base-metal finish having thousands of microscopic pockets that are ideal for supporting a uniform lubrication film.

Honing machines will produce precision bores economically. 80–2 (Page 412). They handle inside diameter (I.D.) ranges from 0.060″ to 6.000″ and from the shortest bore to bore lengths many times their diameter.

With honing tools, only a minimum amount of stock need be removed to correct all previous machining errors and produce a geometrically perfect bore—but, when necessary, substantial amounts of stock can be removed rapidly. 80–3. Complete tooling in pre-assembled sets allows practically instant setup to any bore size, and often the whole job is completed in less time than is required just for setting up other types of equipment.

No chucking is required since bores are self-aligning on the honing tool, eliminating expensive jigs and fixtures.

As the honing tool rotates, the workpiece is stroked back and forth to develop a true bore from end to end. This stroking action also generates a cross-hatch honing pattern.

Coolants are used to flush away small metal chips and keep temperatures uniform. Lard oil or sulphurized mineral-base oil

80–1. Examples of portable hones.

Sunnen Products Co.

mixed with kerosene is generally used.

LAPPING

Lapping is an operation used to: (1) produce true surfaces, (2) improve dimensional accuracy, (3) correct minor surface imperfections, and (4) provide a close fit between two surfaces.

Lapping is used on various types of surfaces—flat, cylindrical, spherical, or specially formed.

Lapping is accomplished by bringing the workpiece in contact with a grooved metal surface or lap. Fine, loose abrasive mixed with a vehicle such as oil, grease, or water is used between the lap and workpiece to provide the necessary abrading. Both the workpiece and lap are in motion with one another so that fresh contacts are constantly being made. Bonded abrasive wheels or coated abrasives are sometimes used and the lapping operation in this instance is very much like that in centerless or vertical spindle surface grinding. The face of the lap is usually of soft, close-grained cast iron. The abrasive grains are usually silicon carbide, aluminum oxide, or boron carbide in fine-screened sizes. Most lapping is done by spreading the lapping mixture on the lap. The face of the lap becomes charged with abrasive grains and the grooves across the face of the lap collect excess abrasive and foreign particles. Lapping is not normally done on softer materials because the abrasive particles have a tendency to become embedded in the workpiece.

The *vertical* lapping machine is used to lap flat or round sur-

TAPER	BELLMOUTH
BARREL	WAVINESS
RAINBOW	OUT-OF-ROUND

80–3. A few of the most common bore problems resulting from previous types of operations. These problems can be corrected, with minimum stock removal, by honing.

faces between an upper and lower lap. The upper floating lap is stationary; the lower lap supports the work and revolves at 45 to 65 rpm.

The *centerless* lapping machine is a production machine and is used for lapping round parts such as piston pins, shafts, valve tappets, and bearing races and cups.

Operation is quite similar to that of a centerless grinder. High production rates can be obtained and yet tolerances of 0.00005″ for diameters and one-half this amount for roundness and straightness are common.

Crankshafts and camshaft bearing surfaces can be lapped on abrasive belt lapping machines.

SUPERFINISHING

Superfinishing is a trade name given to an operation that utilizes

80–2. Manually stroked precision-honing machine. The honing operation is performed on a small connecting rod.

Sunnen Products Co.

HONE

WORKPIECE

abrasive stones to produce a very smooth and uniform honed surface. Superfinishing is a method of improving the surface of a part by removing the undesirable fragmentation metal and leaving a base of solid crystalline metal. Although this process is somewhat similar to honing, the motions of the abrasive stone are so controlled that a single abrasive stone never traverses the same path twice. 80–4.

Both cylindrical and flat surfaces can be Superfinished. In cylindrical Superfinishing, a bonded-form abrasive stone is employed with a very light controlled pressure (10 to 40 psi). The motion of the stone is oscillating, with short strokes less than ¼″ in length. The strokes are quite rapid—around 400 strokes per minute. The workpiece is rotated at a rate of around 50 sfpm and copious amounts of controlled low-viscosity oil are flooded over the rotating surface. The oil serves to carry away the abraded particles by motion of the stone strokes. 80–5.

Flat surfaces are Superfinished by using a cup-shaped abrasive stone. The workpiece is held on a circular table which is carried by a rotating spindle, giving an additional oscillating movement to the stone.

The lubricant introduced between the two machined surfaces will separate them, preventing any actual contact between the two surfaces if a controlled pressure is used. With a given pressure and by use of a lubricant of the proper viscosity, the workpiece can be brought rapidly to the proper degree of smoothness.

Spitfire Tool & Machine Co.

80–4. All-purpose abrasive cylindrical lapping machine designed to deliver finish with a tolerance of 1 rms (root-mean-square) (0.000016) or less.

80–5. Close-up of the working area of the fixed Superfinish arms applying the stones to main bearings and the cam-operated arms for following the crankpin bearings.

Gisholt Machine Co.

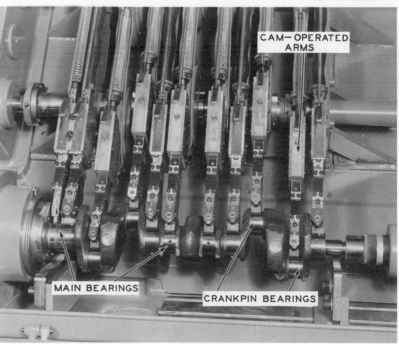

CAM—OPERATED ARMS

MAIN BEARINGS

CRANKPIN BEARINGS

Check Your Knowledge

1. Name some of the important advantages of grinding operations.

2. Define an abrasive.

3. Can the abrasive properties of manufactured abrasives be closely controlled?

4. Describe briefly the manufacture of silicon carbide abrasive.

5. Why are manufactured abrasives more effective than natural ones?

6. What are the two principal components of an abrasive wheel?

7. What is a vitrified abrasive wheel?

8. What are the common materials used today in making grinding wheels?

9. What factors should be considered in selecting a grinding wheel?

10. What are the three fundamental functions of grinding wheels basic to all grinding operations?

11. Describe the standard system for marking grinding wheels.

12. Does the grade letter "H" indicate a relatively soft or hard grade of hardness? The grade letter "S"?

13. How is the structure or grain spacing in a grinding wheel marking indicated?

14. What factors should be considered in the selection of a grinding wheel?

15. What is a coated abrasive? Describe the manufacturing process.

16. What are the two basic types of surface grinders?

17. What is the most common type of surface grinder?

18. How is the size of a surface grinder designated?

19. How is the workpiece held on the surface grinder?

20. Name two types of cylindrical grinding operations where the workpiece is held between fixed centers.

21. What is "plunge-cut" grinding?

22. Describe a universal grinding machine and the operations that it can perform.

23. What are the three fundamental components of centerless grinding?

24. Name the principal classes of centerless grinding.

25. What are the advantages of centerless external grinding?

26. What are the three types of internal grinders?

27. What are the basic features of a tool-and-cutter grinder?

28. Describe the electrochemical or electrolytic grinding process.

29. Name two primary functions of the electrolyte.

30. What are the main advantages of abrasive machining?

31. What is the difference between honing and lapping?

32. What are the functions of the lubricant in Superfinishing?

References

American Society of Tool and Manufacturing Engineers, *Tool Engineers Handbook,* New York, McGraw-Hill Book Co., 1959.

The Carborundum Company, *Handbook on Grinding,* 1967.

The Norton Company, *Lectures on Grinding, Abrasives, Machines, and Methods,* 1961.

Coated Abrasives Manufacturers' Institute, *Coated Abrasives— Modern Tool of Industry,* New York, McGraw-Hill Book Co., 1958.

Section Eighteen

Screw Threads

THE development of the screw thread goes back many centuries. The concept of the screw thread seems to have occurred first to Archimedes, who was a mathematician in the third century B.C. Then followed a long period of development, until in the sixteenth century screws appeared in German watches and were used in the construction of armor. Bolts and nuts were made by hand for a long period of time.

In the eighteenth century, screw manufacturing was started in England during the Industrial Revolution. There was no such thing as standardization at first. Nuts produced by one manufacturer would not fit the bolts of another. In 1841 Sir Joseph Whitworth in England started crusading for a standard screw

thread and developed the Whitworth thread. In 1864 William Sellars, an American, developed a thread which was adopted in the United States. The Sellars thread was recommended by a committee named by the Franklin Institute but the Sellars nut would not fit the Whitworth bolt as the thread angles were different.

The American Standard thread was adopted in 1935, with the 60° form of the old Sellars thread. There still was no standardization of threads between countries. During World War I it had proved to be a serious inconvenience. Finally, during World War II, an agreement was reached between the Americans, British, and Canadians on the unification of American and British screw threads. The result was the development of a new standard called the Unified screw thread which allowed complete interchangeability of threads in the three countries.

Screw threads today are vital to our industrial progress. They are used for hundreds of different useful purposes. The three basic applications are: (1) to hold parts together, (2) to adjust parts with reference to each other, and (3) to transmit power.

Unit 81. Screw Thread Terms and Forms

TERMS

A screw thread can be defined as a ridge of uniform section, in the form of a helix, on the external or internal surface of a cylinder.

A screw thread may be visualized as a flexible form like a piece of string that has been wrapped around a cylinder, or wound down inside a hole, at a uniform rate of advance, producing a helix. 81–1.

All thread designations give the number of threads per inch. The number may be measured with a rule, counting between each 1″ mark and the next. 81–2. A thread pitch gage may also be used for checking the pitch.

Major diameter refers to the largest diameter of a straight thread—both internal and external.

Minor diameter is the diameter of an imaginary cylinder, the surface of which would pass through the threads and the width of the spaces cut by the surface of the cylinder.

The *pitch* is the distance from a point on a screw thread to a corresponding point on the next thread, measured parallel to the axis and on the same side of the axis. The pitch (P) is equal to 1 divided by the number of threads per inch.

Lead is the distance a screw thread advances axially in one turn.

Angle of thread is the angle included between the flanks of the thread, measured in an axial plane.

The *crest* is the top surface joining the two flanks of the thread.

The *root* is the bottom surface joining the flanks of two adjacent threads.

The *flank* is the surface of the thread which connects the crest with the root.

The *axis* is the longitudinal central line which goes through the screw.

Depth of thread is the distance between the crest and the root of the thread, measured normal to its axis.

Form of thread is the cross section of the thread cut by a plane containing the axis.

Series of thread refers to the standard number of threads per inch for various diameters.

FORMS

Various forms of threads are in use to meet the general functions that have been described in the previous definitions.

The American National thread is one of the most widely used thread forms in the world. 81–3 & 81–4. This thread form (see drawing), formerly known as the "United States Standard," is as follows:

A=60° angle of thread.

a=30°=½ angle of thread.

F=0.125000p, or ⅛= width of flat at crest and root.

f=0.108253p, or ⅛H. or ⅙h=depth of truncation.

H=0.866025p=depth theoretical V 60° thread.

h=0.649519p, or 6/8 H =depth American National form thread.

n=number of threads per inch.

$$P=pitch=\frac{1}{No.\ threads\ per\ inch}=1/n.$$

Standard thread forms in commercial use are the NC (National Coarse), NF (National Fine), NEF (National Extra Fine), and N (National) for 8, 12, and 16 pitch. The Unified thread is the new standard agreed upon by the three countries, as previously mentioned. 81-5.

While the illustration shows the theoretical form of the Uni-fied thread, it is to be kept in mind that actually neither the British or American industry will make the complete change indicated by the illustration except that the British will continue making threads with rounded crests and roots and Americans will make them with flats. However, the two types of threads will usually interchange.

The Unified screw thread system includes three classes of external threads, 1A, 2A, 3A, and three classes of internal threads, 1B, 2B, 3B.

The square thread is ideal for power transmission, since its force is nearly at right angles to its axis.

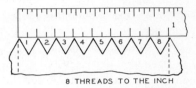

81-2. The number of threads per inch may be measured with a rule.

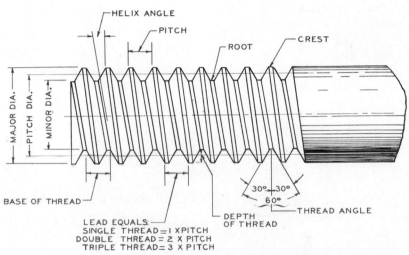

81-3. American National thread form.

81-4. American National thread form.

Greenfield Tap & Die Corp.

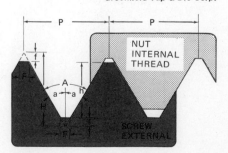

81-1. A screw thread visualized as a flexible form like a piece of string.

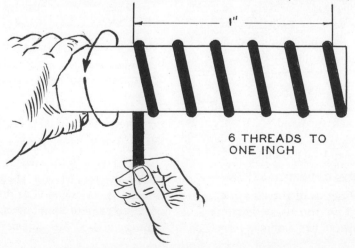

6 THREADS TO ONE INCH

However, the Acme thread, a modification of the square thread has largely replaced the square thread in many applications because it is a much stronger thread. 81–6.

The standard worm thread is similar to the Acme thread but is deeper.

The Whitworth thread, which has been the British standard, is being replaced by the American National standard.

The buttress thread is designed to transmit power in one direction only.

The American Standard pipe thread is the standard tapered thread used on pipe joints in the United States. The taper is ¾″ per foot.

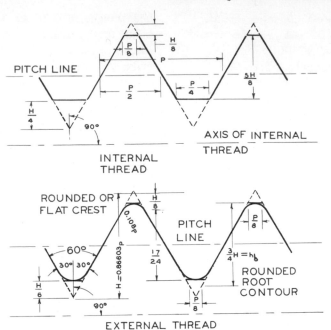

81–5. The basic form on internal and external Unified screw threads.

81–6. Cross section of several forms of screw threads.

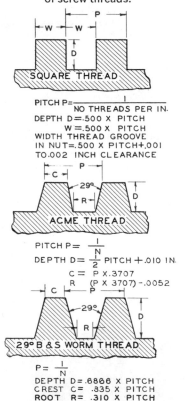

SQUARE THREAD

PITCH P= $\frac{1}{\text{NO THREADS PER IN.}}$
DEPTH D =.500 X PITCH
W =.500 X PITCH
WIDTH THREAD GROOVE
IN NUT=.500 X PITCH+.001
TO.002 INCH CLEARANCE

ACME THREAD

PITCH P= $\frac{1}{N}$
DEPTH D= $\frac{1}{2}$ PITCH +.010 IN.
C = P X.3707
R (P X.3707) -.0052

29° B & S WORM THREAD

P= $\frac{1}{N}$
DEPTH D=.6866 X PITCH
CREST C= .335 X PITCH
ROOT R= .310 X PITCH

Unit. 82 — The Manufacture of Screw Threads

Screw threads are usually manufactured by one of the following methods:

External threads

Cutting: (1) on some type of engine lathe or screw machine, (2) with die and stock by hand, (3) automatic die-head, and (4) milling; rolling between dies; die casting; and grinding.

Internal threads

Cutting: (1) tap and tap wrench by hand, (2) on engine lathe, (3) automatic collapsible tap, and (4) milling.

THREAD DESIGNATION

A series of thread symbols are used in thread designations, as shown in next column:

Nominal size	No. of threads per inch
½	13

Thread series	Class of thread
UMC	2A

When a left-hand thread is to be designated, the letters LH are added after the class of thread symbol.

CUTTING SCREW THREADS WITH TAPS AND DIES

A tap is a tool used for the purpose of cutting internal threads. 82–1(A&B). The threads on a tap are not continuous. The cutting edges are formed by

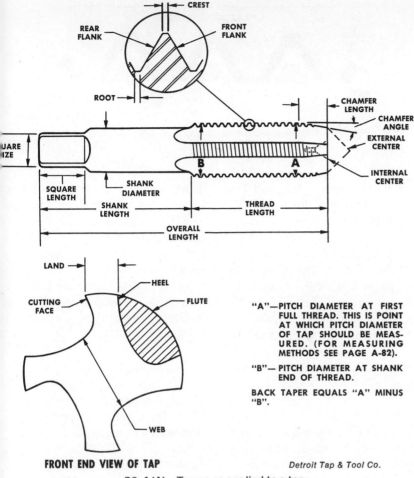

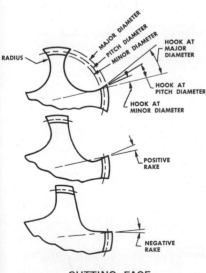

FRONT END VIEW OF TAP

Detroit Tap & Tool Co.

82–1(A). Terms as applied to a tap.

"A"—PITCH DIAMETER AT FIRST FULL THREAD. THIS IS POINT AT WHICH PITCH DIAMETER OF TAP SHOULD BE MEASURED. (FOR MEASURING METHODS SEE PAGE A-82).

"B"—PITCH DIAMETER AT SHANK END OF THREAD.

BACK TAPER EQUALS "A" MINUS "B".

flutes that are cut lengthwise across the threads.

Taps are made with two, three, or four flutes. They are available in standard machine screw sizes.

Machine screw diameters under ¼″ are designated by gage number, such as 6, 8, 10, and 12. A typical designation may be a 10–32 NF thread. The diameters of machine screws can be calculated by multiplying the number of the screw by 0.013 and adding 0.060″.

EXAMPLE:

Find the major diameter of a 6–32 NF machine screw.

$$6 \times 0.013 + 0.060″ = 0.138″$$

Styles of Taps

The most widely used tap today for production tapping is the plug hand tap, although originally hand taps were intended for hand use. 82–2 (Page 420). As a rule, when used by hand, such taps are furnished in sets of three of a size, taper, plug, and bottoming.

Taper, plug, and bottoming taps are identical in size and length, the only difference being in the chamfered threaded portion at the point. The taper tap has the longest chamfer, 8 to 10 threads. The plug tap has a 3- to 5-thread chamfer, and the bot-

82–1(B). Relief and cutting face of a tap.

Detroit Tap & Tool Co.

CUTTING FACE

RELIEF

419

toming tap only a 1- to 1½-thread chamfer.

When tapping in through or open holes, the taper tap should be used for coarse pitch threads. It is also recommended for harder metals. The plug tap can be used in such holes when tapping soft metals or fine pitch threads. In the case of blind holes when tapping to the bottom, taper, plug, and bottoming taps should be used in the order named.

Serial Taps

Serial taps are used for tapping deep holes, open or blind, especially in tough metals, for they cut more easily than ordinary hand taps. 82–3. They are

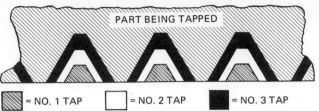

PART BEING TAPPED

▨ = NO. 1 TAP   ☐ = NO. 2 TAP   ■ = NO. 3 TAP

Greenfield Tap & Die Corp.

82–4. Section showing approximate amount of material removed by each serial tap.

similar to taper, plug, and bottoming taps but differ from the latter in that each tap cuts only a certain percentage of the thread to be produced.

The No. 1 tap makes the roughing cut, No. 2 cuts the thread a little fuller, and the No. 3 tap produces the finishing cut. A section showing the approximate amount of material removed is shown in the illustration. 82–4.

Acme Taps

Acme taps are made in sets of two or three. 82–5. The roughing tap is used first to remove some of the material and for cutting the thread to partial

depth. The final depth is obtained with the finishing tap.

Acme taps are used in the manufacture of feed and operating nuts for various types of mechanisms.

NOTE: It is important to furnish the manufacturer with sketches or blueprints of the taps required.

Gun Tap

The gun tap is a production tool not intended for hand use. 82–6. It is used in tapping machines of various types.

The flutes of this tap are divided into two sections—the conventional straight flute and the angular section at the point.

TAP STYLES

TAPER

PLUG

BOTTOMING

Winter Brothers Co.

82–2. Taper, plug, and bottoming taps.

82–3. Set of serial taps.

Greenfield Tap & Die Corp.

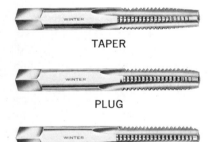

No. 1

No. 2

No. 3

Winter Brothers Co.

82–5. Acme tap.

Winter Brothers Co.

82–6. Plug gun tap.

82–7. Gun flute plug tap.

Greenfield Tap & Die Corp.

The angular design of the cutting point causes the chips to be deflected so that they curl out and ahead of the tap. This tap has fewer flutes than a standard hand tap and they are shallow, giving the tap greater strength, which is a necessity for machine tapping.

The gun flute plug tap is used for tapping shallow through holes not more than one diameter in depth. 82–7. Because there are no flutes in the body, the tap is stronger than the plug gun tap. This type of tap is used for tapping soft, stringy materials such as copper, brass, and similar materials.

Spiral Fluted Taps

Helical-fluted taps, more commonly called spiral fluted taps, are made with spiral instead of straight flutes. 82–8. This feature helps draw the chips out of a hole or bridge a keyway or other gap inside a hole. These taps are used to draw the chips out of a blind hole in stringy materials and are very useful when tapping brass, aluminum, copper, and other nonferrous metals. The cutting angle on the tap causes

82–8. Spiral fluted tap.

Greenfield Tap & Die Corp.

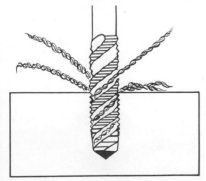

the chips to spiral upward; then as the tap revolves, the spiral flutes draw the chips out, preventing clogging of chips in the hole and consequent damage to tap threads and product threads. 82–9.

These taps are available in ground-thread plug and bottoming styles, 3 to 12 machine screw sizes, and ¼″ to ½″ fractional sizes.

Pipe Taps

Pipe taps cut a tapered thread so that a wedging action is created to obtain a leak-tight joint. 82–10.

Three types of American Standard pipe threads are commonly used: (1) American Standard taper pipe thread (NDT), (2) American Standard straight pipe thread (NDT), and (3) American dryseal pipe thread (NPTF).

HAND TAPPING

Before a tap can be used, a hole must be drilled in the workpiece with a tap drill of the correct size.

Theoretically, a hole drilled to the size of the minor diameter should be correct for tapping the thread. However, for practical purposes the hole would be too small, or tight, as it does not allow sufficient working clearance. Therefore, the diameter of the drilled hole must necessarily be slightly larger than the minor diameter of the thread.

One generally accepted rule for this is that the diameter of the tapped hole should be approximately equal to the major diameter of the screw, less 75% of the double depth of the thread.

In cutting internal threads with a tap, the tap should be squared up with the face of the workpiece. A small square can be used to help check the squareness of the tap. 82–11. A special

Greenfield Tap & Die Corp.

82–9. Machine tapping with a spiral fluted tap.

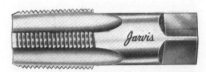

Greenfield Tap & Die Corp.

82–10. Pipe tap.

82–11. Using a square to check tap for squareness with the workpiece.

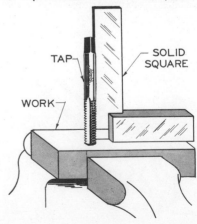

82–12. Device used for keeping the tap square.

H. B. Tools

device, as shown, can also be used to start the tap. 82–12.

Generally considered, of course, there are two types of holes, open or through, and blind or bottoming.

After the tap has been started in the hole, a cutting oil is used, except on cast iron. The tap is turned two or three turns; then the tap is reversed one turn to break the chips. This aids in chip removal, preventing tap breakage and damage to the threads.

82–13. Collapsing tap with radial cutters.

Geometric Tool Co.

The correct tap drill size may be found by referring to a table. If no table is available the correct tap drill size may be calculated as in the following example:

Determine the tap drill size for a ⅜–16 UNC thread of approximately 75% thread depth.

Rule 1: If a hole is to be tapped ⅜–16 NC, the tap drill size may be found by subtracting the pitch from the diameter:

$$⅜ — 1/16, \text{ or } 5/16$$

Rule 2: From the major diameter of the screw, subtract 75% of twice the depth of the threads:

$$⅜–16 \text{ cap screw h} = \frac{.6495}{16},$$

or .04059
2h=2x0.04059, or 0.08118
0.3750—.75x0.08118
0.3750—0.06089, or 0.3141

Correct to the nearest $1/16''$; this is $5/16''$.

A hole drilled this size for a ⅜–16 thread will give 75% depth of thread, which determines the necessary thread strength.

Caution: Taps are subject to severe conditions due to the difficulty of chip removal. A great deal of care in their use when hand tapping is essential; a proper cutting oil is necessary and the tap should be reversed a partial turn after one or two turns to break the chips.

Collapsing taps operate similarly to self-opening die heads and are used on turret lathes and automatics. 82–13. The thread chasers collapse inward automatically when the thread is completed. The tap can then be withdrawn without unscrewing

it from the thread. There are two types of collapsing taps in general use: (1) those having radial cutters and (2) the type employing circular cutters.

THREAD CUTTING DIES

Threading dies are used to cut external threads. They are designed with internal threads having grooves or flutes that intersect the thread to provide space for the chips to escape.

The *round split die* is a single-piece, adjustable die. 82–14. For hand threading operations, it is mounted in a die stock. 82–15. When used on a turret lathe or screw machine, it can be mounted in a special die holder.

This type of die is adjustable so that it can be used to cut a thread with a loose or snug fit.

Solid dies are usually of the square type and are not adjust-

Greenfield Tap & Die Corp.

82–14. Round adjustable die.

82–15. Die stock.

Greenfield Tap & Die Corp.

able. 82–16. These dies are not used to any great extent due to this fact.

Adjustable two-piece dies are assembled in collets consisting of a cap and guide. 82–17. The die halves are inserted in the beveled cap and held in place by the guide, which is screwed to the cap.

Self-Opening Die Heads

A large percentage of external threads cut on a production basis are produced with *automatic die heads.* 82–18.

Greenfield Tap & Die Corp.

82–16. Solid square die.

82–17. Two-piece threading die.
Greenfield Tap & Die Corp.

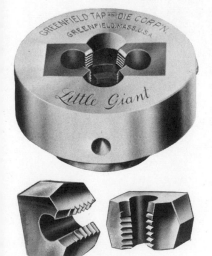

The die head has a body in which four chasers can be mounted. Their blades are made of carbon tool steel, high-speed steel, or cemented carbide. The chasers can be removed when dull and replaced by reground or new chasers. The chasers are mounted radially in some die heads or positioned tangentially in other types of die heads. 82–19. Radial cutters can be changed quickly and are used for threading materials which are hard to cut. Chasers mounted tangentially have less friction and can cut at higher speeds.

The die head opens at the end of the cut, releasing the chasers from the workpiece, thus permitting return of the head without reversing the spindle.

Self-opening die heads are designed for stationary or rotary applications. The stationary type is used on machines which rotate the workpiece, while the rotary type is employed on threading machines where the workpiece remains stationary.

Since the chasers are removable, they may be interchanged for other thread chasers for different size threads and a single die head can be used to cut a variety of threads. 82–20.

The retraction of the chasers occurs when the thread has been cut the required length. On a turret lathe or screw machine, a stop serves to halt the forward movement of the turret lathe and allow the die head to be tripped at the required thread length.

Self-opening die heads on automatics have an automatic tripping mechanism which closes the cutters on each cycle.

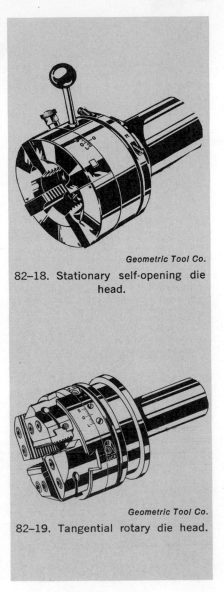

Geometric Tool Co.

82–18. Stationary self-opening die head.

Geometric Tool Co.

82–19. Tangential rotary die head.

82–20. Tangential design of a die-head chaser. This design provides a line contact with the workpiece to furnish a natural clearance.

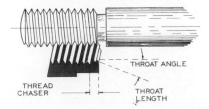

THROAT ANGLE

THREAD CHASER

THROAT LENGTH

Unit 83.

Tapping and Threading Machines

Machine tapping can be done on a variety of machines such as lathes, drill presses, turret lathes, automatics, and machines built especially for this purpose. 83–1.

Drill presses can be equipped with tapping attachments fastened to the spindle. Machines equipped with reversing spindles use a nonreversing tap driver which backs off the tap by reversing the spindle. Machines not equipped with reversing spindles use a nonreversing tap driver which causes the tap to rotate in a direction opposite to spindle rotation while the tap is being withdrawn from the hole.

Some types of tap drivers are provided with friction clutch mechanisms, which prevent tap breakage.

SPECIAL TAPPING MACHINES

There are many types of special tapping machines for tapping nuts and small parts. These machines are made in a variety of designs with from one to eight spindles. 83–2. Some machines are of vertical design while others are horizontal or of the angular type. 83–3.

The machines are designed for automatic or semi-automatic operation. High-speed drilling, tapping, and threading can be done automatically. The basic machine is equipped with devices for parts feeding orientation, locating, holding, clamping, and ejecting.

The blanks are fed automatically from a hopper to a holding device where drilling and tapping are done. 83–4. Then the blanks are fed onto the tap one at a time. When the operation is completed, they are fed out and ejected.

The machine has lead screw adapters for all standard pitches.

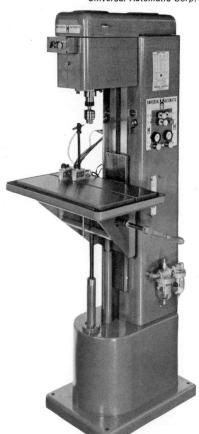

83–1. Vertical tapping machine.
Universal-Automatic Corp.

83–2. A 90°, two-spindle, horizontal tapping machine.
Universal-Automatic Corp.

THREAD MILLING

Hob type or standard cutters can be used to cut large size threads on a thread milling machine, which resembles an engine lathe. 83–5 & 83–6 (Page 426). The milling attachment is mounted at the rear of the machine and the workpiece is held either in a chuck or mounted between centers.

This type of thread manufacture may be done with either single or multiple-form cutters.

A *single-form* cutter resembles a gear tooth cutter. In operation it is tilted through an angle equal to the helix angle of the thread. The workpiece remains stationary while the cutter is fed radially to the full thread depth. The workpiece is then rotated and the cutter is moved in a longitudinal direction similar to the carriage movement of an engine lathe.

For cutting multiple threads the cutter is provided with several rows of teeth which are perpendicular to the axis of the cutter. The rows of teeth do not have any lead. In operation the cutter is set with its axis parallel to the axis of the workpiece.

Milling with multiple form cutters is often as fast as producing threads with self-opening dies and collapsible taps.

The feet in thread milling is expressed as cutter advance per tooth by the following formula:

$$f = \frac{3.1416 \times d \times s}{nN}$$

Where f = feed
d = nominal diameter
of threads in
inches
s = rpm of workpiece
N = rpm of the cutter
n = number of teeth
in cutter

TAPPING SPEEDS

The best and most efficient operating speeds for taps is rather difficult to determine as compared to speeds of many other metal cutting tools.

There are several factors that have to be taken into consideration in determining the best tapping speeds: (1) kind of material to be tapped, (2) length of hole, (3) chamfer length on tap, (4) pitch of thread, (5) percentage of full thread to be cut, (6) cutting fluids, (7) type of equip-

83–3. Angular nut tapping machine.

Universal-Automatic Corp.

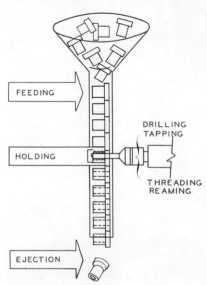

83–4. Blanks are fed automatically from hopper to a holding device where drilling and tapping are done.

ment, and (8) vertical or horizontal tapping.

In machining operations on other types of machine tools, the feed per revolution can be set at any desired point. This feed can be changed to meet certain conditions. In a tapping operation the tap must always be advanced through the workpiece at a rate equal to one lead for every revolution.

The type of tap being used may vary the procedure. For example, bottoming taps are run slower than plug taps. In a taper tap, a number of threads do their full share of cutting before the full height of thread is reached. A coarse thread tap will advance a greater distance per revolution than a fine tap and remove a greater amount of material.

The type and condition of machine as well as the method of

Table 83. Tap Cutting Fluids	
Material Being Tapped	Fluid
Aluminum	Kerosene and lard oil
Brass	Soluble oil or light-base oil
Bronze	Soluble oil or light-base oil
Copper	Light-base oil
Duraluminum	Soluble oil or kerosene and light oil
Die-castings—zinc	Soluble oil
Die-castings—aluminum	Kerosene and lard oil
Iron—cast	Dry or soluble oil
Iron—malleable	Soluble oil or kerosene and lard oil
Steel	Sulphur base oil

feeding have an influence on machine speeds. The mechanical feeding of a tap is more efficient than other methods when the tap is allowed to feed itself and pull the spindle along with it.

CUTTING FLUIDS FOR MACHINE TAPPING

Taps can easily be destroyed by not using the proper lubricant in machine tapping. Taps have a tendency to "burn up" more easily than other cutting tools. A few teeth do all the work, and the actual cutting surfaces are very small. Unless the proper lubrication is applied, excess friction can be created, causing the teeth to heat up. This in turn

causes the metal being tapped to adhere to the tap, causing loading, poor threads, and subsequent tap breakage. Machine tapping operations require proper lubricants that have specific compositions developed for use under certain conditions and for definite requirements. *There is no one lubricant or oil* that can be applied under all operating conditions.

83–5(A). Thread milling with a single-form cutter.

Lees-Bradner Co.

83–5(B). Thread milling cutter.

DoAll Co.

83–6. Another type of thread milling operation.

Lees-Bradner Co.

In all machine tapping operations the lubricant should reach the cutting lands of the tap at all times, especially the point or chamfered portion.

THREAD GRINDING

Thread grinding is used either for finishing coarse threads that have been previously machined and then heat-treated or forming threads from solid, hardened material.

The grinding wheel may be of two types: (1) a single wheel or (2) plunge type wheel. 83–7.

A *single wheel* ground to the desired form traverses the length of the screw. The wheel is rotated against the workpiece at speeds ranging from 750 to 10,000 sfm. The wheel traverses the length of the workpiece, the pitch of the thread determining the speed. Generally, two passes of the wheel are required to cut a thread, the last pass removing only a few thousandths of an inch for finish and accuracy. A tolerance of plus or minus 0.0002″ can be held on the pitch diameter.

Fully automatic machines have been developed for precision thread grinding. Feeds, sizing operations, and wheel dressing are automatically done. 83–8.

When short threads are required, the *plunge-cut* method can be used. The wheel is rotated and fed the depth of the thread before the workpiece is rotated. The workpiece then makes one complete revolution while traversing a distance equal to one pitch, completing the thread.

The grinding of good threads is dependent upon the proper

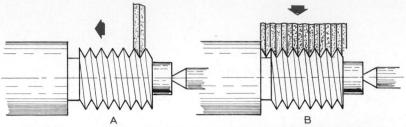

83–7. Two types of thread grinding: (A) single wheel and (B) plunge-cut.

dressing of plunge-cut wheels. The most common method is by the crush-roll process, whereby the grinding wheel is slowly rolled in a crushing contact with a hardened roller having the same type of threads that will be plunge-ground upon the workpiece. This method of wheel dressing is rapid, yet capable of producing sharp, accurate threads. Wheels of the vitrified type are used.

The thread grinding process is used when precision threads are required, generally after the workpiece has been hardened. Any distortion in the workpiece is eliminated and threads of ten pitch or finer can be ground from solid hardened pieces.

THREAD MEASUREMENT

Screw threads may be checked by measuring pitch and pitch diameter. A screw thread pitch

83–8. Internal thread grinding machine.

Jones & Lamson

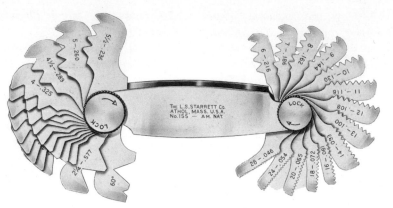

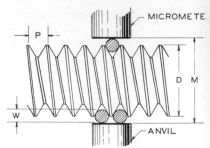

83–12. The three-wire method for measuring pitch diameter of V threads.

L. S. Starrett Co.

83–9. Screw thread pitch gage with locking device and 60° center gage. V-type, American National and U.S. Standard 60° threads—27 pitches, range 2½ to 28 threads per inch.

gage can be used for checking pitch and either a thread michometer caliper, or what is called the "three-wire system," can be used for checking the pitch diameter. 83–9.

In checking pitch with a pitch gage, each leaf of the gage, for a given type of thread form, is stamped with the number of threads per inch. The notches in a selected pitch gage will fit into a thread of correponding type and pitch. 83–10.

A thread micrometer caliper can also be used to measure the pitch diameter of a thread. 83–11. This type of micrometer has a V-shaped anvil that fits over a thread form and a cone-shaped

spindle that fits into the opposite thread groove.

The three-wire system is more accurate but more intricate. Three hardened and lapped wires ground to a specific size for a given thread form are employed. 83–12. Two wires are placed in the thread on the anvil side and one wire on the spindle side of a micrometer caliper. The diameter of the wires varies with thread size. The wires extend beyond the crest of the thread. The anvil and spindle are placed against the three wires and a reading taken. The micrometer reading is then interpreted in terms of pitch diameter. The following formula can be used in

measuring Unified National Coarse threads.

$$M = D + 3W - \frac{1.5155}{N}$$

Where: M = micrometer measurement of wires

D = diameter of thread

N = number of threads per inch

W = diameter of wire used

EXAMPLE: Determine M for ½″ — 12 pitch UNC thread.

$$M = 0.500 + 0.14433 - \frac{1.5155}{12} = 0.51803$$

When measuring a Unified National Fine thread, the constant, 1.732, should be used instead of 1.5155.

83–10. Screw pitch gage with tops of teeth flattened. This permits the use of a single gage for either National form or V threads.

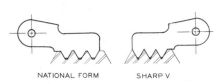

NATIONAL FORM   SHARP V

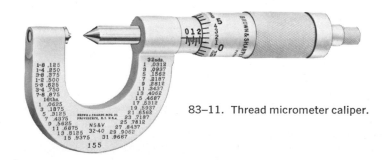

83–11. Thread micrometer caliper.

Check Your Knowledge

1. Write a short history of the development of the screw thread.

2. Define a screw thread.

3. What is the difference between pitch and lead as applied to screws?

4. Explain what is meant by the pitch diameter of a thread.

5. Explain the basic difference between the first standardized thread system used in Great Britain and that used in the United States.

6. Are American National standard threads and Unified standard threads interchangeable? Explain.

7. Of what significance are the Unified and American National screw thread standards adopted in 1949 and 1969?

8. Name some of the methods of manufacturing screw threads.

9. Explain why pipe threads are made on a taper.

10. What advantage does the Acme thread have over the square thread?

11. What threading tool is used to cut internal threads in a blind hole?

12. How are machine screw diameters under ¼" designated?

13. What is the most widely used tap for production tapping?

14. Explain the difference between taper, plug, and bottoming taps.

15. What is a serial tap? Describe its uses.

16. What are the advantages of a spiral fluted tap?

17. Why are internal threads usually tapped only 75% of the full depth for most thread applications?

18. On what types of machines are collapsible taps used?

19. Name two types of collapsing taps in general use.

20. Name one of the disadvantages of a solid type die.

21. What type of tool is used to cut external threads on a production basis?

22. What is a thread chaser?

23. What is the advantage of a tapping machine in producing internal threads?

24. What is thread milling?

25. Name several factors that must be taken into consideration for the most efficient tapping speeds.

26. How are screw threads measured?

27. Describe the three-wire system of thread measurement.

28. Why is the use of proper lubricant so important in machine tapping?

Problems

1. Calculate the tap drill size for a ⁵⁄₁₆-18 UNC thread with approximately 75% thread depth.

2. Find the major diameter of an 8-32 UNF machine screw.

3. Find the best wire size and measurement over three wires for a ½-13 UNC thread.

4. Determine the feed per tooth of a 24-tooth thread milling cutter turning at 60 rpm and the workpiece at 10 rpm.

References

Boston, O. W., *Metal Processing,* New York, John Wiley & Sons, Inc., 1951.

Doyle, L. E., *Metal Machining,* Englewood Cliffs, N.J., Prentice-Hall, Inc., 1953.

Shaw, M. C., *Metal Cutting Principles,* 3rd ed., Massachusetts Institute of Technology, 1954.

Cutting threads with a thread dial indicator.

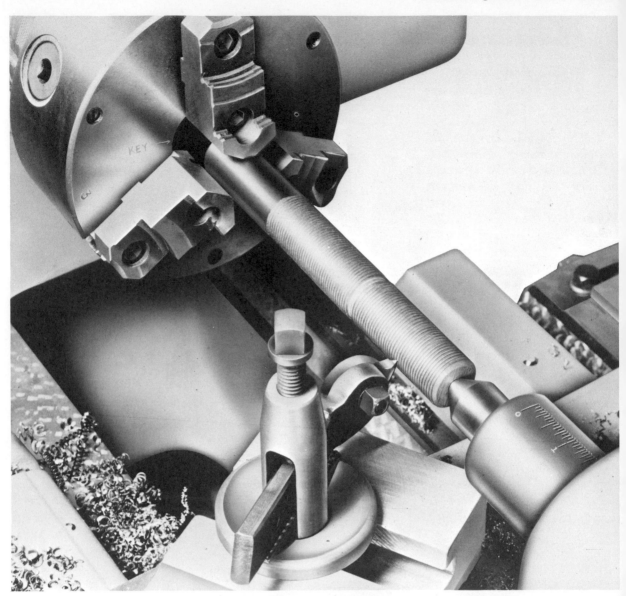

Cutting a thread with a formed threading tool.

Section Nineteen

Gearing

GEARS are used to transmit motion, rotating or reciprocating, from one machine part to another. Gears may be classified according to the position of the shafts that they connect. Parallel shafts may be connected by spur gears, helical gears, or herringbone gears. Intersection shafts may be connected by bevel gears which may have straight, skew, or spiral teeth. Nonparallel, nonintersecting shafts may be connected by crossed helical gears, hypoid gears, or worm gears. Rotary motion can be converted to reciprocating motion by a spur gear meshed to a rack.

Unit 84.   Gear Terminology

Friction wheels will transmit power from one shaft to another parallel shaft. However, such friction wheels are inefficient, since they are subject to slipping, and excessive pressure is required between the wheels to prevent this by frictional force. Pulleys and a crossed belt can also be used, as shown in the illustration at B. If, however, uniform angular motion must be transmitted, neither of these two methods is satisfactory. Yet, pulleys and a crossed belt are more dependable than friction discs but, because of the lack of positive driving contact, belt slippage can occur when too great a load is applied upon the driven pulley. By adding teeth of the proper shape on the cylindrical surfaces of the friction discs, the resulting spur gears will transmit motion and power without slipping and at a completely uniform rate. The addition of teeth does not change the relative velocities of the friction discs and shafts. 84–1.

If gears are to operate smoothly with a minimum amount of vibration and noise, the curved surface of the tooth must have a definite geometric form. The most common form in use today is known as the *involute* system.

In the *involute system* the shape of the tooth depends basically upon the pressure angle which determines the size of the base circle, from which the involute curve is generated. 84–2. The involute curve is generated on any point on the pitch circle, the normals of which are all tangent to this circle. The method of generating an involute is shown. If a pencil is inserted in the loop of a string wound about a cylinder and held taut as the string is unwound, the curve described is an involute. The cylinder on which it is unwound is called the *base circle.*

Involute-form gear teeth are used because: (1) the tooth form provides a pure rolling action, (2) the common normal at the point of contact between mating teeth will always pass through the pitch point, (3) the path of contact is a straight line which passes through the pitch point and is tangent to the base circles of the two gears, and (4) a true involute tooth form can be generated by a rack which has straight-sided teeth.

Proportions and shapes of gear teeth are well standardized. 84–3.

84–1. Three means for transmitting rotary motion from one shaft to another.

Fellows Gear Shaper Co.

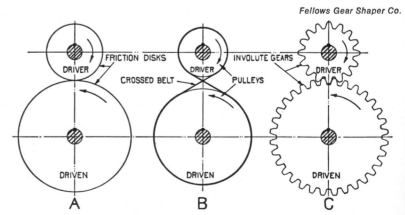

This standardization was initiated by the American Gear Manufacturers Association (AGMA).

The following symbols (from ASA B6.5-1954) and abbreviations are used in conjunction with spur gear formulas:

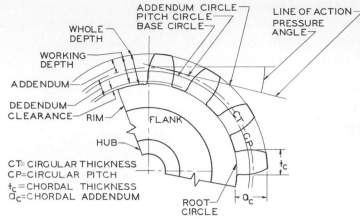

84-3. Gear nomenclature.

Symbol	Term	Abbreviation
P	Diametral pitch	DP
p	Circular pitch	CP
D_o	Pitch diameter	PD
D	Outside diameter	OD
N	Number of teeth	N
t	Circular thickness	CT
a	Addendum	A
b	Dedendum	D
h_k	Working depth	WkD
h_t	Whole depth	WD
c	Clearance	C
C	Center distance	C
L	Length of rack	

The principal definitions and tooth parts for standard $14\frac{1}{2}°$ and 20° involute gears are given below:

Addendum. The radial distance from the pitch circle to the top of the tooth.

Dedendum. The radial distance from the pitch circle to the bottom of the tooth space.

Circular pitch. The distance from a point on one tooth to a corresponding point on the adjacent tooth, measured on the pitch circle. $P = \dfrac{\pi D}{N}$

Diametral pitch. A ratio equal to the number of teeth on a gear per inch of pitch diameter. $P = \dfrac{N}{D}$

Tooth thickness. The thickness of a tooth, measured along the pitch circle. For cut gears, the tooth thickness and tooth space are equal.

Face width. The length of the gear teeth in an axial plane.

Tooth flank. The surface between the pitch line element and the bottom land. It includes the fillet.

Clearance. The amount by which the dedendum in a given

84-2. Method of generating an involute curve by unwinding a string from a cylinder.

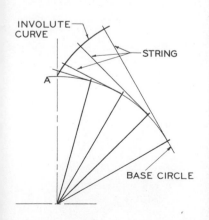

	20° Full Depth	12½° Full Depth	20° Fine Pitch	20° Stub Tooth
Table 84. AGMA Standard for Involute Gearing				
Addendum	$\dfrac{1}{P}$	$\dfrac{1}{P}$	$\dfrac{1}{P}$	$\dfrac{1}{P}$
Clearance	$\dfrac{0.250}{P}$	$\dfrac{0.157}{P}$	$\dfrac{0.2}{P} + .002$	$\dfrac{0.2}{P}$
Dedendum	$\dfrac{1.250}{P}$	$\dfrac{1.157}{P}$	$\dfrac{1.2}{P} + .002$	$\dfrac{1}{P}$
Outside diameter	$\dfrac{N+2}{P}$	$\dfrac{N+2}{P}$	$\dfrac{N+2}{P}$	$\dfrac{N+1+6}{P}$
Pitch diameter	$\dfrac{N}{P}$	$\dfrac{N}{P}$	$\dfrac{N}{P}$	$\dfrac{N}{P}$

Gears within the $14\frac{1}{2}°$ composite system have full-depth teeth with a pressure angle of $14\frac{1}{2}°$. The sides of the teeth of the basic rack curve slightly from a straight line near the top and bottom. This form of gear tooth is used for gears that are machined on milling machines with form-type rotary cutters.

gear exceeds the addendum of its mating gear.

Whole depth. The total depth of a tooth space, equal to the addendum plus dedendum; also equal to the working depth plus clearance.

Working depth. The depth of engagement of two mating gears—that is, the sum of their addendums.

Lead. The axial advance of a helix for one complete turn, as in the threads of cylindrical worms and teeth of helical gears.

Four shapes of involute gear teeth have been standardized by the American Standards Association since 1932 (ASA B6.1).

1. The 14½° composite system.

2. The 14½° full-depth involute gear teeth.

3. The 20° full-depth involute system.

4. Stub tooth involute system. Table 84, page 433.

The 14½° full-depth involute system uses full-depth teeth with 14½° pressure angle. This type is satisfactory when the number of teeth are large enough to avoid excessive undercutting of the tooth form.

The 20° full-depth system uses full-depth teeth with a 20° pressure angle. Gear teeth of this system are somewhat stronger because the tooth is thicker at the base.

In the 20° stub-tooth system the tooth form is a true involute. The addendum distance is shortened by 20%. The shorter tooth with a 20° pressure angle provides for stronger teeth on pinions with only 12 to 13 teeth, without undercutting.

Unit 85. Types of Gears

Many types of gears are produced today, some on milling machines. Others require special machines.

There are also many different types of gears used in the design of machines. These include spur, helical, bevel, miter, hypoid, internal, herringbone, Spiroid, Helicon, and worm gears. This unit also includes a description of special gear designs (coniflex), which limit production methods to specialized machinery and tooling.

SPUR GEARS

Gears most commonly used are those that transmit power between parallel shafts. 85–1. The pitch surfaces of both gears are of cylindrical shape and are tangent to each other at all times.

85–1. A 94″ alloy cast steel spur gear—12″ face 1DP.

Illinois Gear & Machine Co.

Normally they are used under conditions of moderate speed and moderate tooth load. A spur gear rack has teeth at a right angle with the axis of motion. 85–2.

HELICAL GEARS

Helical gears are similar to spur gears. The teeth form a helix, twisting around the body of the gear. These gears cannot only transmit more power but are quieter in operation than spur gears because the teeth engage gradually, thus reducing vibration and noise. 85–3(A).

Illinois Gear Div., Wallace-Murray Corp.
85–2. Cut rack and pinion.

85–3(A). Double-reduction helical gear train.

Illinois Gear Div., Wallace-Murray Corp.

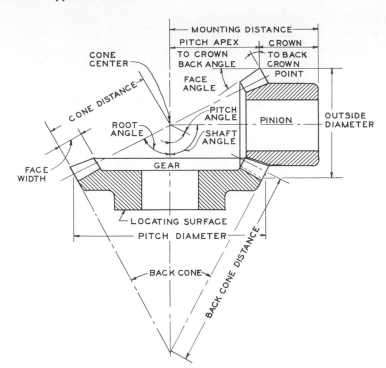

85–3(B). Bevel gear and pinion nomenclature.

Gleason Works

85–4. Straight bevel gear set.

BEVEL GEARS

Bevel gears are the most efficient means of transmitting rotation between angularly deposed shafts. 85–3(B).

There are three basic types of bevel gears—straight, spiral, and Zerol. 85–4. Each can be made with various tooth forms.

Straight bevel gears are the oldest, the simplest, and still the most widely used. 85–5. The teeth are straight and tapered and, if extended inward, would intersect the gear axis. 85–6. In recent years straight bevel-gear-cutting machines have been designed to crown the sides of the teeth in their lengthwise direction. These are known as *Coniflex* gears.*

---

* Zerol and Coniflex are registered trade names of the Gleason Works.

Illinois Gear Div., Wallace-Murray Corp.

85–5. Bevel gear and pinion, with gear having unusually long front hub projection.

85–6. All elements of the teeth of straight bevel gear intersecting at a point.

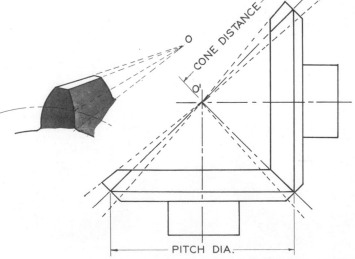

Miter gears—two bevel gears of equal size, with an equal number of teeth—are designed for use on shafts at a right angle. 85–7. *Spiral* bevels have curved oblique teeth which contact each other gradually and smoothly from one end to the other. 85–8. Cut a straight bevel into an infinite number of short face-width sections, angularly displace them relative to one another, and you have a spiral bevel gear. The overlapping tooth action transmits motion more smoothly and quietly than straight bevel gears. Well-designed spiral bevels have

two or more teeth in contact at all times.

Zerol bevels have curved teeth similar to those of spiral bevels but with a zero spiral angle at the middle of the face width and little end thrust. 85–9. Both spiral and Zerol gears can be cut on the same machine with the same circular face-mill cutters or ground on the same grinding machines.

Zerol bevels are widely employed in the aircraft industry, where ground-tooth precision gears are required.

HYPOID GEARS

"Hypoid gears are different from bevel gears. 85–10. Bevel

gear pairs always have intersecting axes. Hypoids never do. Their axes cross instead—which enables them to transmit power between shafts which have to lie in different planes.

"Bevel gears are conical in form. Hypoid gears are based on segments of bodies called 'hyperboloids of revolution'—more uniquely shaped as cones, yet also able to roll together very smoothly when properly designed.

"For the same size gear and with the same number of teeth, a hypoid pinion can be larger and stronger than a corresponding bevel pinion. Greater size enables it to pass along greater power—a fact which most modern passenger car designers have learned to exploit. The axis of a hypoid pinion can be 'offset' either above or below the axis of its gear as application may require."*

---

* The Gleason Works.

85–11. Internal gear for planetary gear train drive.
Illinois Gear Div., Wallace-Murray Corp.

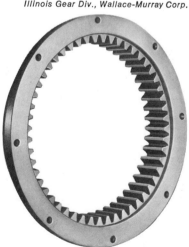

Gleason Works
85–7. Miter spiral bevel gear set.

Gleason Works
85–9. A Zerol bevel gear set.

85–8. Spiral bevel gear set.
Gleason Works

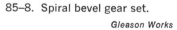

85–10. Hypoid gear set.
Gleason Works

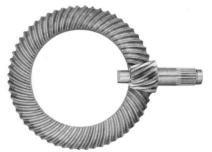

INTERNAL GEARS

Internal gears have teeth on the inner surface of a solid ring, pointing toward the center of the ring. 85–11. Gears may have spur, bevel, or helical teeth.

HERRINGBONE GEARS

Herringbone gears resemble a pair of right- and left-hand helical gears located side by side. 85–12. Hence they are frequently called double-helical gears. They are designed for operation on parallel shafts. Side thrust, which normally results from the sliding action which is common in single-helical gears, is neutralized and thus eliminated. Herringbone gears do away with the need for thrust bearings.

WORM GEARS

Worm gears are used when large speed reduction is required. 85–13. The worm is the small driving gear and the driven gear is the wheel. The helical tooth on the worm, a form of thread, is often simply called a thread. The teeth on the wheel are helical and conform to the diameter of the worm. The shafts for worm gears are at right angles but are not located in the same plane.

Worms may have single, double, or triple threads.

"SPIROID" AND "HELICON" GEARS

These gears are a recent addition to the skew-axis gear family. Spiroid and Helicon gears are screw-type gears, while bevel, spur, and helical gears are primarily rolling types. 85–14.

Spiroid gears offer important design advantages: positive back-

Gould & Eberhardt Gear Machinery Corp.

85–12. Hobbing a double-helical or herringbone gear.

85–13. Bronze worm gear and multiple thread worm.

Illinois Gear Div., Wallace-Murray Corp.

85–14. (A) Spiroid gear. (B) Helicon gear.

Illinois Tool Works, Inc.

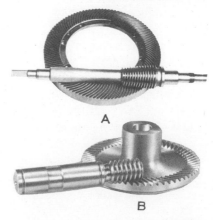

A

B

437

lash control, greater shock strength, liberal mounting tolerances, increased efficiency, more power in less space, and ratios over the range of 10:1 to 400:1.

The illustration shows a comparison of Spiroid gears with cross axis and other skew-axis gears. 85–15. The Spiroid pinion is positioned between the extreme positions of bevel and worm pinions. With the range of Spiroid positions, these gears have many more teeth in contact than a worm gear of equal diameter.

Spiroid and Helicon gear sets consist of two members: pinion and gear. By definition, the pinion has fewer teeth and is normally the driving member while the driven gear is a face member resembling a spiral bevel or hypoid gear. The pinions are often tapered, usually 5° on one side or 10° included angle. In some cases larger or smaller angles may be used.

One such smaller angle is a zero taper angle. In this case the pinion is cylindrical. Because of several practical advantages, cylindrical pinions and their mating gears have acquired their own name, Helicon.*

The gear member of a Spiroid or Helicon gear set is always initially produced by hobbing. (See Unit 86.)

In ratios of less than 5:1, hobbing is uneconomical and gears in production quantity must be sintered or molded. Above 10:1 all Spiroid gears can be hobbed. On larger gear sets pinion threads

---

* Spiroid and Helicon gears have been developed by the Illinois Tool Works, Inc., Chicago, Illinois. The names are registered trade names of the company.

can be produced by thread milling.

Spiroid and Helicon gears have many applications. They are used in power tools, precision power drives on machine tools, in military and precision custom applications, and in many industrial applications such as track drives for power cranes, rotary tillers, slicing machines, lawn mowers, and snow blowers.

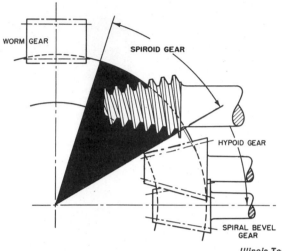

WORM GEAR
SPIROID GEAR
HYPOID GEAR
SPIRAL BEVEL GEAR

Illinois Tool Works, Inc.

85–15. Spiroid gears located between spur and hypoid gears.

Unit 86. Gear Manufacturing Processes

There are many different methods of producing gears. However, most of the gears produced today are by some machining process.

Some types of gears are made by sand-casting, die-casting, or investment-casting processes. Sand-cast gears can be used under conditions where the gear moves slowly and where efficiency in power transmission is not too important.

Gears which are produced by the die and investment casting processes are satisfactory for car-rying light loads. They have a fine surface finish and can also be made dimensionally accurate. However, these gears are made from low-melting alloys and metals which do not have the wearing qualities of heat-treated steel gears.

Some types of gears are made by blanking in a punch press. They are of thin sheet metal for watches, clocks, meters, and calculating machines.

Gears are also made by extrusion, rolling, sintering, and injection molding processes.

Gould & Eberhardt Gear Machinery Corp.

86–1. Form cutting process of cutting gears with a single-point tool—75 S, cutting 88 T, 1½ DP, 5″ face gear.

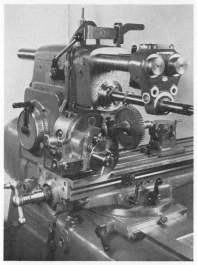

Brown & Sharpe Mfg. Co.

86–2. Cutting a spur gear with a form cutter. The dividing head is mounted on the table of a horizontal milling machine.

Machining processes for producing gears may be: (1) form cutting, (2) template machining, and (3) gear generating.

FORM CUTTING

The form cutting method of producing gears employs a cutter having the same form as the space between the teeth being machined. 86–1. The cutter employed may be a rotating cutter on a milling machine, a single-point tool on a shaper, planer, broach, or a special gear cutting machine.

A formed milling cutter mounted on the arbor of a plain or universal milling machine is commonly used for cutting a spur gear. A gear blank is mounted on an arbor held between the centers of a dividing head. 86–2.

In form cutting gears on a milling machine, standard cutters can be used. They vary from No. 1 to No. 8. These eight standard involute cutters are listed in Table 86.

A single cutter will not produce a theoretically perfect tooth profile for all sizes of gears. However, it is possible to use one cutter for several gears having different numbers of teeth without affecting their operating action to any great extent.

CUTTING A SPUR GEAR

Press the proper size gear blank on a tapered arbor.

Secure the dividing head and tailstock on the machine table as close to the column as the nature of the work and the dividing head will permit. Check the alignment of the headstock and tailstock centers by measuring with a rule and square head from the column face of the machine to each center point. Place a proper type dog on the mandrel and mount the blank between centers of the dividing head. Attach the proper plate to the dividing head. The plate to use can be determined by the calculations given in Section 14 on the dividing head.

Center the cutter so that the cutter line of the gear teeth will

Table 86. Involute Cutters			
No. 1	125 teeth to a rack	No. 5	21 to 25 teeth
No. 2	55 to 134 teeth	No. 6	17 to 20 teeth
No. 3	35 to 54 teeth	No. 7	14 to 16 teeth
No. 4	26 to 34 teeth	No. 8	12 to 13 teeth

439

be radial to the axis of the gear. The table of the machine is raised until the cutter just touches the workpiece. *Test* with a piece of tissue paper placed between the workpiece and cutter. The vertical feed dial is then set to zero. Move the table back until the near edge is to the rear of the front of the cutter. The table is raised to an amount equal to the required tooth depth, or a lesser amount if two or more cuts are to be made. The automatic longitudinal feed is then engaged and the cut is made. At the end of the cut, the feed is disengaged and the table movement is reversed until the cutter is free of the blank.

The blank is then indexed to the required distance for cutting the next tooth space. When all teeth have been formed, the ma-

chine can be set for a finishing cut, if so required.

If large roughing cuts are to be made, a stocking cutter can be used prior to the finishing cut that is made with a formed cutter. The chip breaking action of the teeth on a stocking cutter allows heavy cuts at fast speeds and feeds.

A minimum amount of power is consumed in cutting. While often used singly to advantage, stocking cutters also can be used many times in combination with a finishing cutter on a semi-automatic gear-cutting machine, so that the stocking cutter is roughing while the finishing cutter is finishing.

SPEED, FEED, AND DEPTH OF CUT

The type of material being cut will govern the operation speed of the cutter. The speed should be somewhat under that of an ordinary milling cutter and approximately the same as used for other formed cutters.

The feed will also be slightly under that of ordinary milling operations. The feed will vary

according to the hardness of the material being cut. In milling softer materials, it can be increased considerably.

With some materials the whole depth of cut can be made in one pass. Harder materials may require two or more cuts, depending upon the type and condition of the machine.

GENERATING GEARS BY HOBBING

Hobbing is a nearly universal process which can be used to manufacture spur and helical gears of all types, splines, ratchets, worms, sprockets, Spiroid and planoid gears. 86–3. Hobbing has been used for producing gears smaller than $\frac{1}{10}''$ and up to 200″ in diameter, with pitches coarser than 1 and as fine as 300.

The tool used in this process, a hob, is a special form of mill-

86–3. Plain hobber with special auto cycle, special motor drive, chip conveyor, special auto hob shift, lead gears omitted, and finished stack of Ford starter ring gears, without guards—close-up of operator's side.

Gould & Eberhardt Gear Machinery Corp.

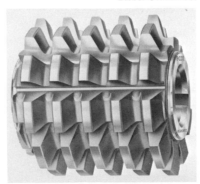

86–4. A typical gear hob used to cut gear teeth.

Barber-Colman Co.

86–5. Cutting action with a hob is continuous. As many as four or five teeth will be cutting at the same time.

Barber-Colman Co.

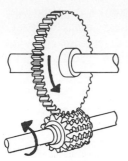

86–6. Speeds between gear blank and hob are proportional.

Barber-Colman Co.

ing cutter designed to cut teeth on a continuous basis. 86–4. The hob is essentially a worm which has been interrupted by a series of transverse gashes to form teeth and cutting faces. Tool relief is obtained by "backing off" the teeth so that the form remains constant but moves closer to the center of the tool as it recedes from the cutting face.

A hob of a given pitch and pressure angle is capable of cutting any gear of the same pitch and pressure angle, regardless of the number of teeth.

The Hobbing Process

Hobbing can be compared to wood carving in certain respects. A carver removes small amounts of wood at a time to obtain the desired curves in the object being carved. A hob removes metal in somewhat the same manner as it "generates" the tooth form.

The teeth on a hob cut into the gear blank one after the other, each tooth in a slightly different position. As many as 30 or 40 hob teeth will each take out a small chip to form a complete tooth profile.

Cutting action is continuous and as many as four or five teeth will be cutting at the same time, machining different parts of adjoining gear teeth. 86–5.

The gear blank and cutter both rotate. The hob, gear blank, and feed are interrelated.

The speeds are arranged so that the hob (*single thread*) makes one complete revolution for each gear tooth that passes by it. 86–6. In cutting a thirty-tooth gear, the hob will rotate thirty times while the gear blank rotates once.

Some hobs have more than one row of teeth. A hob with *two threads,* which is similar to a screw with two starts, will make one revolution for each two gear teeth that pass it, and so on. 86–7.

During the cutting process, the hob is moving through the gear blank from one side to the other. It generates tooth profiles in successive layers, all the way around the blank, as it feeds. When the hob has moved entirely across the thickness of the gear blank, the teeth are complete. For each turn of the blank, the cutter will have moved a regulated distance. The *feed* is expressed in thousandths of an inch per revolution of the workpiece.

A given hob is capable of cutting any size involute gear which has the same number of teeth per inch of gear diameter (diametral pitch).

When hobbing helical gears, the blank is "mis-indexed" to advance or retard its relationship to the hob. Hob feed and index speed must be accurately coordinated to the correct tooth

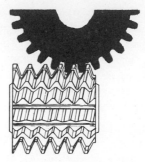

DOUBLE-THREAD HOB

Barber-Colman Co.

86–7. A hob with two threads is like a screw with two starts; it will make one revolution for each two gear teeth that pass it.

angle. 86–8. Instead of cutting straight ahead, the hob is going to cut in a diagonal direction. This means that in order to cut diagonally the hob would have to be moved endwise as well as straight

86–8. Cutting teeth in a helical gear on a 16', heavy-duty, gear hobber.

Mesta Machine Co.

ahead. 86–9. Such a movement is not practical since it would require a very long hob. To remedy this, the indexing head of the workpiece is slowed a small amount so that it does not make a full revolution for each revolution of the hob. For each advance of the hob, the point of the cutting action is offset a trifle from its position at the preceding cut.

By combining these successive cuts, a helical gear is produced.

Some hobbing machines are equipped with a differential, permitting independent motion of the hob carriage without loss of relationship between the work and hob. 86–10.

Many special forms can be generated by the hobbing process, using specially designed hobs. Generally speaking, a hob can be made to generate almost any part that has forms equally spaced around a center.

Hobbing is a fast and accurate method of producing gears. Today's consumer demands quiet running gears in machines such as automatic washers, automobiles, lawn mowers, and other products that he purchases. Inaccuracies of less than .001″ will produce unsatisfactory results.

GENERATING WITH A RECIPROCATING TOOL

The cutter-gear generating process, commonly known as gear shaping, is a continuous indexing gear-cutting process. 86–11. The shaper cutter and work rotate in constant relationship while the cutter reciprocates across the face of the work. 86–12. It is a generative process quite similar to hobbing except that shaping differs; the work and cutter rotate in the same plane. Infeed is accomplished by moving the centers closer together.

The tool used in gear shaping is essentially a gear which has been relieved to form cutting teeth. 86–13.

The face of the tool is "dished" slightly, which provides the teeth with a positive rake. The teeth are elongated in the tip area in order to cut sufficient root clearance in the gear. This method of gear cutting is based on the principle that any two gears will mesh if they are of the same pitch, pressure angle, proper helix angle, and proper tooth depths and thicknesses. 86–14(A) (Page 444).

The cutter is actuated by a crank and reciprocates past the blank. Cutter and workpiece rotate on parallel axes. This motion requires a second index worm and worm gear in the gear train.

On the return stroke of the cutter, the tool must be relieved to avoid rubbing the workpiece. Any rubbing would dull the cutting edges. By moving the cutter head away from the workpiece slightly, or moving the table, this condition can be avoided.

By moving the axes of the workpiece and cutter closer together, infeeding is accomplished. In operation the cutter is fed into the workpiece to the required

86–9. Hobbing double-helical gear with 268 teeth, 3 DP, 84″ diam.

Gould & Eberhardt Gear Machinery Corp.

86–10. Hobbing machine.

Barber-Colman Co.

depth and the feed is stopped and cutting continues until all the teeth are machined to the proper depth. Sometimes more than one cut is necessary. The operation is then repeated until the prescribed depth is reached.

That portion of a gear tooth lying inside the base circle from which the involute is developed is of noninvolute shape. The illustration shows how this shape is produced by the gear shaper cutter.

In the tooth space to the right are shown the successive portions taken by the cutter as it "rolls" into the tooth space. 86–14(B). The cutter teeth are longer than the gear teeth, so as to provide clearance at the bottom of the tooth spaces for the mating gear.

The illustration also indicates the nature of the chip taken by the cutter—the heaviest portion of the chip, after reaching full depth, being in the flank and

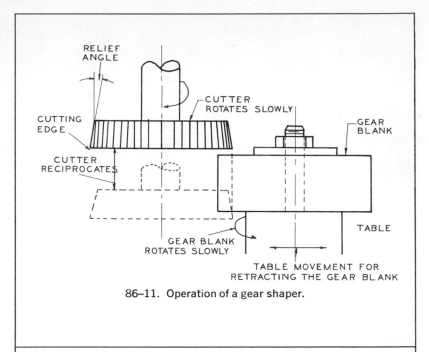

86–11. Operation of a gear shaper.

86–12. Fellows-brand gear shaper.

Fellows Gear Shaper Co.

86–13. Fellows gear shaper cutter form-cutting spur gears. Clearances are provided both on the ends and sides of the teeth.

Fellows Gear Shaper Co.

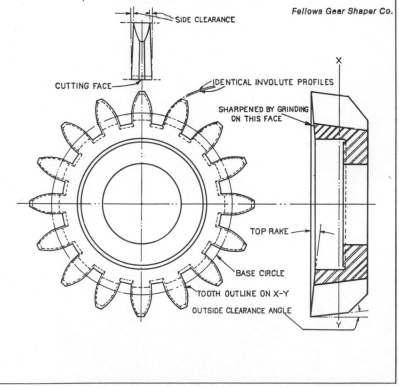

86–14(A). Fellows gear shaper cutting an internal gear.

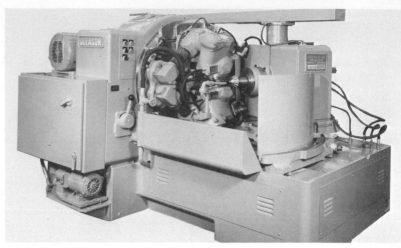

86–15. Straight bevel Coniflex generator.

fillet, and the lightest chip being on the involute portion of the tooth, assuring a fine finish.

Some types of shapers have a hydraulic infeed control while other machines control infeed with a cam.

Spur and helical gears of all types, ratchets, splines, sprockets, herringbone gears, sector gears, and special shapes which may be symmetrical can be produced by gear shaping. Gears from $\frac{1}{16}''$

up to 23′ in diameter have been produced by this process.

Gear generating is a faster method of producing gears than form cutting. Many gears are semifinished by hobbing and shaping and are finished by other methods which are described later in this unit.

An important point in connection with the application of the generating principle is the cutting tool used and its method of

operation. Reciprocation of the cutting tool makes possible its application to the generating of external and internal surfaces, and also permits operating the tool in a comparatively narrow recess. Without this reciprocating motion to the cutting tool, the generating principle is greatly limited in scope.

In shaping helical gears, the lead on the guide must be the same as the lead on the cutter, and the helix angle on the cutter must be the same as the helix angle on the part.

The Sykes gear-generating machine is used in cutting continuous herringbone teeth. Two cutters are mounted in a horizontal position and the cutters are given a reciprocating motion, one cutting in one direction toward the center of the gear blank and the other cutting to the same point when the motion is reversed. Also, the cutters are given a twisting motion according to the helix angle. This type

86–14(B). The action of a Fellows gear shaper cutter, showing how the involute portion, flank, and fillet of the teeth are produced.

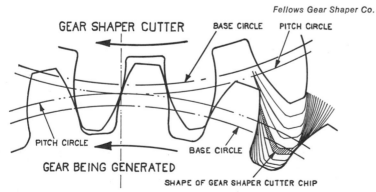

Illlnois Gear & Machine Co.

86–16. Straight bevel Coniflex generator employing two reciprocating tools. This machine can produce bevel and miter gears to 36″ diam.

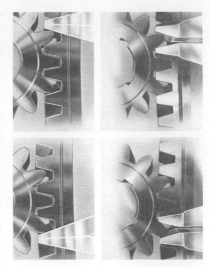

Gleason Works

86–17. Teeth of Coniflex gears are generated by means of a relative rolling motion between work and cutters or tools.

of gear generating is quite similar to that of a Fellows gear shaper.

BEVEL GEAR GENERATORS

Two different types of gear generators are used in the production of straight bevel Coniflex® gears—a generator with rotating interlocking disc cutters, and a two-tool generator with two reciprocating cutting tools. 86–15. On both machines, the tooth profile shape is produced by the generating method, which involves a relative rolling motion between the gear blank and the cutters or tools. The action is as though the gear blank being cut were rolling with a mating generating gear. In the case of the rotary cutter generator, the cutters represent a tooth of this mating gear, whereas with the two-tool generator, the tools rep-resent sides of the adjacent teeth of the generating gear.

On the two-tool completing generator, the gear blank is mounted in a work spindle which rotates in timed relationship with the cradle on which the cutters are mounted. A feed cam moves the workhead and gear blank into cutting position, rough cutting the tooth, without roll, until the cut is just short of the full tooth depth. The cradle, on which the cutter is mounted, and the work then roll to the bottom of the generating roll, rough shaping the tooth. The work is next fed into full depth and then a fast up-roll finish generates the tooth. At the top of the roll, the workpiece backs out, and the cradle and workpiece roll down again into roughing position. During this short down roll, the blank is indexed for cutting the next tooth. 86–16.

In the illustration (Fig. 86–17, left) two positions of the rotary cutter and work are shown, at the beginning of the finishing generating roll and at the end.

Gleason two-tool generators use the same generating method just described. The two reciprocating tools represent the sides of a tooth space of a generated gear as illustrated (Fig. 86–17, right).

Spiral bevel gears are also produced by the generating principle. 86–18 (Page 446). The cutter for generating these gears is circular and is similar in operation to a face milling cutter. The spiral teeth cut by this method are curved on the arc of a circle, the radius being equal to the radius of the cutter.

The teeth are first roughed out and the true shape is then generated as shown.

445

Hypoid gears, widely used in automobile and motorcycle drives, can be cut on the same type of machine. 86–19.

GEAR BROACHING

Gear broaching differs in no respect from regular broaching. Gear broaching is a high-production method of producing internal spur gears and helical gears with helix angles up to 30°. 86–20. Some types of external gears are also produced by this method.

The broaching tool is shaped to conform with the tooth space, quite similar to the formed-tooth principle for producing gears on a milling machine. In most cases all teeth can be cut at once with either push or pull broaches.

Roughing and finishing operations are usually accomplished in one pass. Broach design is standard and is used on standard machines. Helical gears are cut on a machine equipped with a drive head to rotate the broach.

When broaching more than one part at once, both faces of the pieces must be parallel to avoid lead errors. For best results, broaching requires a through hole in the part.

SHEAR CUTTING OF GEARS

Shear cutting of gears is very similar to the broaching process because all the teeth are cut at the same time. This process is also similar to gear shaping because the cutting is a reciprocating action. The gear blank is reciprocated past the tool while it is fed to the proper depth.

The cutting tool resembles a set of form tools that are held in a special holder. When the tool is worn or broken, it can be replaced. The machine is designed to withdraw the tool from the work on the return stroke to avoid wear on the cutter.

This is a high-production method limited to coarse pitch gears from 2 to 12 DP.

GEAR FINISHING

Gear finishing is used to correct any inaccuracies that may have been produced by hobbing, generating, or other methods. Generally these inaccuracies are very small dimensionally but even a slight amount can cause wear and noise at high speeds. Only a few thousandths of an inch is left on the gears for finishing.

GEAR SHAVING

Gear shaving is a finishing operation which improves tooth profile and surface finish. 86–21.

Rotary gear shaving is based on the use of a gashed rotary cutter in the form of a helical gear and a crossed axes relationship between the cutter and work gear which have different helical angles. The axis of the work and axis of the shaver cutter cross at an angle of 3° to 15°.

The gashes in the cutter teeth which provide the cutting edges are normal to its axis. They extend from the top to bottom through each tooth.

All principal cutter elements are held to a tolerance of 0.0002″.

Cutter speed is high and feed is light with tool contact zone restricted. The result is fine, hairlike shavings similar to those produced by the diamond boring tool.

There are three kinds of traverses used in shaving: (1) the axial traverse, (2) the right-angle traverse, and (3) the angular traverse. The latter type is up to 50% faster than others. A right-angle traverse is often used when a feature of the part

86–18. Principle of bevel gear generating machines.

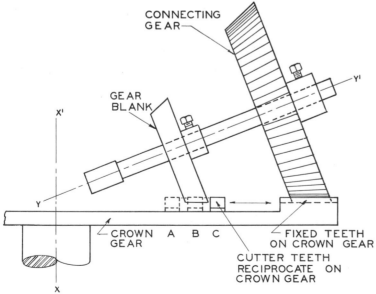

86–19. Hypoid generator.

Gleason Works

National Broach & Machine Co.

86–21. Gear shaving cutters.

would interfere with axial traverse motion.

In order to reduce profile errors, it is important that the cutter not contact the gear tooth gullets.

In the operation the workpiece is mounted between live centers, raised against the cutter, and reciprocated while being driven.

The workpiece, which freewheels in the live centers, is driven by the cutter. At the end of each table stroke, the cutter reverses direction to shave the opposite side of the gear teeth and the work feeds into the cutter. 86–22. NOTE: Some machines are designed to reciprocate perpendicular to the work axis in addition to reciprocating axially.

In rack-type gear shaving, the shaving cutter is in the form of a rack. The rack is mounted on the table of the machine, which reciprocates. The gear to be shaved is mounted above the rack between live centers. The gear is driven by contact with the cutting rack. The gear is reciprocated sideways and fed into the rack. At each stroke the gear is fed down into the rack cutter until the desired tooth depth is reached.

Gears are usually shaved before heat treatment is done. In order to compensate for distortion from heat treating, modified

86–22. Gear shaving machine.

National Broach & Machine Co.

86–20. Broaching external gear teeth on a broaching machine.

Detroit Broach & Machine Co.

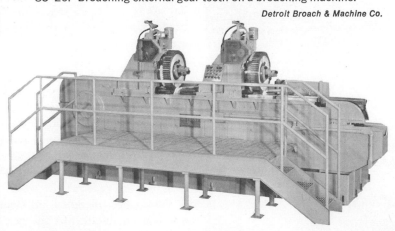

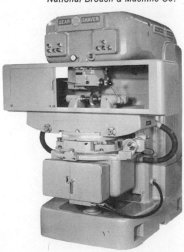

cutters are used for such an operation.

Gear shaving is a low-cost production process. Shaving can be used to finish external spur and helical gears and splines with diameters from ¼″ to 200″. On internal gears with diameters from 22″ to 48″, shaving is an important operation because it can reduce tooth profile errors as much as 50%. This method of finishing is applicable to all gear materials, and to hardness as high as 40 Rockwell C.

GEAR GRINDING

Gears that have been hardened can be finished by grinding. Wheel selection, speeds and feeds, coolant, and heat-treat requirements are the same for gear grinding as in general grinding practice.

There are two types of grinding methods used for finishing gears: (1) form grinding and (2) generating grinding. 86–23. In the former the grinding wheel is dressed to the proper shape and then passed through the gear tooth. Both sides of the tooth are formed at once, and stock removal is controlled by radial infeed. Index plates are used to control indexing of the gear being ground. The usual procedure is to rough-grind the gear and then finish-grind with the trued wheel set to depth. External and internal spur gears, splines, and similar parts are ground in this manner.

In the generating method of grinding, the surface of the wheel is accurately trued to represent one side of an involute-rack tooth. The workpiece is carried under a reciprocating wheel and rolled as though it were in mesh with a rack. The work, rolling with the theoretical rack, generates a correct involute-gear-tooth profile on the side of the tooth. After one side of the tooth is ground, the grinding wheel is returned to its original position. The work gear is then indexed for grinding the side of the next gear tooth.

GEAR LAPPING

Gear lapping is used to finish hardened gears by correcting small errors in spacing, profile, helix angle, and eccentricity. The operation is performed with all forms of gears running together with mating gears, or work gears, and cast iron toothed laps, under a flow of fine oil mixed with an abrasive compound. Lapping is achieved by a sliding action above and below the pitch line, which provides the motion necessary to lap a gear. A reciprocating motion similar to a gear shaver achieves lapping at the pitch line. The work is turned first in one direction, then in another, to lap both surfaces of the teeth. The lapping action can be increased by increasing the pressure between the lap and workpiece (cramp lapping) or by applying a hydraulic brake to the driving gear. Several laps, forming a set of slightly dissimilar tools on one gear, can be used to break up tooth spacing errors.

GEAR HONING

This finishing process is used on hardened gears to remove burrs and nicks. 86–24. The operation is similar to gear shaving. The tool used is an abrasive-imbedded plastic cutter, similar to a shaving cutter.

Two basic methods of stock removal are used: (1) the zero-

86–23. Spur gear grinder.

Michigan Tool Co.

MICHIGAN-SPUR- GEAR GRINDER

backlash and (2) constant-pressure method.

With the former, the cutter and work are tightly meshed and the cutter head is locked in position. As honing progresses, the cutting pressure decreases. In the constant-pressure method, the center distance decreases while the work and cutter are held in constant mesh.

GEAR INSPECTION

There are a variety of inspection methods and different types of equipment produced to check and test gears. Universal gear checkers with fine interchangeable heads indicate errors in tooth size, spacing, helix angle, lead, eccentricity, and parallelism, and they disclose wobble. 86–25.

Sound testers are used to check the quietness of the running of a set of gears.

If the sound test reveals objectionable noise, the faulty gears can be routed back for correction.

With a set of gears in a sound-testing machine, tooth bearing can be checked by using marking compound on one and observing its transfer to the mating gear. When the sound test reveals a nicked tooth, the nick may be removed by a pencil grinder while the gear is still in the sound-testing machine.

Since Spiroid pinions have a theoretically defined lead, pressure angle, and taper, they may be inspected on any lead-checking instrument that provides for following the taper. Such instruments may also be equipped to check pressure angles, and the pinion tooth shape can be

National Broach & Machine Co.

86–24. Gear honing machine.

National Broach & Machine Co.

86–25. Universal gear checker with equipment for comparing the lead of a helical gear with a master lead groove and a checking head on the rear of the machine to check eccentricity and helix angle.

86–26. Forged steel equalizer shrouded spur pinions for steel mills with 17 teeth, .625 DP (5.029″ CP), 20° PA, and 10″ face.

Illinois Gear & Machine Co.

checked with an optical comparator.

The most important inspection is the fundamental check where the operating position of gear and pinion is duplicated in a gear rolling machine. In this position the gear set should have proper backlash if both gear and pinion are the correct size.

The control of quality by gear makers is so painstaking that each and every gear must pass a great many exacting inspections before being finally released to the customer. 86–26 & 86–27.

Illinois Gear & Machine Co.

86–27. Checking pressure angle of 3 DP worm on optical comparator.

18. *Explain the basic principle of the Gleason gear generator.*

19. *Describe the operation of a Fellows gear shaper.*

20. *Explain the operation of a Sykes gear-generating machine.*

21. *What is a two-tool completing generator?*

22. *What is gear broaching?*

23. *Explain the principle of gear shaving.*

24. *Name two types of grinding methods for finishing gears.*

25. *Why is the inspection of gears so important?*

Problems

1. *A spur gear is machined with a 6-pitch cutter. Determine the outside diameter if the gear has 34 teeth.*

2. *Find the circular pitch of a gear which has 48 teeth and a pitch diameter of 6".*

3. *Find the diametral pitch of a gear which has 72 teeth and a pitch diameter of 4½".*

4. *Determine the diametral and circular pitches of a gear having a pitch circle diameter of 6" and 48 teeth.*

Check Your Knowledge

1. *How may gears be classified?*

2. *Why must the curved surface of a gear tooth have a definite geometric form?*

3. *Give some reasons why the involute-form gear teeth are used.*

4. *Make a sketch of a gear and show the addendum circle, pitch circle, dedendum circle, and circular pitch.*

5. *Name the four shapes of involute gear teeth that have been standardized by the ASA.*

6. *Define the following: gear, pinion, and rack.*

7. *Describe spur gears and the kinds of applications for which they are used.*

8. *Why are helical gears quieter in operation than spur gears?*

9. *Name three basic types of bevel gears.*

10. *Describe a spiral bevel gear.*

11. *What is a Zerol bevel gear?*

12. *Explain the difference between hypoid and bevel gears.*

13. *For what purposes are the following kinds of gears used: internal gears, herringbone gears, helical gears, and Spiroid gears?*

14. *Name three processes for producing gears.*

15. *Explain the difference between form cutting and generating methods of machining gear teeth.*

16. *Explain why hobbing is the most economical method for machining gears.*

17. *Describe the hobbing process of producing gears.*

References

Coleman, Wells, "Guide to Bevel Gears," Reprinted from: *Product Engineering*, New York, McGraw-Hill Book Co., 1963.

Dudley, D. W., *Gear Handbook*, New York, McGraw-Hill Book Co., 1962.

The Fellows Gear Shaper Company, *The Involute Curve and Involute Gearing*, 1969.

Illinois Tool Works, Inc., *Spiroid Gearing*, 1963.

Section Twenty

Powder Metallurgy

POWDER metallurgy is the processing of metal powders to produce a great variety of formed products. This process is carried out by blending powders, compacting the cold mixture to the required shape in a die, and then heating the ejected form in a controlled atmosphere to atomically bond the contacting surfaces of the particles.

Powder metallurgy has made giant strides in recent years. At least two billion powder metallurgy parts are being made annually. Parts weighing up to 35 pounds are now being made,

compared to the 2-pound parts made only a few years ago.

Parts made by the powder metallurgy process require simpler processing and minimum machining, but strong complex parts are made to extremely close tolerances. Many secondary and finish-machining operations are eliminated. The parts produced do not contain impurities, gas pockets, or internal stresses.

Dissimilar metals, nonmetallics, and materials of widely different characteristics can be combined.

It is thought that powder metallurgy probably existed in a very crude form as early as 2500 B.C. The Egyptians are given credit for producing sponge iron by heating iron oxide with charcoal. The iron particles were hammered into crude shapes and heated. The resulting product had fairly good strength and could be used for simple tools.

The press bonding of metals was accomplished early in the 19th century and was very similar to methods used today. Early in the 20th century, nonferrous bushings were mass-produced and led to a greater interest in powder metallurgical techniques.

During the 1960's a boom began in the production of P/M (powder metal) parts, particularly in the automotive industry.

The future holds much promise for the metalworking industry through powder metallurgy technology.

ADVANTAGES AND DISADVANTAGES OF THE POWDER METALLURGY PROCESS

A primary reason for producing shaped objects by powder metallurgy is that powder metallurgy is an economic fabrication process in which parts can be produced to closely controlled dimensions having adequate mechanical and physical properties at a satisfactory cost.

The powder metallurgist can control his product from the time the powder is produced until the part is produced. The demands of product application can be met by creating properties and characteristics of a product to suit the manufacturer.

Materials that cannot be produced by other methods can be combined in powder form. Ceramics, for example, can be blended with metals to produce products with prescribed qualities.

There is another reason why certain shaped objects are made by P/M, and that is their porosity. Powder metallurgy is probably the only method by which metal objects can be produced and have uniform pores of closely controlled dimensions distributed throughout the metal structure. The pores are so small that they cannot be readily seen by the naked eye. A bronze bearing made from metal powders may look just like a cast bronze bearing, but because of the small, finely distributed pores, its density is only 80% of a cast bearing's density. This type of porosity is used in the so-called self-lubricating bearings, in which the porous structure of the sintered bearing is impregnated with a lubricating oil. The bearing may then serve as its own oil reservoir. As soon as the shaft begins to turn, warming the bearing slightly, enough oil exudes from the bearing to form a thin film between the bearing and shaft surfaces. This self-lubricating feature of P/M parts is often used in applications other than bearings, such as gears and cams. Other porous P/M parts, with porosities of 40% to 50% by volume, are used as filters.

Gears and similar products that are made by this process possess qualities which permit quieter operations.

Machining and finishing operations can be eliminated, resulting in a large saving. Parts can be made with close tolerances and good surface finishes.

Material losses can be held to a minimum, making the operation an economical one.

However, there are some limitations and disadvantages to this process, such as: (1) relatively high cost of equipment, (2) high raw material costs, and (3) certain design limitations.

POWDER METAL PRODUCTS

There are many products made today from metal powders.

Structural parts for aerospace applications are made from alloyed powders to provide super-hard, high heat resistant parts capable of withstanding the environment of outer space.

Other powder metallurgical parts in aerospace applications include the sintered bronze bearings, which operated for 93 days in space on the Explorer III tape recorder, and Alnico 5, used in the de-spin mechanism of navigational satellites.*

The Hallar Division of Federal-Mogul Corporation makes a door lock assembly for Chevrolet and GMC trucks by the P/M process. Each assembly is made of two parts, which are sintered and copper infiltrated together after briquetting to make a single unit which can be parted only by a force of about 4,000 pounds.

The largest customer of P/M parts is the automotive industry which now consumes an estimated 60% of the total U.S. output.

Other products such as cemented carbides, which are combinations of tungsten, other carbides, and cobalt metal, are very important materials for cutting tools and also compacting dies.

Metallic friction materials, which are combinations of the metals copper, tin, and lead, or in other cases iron with friction-producing ceramics, such as silica, are used for brake and clutch linings.

Certain nuclear fuel element materials combine uranium oxide or carbide with metal.

In the appliance industry, P/M parts account for 16% of the P/M parts market. P/M parts are used in such appliances as mixers, blenders sharpeners, slicers, shredders, and grinders.

Business machine manufacturers are also extensive users of P/M parts.

Space does not permit the listing of the many parts made by this process, but there is no question that the number will increase tremendously.

---

* DeGroat, George, Special Report 594, *American Machinist,* October 24, 1966.

Unit 87. Powders

The most common compositions are iron base and copper base powders. Both materials lend themselves well to powder metallurgy. Iron base powders are used in small machine parts while bronze powders are used in porous bearings. Other types of powders in common use are stainless steel, nickel, aluminum, tin, tungsten, graphite, metallic oxides, and carbides.

In some instances pure metal powders are used for some products and in others, alloys. A fine and uniform alloy can be obtained by alloying the metal before it is converted to powder.

Alloyed powder can also be manufactured by mixing together powders containing the desired ingredients.

Powders are usually produced according to such specifications as compressibility, particle size, size distribution, shape, flowability, and apparent density.

Compressibility is quite important in a powder because it is the amount that a powder will compress or increase in density at some designated pressure, the standard pressure being 30 tons per square inch. The better the compressibility, the better the powder, from the manufacturer's point of view. Manufacturers are interested in softer powders that can be pressed to a high density at ordinary briquetting temperatures.

The physical characteristics of powdered metal are quite important. A distribution of particle size is normally desirable.

Consistency of a powder is necessary to insure uniformity of pressing and reduce dimensional changes during sintering.

Particle size distribution is the amount of each standard particle size in the powder and the *size distribution* is tested by screen analysis during the manufacturing process. Powder that does not meet specifications can be milled or ground to the proper size, or size fractions may be separated and reblended in the correct proportions.

The *shape* of a powder is dependent largely on the manufacturing process. The shape might be flat, angular, spherical, or dendritic. Reduction of oxide produces an irregular-shaped or sponge powder. The shape of the powders can affect the flow rate of the powder into the cavity and also the apparent density.

Particle shape has a considerable effect on the way a powder reacts under pressure. Particles with an irregular shape interlock under presure to form a strong unsintered part. Spherical powders are dependent upon cold welding for green strength.

The *flowability* of a powder is important because the ability of the powder to flow readily under pressure controls the rapidity of the pressing cycle.

Apparent density is the density of unpressed powders expressed in pounds per cubic inch. Compressibility of average powders yields densities of 6.1 to 6.2 gm/cc (grams per cubic centimeter) at pressures of 25 to 35 tons per square inch. A relatively hard powder would require 50 tsi to achieve this density.

Soft steel powders have been developed that have a compressibility permitting densities of 92% to 94% of theoretical maximum with a single pressing. The surfaces of these products can be plated, carburized, or otherwise treated. Parts weighing up to 10 pounds have been made from this powder on ordinary presses without excessive pressures.

High densities can also be obtained with ultra-fine powders, resulting in a great increase in the high-temperature strength of the base metal.

PRODUCTION METHODS OF POWDERS

Powder production methods are somewhat complicated by the fact that there is no such thing as a standard metal powder. This is due to the fact that no two manufacturers use the same method of manufacture.

The most common methods of producing powders are: (1) reduction of oxides and ores, (2) electrolytic deposition from solutions or fused salts, (3) atomizing, (4) mill grinding, and (5) thermal decomposition of carbonyls. There are other processes used on a limited basis, such as precipitation, shotting, granulation, and condensation of metallic vapors. Shotting is the operation of pouring molten metal through a sieve or orifice and cooling by dropping into water. A few metals can be converted into small particles by rapidly stirring the metal while it is cooling.

The *reduction* method is commonly used to produce iron, cobalt, nickel, tungsten, and molybdenum powders. This process is economical.

The *electrolytic decomposition* process is commonly used for the production of copper, iron, tantalum, and silver powders. This method ordinarily requires further processing by grinding the material.

Brass and bronze powders are produced by the *atomizing* proc-

87–1. Light weight, corrosion resistance, high strength, and good ductility are some of the advantages of these aluminum powder metal (P/M) parts.

Aluminum Co. of America

ess. A fine stream of molten metal is broken up with a jet of air. A high velocity flame can also be used to melt and atomize the material simultaneously. Iron and steel powders can be produced by *mill grinding*.

Many special techniques have been developed in the production of powders. One of these involves mixing near-molecular-scale sizes of individual oxides. The total mixture is then reduced to a metallic form, or certain of the oxides can be reduced on a selective basis, leaving other oxides in their natural state. This technique was developed by the Lockheed Missile and Space Company.

Another method of producing powders is the plasma jet proc-

ess. By this method, homogeneous mixtures can be formed directly into dispersion strengthened alloys.

Another development in powder production is high-velocity impacting. This process pulverizes either ductile or brittle metals into very fine particles, free from contamination or the effects of heat generation previously associated with mechanical pulverizing.*

ALUMINUM POWDER

One of the outstanding characteristics of aluminum powder, in comparison to common metal

---

* George DeGroat, "What's New in Powder Metallurgy," *American Machinist,* McGraw-Hill Book Co., October 24, 1966.

powders, is its ability to be compressed. Aluminum powders can be compacted to 90% theoretical density in a pressure of 12 tsi. In other metal powders 50 tsi are required to obtain densities near 90%.

Aluminum powder metal (P/M) parts also offer these advantages not available in parts produced from other commonly used powders: (1) lightweight, (2) corrosion resistant, (3) high strength, (4) good ductility, (5) nonmagnetic properties, (6) conductivity (except coppers), (7) variety of finishes, and (8) comparative costs on a volume per pound basis are competitive with many iron powders and enjoy a cost advantage over copper powders. 87–1 & 87–2.

Aluminum alloys can be made in both pre-alloyed or blended powder forms.

Lower compacting presses can be used for blended forms of powders, with improved sintering, making this process preferable.

Additions of magnesium, copper, silicon, and zinc will produce excellent sintered structures. These solid-solution strengthening elements can be added in combination or individually.

The automobile industry is by far the largest consumer of precision aluminum P/M parts. Many auxiliary components such as distributors, windshield wipers, knobs, latches, and switches can be made from aluminum powders.

Aluminum alloys can be machined to a smooth surface at high cutting speeds.

87–2. The addition of aluminum to the rapidly growing P/M industry offers designers and engineers a range of metal characteristics never before possible in P/M parts. In effect, it provides a completely new dimension in design—with the advantages of aluminum.

Aluminum Co. of America

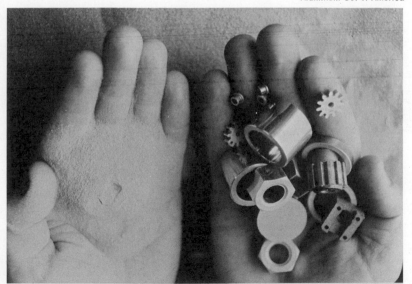

Unit 88. Producing the Part

Powder metallurgy parts are produced in three basic steps: (1) blending, (2) compacting, and (3) sintering. 88–1.

BLENDING

Blending consists of mixing the metal powder with lubricants and, usually, with alloying elements as well.

It is necessary to weigh the material to the correct proportions by mixing it into a homogeneous blend. When the part to be processed uses only one powder and the particle size is correct, no further blending or processing is necessary.

When the powders are alloyed or when nonmetallic powders are added, mixing or blending becomes necessary. The mixing can be done either wet or dry.

To obtain better mixing and to reduce dusting, water or solvent is added to the mix. In order to reduce die wall friction and aid in the ejection of the finished part, most powders have lubricants added during the blending operation.

Increased production rates are obtained and the lubricant is a necessity when using an automatic powder fill. These lubricants may be powdered graphite, stearic acid, or lithium stearate. Flow characteristics of the powder and reduction of die wear are improved with lubricants.

COMPACTING

Compacting consists of automatically filling a die cavity with the required amount of blended powder and then compressing it between punches. 88–2. The required pressure and production rate will vary with the shape, size, and specified density of the part.

The principal steps in the compacting process are as follows: (1) filling the die cavity with powder, (2) compacting or pressing (which may include several press actions), and (3) ejection of the finished part. 88–3.

The first step requires a powder which flows freely and has a very consistent apparent density of loose powder. The mass of powder that fills the die depends upon this. Green density of the part is the density *after* it has been pressed, but before it has been put through the sintering process.

In operation the powder is fed by feeders. There are three basic types of feeders used:

1. The type which provides straight reciprocating action, the

88–1. Diagram of powder metallurgy process.

Powder Metallurgy Parts Mfg. Assn.

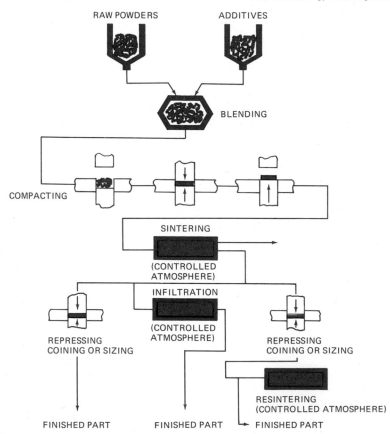

RAW POWDERS   ADDITIVES

BLENDING

COMPACTING

SINTERING

(CONTROLLED ATMOSPHERE)

INFILTRATION

(CONTROLLED ATMOSPHERE)

REPRESSING COINING OR SIZING

REPRESSING COINING OR SIZING

RESINTERING (CONTROLLED ATMOSPHERE)

FINISHED PART   FINISHED PART   FINISHED PART

feed shoe being connected directly to the hopper.

2. A type which pivots from a point on a die table to a position over the die. Agitation aids in filling the die cavity.

3. In some cases a shuttle feeder located under the hopper moves to a position over the die and deposits the correct amount of powder in the die cavity.

The press tooling determines the shape of the compacted part. The vertical dimensions are controlled by upper and lower punches while the die cavity configuration determines the lateral dimensions of the part. Core rods are used to produce holes in the part.

High pressures are required in the compacting process, resulting in considerable wear on the die walls. The dies are usually made of hardened tool steel to resist the abrasive action of the powder particles. For high-production work where highly abrasive powders are used, cemented carbide dies are sometimes employed.

In the compaction process, as the upper punch enters the die and compression of the powder begins, the density of the powder increases at the face of the upper punch. Friction is originated between the partially compacted powder and the walls of the die.

As parts become more complicated, involving different thicknesses, additional press or tool actions are necessary to maintain constant density. A two-level part must be compressed to different degrees at the two levels if uniform density is necessary, because lateral powder flow is very limited. Uniform density is im-

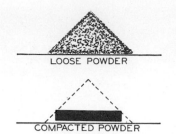

88-2. Loose powder and the same powder after compacting.

portant to insure dimensional stability during sintering.

SINTERING

The most critical stage in powder metal fabrication is the sintering process. The increased usage of sintered metal for applications which require properties comparable to forged, cast, or wrought steel makes control of sintering time, temperature, and atmosphere very important.

Sintering is an operation carried out in powder metallurgy whereby a "green compact" is heated to an elevated temperature.

Sintering is done below the melting point of the powder, which is usually from 60% to 80% of the melting temperature. In this operation the particles are fused together so that the density of the part is increased.

Some parts being sintered may be composed of more than one material. In this case the sintering temperature may be above the melting point of some of the ingredients. When the proper temperature is obtained, diffusion occurs and the particles of powder form a single solid mass.

Sintering time ranges from 20 to 40 minutes, depending upon

the material being sintered. The temperature can range from 1600° F. for copper, 2000° F. for iron, to 2700° F. for tungsten carbide.

The lubricants added to the powders to provide die lubrication are of no value in obtaining good bonding. These lubricants have a tendency to interfere with good sintering and must be expelled before the parts reach the high temperature portion of the furnace.

This is accomplished by providing burn-off chambers to burn off the lubricants before the part reaches the high-heat part of the furnace. The flow of atmosphere is always important in the sintering operation. When the burn-off chamber is attached to the high-heat sintering furnace, sufficient atmosphere gas must be provided and the vapors discharged away from the high-heat zone.

Protective atmosphere gases are used to help reduce surface oxides on powder particles and promote the proper fusion. 88-4 (Page 458). These gases may be

88-3. Press arrangement for compacting the metal powder.

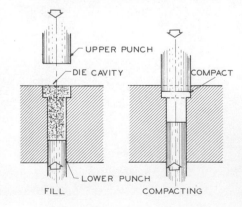

457

hydrogen dissociated ammonia or rich endothermic gas.

The illustration shows a high-temperature furnace for sintering stainless steel compacts. 88–5. A dissociated ammonia atmosphere sinters the parts at temperatures up to 2400° F. The parts are pushed through the furnace on ceramic slabs.

Iron powder metal parts normally are sintered in furnaces operating at lower temperatures and move the parts through the furnace on metal belts. 88–6. These belts could not withstand the temperatures employed for sintering stainless steels.

The careful control of atmospheres and temperatures is particularly important for sintering furnaces. Most furnaces are semi- or fully continuous. These furnaces may either be the mesh-belt, mechanical-pusher, or roller-hearth type. They are provided with several chambers for heating and cooling in separate stages.

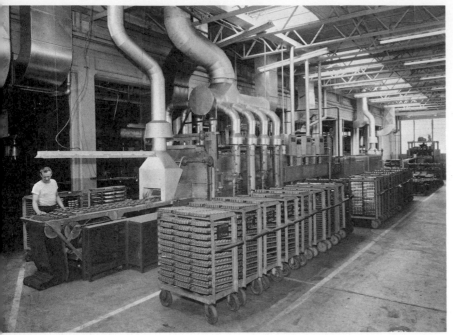

Hallar Div., Federal-Mogul Corp.

88–4. Standard type of sintering furnace with controlled endothermic atmosphere.

88–5. Furnace for sintering stainless steel compacts.

Sintered Specialties Div., Panoramic Corp.

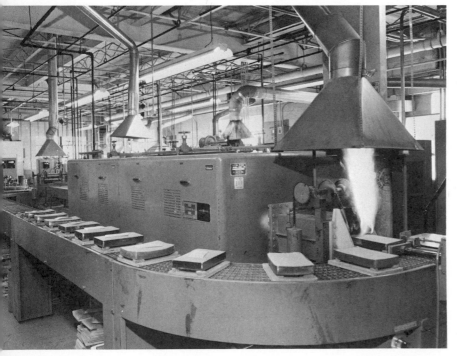

88–6. Standard sintering furnace with gears undergoing simultaneous sintering and copper infiltrating. Note continuous steel-mesh belt conveyor.

Hallar Div., Federal-Mogul Corp.

The future of powder metallurgy lies in the direction of high-strength parts made of 4600 and 8600 series steels. To achieve this goal, furnaces must be improved to sinter the alloys at temperatures above 2100° F. Improvement will have to include better materials for conveyor belts, rollers and other moving devices to withstand higher sintering temperatures.

Spark Sintering

Spark sintering employs a process that combines electrical energy and mechanical pressure to convert metal powder into a solid part of the desired configuration and density.* 88–7.

As previously stated in the conventional method of producing P/M parts, pressing and sintering are performed as two separate operations. Spark sintering combines them into one operation.

The process employs a combination of alternating and direct currents which are passed through the powder material enclosed within a die body. At the same time the powder is subjected to compacting pressure; compacting punches also serve as electrodes.

The parameters of AC current and/or voltage, DC current and/or voltage, and compacting pressure can all be varied independently with time, depending upon the size, shape of the part being made, the material of which it is

* R. W. Boesel, M. I. Jacobsen, I. S. Yoshicka, Lockheed Missiles and Space Co., *Materials Engineering*, October, 1969, issue.

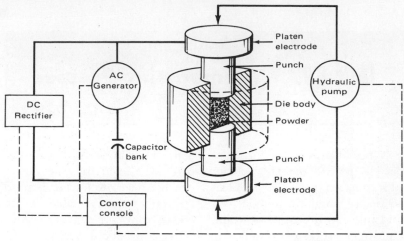

Lockheed Missile & Space Co.

88–7. Spark sintering combines electrical energy and mechanical pressure to simultaneously press and sinter metal powders.

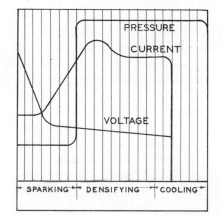

REPRESENTATIVE VALUES
FOR 10 CU.IN. PART

MAX. VOLTAGE	15 VOLTS
MAX. CURRENT	1500 AMPERES/IN.^{2}
MAX. PRESSURE	2,000 PSI
CYCLE TIME	4 MINS.

88–8. Cycle parameters.

constructed, the density, and other properties desired. 88–8. See the illustration.

Tooling can be specially developed materials or graphite and the process can be carried on in air, in a vacuum, or in an inert atmosphere.

The illustration shows a large copper powder ring, an ECM electrode for machining a titanium part produced by the Lockheed Missiles and Space Company. 88–9. This spark sintered copper cathode for ECM is one of the largest intricate copper P/M parts ever made.

88–9. Spark sintered ECM electrode for machining a titanium part is an example of economics inherent in spark sintering.

Lockheed Missile & Space Co.

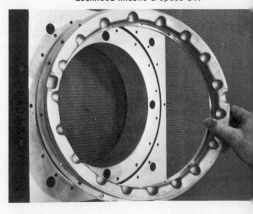

Pennwalt Corp.

89–2. A 20-ton, dual-motion, die set press.

Types of presses used in compacting powder metals include: (1) single-action, (2) double-action, (3) multiple-motion, (4) multiple-motion opposed ram, and (5) rotary compacting presses.

Single-action presses include a die to form the outer contour of the part, an upper punch, a lower punch, and may also include a core rod to form any through holes. 89–1. During the pressing action, the die and lower punch remain stationary. The upper punch compresses the powder against the stationary lower punch and inner surface of the die. Ejection of the green compact can be accomplished by the lower punch raising the part, or the die can be lowered from the part.

Double-action presses apply the forces from opposite direc-tions simultaneously. 89–2. The part is ejected by the lower punch which pushes the part to the top of the die table. These presses can have either mechanical or hydraulic drives.

Multiple-motion presses are used to produce powder parts with more than one level. 89–3. These presses have two or more motions in either top action, bottom action, or both.

The 50-ton Stokes multiple-motion press shown in the illustration has two upper and three lower compacting motions with underfill or resistance pressing controls. 89–4. A third lower motion is used as a stationary, movable, or ejecting core rod; a resistance motion; or a third lower punch, simply by position-ing a selector switch and se-quence dials at the control panel. 89–5.

On *rotary presses* multiple sets of identical tools are mounted on a rotary table. 89–6. The feeding device is in a stationary position and the tools rotate under it. Cams and rolls give pressing and ejection action.

The rotary press in the illus-tration has twenty-three die sta-tions with a maximum pressure of 15 tons on both the upper and lower punch. 89–7 (Page 462). The maximum depth of fill is 1⅜″ with a die diameter of 1⅛″. Compacts per minute are 240 to 720.

Some machines contain as many as fifty sets of punches and dies. For parts with through holes a core rod is used. Gener-ally the rod is raised by means of special camming during ejec-tion. Before scrape-off, it is re-turned to the fill position.

Positive filling action provides for overfill and underfill arrange-

89–1. Schematic of single-action P/M compacting press. A die forms the outer shape of the part; an upper punch and power punches form top and bottom surfaces of the part. An upper punch compacts powder in downward direction only.

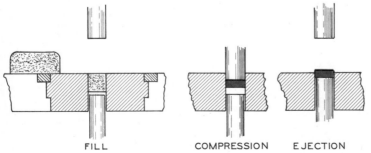

FILL   COMPRESSION   EJECTION

Pennwalt Corp.

89–3. A 50-ton multiple-motion press—three lower motions and two upper motions.

89–4. The operation of a multiple-motion, powder metal press.

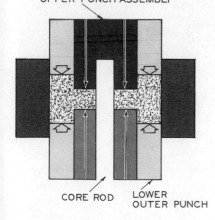

UPPER PUNCH ASSEMBLY

CORE ROD   LOWER OUTER PUNCH

GREEN COMPACT

ments. This action assures that the die is completely filled and results in more uniform parts.

Most compacts require additional pressing operations after initial pressing and sintering, either to increase the density or to secure dimensional tolerances.

REPRESSING

In the repressing operation the pressures used are so high that in most cases they equal the original briquetting pressure. Along with the increase in density will come increased strength and smooth surface finish. The parts are also easier to heat treat and plate. Ductility of parts is usually decreased and the parts have a lower impact strength. The same die is used as in briquetting. Prior to repressing, the parts are lubricated with zinc stearate, molybdenum, or other lubricant.

SIZING

Sizing is done for the purpose of qualifying dimensions. The pressures are usually less than those on the first pressing opera-

tion. The sized part will be straighter, dimensional tolerances will be better, and surface finish will be improved. In this operation, the parts are lubricated with either zinc stearate, oil, or molybdenum disulfide.

COINING

Coining is a pressing operation by which a specified surface

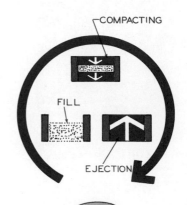

COMPACTING

FILL

EJECTION

COMPLETED PART

Pennwalt Corp.

89–6. Diagram shows the sequence of operation of a rotary, 15-ton P/M press.

89–5. Shows the multiple-motion compacting principle. Parts of more than one level are produced on this type press. Separate punches are used for each level of the part.

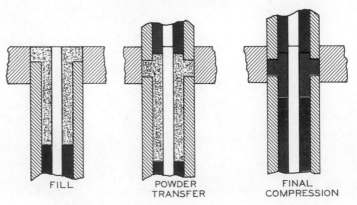

FILL   POWDER TRANSFER   FINAL COMPRESSION

Pennwalt Corp.

89–7. A 20-ton, P/M rotary press.

geometry is formed on the part. 89–8. Coining may be used to raise an embossment on the surface or to form raised or indented letters or numbers on a P/M part. In this process the pressures are quite high because the metal is forced to flow and is cold-worked. Lubricants are also used in this operation.

MACHINING

One of the advantages of the P/M process is the fact that machining processes are eliminated to a large degree. 89–9. There are, however, many parts which require some secondary operations. Some configurations such as re-entrant angles, threads, undercuts, and angular grooves must be machined. Holes that are at right angles to the pressing operation must be drilled on a machine. 89–10.

INFILTRATION

Infiltration is a process used to eliminate the residual porosity that sometimes occurs after compacting and sintering. The absence of metal and the stress-raising action of the pores impair the mechanical properties of porous metals.

Porous metal can be infiltrated with another metal of lower melting point. The molten metal penetrates the pores and is absorbed by capillary action to frequently increase the strength by 70% to 100%. The process is carried out by a heat treatment method with temperatures close to the sintering temperature. This

89–8. Typical coining press. This secondary operation also sizes the transmission gear O.D. and I.D. Safety features evident are safety glasses, shortened shirt sleeves, and wrist shackles. Two-handed tripping is required to activate the press.

Hallar Div., Federal-Mogul Corp.

89–9. Besly double-spindle grinder (grinding faces of powder metal pressure plates).

Hallar Div., Federal-Mogul Corp.

1-INCH GRID

Hallar Div., Federal-Mogul Corp.

89–10. Typical P/M parts. These happen to be transmission gears with end use in automotive, industrial consumer areas.

operation partially hardens the part and serves to drive out volatile materials.

NEW TECHNIQUES

Slip Casting

Slip casting is a method used to manufacture complex shapes from various powdered metals.

The powder is mixed with a liquid vehicle. It is then poured into a mold made of porous material that absorbs the liquid, leaving a product conforming to the shape of the mold, similarly to any casting process. After drying, the green part is ready for sintering.

Isostatic Pressing

In isostatic or hydrostatic pressing, high pressures can be secured to obtain uniform density of the powder during the compacting process. The material to be compacted is put in a flexible mold. The medium is a gas in isostatic pressing and a liquid in hydrostatic pressing.

Pressure applied to the medium acts equally on all areas of the mold, compacting the material equally from all sides. The material takes the form of the mold but is pressed to dimensions proportionate to the pressure applied and the compression ratio of the material.

Internal cavities are made by a metal core or mandrel. The assembly is placed in a pressure vessel, which is the heart of the isostatic system.

Powder metals that have been compacted by this method include aluminum, berylium, magnesium, brass, tungsten, iron, titanium carbide, and stainless steel.

Check Your Knowledge

1. Explain the powder metallurgy process.

2. Why has the powder metallurgy process become so important to the metalworking industry?

3. What are some of the requirements of a good powder?

4. Name some of the most common methods of producing a powder.

5. What types of powders are produced by the reduction method?

6. Why are powders mixed and blended before pressing?

7. Why is it that there is no such thing as a standard metal powder?

8. What is the outstanding characteristic of aluminum powder?

9. Name three methods of producing a part by the powder metallurgy process.

10. Explain the compacting process.

11. What is green density?

12. Name three basic types of feeders.

13. At what temperature is sintering usually done?

14. Why are lubricants added to the powder?

15. Why are protective atmosphere gases used in the sintering process?

16. What improvements have to be made in equipment to produce high strength parts made of 4600 to 8600 steels?

17. Name some types of compacting presses.

18. Name two repressing operations.

19. What is the infiltration process and for what is it used?

20. What is isostatic molding and what advantages are claimed for this process?

References

Boesel, R. W.; Jacobsen, M. I.; and Yoshicka, I. S., "Spark Sintering Tames Exotic P/M Materials," *Materials Engineering,* New York, Reinhold Publishing Corp., October, 1969.

DeGroat, George, "What's New in Powder Metallurgy," *American Machinist,* October 24, 1966.

Tsukerman, S.A., *Powder Metallurgy,* New York, Pergamon Press, Inc., 1965.

"The World of Powder Metallurgy," *Machine Tool Bluebook,* Hitchcock Publishing Co., September, 1969.

Aluminum P/M parts have good conductivity

Aluminum's excellent electrical and thermal conductivity permits aluminum P/M parts to be used in scores of applications where high thermal or electrical transfer properties are required.

Section Twenty-One

Polishing and Finishing Metals

A metal form may have been produced by machining, casting, forging, and other methods. These processes produce different surfaces, and one (or more) subsequent operation is generally required to produce a desired surface. These treatments may be decorative or protective and usually serve to enhance the saleability of the products.

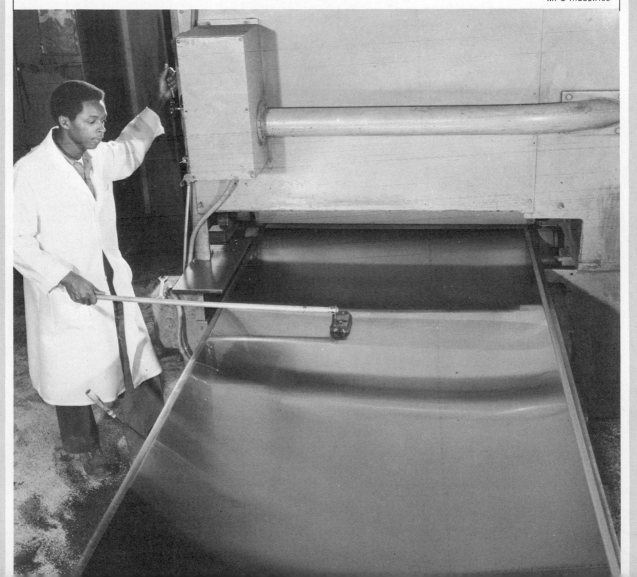

90–3. Cutaway view of blast wheel.

Unit 90.

Cleaning and Smoothing Methods

ABRASIVE CLEANING

One of the first steps in preparing a product for a protective or decorative surface treatment is the removal of sand—in the case of castings—or scale from metal parts. Scale is usually produced on a part when the metal has been heated to elevated temperatures, as in forging or heat-treating operations. These parts are generally cleaned by the use of abrasive particles, such as sand, steel grit, or shot, impelled against the surface to be cleaned.

Some cleaning is accomplished by means of a high-velocity air blast, with the blast directed by hand, as is frequently done when large parts are to be cleaned. In this manual operation, protection is provided for the operator who generally works in a separate and well-ventilated room or booth as a protection against the resulting dust.

One company produces an airless blast machine that cleans by impact. 90-1. It utilizes radial and tangential forces of a rapidly rotating wheel to hurl metallic shot or grit in a controlled stream upon the work to be cleaned. A conveyor gently tumbles the work and uniformly presents all surfaces to the abrasive blast. Upon completion of cleaning, the conveyor is simply reversed and the cleaned work is discharged from the mill. 90–2.

90–1. A 28-cubic-foot model of a Super Tumblast used for blast cleaning.

90–2. Surface of shot-peened steel. Magnification of photo seven times.

In this process, the abrasive is fed from an overhead storage hopper to the center of the wheel, whereupon it is hurled, under perfect control, upon the work to be blasted. 90–3. The blast utilizes all the power supplied by the machine. All traces of sand, scale, oxides, and other material are removed right down to the virgin metal, providing an excellent surface for bonding final finishes.

This airless blast machine is used for cleaning engine blocks, crankshafts, miscellaneous castings, railroad cars, car wheels, oil and gas pipe, steel strip, reconditioning metal products, core knockout, and many other purposes. 90–4.

TUMBLING

One of the most widely used methods of cleaning parts is a process known as tumbling. 90–5.

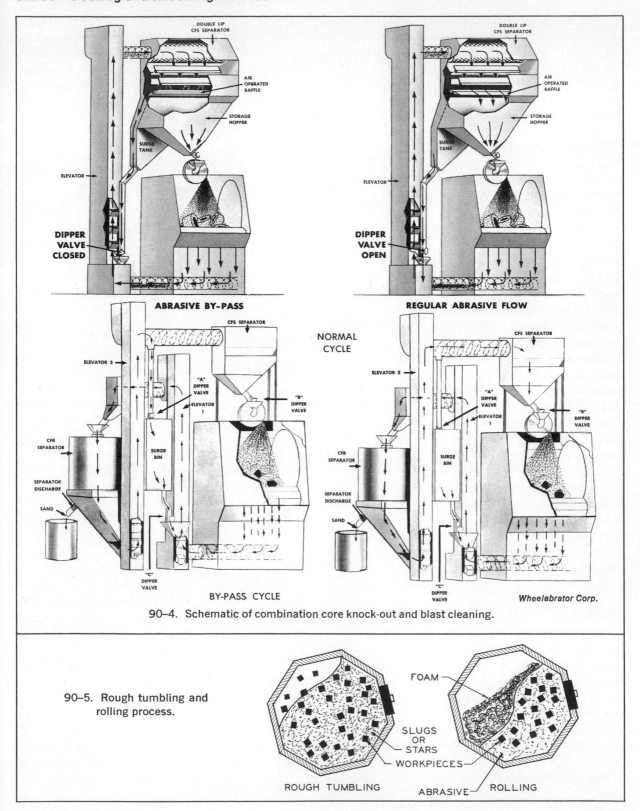

ABRASIVE BY-PASS   **REGULAR ABRASIVE FLOW**

BY-PASS CYCLE

Wheelabrator Corp.

90–4. Schematic of combination core knock-out and blast cleaning.

90–5. Rough tumbling and rolling process.

The operation is accomplished by placing workpieces in a drum or barrel, together with stars, jacks, slugs, or abrasive materials. The abrasive materials can be sand, granite chips, slag, or aluminum oxide pellets.

In operation, the barrel is rotated, and the movement of the workpieces and the accompanying slugs or abrasive material against each other produces a fine cutting action which removes the fins, flashes, and scale from the parts.

An amazing variety of parts can be tumbled successfully if careful attention is paid to a suitable selection of abrasive, fillers, careful packing of the barrel, and correct barrel size and speed.

Tumbling is an inexpensive method for cleaning parts. Care must be taken in the size and shape selection of the slugs so that they will reach into all sections and corners of the parts to be cleaned.

Loading and unloading should be arranged so that it can be accomplished readily. The slug material is generally separated from the workpieces by an arrangement that permits the slugs to drop through suitable grid tables.

BARREL ROLLING

Barrel rolling and tumbling are quite similar operations, except that the barrel is loaded only to 40–60% capacity, while in tumbling the drum is generally packed nearly full.

Rolling can be done by two methods: (1) in open, tilted barrels or (2) in closed, horizontal barrels. Abrasives, such as cinders, slag, granite chips, sharp sand, alundum, or carborundum, are placed in the barrel with the workpieces, along with water or a dilute acid solution. As the barrel turns, the mass is carried about three quarters of the distance up the side of the barrel and then rolls over and falls to the bottom of the barrel. This motion cuts down the surface of the parts. The parts are required to roll freely to provide the proper cutting action. Sometimes mineral matter or scrap punchings are added to the wet rolling. Hardwood dust or leather scraps are used in dry rolling to keep the workpieces separated.

Unit 91. Machine Polishing and Buffing

POLISHING

Polishing is usually undertaken to make metal smoother or to produce a more uniform surface. The amount and degree of polishing needed is determined solely by the characteristics of the metal surfaces. The rougher the metal to start with, and the finer the finish specified, the greater the required work will be. An additional determiner is the hardness of the metal itself; for instance, stainless steel is harder to finish than brass.

Another feature which has to be observed in the finishing of metal is whether the surface has hard or soft crystals. Care must be taken not to use methods which gouge out the soft crystals, leaving the hard areas high, thus producing a mottled effect.

As the polishing progresses, the roughness of the polishing materials must be decreased. Finer abrasives must be used.

Economical finishing requires a thorough understanding of polishing, buffing, burring, and the use of proper materials and equipment so that the desired surface can be produced with a minimum of work and waste.

Such operations are influenced by: (1) the metal itself, (2) the method and amount of forming, (3) the condition of the surface prior to finishing, and (4) the character of the surface finish desired.

Table 91 shows the distinguishing appearance of selected metal finishes.

BUFFING

The function of the buffing operation is to produce a smooth, uniform surface with a high, brilliant luster. 91–1. To do this, it is obvious that the abrading action must be reduced to a minimum. Therefore, a lubricant is usually blended with the abrasive particles.

Buffing can be divided into two operations: (1) cutting down and (2) coloring. The second operation—coloring—produces a high finish or luster. As

Table 91. Finish Appearances from Bright to Dull	
Mirror	No surface defects visible
Buffed bright	No surface defects visible but less brilliant
Bright satin	No surface defects visible but fine finishing lines show
Regular satin	No surface defects visible; heavier finishing lines
Satin	Some slight defects; heavy lines
Dull satin	Very heavy lines
Bright matte	Etched or frosted finish with some luster but no lines visible
Dull matte	Dead etched or frosted finish with no luster and no lines visible

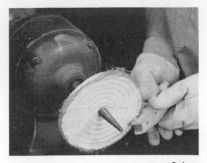

Sebree

91–2. Applying buffing compound to the wheel.

with polishing operations, many variations are obtainable, depending upon the grades of compound and the buffs used.

Hand buffing is still necessary for some operations. 91–2. With this method, the operator applies an abrasive bar against a rotating wheel. Automatic buffing requires piping and injection nozzles that throw the abrasive into the wheel. A timed cycle is generally used to squirt the abrasive on the wheel.

A newer system uses an airless, high-pressure abrasive with an independent air pump and thick compound ten times as viscous as conventional abrasive materials. 91–3. The compound is delivered to carbide nozzles at 2,000 psi in pulses. Older systems used a thinner abrasive solution that was wasted because so much of it flew away from the wheel before it got close to the work.

Semi-automatic machines are sometimes used. These machines carry a series of buffing wheels which can be adjusted to different positions so that all surfaces of the part can be buffed. The workpieces are fastened to a circular table by means of fixtures. The buffing wheels can be adjusted to different positions as the table rotates. The part moves

under the wheels for the buffing operation. It is not possible to buff parts with complex shapes on this machine.

A great deal of decorative finishing today is done by production methods on automatic buffing machines like those shown in the illustrations. 91–4. These machines are capable of providing: (1) improved finish and quality, (2) greater efficiency, (3) savings in time and labor, (4) uniformity of finish, and (5) automation. They are high-production machines which produce a consistently high-quality finish.

The buffing heads on these machines are selected to furnish the necessary contact time for

M & T Chemicals, Inc.

91–3. Automatic airless spray buffing system. Liquimatic buffing compound is sprayed onto buff face and sticks there with little or no overspray or throw-off by centrifugal force.

91–1. A smooth surface is given to the spoon handle with fine abrasive on a high-speed, revolving, buffing wheel.

International Silver Co.

91–4. Automatic buffing machine. The size of piece being processed determines the spacing of work spindles mounted in a conveyor carriage.

Harper Buffing Machine Co.

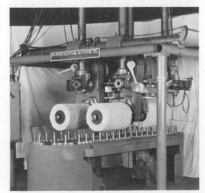

91-5. Automatic buffing machine. Straight travel of work as opposed to rotary travel assures constant, maximum, buffing-wheel performance.

Harper Buffing Machine Co.

Setco Industries

91-6. Large polishing lathe used in industrial applications.

91-7. Silverware that has been color buffed to bring out the beauty of the metal.

International Silver Co.

cut and/or color to finish the part to the necessary requirements. 91-5.

Conveyor size and type are governed by the number of heads needed to supply the wheel contact time required.

The compounds and wheels selected are governed by the geometry of the part, the material of which it is fabricated, and the appearance of the product desired.

For ordinary polishing and buffing operations, polishing and buffing wheels are mounted on floor polishing lathes. 91-6.

Color buffing is a finishing process used to bring out the color and luster, particularly on decorative and contoured parts, and can be done by hand. 91-7.

POLISHING AND BUFFING WHEELS

Polishing Wheels

Commonly used polishing wheels are constructed of canvas, muslin, felt, and leather.

In general, the more rigid polishing wheels are used when there is a need for rapid metal removal and where there are no contours and a flat surface is to be maintained. Conversely, softer polishing wheels are used when

there are irregularities in the surface and the fast removal of metal is not a prime requisite.

Felt polishing wheels are coated with hot glue and, when almost dry, they are rotated, scraped smooth, and shaped. 91-8. When the wheel is dry, it is recoated with hot glue or waterglass and, while it is wet, rolled in aluminum oxide abrasive. Silicon carbide abrasive may be preferred because of its faster cutting properties, but it does not bond as well to the conventional wheel.

Generally, the felt wheel is charged with No. 100 to 220 grit, depending upon the operation. Buffing tallow, oil, or beeswax will serve as a lubricant.

Buffing Wheels

Buffs are flexible wheels made of cotton cloth, canvas, linen, flannel, or wool discs. 91-9. Canton-flannel or wool-cloth buffs are used for high coloring on the noble metals (gold, silver, and platinum). In addition, loose buffs made of sheepskin can be used for final coloring of precious metals.

91-8. Felt polishing wheel.

91-9. Felt buffing wheels.

Frederic B. Stevens, Inc.

The material most widely used for buffs is muslin, bleached and unbleached, with thread counts up to 86 x 93. Higher-count sheeting is, of course, more expensive, but the greatly increased wearing quality makes buffs of this type more economical.

The high thread count buffs are used for heavy, hard service on brass, copper, or nickel-silver surfaces, as well as on heavy nickel stock.

POLISHING AND BUFFING COMPOUNDS

Polishing and buffing compounds, like wheels, are usually divided into two broad categories: (1) cutting down, the removing of scratches and grain lines from previous operations and (2) coloring, which gives the product the final, bright, deep luster.

Buffing compounds can either be greaseless or have a grease base. (Compounds that combine cut and color are usually medium to dry as far as greasiness is concerned.)

A mixture of glue base, a softening agent, and a mineral make up a greaseless compound. This generates a satin finish and is also used in cutting down prior to coloring. Sometimes a greaseless compound is followed by a cutting compound and then a coloring mixture. Many abrasive elements are used for the coloring compound, such as red rouge, green rouge, crocus, and white coloring compounds.

Grease buffing compounds use oil, tallow, and other bonds. The bonding material not only serves as a lubricant but also causes the abrasive to adhere to the wheel.

The selection depends upon the type of work to be done, the equipment available, and the finish required. For cutting operations, emery abrasive and tripoli do a good job.

POLISHING METALS WITH ABRASIVE BELTS

Coated abrasives have become a major production cutting tool for the polishing of metals in the modern metal industry. 91-10. Coated abrasive machines are of three types: (1) manually operated, (2) semi-automatic, and (3) fully automatic.

The versatility of coated abrasive belts and brushes is recognized by industry today. One very important benefit provided by abrasive belts is the quick change that is possible from a used belt to a new one, or from one grade to another. The belts used for polishing are coated with resins and hide glues, followed by either emery, flint, crocus, garnet, aluminum oxide, or silicon carbide.

Belts can be made in any desired length and range in width from ⅛" to 86". There are a few applications where the size of the workpiece prohibits the use of a belt. The belts ability to remove stock rapidly and produce fine finishes, plus its ability to produce a very fast and extremely cool cut, has led to the rapid development of coated abrasive machines. 91-11.

91-10. Fine abrasive belts are used to polish edge surfaces of spoons and all other articles of flatware to a smooth finish.

International Silver Co.

91-11. This planetary polishing machine consists of two abrasive belt heads which revolve as a unit around the work. The work does not rotate.

Murray-Way Corp.

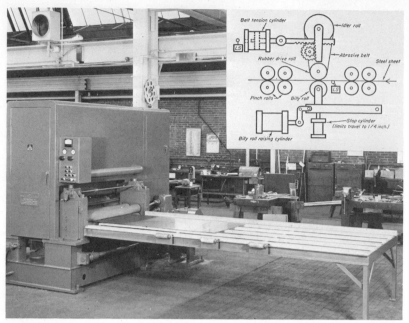

91–12. Pinch roll polishing and grinding machine.

Hill Acme Co.

There are many different machines made by manufacturers. The illustration shows a pinch roll machine which is designed for either single- or multiple-unit operation to produce highly polished surfaces on ferrous or nonferrous material. 91–12. Normal minimum length of the work material is 34″.

Two sets of vertically adjustable feed rolls, are built onto the "run-in" and "run-out" sides of the machine to carry stock under the abrasive belt polishing head. These rolls may be either plain or serrated rubber covered and are vertically adjustable. Power is delivered to the feed rolls through a six-speed transmission unit and gear boxes which produce stock feed from 20 to 70 fpm.

This machine can be used for polishing stainless steel, finishing photolithograph plates, sizing steel sheets for aircraft, and finishing aluminum sheet and plate.

The coiler type strip grinding and polishing machine is recommended for processing coiled strip material in either finishing or salvaging operations. 91–13.

The basic parts of this machine are all mounted on a heavy fabricated steel base and frame. A ten foot endless abrasive belt travels over a top steel idler roll and a lower rubber contact roll.

A billy roll, directly beneath the contact roll, exerts upward pressure against the work being processed.

A brake acting on an extension of the main drive spindle or motor automatically stops the rotation in case of belt breakage, preventing damage to the machine and to the work in process.

Steel or rubber covered guide rolls on the work in process provide an angle of "break" over the billy roll.

POWER BRUSH FINISHING

Power brushing methods are finding additional use as production tools for metal finishing operations. A major advantage of the power brush is that it can be

91–13. Strip or coiler type, abrasive belt, polishing and grinding machine.
Hill Acme Co.

Osborn Mfg. Co.

91–14. Removing scale from a heat-treated part with a power brush.

can be brushed, but proper brush selection depends upon hardness and electrolytic corrosion characteristics. There are many kinds of fiber brushes. Only fiber brushes are used for a relatively soft metal such as zinc. For stainless steel, aluminum, and magnesium, fiber brushes can be used alone or after previous wire brushing.

Wire wheel brushes are best for general purpose jobs and such metals as steel, stainless steel, nickel alloys, brass, bronze, and copper. 91–14.

Cord brushes are used with abrasive compounds for polishing, finishing, and burring metal parts.

Treated Tampico fiber brushes, used with abrasive compounds, are outstanding for removing burrs and tool marks and for blending junctures. In the latter stages of the polishing procedure,

Osborn Mfg. Co.

91–15. Power brushing has removed tiny burrs and polished an electric shaver head.

used in manual, semi-automatic, or integrated methods.

Polishing, as a part of the finishing process, has a double meaning. One meaning is broad: the preparation of any surface for further treatment. The other meaning is narrow and deals with the final preparation of the surface.

Two basic factors generally control the finish of any product: (1) the material being finished and (2) the selection of the proper power brush. It is generally known that a hard material such as steel will take a higher luster than a soft material such as aluminum. Treatments that affect the hardness of metal —such as drawing, rolling, and heat treating—have a bearing on the luster. Brushes are selected accordingly. The correct brush with the proper buffing compound is important for a good finish.

Many brushes are used for polishing metals. These include wire, fiber cord, and Tampico fiber brushes. All common metals

these brushes are used more like a buffing wheel in that the compound is applied loosely rather than as a fixed abrasive. 91–15.

The illustrations show what can be done by power brush finishing. 91–16.

91–16. Casing ring before and after power brushing.

Osborn Mfg. Co.

Unit 92.

Decorative and Protective Metal Finishes

CHEMICAL CLEANING

Before any finishing process can be employed, it is usually necessary to remove oil, dirt, and any foreign material from the part. The most widely used methods for doing this are: (1) vapor degreasing, (2) alkaline cleaning, and (3) emulsified solvent cleaning.

Vapor Degreasing

Vapor degreasing is a rapid method used on metals like aluminum and zinc which cannot be cleaned by alkaline cleaning. In this process a solution known as trichlorelylene is heated to its boiling point. A vapor is produced, and the parts to be cleaned are suspended in this vapor. The condensation of the vapor on the work removes all the grease and oil.

Alkaline Cleaning

In this process a bath is prepared from agents such as caustic soda or sodium metasilicate. These materials are added to some type of soap to aid in mulsification. The mixture produces an alkali which serves as the cleaning agent. Parts are thoroughly rinsed after cleaning. This process is used on all metals except zinc, lead, and aluminum.

Emulsified Solvent Cleaning

Solvent cleaning is used on such metals as zinc, lead, and aluminum since their surfaces might be attacked by alkaline cleaners.

In this process an organic solvent is mixed with a hydrocarbon-soluble emulsifying agent. The agent may be a soap and kerosene mixture with a small amount of water or a mixture of sulfonated castor oil and water. Cleaning is accomplished by dipping the part in the solution and then rinsing. Parts to be electroplated should be treated with an alkaline cleaner after the solvent cleaner to remove any organic material.

PICKLING

It is often necessary to remove oxides and rust from the surface of products. This is generally accomplished by dipping the product in a pickling solution of 10% sulfuric acid at temperatures of 150° to 185° F. Muriatic acid can also be used either hot or cold as a pickling solution. Alkaline cleaning of the part should be used first to remove all dirt and oil in order to obtain an even removal of the oxides during the pickling process. Sometimes it is necessary to add pickling inhibitors to decrease the action of the acid upon the metal.

After removal of the part from the pickling solution, a thorough rinsing is necessary to remove all traces of acid. To prevent rusting, the part is then dipped in a slightly alkaline bath.

ELECTROPLATING

Electroplating consists of covering by electro-deposit a surface or object (usually metallic) with a thin adherent coating of the same or other metal. The form and details of the original part are retained.

There are many electrolyte plating solutions. A different one is necessary for each type of metal plating. The electrolyte must contain a chemical compound of the metal, to be deposited on the surface of the part.

All electroplating is done with the use of direct-current electricity at low voltages. Proper current density, expressed in amperes per square foot, is important in obtaining smooth, dense deposits; thus, in addition to a rheostat for each tank, it is also desirable to have an ammeter and voltmeter in the line.

Preparation for Plating

Electro-deposited metal will adhere firmly only to a clean surface. Also, the deposited metal is a thin film that reproduces an almost precise image of the surface on which it is deposited, making a thorough cleaning even more necessary. All surface irregularities will be carried through to the finished product.

Therefore, operations of cleaning and polishing may involve one or both of the following steps: (1) removal of all oil, grease, or organic material and (2) removal of surface irregularities, scale, and oxides by pickling or by use of a file, abra-

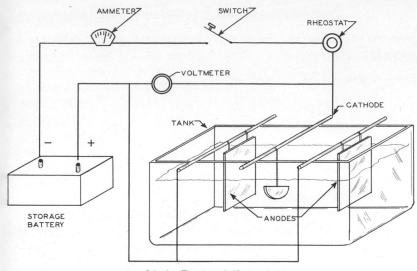

92–1. Electroplating setup.

sive wheel, wire brush, or polisher.

The illustration shows an electroplating setup. 92–1. The plating solution (electrolyte) is placed in the tank. The electrolyte contains some salt of the metal to be plated, and usually other salts, acids, or alkalies, to improve the action of the electrolyte.

The positive electrodes (anodes) of pure metal are suspended in the bath from suspension bars connected to the negative terminal. The object (cathode) to be plated is connected to the negative terminal and suspended in the plating bath.

As the current is passed through this circuit, metallic ions migrate to the cathode and, upon losing their charge, are deposited as metal upon it.

Copper Plating

Copper's role in the electroplating of metals in recent years is growing rapidly as the sustained shortage of nickel causes platers to turn to copper plating for leveling.

Nickel has been in short supply since 1964 and experts expect it to remain so for some time to come. The result of this has been a shortage and rising cost of decorative chromium plating using nickel.

Putting more copper instead of nickel under the chrome is a good method which platers recognize, and, on that basis alone, copper use is growing. But a bigger impetus is directed toward the use of new bright acid copper plating systems which produce a hard, ductile, bright deposit with excellent leveling ability to fill pores.

In light of these developments, experts see three main trends dominating copper plating technology: (1) all plating bath systems, bright acid, cyanide, and pyrophosphate, will improve and be in great use, (2) copper plating on plastics will become even more popular, and (3) new anodes and anode systems, which allow automatic feeding to maintain constant bath conditions, will be used more often.

The greater portion of copper plating is done in one or both of two baths—copper cyanide or an alkaline solution.

In depositing copper on an iron base, the plating solution will contain copper sulphate. Upon the addition of water, positive copper ions and negative sulphate ions are formed. When a direct current is passed through this bath, the copper ions will be attracted to the negative electrode—the workpiece—and the sulphate ions will be attracted to the positive electrode of pure copper. The positive copper ions obtain electrons from the workpiece, and neutral copper atoms are formed which adhere to the surface of the iron, forming a copper coat.

Copper coatings are now widely used as decorative finishes on a variety of plastics, providing a bright attractive finish coupled with the high ductility required by the differential plastic and metal expansion rates. 92–2.

92–2. This shower head is made from plastics and exhibits the excellent chromium plating that can be applied to copper coatings.

Amax Copper Co.

92–3. Silver plating. The forks rotate in a plating tank containing cyanide solution and bars of pure silver. The amount of electric current and length of time the pieces remain in the tank determine the amount of silver on each piece.

Copper is plated on plastics for two main reasons: (1) to form a decorative coating or (2) to provide electrical conductivity between components on printed circuit boards.

Plating plastics with copper deposits from 0.5 to 1.5 mils thick provides an adherent coating that is used on a number of different plastics and all sorts of parts from car instrument panels to kitchen appliances and from small boat fixtures to radio and television sets.

Bright acid copper provides a smooth, ductile, and bright copper deposit that can be a decorative final coating, provide an electrically conductive path on the plastic surface, form a good plastic-to-metal bond, and serve as a base for other metals, chiefly nickel and chromium.

The production of plated plastics was estimated at 5 million pounds in 1968 and that figure is climbing rapidly.

Silver Plating

Silver is seldom plated directly on steel. 92–3. Copper, is often used as an undercoat for subsequent silver plating. The first layer of copper plating, the strike, is not adherent but provides a displacement film of copper. The thickness of the strike ranges from 0.025 to 0.075 mil. It can be followed by either bright cyanide or bright acid plating to develop the full copper thickness.

If silver is to be directly plated on steel, the part is usually given a first strike in a solution containing less than 2 grams of silver per liter (0.2 ounces) per gallon followed by a second strike to build up the silver coating. Only one silver strike is necessary for silver plating brass, copper, nickel, and britannia metal.

Chrome Plating

Chrome plating is used when wear and abrasive resistant surfaces are desired. Coatings are seldom less than 0.002″ thick and may even be considerably thicker as conditions demand.

As a preliminary to chrome plating, an acid copper is used to provide a base for the chrome. 92–4. This procedure is widely used on steel parts such as bumpers for the automotive industry. The copper plating is used as a preplate for chromium because it provides a coating that fills most scratches and irregularities. It is relatively free from stress and is therefore ductile, adherent, and durable.

The electrolytic plating process is carried out by passing an electric current from an anode to a cathode (the car bumper or some other part to be plated) through a suitable electrolytic solution in the presence of a catalyst. The electrolyte is made up of a solution of chromic acid with a high degree of saturation. The surfaces of the work must be cleaned and polished before placing in the plating solution. It is necessary that the parts be kept in the plating tank for several hours because the rate of deposition is rather slow for heavy plating.

COLOR ANODIZING

This process gives intense chemical dye-coloring to aluminum. The article to be anodized is cleaned with an aluminum degreasing agent or a hot household detergent solution and rinsed in cold water.

A solution of sulfuric, oxalic, or chromic acid is used as an electrolyte. The workpiece is now the anode, and the process is somewhat the reverse of electroplating. Instead of simply adding the material to the surface as

92–4. A wide variety of cast metal parts are preplated with copper before final nickel and chromium coatings are applied.

with electroplating, the reaction progresses inward from the surface of the piece. This makes it a permanent part of the original base material. The process produces an oxide coating that is hard and porous.

The oxide coating provides a base which makes it possible for dyes to be applied to the surface of the aluminum. The dye is made by mixing commercial dyes in a proportion of 2 grams of dye per 1 liter of water. The dye solution is heated to 150° F. and the article is immersed in the solution for about 10 minutes. By varying the immersion time, lighter or darker shades can be obtained.

The article is rinsed in cold, running water after it is taken from the dye solution. The article is then sprayed with a clear metal lacquer, or a chemical sealing process is used to make the colors more permanent.

PROTECTIVE METAL FINISHES

Most metals will tarnish or oxidize when exposed to moisture and air. Silver, copper, and aluminum are no exceptions. It is therefore necessary to apply some protective coating to preserve the surface and finish. Among the many protective coatings are primers, metal fillers, enamels, and lacquers.

Primers

In order to secure the proper cohesion of most paints and enamels to metal surfaces, a primer has to be applied first. There are many types. Some are made especially for application to steel, such as on automobile bodies. These are lead primers. Zinc and lead chromate primers can be used on steel, zinc, and aluminum with satisfactory results.

Metal Fillers

Blemishes such as dents, pits, and tool marks may be filled with a metal filler after the primer has been applied. The fills can then be sanded smooth by hand or with a power sander, using No. 280 or 320 abrasive paper. This is done when repairing automobile bodies.

Metal Enamels

Enamels are used for decorating and protecting metal surfaces. They are highly durable and resistant to moisture. Enamels may be flat, semi-gloss, or gloss, depending upon the product and the finish desired. Today they are made from synthetic resins mixed with drying accelerators to facilitate the drying process. "Porcelain" enamels are baked on. A better job can be obtained by spraying than by brush application. Curing can be done in a kiln or oven.

Lacquers

Lacquers provide a hard, durable finish if a nonlacquer prime coat is first applied. A considerable amount of skill is required in their application. This finish uses a fast-evaporating solvent as a drying agent and carrying vehicle for pigments.

Lacquers provide a harder finish than most enamels and are more mar and abrasion resistant. They resist fading, wear, and most mild chemicals. Due to their fast drying characteristics, they are best applied by spraying.

MANUFACTURING PAINTING SYSTEMS

Industry uses four methods of applying paints and enamels to products: (1) hand spraying with spray guns, (2) automatic spraying, (3) electrocoating, and (4) dip painting. 92–5.

In all of these methods a prime coat is applied first, followed by a light sanding. The

92–5. Horizontal transverse automatic spray machine.

De Vilbiss Co.

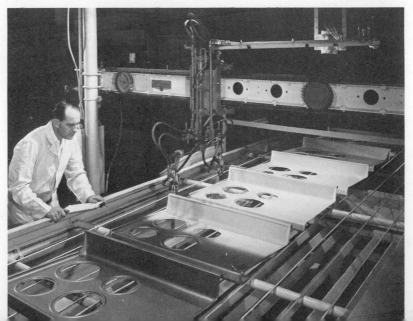

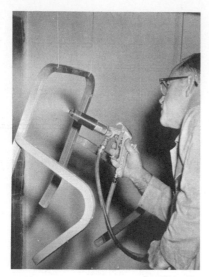

De Vilbiss Co.

92–6. Manual electrostatic paint spraying.

purpose of the prime coat is to obtain good cohesion of the metal for the finishes that are to follow. Small scratches and imperfections can also be filled in with the prime coat.

The *hand spraying* process is one that requires a great deal of skill by the operator to obtain proper coverage and build up the proper thickness of paint without obtaining "runs" or "drapes." 92–6. While this method is used to a great extent by industry and does produce good results with skilled operators, it is a costly operation due to high labor costs today.

The cost of spray-painting by industry can be reduced considerably by the use of *automatic spray-painting* equipment.

The automatic painting system can be advantageously used when the product design and volume of production warrants the purchase of this equipment.

In the automatic painting system, parts are carried on a chain conveyor past a series of sprayheads which are so arranged to give the proper paint coverage. Special spray-heads have to be used to reduce the wastage of paint, and touch-up is sometimes needed with a hand spray gun.

The most efficient method of automatic spray-painting, *electrocoating* is based on the electrostatic principle. 92–7. The product to be painted is an electrode of a high-voltage circuit. A grid, which is positioned close to and between the spray nozzles and the part, is used as the other electrode. A DC current is applied to the two electrodes, and the part is sprayed through the grid. The paint particles pick up ions and become charged electrostatically.

The work electrodes attack the charged paint particles and are deposited on the work. The efficiency of this method of spray-

painting is much higher than others.

One of the most economical methods of painting is *dip painting*. 92–8. In this method the product is dipped into the paint while moving on a conveyor. Some advantages are that dipping: (1) is an economical method, (2) can be used for complex shapes that would not be suitable for spray-painting methods, and (3) can be used for small parts without loss of paint, which might occur in spray-painting.

One of the disadvantages of this method is that the paint has a tendency to run downward, producing a somewhat wavy surface. With some products, such as farm implements, this is not a great disadvantage, but with other products it can make a difference.

GALVANIZING

Galvanizing is done by dipping low-carbon steel in molten

92–7. Electrostatic coating system.

De Vilbiss Co.

De Vilbiss Co.

92–8. Conveyorized dip coater.

zinc. First the metal is cleaned and usually fluxed by dipping the material in a solution of zinc chloride and hydrochloric acid. The metal is then ready to be dipped in the zinc bath. The zinc-coated material is rendered corrosion resistant by this process.

TIN COATING

Tin coating is usually applied to sheet steel by hot-dipping or by electrotinning.

In the first method, the tin coating is applied by dipping the material into molten tin at temperatures of approximately 600° F. which gives a coating about 0.0001″ thick.

With electrotinning, the metal is immersed in an electrolyte and a current is passed from the electrode to the metal part.

PARKERIZING

As mentioned before, most enamels and paints require a base or primer. Parkerizing is a process for placing a thin phosphate coating, which serves as a primer, on steel. The steel is dipped in a solution of manganese dihydrogen phosphate, which has a temperature of 190° F., and is held there for about 45 minutes.

Parkerizing is employed to provide corrosion resistance to metal surfaces. However, corrosion will occur after an extended period. Therefore, it is a good idea to apply paint to such surfaces after parkerizing to insure a long-lasting finish.

Check Your Knowledge

1. What is the purpose of abrasive cleaning?

2. What materials are used for abrasive blast cleaning?

3. Name one method used to impel the abrasive particles.

4. What is tumbling? Explain its uses.

5. Compare tumbling and barrel rolling operations.

6. Name two methods of barrel rolling.

7. Explain how the design of a workpiece can affect the various methods of surface finishing.

8. What elements affect the economical finishing of materials?

9. What is the function of a buffing operation?

10. Name two main buffing operations.

11. From what materials are buffing wheels made?

12. What type of abrasive is most commonly used on polishing wheels?

13. What is coloring as applied to buffing?

14. Why are most polishing operations done with abrasive belts today?

15. Name some advantages of the abrasive belt polishing method.

16. What is power brush finishing?

17. What are the advantages of power brush finishing?

18. Name three chemical cleaning methods.

19. Explain the vapor degreasing process.

20. What is the purpose of pickling?

21. What is the important factor in obtaining smooth, dense deposits in electroplating?

22. Explain the electroplating process.

23. Compare the process of copper plating with that of silver plating.

24. How does anodizing differ basically from the electroplating process?

25. Name three methods used by industry for applying paints and enamels.

26. What are some of the advantages of electrostatic painting?

27. What is the coating material used in the galvanizing process?

28. What is parkerizing?

Reference

American Society of Tool and Manufacturing Engineers, *Tool Engineers Handbook,* New York, McGraw-Hill Book Co., 1959.

Silverware that has been polished to a fine finish.

Section Twenty-Two

Recent Techniques in

Metalworking

Bendix Automation & Measurement

Unit 93. Chemical Milling

Chemical milling is an important process used to shape metals to an exacting tolerance by the chemical removal of metal or deep etching of parts, rather than by conventional mechanical milling or machining operations.

The chem-mill process permits the fabrication of lightweight, high-strength parts, which were heretofore either too expensive or impossible to manufacture, using the most modern machine tools available.

Chem-milling and machine milling have one thing in common: both are basic production methods of removing metal. However, the two techniques are so different that neither one entirely replaces the other.

Mechanical methods of removing metal are limited to the removal of metal from simple planes. 93–1. In the chemical method, however, metal can be removed from all surfaces of the entire part at one time and also from the most complex surfaces.

Chemical milling was used extensively in the fabrication of Apollo and Saturn hardware in the space program. The Apollo command module, which made the journey to the moon and back, met all the requirements for lightweight strength through the chemical milling process.

The basic chemical application has three uses: (1) *weight removal,* (2) *cutting,* and (3) *tapering*. The most important of the three is weight reduction.

While chemical milling was previously limited to shallow cuts on thin sheets, work is now being done on "gore segments" of 33′ diameter, fuel-and-oxidizer-tank bulkheads, where depths of cut by etching exceed ½″. Stainless steel parts are chemically milled to tolerances of plus or minus 0.001″ on a production basis.

THE PROCESS

In this process the entire part is cleaned to remove all dirt and grease. The part is generally degreased with trichlorethylene, alkalined for 15 minutes in aviation cleaner, and rinsed for 5 minutes at 110° to 120° F. Next it is deoxidized for 10 minutes in a chromic deoxident, rinsed, and dried.

Technicians then apply a rubber coating material (maskant) to the part. 93–2. The maskant is applied by "flow coating," to obtain a uniform film of controlled thickness. Large parts are masked by using electro-spraying, which produces a smooth uniform coating. Maskants are also applied by airless spraying.

The part is then cured for 1 hour at 210° F.

A template is placed on the part, and areas to be exposed to the etch are scribed by trained workers using scribing tools to remove the cured rubber coating only in areas to be milled. 93–3.

93–1. This aluminum forging was chemically milled to reduce web thickness and save weight.

North American Aviation, Inc.

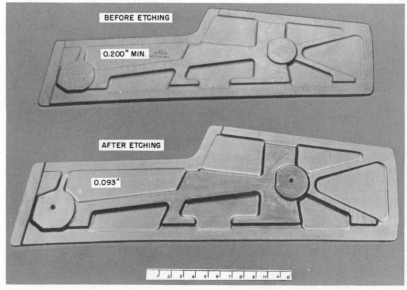

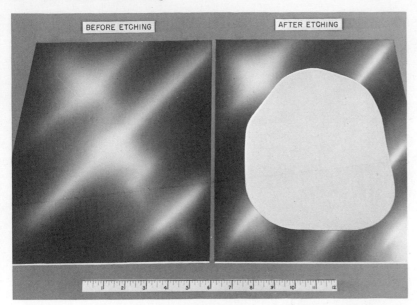

BEFORE ETCHING AFTER ETCHING

Automation Industries, Inc.

93–2. This illustration shows a part covered by maskant before etching and after the part has been chem-milled.

Automation Industries, Inc.

93–3. Trained workers follow formed pattern tools with scribing instruments, taking care to remove cured rubber coating only in areas to be milled.

93–4. Part being lowered into caustic etchant to be chem-milled.

Automation Industries, Inc.

Next the part is lowered into the caustic etchant at 195° F. long enough to dissolve (etch) the indicated metal. 93–4. Temperature control is maintained thermostatically.

Due to the fact that the etchant removes metal at an equal rate in all directions, the maskant must extend onto the etch area for a distance equal to the total depth of the etched portion. The allowance is the "eat-back." 93–5 (Page 484).

After rinsing in cold water, the part is lowered into a solvent tank which releases the maskant bond. The maskant is then stripped off.

To brighten, the part is dipped in chromic deoxident for 3 to 5 minutes and rinsed. The part is then dried in an oven.

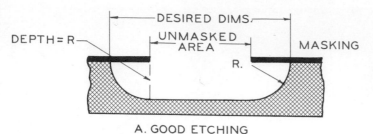

A. GOOD ETCHING

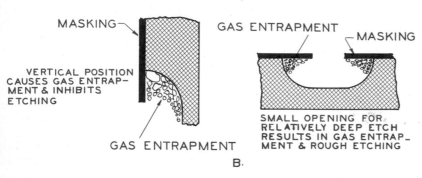

B.

93–5. (A) Chemical milling eats back under maskant just as far as it etches down into metal. Allowances must be made in the template to allow for eat-back. (B) Undesirable etching conditions.

North American Aviation, Inc.

93–7. Close tolerances may be held in chemical milling.

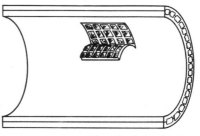

Automation Industries, Inc.

93–8. Thin web sections can be produced by chemical milling.

93–6. The part after etching has taken place. Note the smooth finish and the sharpness of the etch.

North American Aviation, Inc.

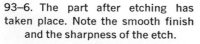

If the part is to be etched at several depths, the maskant is removed from the deepest part first and other areas are unmasked at the time intervals proportionate to the differences in depth. 93–6. After the part has been etched, it is given a final inspection.

ADVANTAGES OF CHEMICAL MILLING

● A part may be chemically milled on both sides simultaneously.

● Production capacity is increased since many parts can be chemically milled at the same time.

● Close tolerances may be held. 93–7.

● Using this process, parts may be produced with thin web sections without fear of excessive warpage or distortion. 93–8.

● Various tapers may be made on one or both sides of a part. 93–9.

● With chemical milling, a casting can be designed uniformly oversized, heat-treated with little or no warpage and then chemically milled to achieve the desired final dimensions. 93–10. Many times the resultant surface finish can be reduced from over 200 rms to 40–66 rms.

93–9. Parts may be tapered by the chem-mill process.

Automation Industries, Inc.

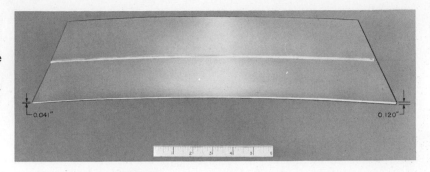

93–10. Comparison of machine milled and chem-milled surfaces.

Automation Industries, Inc.

CHEM-MILLED

MACHINE-MILLED
POLISHED

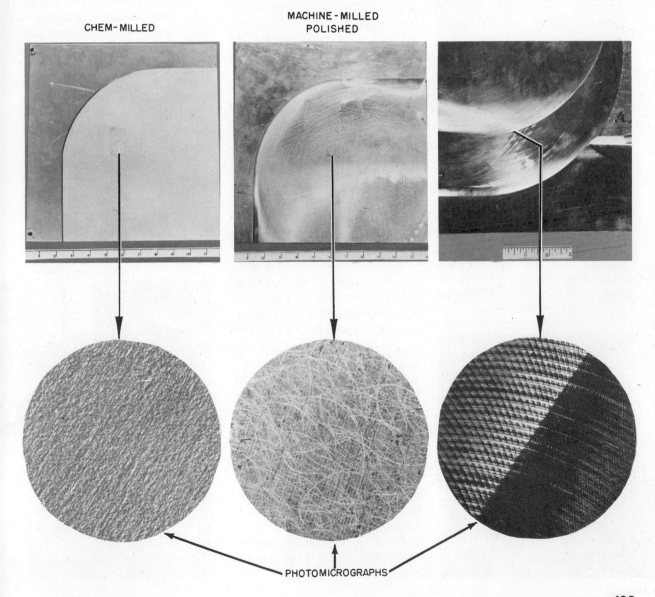

PHOTOMICROGRAPHS

Unit 94. **Flame Spraying**

Flame spraying has become a widely recognized process in industry. It can be defined as the process of melting materials in a heating zone and propelling them in a molten, or heat-softened, condition onto a target to form a coating. There are three types of flame-spraying processes: (1) metallizing, or the wire process, (2) the powder, or Thermo-Spray, process, and (3) the plasma flame process.

METALLIZING PROCESS

Metallizing is the process of spraying a molten metal onto a surface to form a coating. Pure or alloyed metal is melted in a flame and atomized by a blast of compressed air into a fine metal spray. This spray builds up on a surface that has been prepared in advance and forms a solid metal coating. The object being sprayed does not heat very much due to the fact that the molten metal is cooled by a strong blast of air.

In the metallizing process the metal to be sprayed is fed into the gun by an atomic feed mechanism and through the gun into a gas-oxygen flame. 94–1. Compressed air restricts the flame and causes it in turn to blast the molten tip of the wire, producing a fine metal spray which interlocks and meshes to produce a coating.

The structure of sprayed metal is quite different from that found in rolled, drawn, or cast form. As the small molten particles are sprayed from the gun, they strike the surface, flatten out, and cool almost instantly.

Sprayed metal is used for building up worn parts and salvaging mis-machined products. 94–2. It is also used to apply corrosion-resistant materials to iron and steel. Aluminum and zinc are used on structural steel elements such as bridges, lock gates, ships, and other marine structures.

Wear resistance usually exceeds that of the same metal in wrought or cast form.

The metallizing process should not be used when the sprayed metal will be subjected to sharp impact, edge strain, or continued pounding at one point.

POWDER, OR THERMOSPRAY, PROCESS

The ThermoSpray process uses a technique which permits the application of metals, ceramics, alloys, and cermets—available in powder form. 94–3. The equipment used makes it possible to flame-spray materials that cannot be drawn into wire. Special alloys are used for hard-facing critical areas of parts that must operate under severe conditions.

The powder is applied with a gun and fed by gravity. 94–4. Ordinarily the gun requires no air, and only two lightweight hoses are used to supply oxygen

94–1. Metallizing traction motor armature shaft with No. 2 stainless steel 11 gage wire. Metallizing operation took 15 minutes to complete. Approximately ½ pound of stainless steel wire was used.

Metco, Inc.

94–2. Sprayed metal is used to build up worn parts.

Metco, Inc.

and fuel gas. The powder is fed from a canister attached directly to the gun, eliminating separate hoppers and hoses. The powder is melted almost instantly by an oxyacetylene or hydrogen gas flame.

An air cooler may be attached to reduce overheating on small workpieces or thin sections. A trigger-actuated vibrator is used with ceramic powders.

Many special-purpose refractory and cermet (titanium carbide) coatings may be sprayed, but alumina and zeronia are the materials most widely favored. Zeronia is used principally as a thermal barrier for high temperature service. Alumina is used as a heat barrier and for wear resistance.

PLASMA FLAME PROCESS

"Plasma" is the name used to describe vapors of materials which are raised to a higher energy level than the ordinary gaseous state. Ordinary gases consist of separate molecules, while plasma consists of these same gases which have been broken up and dissociated so that some of the electrically charged particles have been separated.

The plasma flame-spray process is accomplished through the use of a spray gun which utilizes an electric arc that is contained within a water-cooled jacket. 94–5 (Page 488). The plasma flame permits the selection of an inert or chemically inactive gas for the flame medium so that oxidation can be controlled during the heating and application of the spray material. Passing

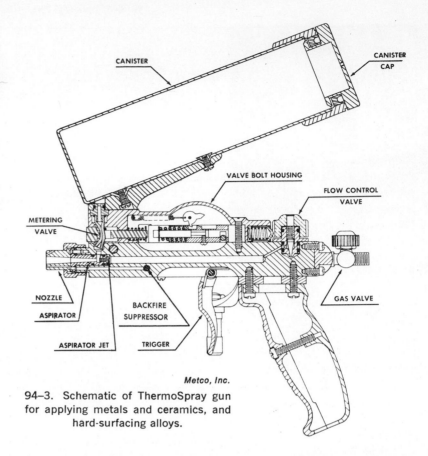

Metco, Inc.

94–3. Schematic of ThermoSpray gun for applying metals and ceramics, and hard-surfacing alloys.

94–4. ThermoSpray gun spraying alumina onto a pump part for protection against corrosion and abrasion.

Metco, Inc.

Metco, Inc.

94–5. Plasma flame gun applying a self-bonding undercoat.

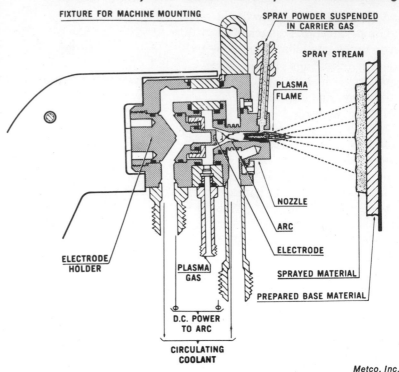

FIXTURE FOR MACHINE MOUNTING

SPRAY POWDER SUSPENDED IN CARRIER GAS

SPRAY STREAM

PLASMA FLAME

NOZZLE

ARC

ELECTRODE

SPRAYED MATERIAL

PREPARED BASE MATERIAL

ELECTRODE HOLDER

PLASMA GAS

D.C. POWER TO ARC

CIRCULATING COOLANT

Metco, Inc.

94–6. Cross section of plasma flame spray gun.

the gas through the electric arc makes it possible to obtain temperatures to 30,000° F.

The powder used is fed into the plasma flame through the side of the nozzle. 94–6. The high velocity of the flame propels the powder toward the surface to be coated. While doing so, the ions and electrons are recombining into atoms, releasing energy as heat which is absorbed by the powder until the particles reach a molten state.

This process offers coatings of previously unworkable materials that add extra life and superior resistance to heat, wear, and erosion on parts and products of almost any base material.

Flame-spraying techniques are used in applications that involve wear and high-temperature problems. Missile nose cones, rocket nozzles, jet turbine cases, electrical contacts, jet engine burner cam clamps, and many aircraft parts are some of the many applications.

Unit 95.   Laser Machining

Dr. Fred P. Burns, manager of operations at Korad Corporation, Santa Monica, California, has said that "Lasers are about as magical as a flashlight beam." The laser in reality is a very strong monochromatic beam of light which is highly collimated, producing a narrow and intense beam of light that can be focused optically onto an area only a few microns (thousandths part of one millimetre) in diameter. In other words it is little more than a beam of light. However, with the laser, it is possible to instantaneously create temperatures up to 75,000° F. at the point of focus, depending upon the initial source used to activate the laser.

In metal removal the process depends upon the concentration of this intense heat but instead of a melting operation, the metal is caused to react with its environment—a somewhat more violent application of concentrated heat.

In the laser method of machining, metal removal rates are so small, however, that lasers

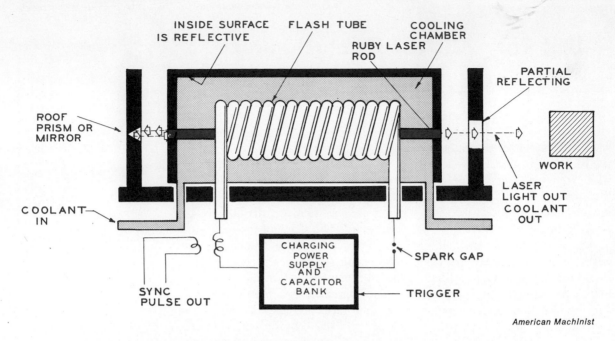

INSIDE SURFACE IS REFLECTIVE

FLASH TUBE

COOLING CHAMBER

RUBY LASER ROD

PARTIAL REFLECTING

ROOF PRISM OR MIRROR

WORK

COOLANT IN

LASER LIGHT OUT COOLANT OUT

CHARGING POWER SUPPLY AND CAPACITOR BANK

SPARK GAP

SYNC PULSE OUT

TRIGGER

American Machinist

95–1. Typical of lasers for microfinishing is this Korad unit with an energy output of 15–20 joules. A light beam is directed along the axis of the ruby rod to impinge upon the work.

are pretty much confined to what might be called "micromachining"—the precise removal of small amounts of metal. Examples include drilling almost microscopic holes in rocket engines and drilling holes in diamond wire drawing dies and other parts made of such materials as stainless steel, tungsten carbide, alumina, or other ceramics. Hole sizes run as small as 0.001″ diameter through such materials in thicknesses of 0.010″ to 0.065″.*

TYPES OF LASERS

There are four types of lasers in current operation: (1) solid state, (2) gaseous state, (3)

* DeGroat, George, "Lasers: Tools not Toys," *American Machinist,* October 23, 1967.

liquid state, and (4) semiconductor lasers.

All four involve the use of a beam of light, made up of photons, or unchanged particles with zero rest mass. Differences between the laser beams determine their general field of application. The coherent beam is a measure of the lasers concentration. Essentially, this means that all the photons generated in the lasers material are directed along its axis to end up in a concentrated spot at the work.

In the solid state the active medium is solid, such as a ruby or doped glass. Argon, carbon dioxide (CO_2), or another gas can be used in the gaseous state laser. In the liquid state laser,

the active medium is a fluid such as a dye solution. The semiconductor lasers use gallium arsenide chip as the active material.

The illustration is a typical laser for micromachining. This is a Korad unit with an energy output of 15–20 joules (a unit of work or energy equal to 10^7 ergs). 95–1. The light beam is directed along the axis of the ruby rod to impinge on the workpiece.

The pulsed solid state laser built by Korad for metalworking operations makes use of ruby rods 3/8″ in diameter and 4″ long. For micromachining they usually operate at 2.5 to 3 microseconds and at 2.5 to 3 milliseconds for welding.

Unit 96. Ultrasonic Machining

Ultrasonic cutting is done by abrasive grains driven into the workpiece by linear oscillation of the tool. 96–1. The high velocity with which the grit bombards the workpiece machines away microscopic particles without perceptible heat.

Abrasive grains are the cutting edges of the tool. They are carried, in granular form, in a liquid that flows between the workpiece and the tool, and are recirculated for continued use.

The same types and grit sizes found in commercial grinding wheels are used in ultrasonic machining. Types and grit sizes are selected in accordance with the nature of the operation and the surface finish desired. Most universally used abrasives are boron carbide, silicon carbide, and aluminum oxide. Coarse grit is used for rapid cutting and fine grits for finishing.

A tool stroke of a few thousandths of an inch and oscillating linearly approximately 20,000 times per second drives the abrasive grains. The shape of the tool determines the precise bombardment pattern of the grit against the workpiece.

The extremely fast motion of the tool face produces a cavitation of the abrasive liquid carrier necessary for material cutting. This turbulent action of the liquid acts as a pump for the abrasive grains and the minutely cut particles in the cutting area.

TOOLING FOR ULTRASONICS

Tools are made preferably of annealed alloy steels, although

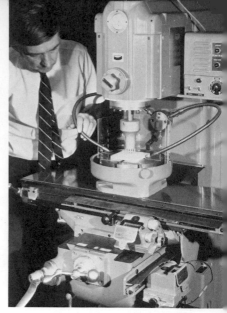

Bendix Automation & Measurement

96–2. Ultrasonic machine tool.

semi-hard tools are occasionally used. 96–2. The shape of the formed tool must be the mate of the surface to be machined. There is practically no limitation on the profile.

Tool size is governed by the degree of accuracy and type of finish required. The cutting tool is usually mounted to the toolholder by brazing, but may, in

96–1. Principles of ultrasonic machining.

96–3. Ultrasonic toolholders.

Bendix Automation & Measurement

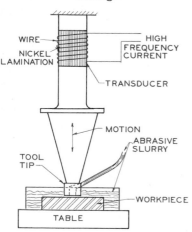

WIRE

NICKEL LAMINATION

HIGH FREQUENCY CURRENT

TRANSDUCER

MOTION

ABRASIVE SLURRY

TOOL TIP

WORKPIECE

TABLE

certain instances, be soft soldered or mechanically fastened. 96–3. Toolholders are quickly interchangeable, being threaded to the transducer.

MACHINING RATES

Two factors govern the rate at which stock is removed by the ultrasonic tool. 96–4. They are: (1) the hardness, brittleness, or density of the workpiece material and (2) the coarseness of the abrasive grains. For example, the more brittle the material and the coarser the grit, the faster the stock is removed.

MACHINING CAPACITY

Maximum, tool, cross-sectional area is governed by the power capacity of the transducer. The largest is capable of machining a 3½" diam. Depth of cuts up to 1½" may be attained with standard techniques. Special tooling permits depths to 5".

FINISH AND ACCURACY

The finish and precision of ultrasonic machining depends upon the size and finish of the tools, fineness of abrasives, and the material being machined. 96–5.

In roughing operations, a 25 microinch finish may be obtained with 280 grit. A 10 microinch finish requires up to 800 grit. Tolerances of 0.001" to 0.0005" may be obtained.

Maximum finishes and the smoothest finishes are attained by the use of more than one tool and more than one grit size for any individual profile cut.

Bendix Automation & Measurement

96–5. This ½" glass bearing plate for aerospace ground support equipment has been ultrasonically machined to produce the precise hole pattern. The cutting tool head shown at the left makes two "butterfly wing" holes.

96–4. Molybdenum disc .010" thick and 1.5" in diameter machined to produce 2,025 square holes each 0.052" square, leaving a grid 0.0015" to 0.002" thick. The device is used to shape electrostatic fields for an ion optical system.

Bendix Automation & Measurement

| **Unit 97.** | **Electron Beam Machining** |

Electron beam machining (EBM) involves the emission of electrons which have charge and mass and which are accelerated by high voltages in a high vacuum to impinge upon the workpiece where their energy is converted to heat.

The EBM machine can be focused to a very sharp point, and cutting is accomplished by alternately heating (voltages around 30,000) and cooling the area to be cut. 97–1 (Page 492). Heating and cooling must be controlled carefully so that the workpiece at the point of focus is properly heated to avoid melting the surrounding metal. This is accomplished by a pulsing technique. 97–2 (Page 492). The beam is left on for a few milliseconds and then turned off for a certain period of time. Instead of just melting the metal as in electron beam welding, electron beam machining vaporizes the metal. This facilitates the removal of the metal from the cut. Very high temperatures are reached at the focal point of the beam and a clean edged hole can be produced. Extremely small holes, less than 0.001", can be produced by this process because the beam can be focused to a very fine point.

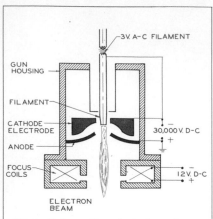

97–1. Schematic of electron beam machine.

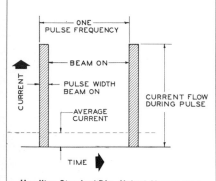

Hamilton Standard Div., United Aircraft Corp.

97–2. Beam pulsing.

97–3. Path of cut can be controlled by deflecting the electric beam.

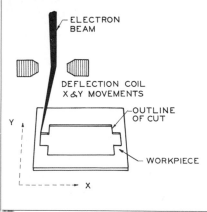

The smaller the hole diameter, the lower the energy that will be required.

The geometry of the cut is governed by the movement of the worktable in the vacuum chamber. A deflection coil is also used to bend the beam of electrons to the proper cutting path. 97–3. Depths of holes and slots produced by EBM are limited to less than ½".

In normal operations cuts are made completely through the workpiece. However, bottoming cuts can be accurately made by controlling energy input, beam concentration, and length of dwell.

Electron beams generate X-rays at the work upon deceleration and, for this reason, the beams are shielded to protect the operators.

Metal removal rates are faster with EBM operations than with the laser, and more energy can be delivered to the workpiece. However, EBM units require a high vacuum and protective shielding which are not needed in laser operations.

Unit 98.   Electrical Discharge Machining

Electrical discharge machining (EDM) is the process of removing metal (or conductive materials) by means of an electric discharge (spark) in the presence of a dielectric. 98–1.

EDM TERMS

Understanding this process requires knowing some basic terms: (1) rate (amperes), (2) frequency, (3) electronic envelope, (4) coolant, (5) electrode material, and (6) workpiece material.

Rate and Frequency

Metal-removal rate depends upon the volume of metal removed by each spark and by the frequency with which the sparks occur. 98–2. The amount of metal removed per spark can be increased by feeding more current to the tool. The chips are removed mainly by heat, and the volume of metal removed varies with the type of material being machined.

To understand the way in which current regulates the metal-removal rate, consider three similar machining conditions. As the drawing shows, in each case there is only one spark. The electrode and workpiece materials remain the same.

The only factor that changes is the current (amperes). A spark of one ampere contains a certain amount of energy. Consequently, it will remove a certain amount of material from the workpiece. When the current is doubled, twice the amount of material is removed.

One other condition changes with increasing amperage. That is surface finish. As the amperage is increased, the spark cavity size in the workpiece also increases, which roughens the surface more. However, doubling the amperes does not cause the surface finish to be twice as rough.

As with any machining operation, surface finish of the machined area is of prime importance. Rough cutting of any kind is normally accompanied by a rough surface finish. Finish machining calls for a fine surface finish. EDM is no different, so a surface finish selector (frequency control) is built into each power supply. The frequency is controlled by the number of sparks per second between the electrode and workpiece, with frequencies ranging from 2,000 to 260,000 sparks per second.

Frequency control affects the surface finish. 98–3. As shown in the illustration, a setting of 5 amperes at a hypothetical frequency of two sparks per second divides the energy between the two sparks. Each of the two sparks removes a smaller amount of metal than a single, 5-ampere spark, producing a better surface finish.

A 5-ampere spark will machine a given amount of material from the workpiece. The cavity created is of a given size and determines the surface finish.

By doubling both the amperes and spark frequency, there would be two sparks of 5 amperes each (or 10 amperes) per second. Metal removed per 5-ampere spark remains the same, as shown in Fig. 98–4, so that the re-

sulting surface finishes of A and B are the same. Machining time is dependent upon cutting amperes, therefore it will take half as long to remove a given amount of material at 10 amperes as compared to 5 amperes. Since there is no change in surface finish for each operation, the 10 ampere rate can be used, doubling the machining rate.

Electronic Envelope (Overcut)

EDM requires that the operator understand the way in which clearance between the electrode and workpiece is obtained and how it is controlled. An electronic envelope or cloud (space) surrounds the electrode. The size of this envelope is determined by the amount of machining am-

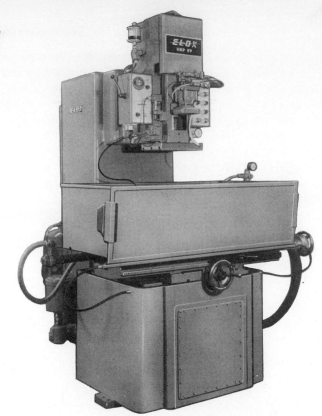

Colt Industries, Elox Inc. Div.

98–1. An electrical discharge (EDM) machine.

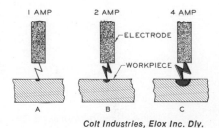

Colt Industries, Elox Inc. Div.

98–2. Metal removal, one discharge.

98– . y increasing discharge frequency, the surface finish can be improved. Often you can double both frequency and amperage for maximum machining rates.

Colt Industries, Elox Inc. Div.

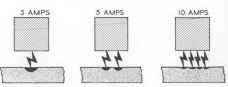

493

peres, spark frequency, and the condenser value used, measured in microfarads (units of measurement in electronics).

The diagram illustrates the electronic envelope from the cutting end. Shown are round-, square-, and irregular-shaped electrodes. 98–5. The electronic envelope follows the shape of the electrode. The clearance or over- cut between the electrode and the machined surface will be identical for the entire electrode.

Coolant

A dielectric fluid (coolant) is used in the EDM process. The coolant serves three functions: (1) forms a dielectric barrier between the electrode and work- piece at the arc gap, (2) "cools" the eroded particles of the work- piece, and (3) flushes the eroded workpiece particles out of the arc gap.

Several types of coolants can be used: mineral and silicone oils, distilled water, certain com- pressed gases, sodium silicate solutions, glycerol, and kerosene. 98–6. Mineral oils are most commonly used.

Electrode Material

There is no best electrode ma- terial for all applications, al- though some are more versatile than others. The ideal electrode material, however, has to have the following characteristics: (1) machinability, (2) reasonable material price, (3) good wear rate, and (4) be a good conduc- tor of heat and electricity.

Some electrode materials have good wear rates but are difficult to fabricate and may be quite expensive. The following is a list of known acceptable electrode materials.

Tungsten	Brass
carbide	Copper
Tungsten	Zinc alloys
Silver tungsten	Copper
Copper tungsten	graphite
Graphite	

New electrode materials are constantly being developed; how- ever, most of these are refine- ments.

Workpiece Material

The material being machined is the factor over which there is the least control. The material must be a conductor of elec- tricity. Unlike regular machining, the hardness of the workpiece

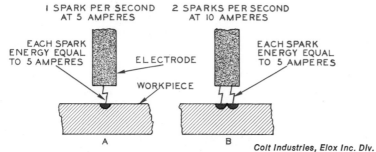

98–4. Surface finish as affected by spark frequency and amperes.

Colt Industries, Elox Inc. Div.

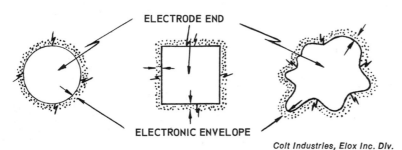

98–5. Round, square, and irregular shapes show that the envelope follows the shape of the electrode. Electrodes may be any shape.

Colt Industries, Elox Inc. Div.

98–6. Types of coolant flow.

Colt Industries, Elox Inc. Div.

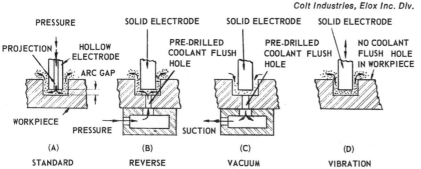

does not determine whether or not it can be machined. For instance, a brass electrode may be used to machine soft steel, hardened steel, or even carbide. This is one of the greatest advantages of EDM.

By machining material in their hardened state, expensive operations which can cause distortion or breakage that might make the part useless, can be eliminated before heat-treating the part. EDM also eliminates the need for burring operations.

Materials that are machined by the EDM method include:

Aluminum	Molybdenum
Brass	Stainless steel
Beryllium	Steel
Carbide	Tungsten
Magnesium	Titanium

THE PROCESS*

The EDM process depends upon the periodic flow of sparks between two conductors of electricity, both of which are submerged in a dielectric fluid.

In this process the workpiece is mounted on the bed of the EDM machine. The tool is fed down but never touches the workpiece. When the tool reaches a preset distance from the workpiece, sparks begin to materialize. The preset distance is known as the overcut. The pulsating charges (DC) come from a special power supply. 98–7.

There are thousands of sparks per second. As the sparks travel from cathode to anode, they cut the workpiece to the exact shape of the tool. A crater is produced on both the tool and workpiece

---

* Colt Industries, Elox Div., *Fundamentals of EDM*, 1964.

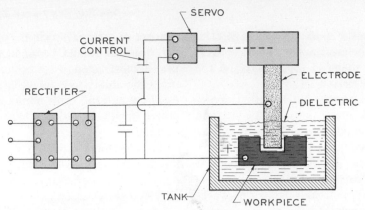

98–7. In EDM the servomechanism monitors gap voltage changes. The tool is fed into or out of the workpiece as required. The rectifier changes AC current to DC.

by each spark. The heat generated by the spark provides the energy for metal removal. The fluid near the discharge is vaporized and decomposed by the heat from the spark. 98–8. Chips are produced in the form of hollow spheres.

In the process it is necessary to know the depth of cut and the speed at which the material can be removed so that good dimensional control can be obtained from any soft or hard material.

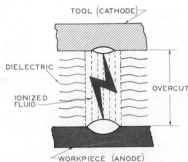

98–8. When electrical energy ionizes a portion of the dielectric fluid, a spark from the tool erodes a tiny crater on both the tool and workpiece.

Unit 99. Electrochemical Machining

Electrochemical machining (ECM) differs from other metalworking techniques in that electrical and chemical energies act as the cutting edge of the tool. 99–1 (Page 496). ECM is a metalworking process based on reverse plating since metal is removed from the workpiece rather than deposited upon it.

In this process the workpiece is connected to the positive terminal of a high-frequency, DC power supply. A tool or cathode, connected to the negative terminal, is advanced toward the workpiece through an electrolyte that completes the electrical circuit between the anode and cathode. Metal is then removed from the workpiece through electrochemical action, and the cathode shape is reproduced on the workpiece.

In conventional plating operations metal ions removed from the anode generally move to the cathode and plate out. However, in the ECM process hydroxyl ions of the electrolyte combine with metal ions from the workpiece and form insoluble metal hydroxides.

In the ECM process the electrolyte, pumped at high pressure through the gap between the workpiece and tool, conducts current between them, and the electrochemical reaction produced in the tiny gap rapidly dissolves the metal from the workpiece. 99–2. The tool does not contact the workpiece (no direct friction) and, therefore, no heat build-up occurs.

The cathodes do not wear and are generally fabricated from conductive materials such as copper, brass, or stainless steel. Copper is most often used because it has the ability to conduct large electrical currents with minimum power losses and low thermal heating.

The electrolyte bath is pumped through the tool to the gap and must be circulated at a rate sufficiently high to carry away heat.

The electrolytes used in ECM are water solutions of sodium chloride, sodium chlorate, or sodium nitrate. The most commonly used is the sodium chloride solution, as it is inexpensive, readily available, and easily handled.

Since there must not be contact between the workpiece and tool, a gap is present. This is known as the "machining gap," which is .001″ to .003″. The space between the tool and the sides is somewhat larger. A dune of uncut metal is left at the cen-

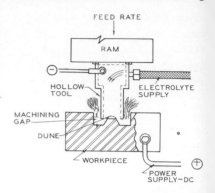

American Machinist

99–2. A machining gap is necessary for operation of the ECM system. Current from an electrode tool speeds the chemical reaction between the electrolyte and the metal being machined.

ter as shown in the illustration. The rate of metal removal is directly proportionate to the current flowing across the gap for a given tool, workpiece, and electrolyte.

ECM machines all materials at approximately the same rate. ECM does not depend on the mechanical properties but rather on the chemical and electrical properties of the materials. In this process there is no surface hardness because there is no contact with the workpiece. High penetration rates are obtainable with ECM. (See Table 99–A.)

99–1. Electrochemical machine.

Cincinnati ECM

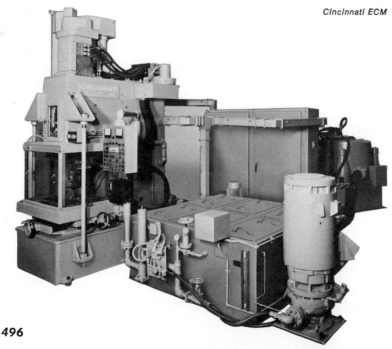

Table 99-A. Typical Penetration Rates		
Machining operation	Penetration rate (in./min.)	CD multiplication factor
Round through holes	0.5	5.0
Square through holes	0.4	4.0
Blind holes (round and square)	0.3	3.0
Simple cavities	0.25	2.5
Planing	6.0	5.0
Wire cutting	(Depends upon size of area machined)	

The requirements for any machining operation are easily found by multiplying the current density (CD value—Table 99–B) by

Table 99-B. Current Density of Metals	
Material	CD/0.100 in./min. penetration rate
Iron (steel)	1100
Nickel	1200
Cobalt	1195
Aluminum	1190
Titanium	1490
A-286	1100
Rene 41	1350
17–7ph	1180

the current density multiplication factor in Table 99–A. The total current necessary for the operation may be found by multiplying the maximum current density by the surface area between the tool and workpiece.

ADVANTAGES OF ECM PROCESS

1. Low unit cost of manufacturing is made possible by the high rates of metal removed.
2. Tool life is extremely long.
3. Square or curved holes and other unusual shapes are easily generated.
4. Properly controlled machining induces no thermal damage, residual stress, or burrs.
5. Thin delicate workpieces can be machined without distortion.
6. Simple tool motions are used.
7. ECM can compete with most conventional machining processes with the exception of grinding, honing, lapping, and super finishing.

Chemical machining is a process which removes metal by chemical action. 100–1. This new technique is ideally suited for production of flat, relatively thin parts of unlimited configurations and for other jobs requiring area, point, or line removal of metal.

PROCESSING STEPS

There are four basic steps in chemical machining: (1) artwork and negative preparation, (2) metal preparation, (3) image printing and developing, and (4) etching and resist removal. 100–2 (Page 498).

Artwork and Negative Preparation

Preparation of an accurate image of the part is necessary. The artwork is made on mylar and true black ink is used. The artwork master is cut from two to one hundred times actual size to assure the closest possible tolerances. The artwork is then reduced photographically.

From the camera, the negative goes to a step-and-repeat vacuum frame, where the image of the part is duplicated on one large film. This is done so that multiple images can be exposed at one time on a single piece of metal.

Metal Preparation

To prepare the metal panel that will go into the negative

"envelope," grease and oxides are removed from the metal panel. After cleaning, the panels are dipped into a vat containing a photo resist, and then hung vertically to drain. This is done under controlled temperature and humidity. Most panels are dried in an oven or air-dried in a dust-free atmosphere.

The metal is etched from both sides to facilitate etching accuracy and speed. For this purpose, a mirror-image negative is made from the multiple-part negative already produced on the step-and-repeat frame. If only one side is to be etched, it is not necessary to make mirror-image negatives.

The multiple-part negative and its mirror image are placed with

100–1. Chemical machining process.
American Machinist

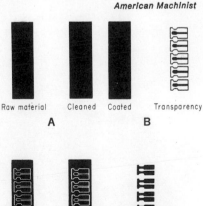

Raw material   Cleaned   Coated   Transparency
A   B

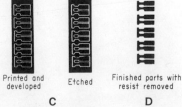

Printed and developed   Etched   Finished parts with resist removed
C   D

Chemcut Corp.

100–2. Examples of parts that can be produced by chemical machining.

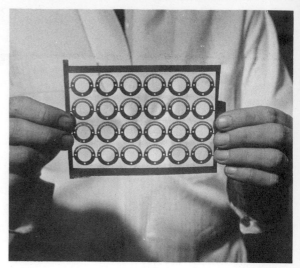

Chemcut Corp.

100–4. Quantities of small parts are held together by metal tabs incorporated into the original artwork.

their emulsion sides together and secured together on two opposite edges. This negative "envelope" is now ready to accept the sensitized metal panels.

Image Printing and Developing

To get the part images onto metal, the photosensitized panel is placed into the negative "envelope." This "sandwich" goes into a vacuum printer, where an ultraviolet light source exposes both sides of the panel simultaneously.

After printing, the panel is developed in a solvent spray. This removes the photo resist from the panel, except in areas which have been converted by ultraviolet light to etch-resistant images of the part.

Etching and Resist Removal

In the etcher all areas not protected by the photo resist are dissolved, leaving only the finished parts. 100–3. Quantities of small parts are held together by

100–3. A conveyorized etcher. The horizontal spray etcher permits continuous high-speed volume etching with exceptional uniformity and speed.

Chemcut Corp.

metal tabs incorporated into the original artwork or by an adhesive or plastic-laminated backing. 100–4. After etching, the remaining photo resist is ordinarily removed from the parts.

ABRASIVE JET MACHINING

A mechanical process for cutting hard brittle materials is known as abrasive jet machining (AJM). The process is somewhat similar to sand blasting but uses finer abrasives. The particle size and velocity of the abrasive jet is kept under close control during the operation. The illustration is a schematic of this operation, the carrying medium for the abrasive being air or CO_2. These abrasive particles contact the work at velocities from 500 to 1100 fps. The abrasive used for cutting can be either silicon carbide or aluminum oxide particles. 100–5. Cleaning, etching, or polishing is usually done with softer powders such as sodium bicarbonate or dolmite.

The process is limited to the harder type materials as the abrasive has a tendency to become embedded in softer materials. Material removal rates are slow.

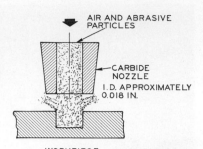

100–5. Abrasive jet machining using silicon carbide particles.

This special type of machining is useful for: removing oxides from surfaces, frosting glass, etching, and cutting thin sections of metal.

Check Your Knowledge

1. Describe the chem-mill process.

2. What are the advantages of chemical milling over conventional machining processes?

3. Name some of the chemical-milling applications.

4. Describe the metallizing process.

5. Name the major uses of the metallizing process.

6. Explain the ThermoSpray process. How does it differ from the metallizing process?

7. What type of spraying material is used in the ThermoSpray technique?

8. What are some of the advantages of this technique?

9. Describe the plasma flame process.

10. For what type of machining are lasers used?

11. Name four basic types of lasers.

12. Describe the ultrasonic machining process and give its advantages.

13. What two factors govern machining rates in ultrasonic machining?

14. Describe fully the EDM process.

15. What effect does the increase in amperage have on the spark cavity size in the EDM process?

16. Name some of the characteristics of electrode materials.

17. Why does the material being machined have to be a conductor of electricity? Explain why hardness of the material is not a machining problem.

18. Explain the difference between ECM and electroplating.

19. Does the hardness or toughness affect the rate of metal removal? Explain.

20. What is the function of the coolant of ECM?

21. What is meant by the term "machining gap?"

22. Describe the procedure for chemically blanking a part.

References

Colt Industries, Elox Div., *Fundamentals of EDM,* 1964.

DeGroat, G., "Lasers," *American Machinist,* October 23, 1967.

"Electrochemical Machining," *American Machinist,* Special Report No. 609, October 23, 1967.

Sandford, J., "Cutting with a Spark," *American Machinist,* Special Report No. 590, July 4, 1966.

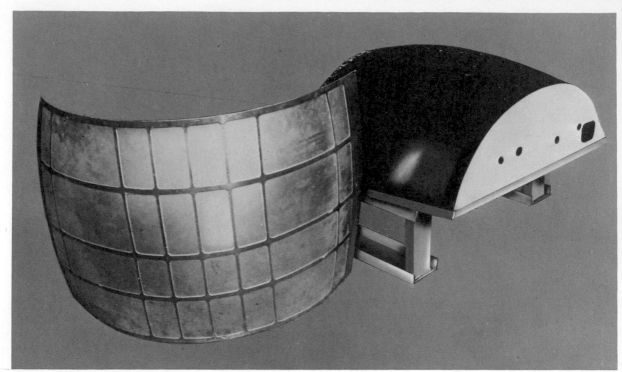

Chemical milling.

Section Twenty-Three

Numerical Control Machining

Superior Electric Co.

Unit 101.

What is "Numerical Control" and How Does it Work?

Numerical control is the most significant breakthrough in manufacturing processes since the invention of the production-line technique to mass-produce identical interchangeable parts. The primary machine functions have not changed; efficiency and methods have. With other processes, in order to make certain machine movements, the *operator* turned cranks and read scales to be sure the machine did the specified work. In numerical control machining, however, the *control* tells the machine to move to a specified point to perform some desired operation. The machine automatically measures, knows when it reaches a specified point, and relates back to control, through the "closed loop" system, that it has completed the instructions fed through the tape.

It might be said that numerical control is control by numbers. This takes a great step beyond automatic control, because it reduces jigs, fixtures, and setup. The short-cut handling of tooling gives a practical answer for the production of parts when they are needed, whether 5 pieces or 5,000 pieces are involved. Numerical control of machines also cuts down large inventories and production costs because the stored knowledge can be used almost instantly to produce a few pieces to many thousands.

The idea of numerical control is to use any of the basic machine tools in which one, two, or more multiple motions are easily coordinated, sequenced, or otherwise manipulated from data prepared in advance. In a broad sense N/C requires only counting and measuring functions of numbers. It directly converts numerical values into physical values, such as quantities and dimensions.

Transducers have been developed which measure with surprising accuracy the distance a machine tool or table has traveled.

Electronics plays an important part in numerical control. It is from this science that electronic tools have been produced to work with a high degree of accuracy, efficiency, and speed. Electronic circuits have been designed with the ability to "remember" a number and to turn a switch on or off when that particular number is reached. This means that if a control unit can be designed to measure and "remember" numbers, the unit then has the ability to run a machine, as long as a method is provided that tells the machine what the operator wants it to do.

The common on and off switch is well suited to a simplified N/C system since its function is turning on or off the

101–1. Vertical milling machine equipped with Slo-Syn N/C controls.

Superior Electric Co.

CONTROL UNIT

MOTOR

control motors that drive the machine table. The switch is then an important part of the N/C system, as it is the key to converting the information or directions on the tape into electrical impulses which control the machine tool.*

Our basic counting system—0, 1, 2, 3, 4, 5, 6, 7, 8, and 9—which contains the ten distinct digits, is overly complicated in an N/C system and has to be converted to a code capable of controlling the on or off switch signals. This code, known as the binary coded decimal system, uses a series of symbols, each representing a definite letter or number and each a combination of on and off signals.

BASIC COMPONENTS OF AN N/C SYSTEM

An N/C system has the following components:

1. The *control unit,* which interprets the coded instructions and directs the machine through the required operations. 101–1.
2. The *tape,* which is punched full of holes, with each hole providing an electronic pulse. 101–2.
3. The *motor,* which supplies the power to move the tool or table of the machine.
4. The electronic *feedback* device (*transducers*), which tells how much movement has taken place.

The console, or controller, is the heart of an N/C system. 101–3. It "reads" the control tape and contains the electronic circuits that translate the coded data to machine-tool instructions.

* Stocker, Wm. M., Jr., "The ABC's of Numerical Control," *American Machinist,* August 8, 1960.

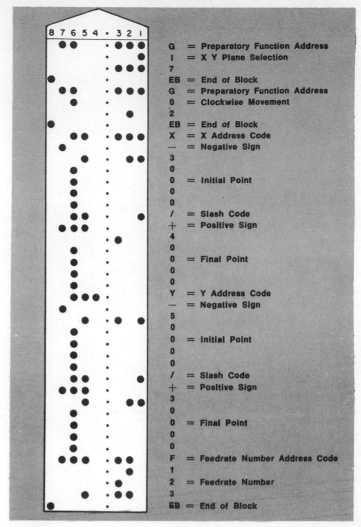

8 7 6 5 4 · 3 2 1	
G	= Preparatory Function Address
I	= X Y Plane Selection
7	
EB	= End of Block
G	= Preparatory Function Address
0	= Clockwise Movement
2	
EB	= End of Block
X	= X Address Code
—	= Negative Sign
3	
0	
0	= Initial Point
0	
0	
/	= Slash Code
+	= Positive Sign
4	
0	
0	= Final Point
0	
0	
Y	= Y Address Code
—	= Negative Sign
5	
0	
0	= Initial Point
0	
0	
/	= Slash Code
+	= Positive Sign
3	
0	
0	= Final Point
0	
0	
F	= Feedrate Number Address Code
1	
2	= Feedrate Number
3	
EB	= End of Block

Pratt & Whitney

101–2. This tape is punched full of holes, with each hole providing an electronic pulse.

101–3. Close-up view of N/C control unit.

Superior Electric Co.

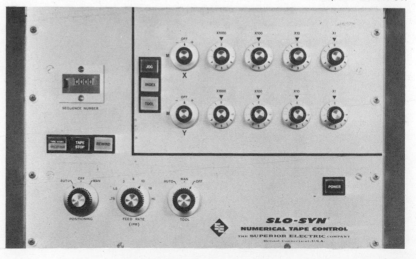

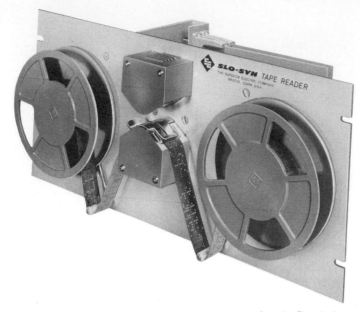

Superior Electric Co.

101–4. N/C tape reader.

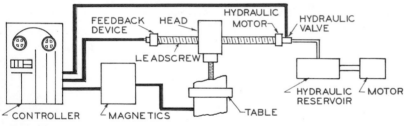

101–5. How the tape "talks" to the machine tool. The controller "reads" the control tape and contains the electronic circuits that translate the coded data to machine-tool functions.

101–6. Schematic illustration of a digital transducer, an analog transducer, and the resulting output signals.

Norden Div. of United Aircraft Co.

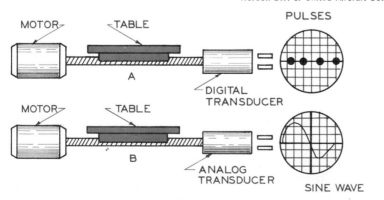

101–4. Holes are punched in a piece of tape, and when the tape passes over the tape reader, a finger drops through and punches a small key. The key is connected to the electronic circuit, and when the key is pushed, an electrical pulse is transmitted to a sensing device on the controls which "tells" the worktable when to move, in what direction, and how far. 101–5. Pulses also control other machine functions, such as the action of the coolant pumps.

A feedback device quantitatively records the motion of the lead screw and sends information back to control. The control compares these signals with the input signals on the tape, and continues to regulate the lead screw motions until the command signals from the tape balance the feedback signals which indicate the actual motions of the machine. 101–6.

The transducers provide either digital or analog signals. 101–7 (A&B). Analog signals are continuous, modulated by events to provide the message. Digital signals usually are in the form of pulses. A signal from a car speedometer is an analog signal, while a telephone dial taps out digital signals.

Lead screws and hydraulic cylinders, because their functions are continuous, are analog devices. Relays and push buttons are digital devices because they can be only on or off. Most numerical control systems are a combination of the two. For instance, the numerical input can be digital and then converted to an analog signal by a converter

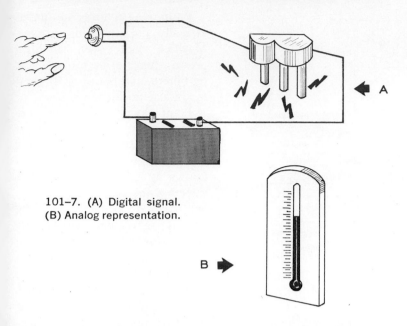

101–7. (A) Digital signal.
(B) Analog representation.

for use by the components of the machine.

More circuits or loops can be added if there is a need to control more motors. The additional motors can be used to control the tool or table movement on any axis that the machine is capable of handling. These movements can be controlled simultaneously, allowing the operator to move the cutting tool and/or table in any direction on any axis. The machine tool may be electrically or hydraulically operated. By using enough motors or circuits and with sufficient control speed to be able to feed and read information instantaneously, the machine can make any cut in any contour within the tool's capability.

HOW NUMERICAL CONTROL WORKS

In the following paragraphs a brief description will be given on how numerical control works.

As the prepared tape passes through the tape reader head, silicon photo diodes sense light as it passes through holes in the tape, causing signals to be sent to the electronic control. The number and location of the holes in each row across the tape conforms to a code with a specific meaning.

The code is interpreted by the control unit, which stores all information until a complete block of information is obtained. This block of information contains the instructions that are necessary to do a required operation. When the end of the block (EOB) signal is received, the unassigned miscellaneous functions and the rapid traverse will be performed first.

The control then causes the motors to make the required number of steps. If motion along two axes is required, the motors will position along both axes simultaneously. If a tool change

or tape rewind code has been programmed, these will be done after the motors have been positioned. If neither function is called for, the control will initiate the tool cycle if the tool switch is at auto or go on the next block, if the tool switch is off, or if the tool inhibit code has been programmed. When the tool switch is in the manual position, the operator must push the tool button to perform the tool cycle.

During the tool cycle, the next tape block will be read and stored. Feedback from a switch on the tool motion prevents table movement until the tool cycle is completed. If the tool switch is at off, the next block will not be read until all functions called for in the previous block are completed.

The principle of the control function can be compared to our modern dial telephone. A control at the telephone exchange takes and stores each number as it is dialed. When the entire number has been dialed, the complete block of information has been programmed so that the equipment is activated and the call is completed.

Using a simple drilling operation to further explain the system of N/C, suppose a drill press operator is to drill a hole in a part 10.375″ to the right of the left edge and 5.250″ from the front edge.

To perform this simple operation by N/C, he can use five calibrated dials. The dials are divided into 10 parts, numbered from 0 to 9. 101–8. The first dial to the left will provide 90,000 pulses for one full turn or a total value of 90″. To the

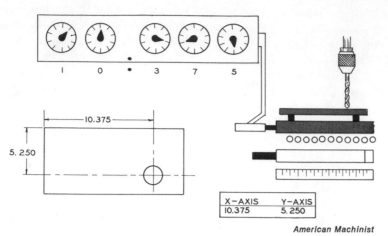

101–8. Numbers are translated into physical distances.

Positioning controls are fundamentally point-to-point systems. Machine tools such as drill presses, turret drills, turret lathes, jig borers, and boring mills commonly use positioning systems.

Point locating systems are used either to locate a point, or a series of points, by moving independently in two dimensions known as X and Y. 101–9. The direction the tool takes to reach the desired locations are not critical movements. The only concern is whether or not the machine can move to its next location without hitting itself or some part of the workpiece. Point-to-point locating systems are the simplest and least expensive for N/C machines.

Contouring, or continuous path, systems differ from point-to-point systems in that they are able to precisely control the tool movement at all times and in all places. They have a complex circuitry which can feed and read information to the tool on a nearly instantaneous basis.

The continuous path is generated by a series of minute, overlapping, straight lines, or parabolas, often as small as 0.0002″ in length. Each of these cuts must be calculated and the dimensions fed into the control. The sum of these lines or cuts produces the desired curve. Contouring N/C's are normally programmed by computers. It is not practical to plot the thousands of required points manually, as it would be a time-consuming task. The speed of the electronic computer is a time-saving method which makes this type of control possible.

right of the dial, a second dial will supply 9,000 pulses, or nine inches, in one turn. Then he comes to an imaginary decimal point.

The first dial on the right of the imaginary decimal point provides the decimal fractions, having a value of 0.900″ per full turn. The next dial value is 0.090″ per full turn and the last dial gives a total range of 0.009″ divided into increments of 0.001″ each. If 0.0001″ increments are necessary, an additional dial may be added.

To move the table to 10.375″, the operator sets the left hand dial to 10 and the next dial to 0. To obtain the fractional number, he sets the dial following the decimal point to 0.3″, the next dial to the right at 0.07″, and the thousandths dial to 0.005″. There have then been 10.375 pulses released by the operator to move the table 10.375″.

A second set of dials positions the table to the 5.250″ dimension. The workpiece to be drilled has then been positioned to two dimensions, X and Y. A third set of dials could be added to provide the depth of the hole, which would provide the vertical, or Z dimension. By inserting a prepared tape the operation can be done automatically.

TYPES OF NUMERICAL CONTROL

There are actually two forms of numerical control: (1) *discrete positioning,* commonly known as *point-to-point* and (2) *continuous path,* or *contouring.*

101–9. The directions the tool takes in a point-to-point N/C system are not critical movements.

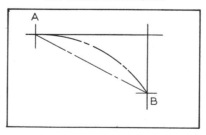

The computer can also be used to punch the tape. Continuous path N/C is most commonly used on milling machines.

MEASURING BASIS FOR N/C CONTROL SYSTEMS

The Cartesian (rectangular) coordinate system is the basis for measuring N/C machine tools. 101–10. In this system all point positions are described in terms of distances from the origin (common point) and measured along lines known as axes. The primary axes are the three basic dimensions—length, width, and height. These are called the X, Y, and Z axes. The X and Y axes are ordinarily located in the horizontal planes and the Z axis is perpendicular to them. Any measurements to the right are considered to be in a +X direction and to the left in a —X

direction. 101–11. The Y axis also has +Y and —Y directions. The same is true of the Z axis.

On a two-axis machine, the tool moves in a horizontal XY plane. 101–12. This movement can be compared to a draftsman who can draw a line anywhere on a plane represented by his drawing board.

All numerical programming has to be done from dimensional drawings.

Some systems operate on what is called an absolute dimensioning system. 101–13. This means that the control relates all dimensions to the original zero point at all times. Some N/C units such as contour control, allow incremental positioning, which means they will accept dimensions from other than the original fixed point. 101–14. In this way, they can use a previous point in a sequence of operations as the reference point for the next operation.

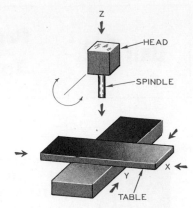

101–11. Motions that can be controlled on an N/C drilling machine.

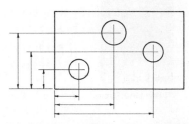

101–13. An example of absolute measuring. All coordinates are measured from a fixed point of origin.

101–10. The Cartesian (rectangular) coordinate system is the basis of all N/C programming. In this system, X and Y axes are horizontal table movements, and the Z axis is a vertical motion of the tool.

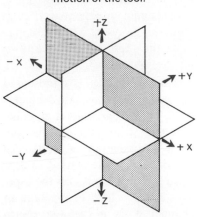

101–12. Areas of tool movement on a horizontal knee milling machine.

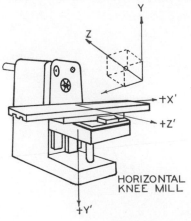

101–14. Drawing shows an example of incremental measuring. This system of measuring can accept dimensions from a point other than the original zero reference. It can use a previous point in a sequence of operations as the reference point for the next operation.

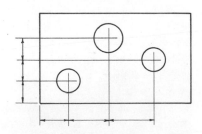

507

Unit 102.

Programming and Tape Preparation

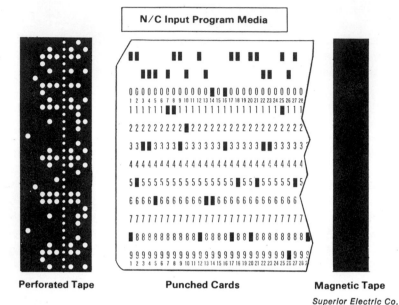

N/C Input Program Media

Perforated Tape   **Punched Cards**   **Magnetic Tape**

Superior Electric Co.

102–1. N/C input program media. Instructions recorded on any of these media are used to control the sequence and performance of many machine-tool operations.

102–2. Filling out the tape preparation sheet from a part print using the word address system. Letters represent functions, and numbers and decimals show dimensions.

Writing the manuscript, or program, and tape preparation is entirely an office-methods engineering procedure, done by a "programmer."

Manual programming is widely used in industry, and the method contains the fundamental elements upon which computer programming methods are based.

Information required to operate both the control system and machine tool must be transcribed on an input medium such as paper tape, magnetic tape, or cards. 102–1. An eight-channel tape is the most commonly used.

The programmer reviews the drawing of the part to be produced to be sure all dimensions are given point-to-point. (Some jobs might require continuous path.) He first establishes a reference point from which to start the job. This is usually the most convenient point from which the operator would choose to work.

After studying the job, a specially designed processing sheet is filled in with the machining data taken from the print. 102–2. Although this is an extremely important step in the operation and very large shops make it the responsibility of the engineering department, an experienced shop man can be relied upon to determine the most expedient way to do the job. 102–3.

The information is represented on tape in sections called blocks. Each block represents a machine function, a machining function, or a combination of both. An end-of-block code is used to separate the data blocks on the tape. This code, a hole in the tape in channel 8, is a carriage return

Seq. No.	TAB or EOB	+ or −	X Increment	TAB or EOB	+ or −	Y Increment	TAB or EOB	M Funct.	EOB	Instructions

102–3. Example of a programming sheet.

command. Each data block is made up of "words," with each word consisting of both alphabetic and numerical characters which supply the information on the different axes positions, feed, and speed.

It is necessary that the programmer have all the necessary information, such as part geometry and a familiarity with both the machine tool and the control unit to be used. 102–4. The programmer should also have the

102–4. Manual programming of the basic sequence.

Technical Education & Mfg., Inc.

ability to: (1) read and interpret blueprints, (2) organize specifications and data for preparing programs, (3) apply the number language for N/C purposes, (4) know about material machinability, (5) know the machine tool, its operations, and the sequencing of these operations, and (6) apply the number language for N/C purposes. These are only some of the things involved in being a programmer. Programmers may be specialists or engineers. Draftsmen, machine operators, and shop foremen can also prepare the program.

Language Codes

Many basic N/C commands have been established and standardized by research and development personnel. These are basic commands that the programmer uses in preparing his program manuscript. The following codes are those used with the Slo-Syn numerical tape controls. This equipment is simple in design and educationally and economically sound for use in schools at secondary and post-secondary levels.

Leader. This is a strip of tape having only the drive sprocket holes. It permits the tape to be threaded without danger of a wrong code being read when the tape reader is started.

Rewind stop (RWS). This code is normally placed in the first block of information. When moving in reverse feed, the tape reader will stop at the rewind stop code.

Tab. This code separates information within a block. The first tab is followed by the X increment, the second tab by the Y increment, and the third tab is followed by miscellaneous function codes.

Plus (+). This plus code indicates travel is to be in the plus direction. This sign may be omitted. Absence of a sign indicates that travel is to be in the plus direction.

Minus (—). The minus code indicates travel in the minus direction.

Numbers. Numerical codes following the first two tabs determine the number of steps the appropriate driving motor will index.

509

End of block (EOB). This code separates information blocks on the tape. It stops the tape reader and tells the system to act on information received.

Delete. Incorrect characters on the tape are punched over with the delete code. The correct codes must then be punched on the next portion of tape.

Tool change (06). When the *tool* switch is at *auto,* this code causes the system to stop after positioning with no tool actuation. The *tool change* lamp will light when the system stops.

Rewind (02). The rewind causes the tape to rewind and resets the sequence counter. All other information in the block will be acted on first. There will be no tool actuation in a block in which a rewind code is programmed.

Hi feed (55). When operating at feed rates from ¾″ to 18″ per minute, the Hi Feed code will cause the system to position at the Hi Feed rate for the block in which it appears.

Tool inhibit (56). When operating with the *tool* switch in *auto,* this code will prevent tool actuation after positioning in the block in which it appears.

Unassigned miscellaneous functions (52, 53, and 54)—These codes control whatever miscellaneous functions are connected to their respective relays. The relays will be actuated before positioning begins. On three-axis models, the 54 code signifies that the increment following the second tab is for the third axis.

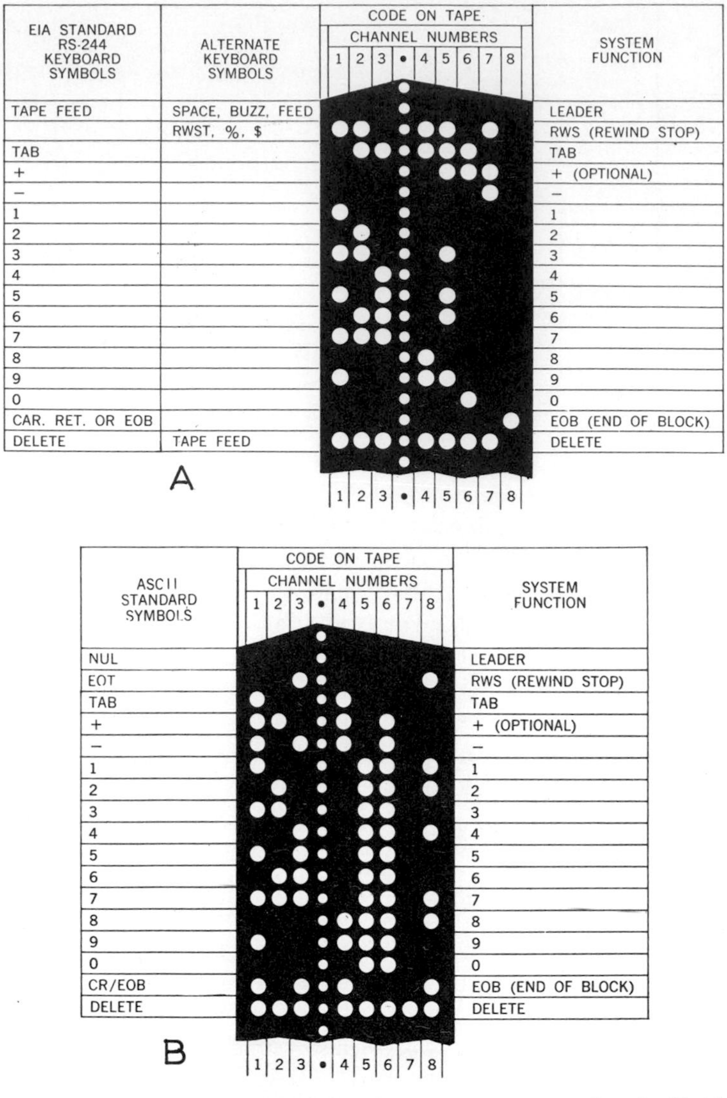

Code on Tape Formats

There are two tape formats that have been standardized: (1)

EIA STANDARD RS-244 KEYBOARD SYMBOLS	ALTERNATE KEYBOARD SYMBOLS	CODE ON TAPE CHANNEL NUMBERS	SYSTEM FUNCTION

ASCII STANDARD SYMBOLS	CODE ON TAPE CHANNEL NUMBERS	SYSTEM FUNCTION

Superior Electric Co.

102–5. (A) Electronics Industries Association Format (EIA) and (B) American Standard Code for Information Interchange Format (ASCII).

the EIA Standard, established by the Electronics Industries Association, and (2) the ASCII, known as the American Standard Code for Information Interchange. 102–5.

The binary number code on each of these two formats is the same. 102–6. Prescribed punched holes in channels 1, 2, 3, 4, and 6 are requirements for the binary number code. The balance of the columns and prescribed combinations thereof are reserved for codes of a non-numerical nature. The illustration shows how the numericals 1 through 0 are represented.

The use of eight-channel tape and binary-based numerical cod-

Note:
 A. All holes punched in channel #1 = 1
 B. All holes punched in channel #2 = 2
 C. All holes punched in Channel #3 = 4
 D. All holes punched in channel #4 = 8
 E. All holes punched in channel #6 = 0

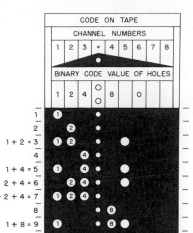

Superior Electric Co.

102–6. Binary number code-on-tape format.

ing is pretty well standardized. The format for presenting the number language on the tape varies. Two of the most common formats are the *word address* and the *tab sequential*.

The tape format must be tailored to the specific requirements of the control unit. Format encompasses the following considerations:

Word address. This format uses an alphabetical character to identify exactly what each numerical word refers to. It allows the words to be placed in any order within a block.

Tab sequential. This system relies on the sequence of the word within a block, rather than an alphabetic character, to identify the quantity specified.

Maximum and minimum number of digits. The number of nu-

merical digits used to represent a given piece of data is usually specified explicitly for each type of machine control. Preparatory functions, called G-address, and miscellaneous functions, M-address, are usually expressed by two digits. Dimensional data may be expressed by five, six, or seven digits, preceded by a minus sign when it is necessary to indicate negative quantities.

Block length. Sometimes limitations in tape-preparation equipment limits the number of characters that can be placed in a block of data.

Function coding. Miscellaneous function coding and corresponding specific functions (M-address) are generally of an on-off nature, controlling the machine tool. G-address functions are used to direct the machine tool control unit through a given operation or for controlling the axes.

Spindle Speeds. These are usually programmed with an S-address prefix and a number of digits to indicate the desired machine speed.

Feed rate. Such codes are prefixed by the letter "F," and feed

changes are specified by a variety of codes.

In addition to tape format, quantities must be considered. This can include the type of dimensioning system used and other factors dictated by limitations of the control unit.

After the process sheet has been prepared, it is turned over to the tape punch operator who punches the tape and then verifies it for accuracy. 102–7.

The tape used is a standard 1″ wide paper or Mylar coated tape and is punched with an eight-unit code. The code perforations are punched across the width of the tape. There are eight positions available for code holes and these positions are called channels. These channels are numbered, 8, 7, 6, 5, 4, 3, 2, and 1, from left to right. Feed holes, which assure proper positioning of the tape in the punch, and the mechanical tape reader, are located between the third and fourth channels and are in line with the code holes.

The tape can be punched with any one of three or four relatively inexpensive special-purpose machines or a standard office

102–7. Converting a machine operation to N/C tape. Device punches the necessary holes in the tape.

Technical Education & Mfg., Inc.

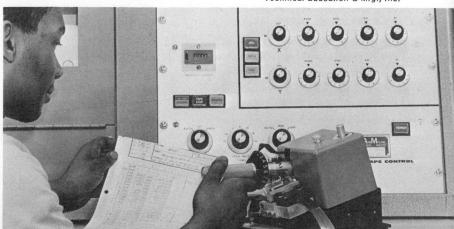

Friden, Inc.

102–8. Information typed on special typewriter with tape attachments, the result being a completely coded and punched tape.

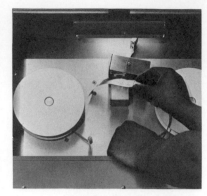

Technical Education & Mfg., Inc.

102–9. Loading the tape in the N/C tape reader.

unit automatically controls the tool after positioning.

Starting from the setup point, each line is given a sequence number which is entered in the column under seq. no. The zero sequence contains no positioning data.

The rewind stop instructions to the tape reader and the EOB code are entered here.

Using the tab-sequential format, X axis positioning commands follow the first tab and the Y axis commands the second tab. Therefore, a tab should be entered in the second column, and the direction (+ or —) and magnitude of the desired X increment should be entered in the third and fourth columns. A tab

Flexowriter. Since this step is similar to using an electric typewriter, many secretaries can do this operation with a minimum amount of training. 102–8. The strip of punched tape is then ready to go to the machine and start producing the part. 102–9.

Programming a Point-to-Point Drilling Operation*

The following paragraphs detail the steps in programming a simple point-to-point drilling program on a drilling machine or vertical mill equipped with the Slo-Syn N/C system.

Using the tab-sequential format and the codes given in Fig. 102–3, eight holes are to be drilled in a part. 102–10. The program is for an incrementally positioning controller. From the original drawing, a sketch is

* Robert Link and Robert Clark, "Taking The Mystery out of Numerical Programming for the Small Shop," The Superior Electric Company.

made of the part and the dimensions are changed to point-to-point increments for the purposes of programming. 102–11. A setup point has been added, and the holes have been numbered in the sketch, showing the drilling order. Arrows on the sketch are added to indicate the plus direction for the X and Y axes. The completed program sheet is shown in the illustration. 102–12.

It should be noted that no tool changes are necessary as all the holes are the same diameter. Each horizontal line of information on the program sheet makes up one sequence or block of operations. It also contains the information for one positioning movement together with any miscellaneous functions, such as tool changes, required in conjunction with the positioning movement. The program shown has been arranged so that the drilling operations will be performed by the control unit after positioning has been completed.

No code is required for the tool actuation, since the control

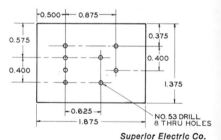

Superior Electric Co.

102–10. Drawing of component board.

102–11. Programmer's sketch of component board.

Superior Electric Co.

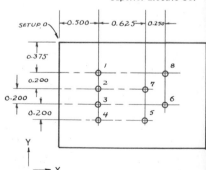

SLO-SYN TAPE CONTROLLED INDEXER PROGRAM

COMPANY NAME _Acme Precision Products_   ADDRESS _Clark St. Podunk, Conn._

PREPARED BY _LH_ DATE _1-26-66_	PART NAME _Component Board_				PART NO. _BC11365_		OPER. NO. _—_
CK'D BY _BWE_ DATE _1-27-66_							
SHEET _1_ OF _1_	REMARKS:						
DEPT _18_	_NCIR24 w/ Backlash Compensation_ _Bridgeport 72421 Machine_ _#53 Drill 8 Thru Holes_						
TAPE NO _105_							

SEQ NO	TAB OR EOB	+ OR	X INCREMENT	TAB OR EOB	+ OR	"Y" INCREMENT	TAB OR EOB	"M" FUNCT	EOB	INSTRUCTIONS
	E									
%	E									LOAD START
1	T		500	T	-	375	E			
2	T			T	-	200	E			
3	T			T	-	200	E			
4	T			T	-	200	E			
5	T		625	E						
6	T		250	T		200	E			
7	T	-	250	T		200	E			
8	T		250	T		200	E			
9	T	-	1375	T		375	T	02	E	

Superior Electric Co.

102–12. Programming sheet for component board.

is entered in the fifth column to indicate that the X axis command is complete and the Y command is to follow. The appropriate Y axis commands are entered in the sixth and seventh columns and a tab code is placed in column eight. Rewind, tool change, and any other miscellaneous function codes required are entered in column nine, and an EOB code is placed in column ten to tell the control unit that the block of information is complete. A space is provided for instructions to the operator.

In sequence 1 on the program sheet, the program calls for movements of 0.500″ in the plus direction along the Y axis. Upon completion of the positioning phase, the control unit will actuate the tool to drill the first hole.

In the same manner, the remaining seven holes will be drilled, each sequence or block of information containing the codes needed to bring the workpiece to the next position to drill a

hole. Upon completion of the drilling operation, the control unit returns the work to the setup point and rewinds the tape. The 02 code in sequence 9 is the numerical code for tape rewind.

With a point-to-point system, straight-line milling programs can be easily worked out. This operation requires raising and lowering the tool and the appropriate "M" function code is inserted in the program. Also in this operation, the diameter of the cutting tool must be taken into consideration.

Sample Milling Program

Focus:

1. Basic programming procedure for milling.

Note:

1. Machine operation will be milling. 102–13.

2. Tool advance, tool retract, and Hi Feed will be actuated from tape. The commands used are:

52	Tool advance.
53	Tool retract.
55	Hi Feed.

102–13. Sample of a simple milling operation on a vertical milling machine equipped with N/C controls.

Superior Electric Co.

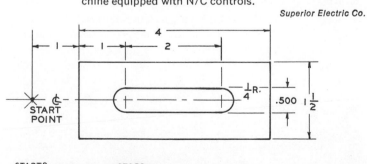

SEQ. NO.3 — RETURNS TO START POINT — HIGH FEED

SLO-SYN™ NUMERICAL TAPE CONTROL **PROGRAM**

COMPANY NAME _____ ADDRESS _____

PREPARED BY DATE		PART NAME			PART NO. Sample Milling Program No. 1		OPER. NO.
CK'D BY DATE							
SHEET	OF	REMARKS:					
DEPT.			Tool Switch—Off		Tools: 1/2″ End Mill		
TAPE NO.			Feed Rate—6 ipm				
			Backlash—No. 1 or No. 2				

SEQ. NO.	TAB OR EOB	+ OR –	"x" INCREMENT	TAB OR EOB	+ OR –	"y" INCREMENT	TAB OR EOB	"m" FUNCT.	EOB	INSTRUCTIONS
									EOB	
0	RWS								EOB	
1	TAB		2000	TAB			TAB	55	EOB	
2	TAB		2000	TAB			TAB	52	EOB	
3	TAB	–	4000	TAB			TAB	02535	EOB	

Superior Electric Co.

102–14. The program for the N/C milling operation.

3. Backlash take-up not required.

Program notes:

1. Console presets: (A) Tool switch is at off. The tool will be advanced and retracted by tape commands. (B) Feed rate switch is at 6 ipm. (C) Backlash switch is at No. 1 or No. 2. The backlash take-up circuit will not operate. 102–14.

2. Sequence 1 statement moves the tool from the starting point to the beginning of the slot. The 55 (Hi Feed) code causes this tool movement to be done at the Hi Feed rate.

3. Sequence 2 statement prescribes the tool motion from the end of the milled slot and has a 52 (tool advance) code. The tool will advance into the work before positioning begins.

4. Sequence 3 statement prescribes the tool motion from the end of the milled slot back to the starting point and contains 02 (tape rewind), 53 (tool retract), and 55 (Hi Feed) codes. The resulting action will be as follows: (1) the tool will retract, (2) the tool will be returned to the starting point at the Hi Feed rate, and (3) the tape will be rewound to the RWS code.

Tape Controlled Continuous Path Milling

The illustration shows an N/C continuous path milling machine. 102–15. This machine features a tape reading, numerical control system that allows automatic, continuous path, contour milling of two- or three-dimensional shapes.

In its operation a numerical drawing is prepared by a draftsman who modifies the original part drawing so that the required dimensions are given in the form of conventional rectangular coordinates referenced to a set of three axes. 102–16.

The process sheet lists the dimensional data from the numerical drawing together with machining sequences, tolerances, pocket milling instructions, cutter diameter, feeds, and auxiliary (bang-bang) functions. 102–17.

The computer input process tape is prepared by a typist on the process tape typing-and-punching unit. The unit automatically condenses this information into coded form on a tape that can be fed into the computer.

The computer carries all routine and detailed mathematical calculations and punches the machine control tape. The operation of the system simply calls for inserting the process tape into a reader that feeds its data to the computer. The computer makes its calculations from the data it receives from the process tape, manipulates it, and outputs

102–15. N/C continuous path milling machine.

Colt Industries and Pratt & Whitney, Inc., Machine Tool Div.

the proper data on the machine control tape. The process planner can check the cutter locations that are being calculated along the path by observing the record produced by a control typewriter.

The machine control unit has the control tape mounted on the reels of the unit's photoelectric reader. The operator then locates the cutter at the setup, or starting point, and selects the desired spindle speed. When the go button is pressed, the reading of the tape, block by block, sends binary information through the electronic circuitry. This information is manipulated and sent

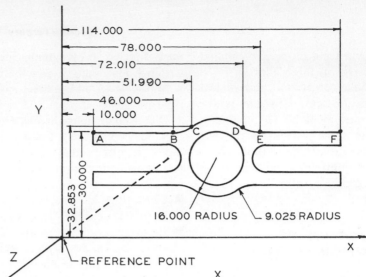

Colt Industries and Pratt & Whitney, Inc., Machine Tool Div.

102–16. The numerical drawing for a typical profile milling operation. The points required to describe the parts geometry are stated relative to the X, Y, and Z axes by rectangular or angular coordinates.

102–17. This process sheet lists the dimensional data from the numerical drawing together with machining sequence, tolerances, cutter diameter, etc.

PRATT & WHITNEY PROCESS SHEET

SETUP POINT				CLEARANCE PLANE	TOLERANCE	TYPE OF APPROX.	DATE				PART NO.				
X	Y	Z	/	z_0							TAPE NO.				
IN.	IN.	IN.		IN. **C**	IN. **E**	**F**	PLANNER **I**				SHEET		OF	**P**	
001.0000	001.0000	012.0000		015.0000	000.0002	/									
END POINT OF SECTION			**B**	INITIAL CLEARANCE	CIRCLE RADIUS	ARC LENGTH	CORNER	TYPE OF POINT	R	FEED RATE	TOOL DIAM.	R	AUX. FUNC.	R	FINAL CUT	ROUGH CUT PASSES	NO. OF SECTIONS	R
X	Y	Z	/	**U**	**D**		**H**		**J** 00	**K**	**L**	**M** 40	**N**	**O** 41	**Q**	**R**	**S**	**T** 01
IN.	IN.	IN.		IN.	IN.	**G**				IN./MIN.	IN.				IN.			
010.0000	030.0000	012.0000	/			0	+1	-2	00	025.0000	-003.0000	40						

TYPICAL LAYOUT

A. Coordinate dimensions from the numerical drawing. These dimensions are listed vertically in the sequence in which they will be machined, beginning with the setup point in the upper left hand corner.

B. A character which separates different groups of information being fed into the computer.

C. The Z-coordinate of a plane parallel to the work surface in which the cutter will clear the work or fixture at all points.

D. The radius of a circular surface that is to be machined (coded for clockwise or counterclockwise). Only the coordinates of the start and the end of an arc need to be specified. The computer interpolates the intermediate points.

E. The allowable mathematical deviation or tolerance for the circular surface (needed for computer interpolation).

F. The type of approximation for the circle (coded for secant, chord or tangent).

G. The length of the arc of the circular surface (coded for straight line, equal to or less than 180 degrees or greater than 180-degrees).

H. The type of corner (coded for inside corner, outside corner or a slow-down at the corner).

I. Indicates whether the X, Y and Z coordinates specify part geometry (section points) or cutter center locus (index points).

J. A key telling type of information (for the computer).

K. The rate of feed of the cutter across the work surface.

L. The diameter of the cutting tool (coded for cutting on right side or cutting on left side).

M. A key telling type of information (for the computer).

N. A key to stop or initiate on-off functions at the machine.

O. A key telling type of information (for the computer).

P. For pocket milling operations.

Q. The amount of material to be removed in the finish cut (coded for a finish cut to follow a rough cut immediately or to carry out a finish cut at a later time).

R. The number of cutter passes in the pocket preceding the finish cut. This determines the amount of overlap between cutter passes.

S. The number of curves and straight lines that enclose the pocket.

T. A key telling type of information (for the computer).

U. Used only for pocket milling to indicate distance from periphery of pocket to cutter center for first roughing pass.

515

out as a train of exact command pulses to all three axes.

These electronic command pulses are converted into power and movement by the operation of the servo valves on the hydraulic drive motor, thus effecting a continuous motion along the path at the feed rates planned.

ADVANTAGES OF NUMERICAL CONTROL*

It takes just as long to mill a surface or drill, bore, or tap a hole with N/C equipment as it does with properly used, late-model, conventional machines.

Thus, the savings and benefits of N/C come not from higher metal-cutting rates, but from "management-managed production"—greater control over the entire manufacturing process. The influence of machine operators on production rates and profits is minimized. Manage-

---

* Sunstrand Machine Tool, Division of Sunstrand Corporation.

ment-directed programming determines machining productivity.

Major direct and indirect savings are achieved.

Direct labor hours involved in N/C machining are a fraction of those required under conventional methods. Large time-savings result from:
● Converting idle machine time to metal-cutting time.
● Performing all, or nearly all, required operations with a single machine, thus reducing the number of setups and eliminating work handling between machines.
● Consistently using the correct speeds, feeds, and tooling to achieve optimum productivity.
● Reducing the number of inspections between operations without loss of accuracy in the finished part.

The indirect influences of N/C go far beyond actual machining to include the following:
● Inventory reduction.
● Profit on increased shipments.
● Fewer machines and operators.

● Floor space savings.
● Less machinist skill required.
● Elimination of jigs and reduction in fixturing costs.
● Assembly time savings.
● Reduced scrap and rework.
● Reduced machine and tool damage.
● Simplified scheduling.
● More accurate time studies and costing.
● Savings in lead time for design and production.
● Greater return per dollar of machine investment.
● Versatility of future requirements.
● Improved product design and quality.

DISADVANTAGES OF NUMERICAL CONTROL

The disadvantages of numerical control are:
● The initial cost is rather high.
● Skilled personnel in the electronics field are required to service machines, as the machines and controls are complicated.
● Additional space is required.

Unit 103. Modern Numerically Controlled Machines

N/C TURNING CENTER
The Omnilathe N/C Turning Center, with 2-axis numerical contouring control, greatly increases the efficiency of small-lot turning of spindles, shafts, toolholders, and other irregularly shaped parts. 103–1. The elimination of templates, coupled with

fast, simple setup, make this machine a practical tool. 103–2 & 103–3.

Setup time is normally 15 minutes maximum. Tool changing is fast—roughly two minutes—and boring tool adapters and tools can be installed in the turret in five minutes. Dial-in tool offsets

provide quick, easy compensation for any deviation in tool-setting or tool wear.

A 3-AXIS MILLING CENTER
The milling center shown in the illustration is a heavy duty, 20 hp, bed type milling and profiling machine with additional capability of boring, drilling, and tapping. 103–4 & 103–5 (Page 518).

This machine finds broad application for production and tool-room work, including die sinking.

This machine is especially valuable to plants making products in a variety of sizes, particularly when the components have a number of surfaces to be machined at varying depths or levels.

Because the N/C provides measurement control for high accuracy and controlled positioning for fast cycling, it is ideal where the variety of milling cycles exceeds the practical capability of conventional milling control.

OMNIMILL 5-AXIS N/C MACHINING CENTER

A tremendous variety of work can be performed on this 5-axis machining center in less time and at less cost than by any other method.

The one-machine production line will mill, drill, bore, tap, and contour all exposed faces of a workpiece at any angle. 103–6. With only one or two setups,

Sundstrand Machine Tool Co.

103–1. Omnilathe N/C turning center.

103–3. The type of OD and ID operations that can be performed with a single 8-position turret on the N/C turning center.

Sundstrand Machine Tool Co.

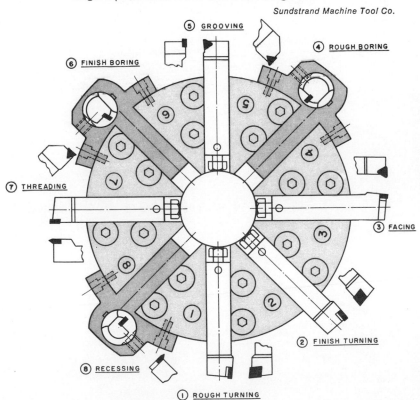

⑤ GROOVING
④ ROUGH BORING
⑥ FINISH BORING
⑦ THREADING
③ FACING
② FINISH TURNING
⑧ RECESSING
① ROUGH TURNING

103–2. Operations that can be performed on the Omnilathe turning center.

Sundstrand Machine Tool Co.

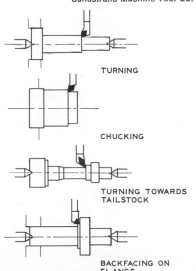

TURNING

CHUCKING

TURNING TOWARDS TAILSTOCK

BACKFACING ON FLANGE

it will perform all operations required on most parts, thus replacing entire groups of conventional machines.

Two independent spindles accommodate all materials. One operates in lower speed range required for hand-to-machine materials; the other operates in higher range for free machining materials.

The high productivity of this machine stems from the programmed N/C operation, fast automatic tool changing (up to 60 different tools), and simple setup. 103–7. An optional automatic pallet changer further reduces idle time by making it possible to set up one workpiece while another is being machined.

N/C MACHINING CENTER

Another type of N/C machining center is shown in the illustration.

Sundstrand Machine Tool Co.

103–4. Sundstrand, OM-2, Omnimil, 3-axis, machining center, equipped with optional 60-position tool storage drum. This machine features a 60"-high column plus wide table to accommodate larger piece parts.

103–5. Operations that can be done on the 20-hp, 3-axis, numerically controlled, 3 Ridgimil milling center.

Sundstrand Machine Tool Co.

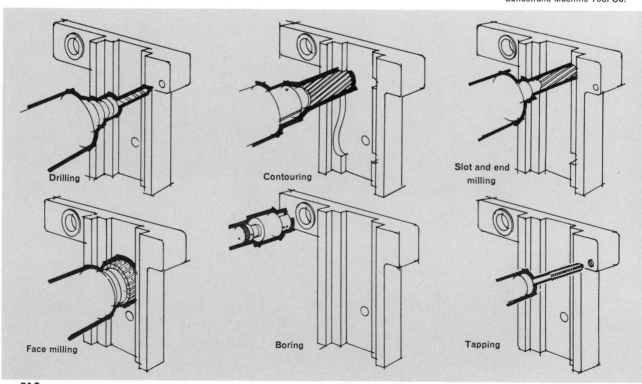

Drilling

Contouring

Slot and end milling

Face milling

Boring

Tapping

On this particular machine up to fifteen preset tools can be loaded, in sequence, in the magazine at any one time. At the start of each machining operation, the magazine is automatically indexed to the first tool position. Thereafter, taped commands rotate the magazine to the next tool during other machining functions.

Maximum tool size for automatic changing is 4″ in diameter and 7½″ in length. 103–8. Larger tools may be used with selective programming or through manual loading. Drills and boring bars to 10″ long can be handled automatically.

This machine can perform milling, drilling, tapping, and boring operations in a single setup.

Sundstrand Machine Tool Co.

103–6. A 5-axis machining center. This machine is used to perform multiple operations on a complex aircraft part.

103–7. Note the large variety of operations that can be performed on a 5-axis Omnimil machining center.   *Sundstrand Machine Tool Co.*

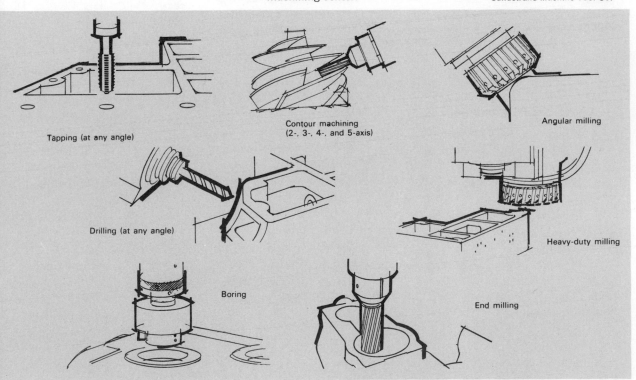

Tapping (at any angle)

Contour machining (2-, 3-, 4-, and 5-axis)

Angular milling

Drilling (at any angle)

Heavy-duty milling

Boring

End milling

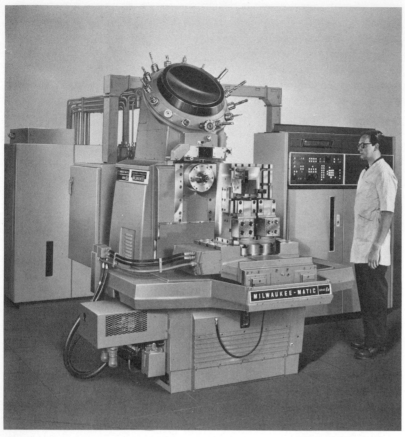

Kearney & Trecker Corp.

103–8. With this N/C machining center, fifteen preset tools can be loaded in the magazine at one time.

Check Your Knowledge

1. What is numerical control?

2. What part does electronics play in numerical control?

3. What signals do transducers provide?

4. Explain the difference between analog and digital signals. Give examples.

5. List the basic components of an N/C system.

6. Give a brief description of how N/C works.

7. Explain the difference between the point-to-point and contouring systems.

8. What is the measuring basis for N/C control systems? Explain.

9. What guides are available to the N/C programmer?

10. What is the function of code-on-tape formats?

11. What is the function of the following: sequence number, tab, and EOB?

12. What is the programmer expected to do and know?

13. Name the two types of standardized tape formats.

14. What operations are best suited to numerical control?

15. What machining operations are best suited to contouring commands?

16. Of what advantage is a computer to N/C operations?

17. How are electronic command pulses converted into power and movement in continuous path machining?

18. Name some advantages of numerical control.

References

The Bendix Corporation, *N/C Handbook,* 1969.

Chandler, Robert, "Design for Numerical Control Machining," *Machining Design,* February 15, 1968.

Conaway, Dr. John W.; Bringman, Dale; and Doane, Dr. Ray C., *Handbook for Slo-Syn Numerical Control,* The Superior Electric Co.

Link, Robert, and Clark, Robert, "Taking the Mystery Out of Numerical Programming for the Small Shop," *Western Machinery and Steel World.*

"Numerical Control for Metalworking Manufacturing," *American Machinist/Metalworking Manufacturing,* New York, McGraw-Hill Book Co., 1960.

Stocker, William M., Jr., "The ABC's of Numerical Control," *American Machinist/Metalworking Manufacturing,* August 8, 1960.

Section Twenty-Four

Welding Processes

WELDING is the joining of two or more metal parts into one homogeneous part by means of heat, pressure, or both.

A weld is defined by the American Welding Society as "a localized coalescence of metal wherein coalescence is produced by heating to suitable temperatures, with or without the application of pressure, and with or without the use of filler metal. The filler metal either has a melting point approximately the same as the base metals or has a melting point below that of the base metals but above 800°F."

Welding is used today in every major industry. There is hardly a product produced that does not contain some weldments. To a large degree, welding has replaced other types of permanent fasteners.

Some welding requires that the metal be hammered, rolled, or pressed to effect a weld. Welding processes that use pressure require that the metal be heated to a designated temperature before pressure is applied to unite the surfaces. Other processes bring the metal to a fluid state, and no pressure is required to weld the surfaces together.

In all types of welding, surfaces must be cleaned and surface oxides removed to prevent them from becoming mixed with the solidifying metal. Oxides are removed in fusible slags by employing a flux which can be part of the electrode or can be in the form of a powder such as that used in gas or forge welding. In some processes, a nonoxidizing atmosphere is formed at the point where welding occurs.

Unit 104. Forge Welding

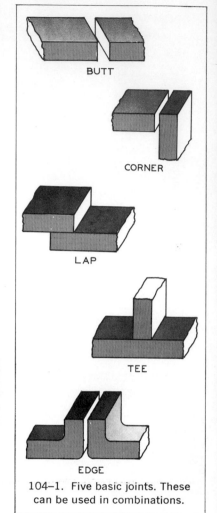

104–1. Five basic joints. These can be used in combinations.

Forge welding can be traced back many years to when the blacksmith developed the basic forging tools—the hammer, forge, anvil, and bellows—for controlling the fire. These tools were forerunners to the modern drop forge, air hammer, and hot forming machines.

The forge welding process, used little today, consists of heating metal in a forge to a plastic condition and hammering the parts together. The heating is done in a forge fired by coal or coke. After pieces to be joined are heated in the forge, they are scarfed (tapered). The ends are then heated again and dipped into borax, which is used as a flux. The metal is next heated again until the workpieces are at the proper welding temperature.

When workpieces are withdrawn from the forge, the scale is knocked off. The parts are placed together and hammered to weld them into one piece.

TYPES OF JOINTS AND WELDS

In general, there are five basic types of joints which are common to both arc and gas welding. The five are: (1) butt, (2) corner, (3) lap, (4) edge, and (5) tee. 104–1.

Each of these types might incorporate several variations to provide for different service requirements. 104–2.

In designing a welded product, the selection of the proper weld joint is governed by: (1) type of loading, (2) cost which involves edge preparation, (3) type of equipment to be used, and (4) process and speed with which the welding operation can be performed.

The basic type of welds are: (1) fillet, (2) groove, (3) plug, (4) bead or surfacing, and (5) arc spot or arc seam weld. 104–3(A&B). Illustration 104–3(B) shown on page 524.

COMMON WELDING PROCESSES

A. Forge welding
  1. Manual
  2. Machine
    a. Hammer
    b. Die
    c. Rolling
B. Gas welding
  1. Oxyacetylene
  2. Air-acetylene
  3. Pressure
  4. Oxyhydrogen
C. Arc welding
  1. Carbon electrode
    a. Shielded
    b. Unshielded
  2. Metal electrode
    a. Gas tungsten inert shielding (TIG)
    b. Gas metal—inert shielding (MIG)
    c. Submerged-arc
    d. Open-arc
    e. Gas metal-arc CO_2 shielding
    f. Micro-wire
    g. Stud
    h. Electroslag
D. Resistance welding
  1. Spot
  2. Seam
  3. Flash-butt
  4. Projection
  5. Percussion
E. Inertia welding
F. Ultrasonic welding
G. Thermit welding
H. Electron beam welding

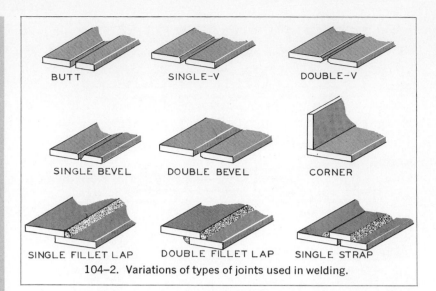

104–2. Variations of types of joints used in welding.

BUTT SINGLE-V DOUBLE-V SINGLE BEVEL DOUBLE BEVEL CORNER SINGLE FILLET LAP DOUBLE FILLET LAP SINGLE STRAP

Fillet welds are used for tee, lap, and corner joints 104–4 (Page 24). Groove welds are used for obtaining full-thickness strength on thick materials. The welds are generally made either in a single pass or by multiple-pass methods, depending upon material thickness. As shown in the illustration, there may be several variations of grooves such as: square, single-vee, double-vee, single-bevel, double-bevel, single-U, etc. 104–5 (Page 524). The thickness of the material governs to a certain extent the type of grooves used, the welding process employed, and the work position.

Plug welds are used when fastening one piece of material on top of another in situations

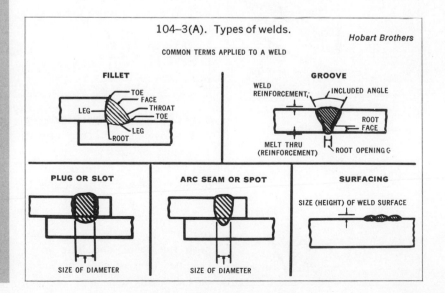

104–3(A). Types of welds.

Hobart Brothers

COMMON TERMS APPLIED TO A WELD

FILLET — TOE, FACE, THROAT, TOE, LEG, LEG, ROOT

GROOVE — WELD REINFORCEMENT, INCLUDED ANGLE, ROOT FACE, MELT THRU (REINFORCEMENT), ROOT OPENING G

PLUG OR SLOT — SIZE OF DIAMETER

ARC SEAM OR SPOT — SIZE OF DIAMETER

SURFACING — SIZE (HEIGHT) OF WELD SURFACE

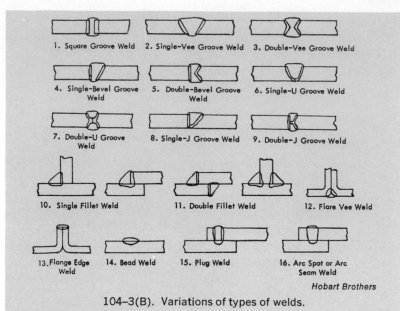

1. Square Groove Weld 2. Single-Vee Groove Weld 3. Double-Vee Groove Weld

4. Single-Bevel Groove Weld 5. Double-Bevel Groove Weld 6. Single-U Groove Weld

7. Double-U Groove Weld 8. Single-J Groove Weld 9. Double-J Groove Weld

10. Single Fillet Weld 11. Double Fillet Weld 12. Flare Vee Weld

13. Flange Edge Weld 14. Bead Weld 15. Plug Weld 16. Arc Spot or Arc Seam Weld

Hobart Brothers

104–3(B). Variations of types of welds.

where bolts and rivets are eliminated.

A bead is a type of weld deposited on the surface of a material when no groove is to be used. It can be used to build up the surface of the material when surfaces become worn.

Arc spot or arc seam welds can be made by an argon shielded electric arc, using a consumable electrode. A small welding gun with a pistol grip is held tightly against the work to be welded. By pressing the trigger, the argon valve is opened, and the current passes through the electrode for a preset interval, creating the weld.

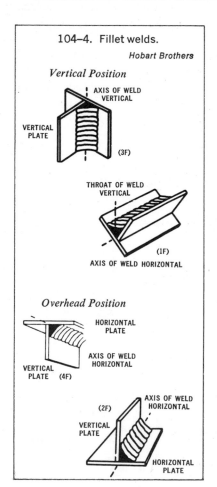

104–4. Fillet welds.

Hobart Brothers

Vertical Position

AXIS OF WELD VERTICAL

VERTICAL PLATE

(3F)

THROAT OF WELD VERTICAL

(1F)

AXIS OF WELD HORIZONTAL

Overhead Position

HORIZONTAL PLATE

AXIS OF WELD HORIZONTAL

VERTICAL PLATE (4F)

AXIS OF WELD HORIZONTAL

(2F)

VERTICAL PLATE

HORIZONTAL PLATE

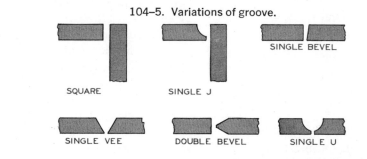

104–5. Variations of groove.

SQUARE SINGLE J SINGLE BEVEL

SINGLE VEE DOUBLE BEVEL SINGLE U

Unit 105. Gas Welding

OXYACETYLENE WELDING

This welding process utilizes a mixture of acetylene and oxygen in the correct proportions to produce a flame hot enough to melt specific metals.

In oxyacetylene welding no pressure is needed to accomplish the weld. The base metal is joined in most cases by fusion of the metal deposited between the two surfaces. In some instances the heated edges can be fused without the use of filler metal.

Such metals as iron, steel, cast iron, copper, brass, aluminum, bronze, and other alloys may be welded. Sometimes it is possible to join dissimilar metals such as steel and cast iron or brass and steel.

Welding Equipment

The basic oxyacetylene equipment consists of an oxygen cylinder, acetylene cylinder, two regulators, two lengths of hose, a welding torch with an assortment of welding tips, and hose fittings. The cylinders can be mounted on a two-wheel truck in order to facilitate moving the equipment.

Oxygen cylinders are charged with oxygen at a pressure of 2,200 pounds per square inch at 70° F. 105–1. The pressure in the cylinder will increase and decrease as the temperature changes, since the volume remains constant. To provide against dangerously excessive pressures, such as could occur if the cylinders were exposed to fire, every valve has a safety device to release the oxygen before there is any danger of rupturing the cylinders.

When a great deal of welding is to be done, as in industrial practices, the oxygen cylinders are frequently connected to a manifold, with pipelines carry-

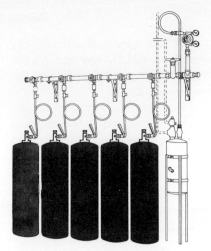

Smith Welding Equipment

105–2(A). Manifold with oxygen cylinders connected to a pipeline.

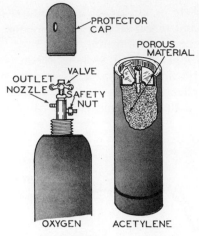

105–2(B). Oxygen and acetylene cylinders are used for storage.

ing the gas to the various welding stations. 105–2(A).

Acetylene cylinders are filled with a porous substance which is saturated with acetone. 105–2(B). Acetylene is not safe when stored at over 15 psi and, for this reason, must be dissolved in acetone. The porous material consists of such materials as balsa wood chips and infusorial earth. The voids in the filler material are filled with acetone which dissolves the acetylene gas under pressure.

When large quantities of acetylene are required as in industrial applications, an acetylene generator is used. 105–3. In operation, controlled amounts of calcium are fed into water, producing acetylene gas. The reaction that takes place in the generator is:

$$CaC_2 + 2H_2O =$$
$$Ca(OH)_2 + C_2H_2$$

CaC_2 = calcium carbide
$2H_2O$ = water
$Ca(OH)_2$ = slaked lime
C_2H_2 = acetylene gas

In the welding process, the oxygen and acetylene gases are fed through a torch or blowpipe which mixes the two in correct proportions. 105–4 (Page 526). This mixture of gases flows to the tip of the torch where it is ignited. Mixtures of oxygen with acety-

105–3. Acetylene generator.

Rexarc, Inc.

105–1. Oxygen cylinder.

Pressed Steel Tank Co., Inc.

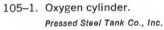

lene or air are highly explosive, and care must be taken in mixing the gases properly.

The typical welding torch is provided with a series of interchangeable tips of different sizes so that the same handle can be used in a variety of different operations. 105–5. The tip sizes are governed by the diameter of the opening. 105–6.

Regulators are used to reduce cylinder pressure to the required working pressure and also to produce a steady flow of gas under varying pressures. 105–7 (A&B). All oxygen fittings have right-hand threads, while acetylene fittings are equipped with left-hand threads.

A sparklighter is used to ignite the torch, and the proper flame is obtained by adjusting the torch which controls the volume of gases delivered to the torch tip.

Three types of flames can be obtained by varying the ratio of acetylene and oxygen. 105–8. A *neutral flame* is obtained if the ratio of oxygen to acetylene is about 1:1 to 1.15:1. The pale blue core of the flame is known as the inner cone. The oxygen required for the combustion of the carbon monoxide and hydrogen in the outer envelope of the flame is supplied by the air. The inner cone of the neutral flame is from $\frac{1}{16}$ to 1″ long, depending upon the size of the welding head. If the size of the head is increased, a larger flame will be produced.

The neutral flame is of particular importance not only because it permits a wide variety of welding and cutting operations but also because it serves as a basis of reference for making other flame adjustments. This flame is used in most welding operations since it has the least chemical effect on most heated metals.

When there is an excess of oxygen over the ratio required for a neutral flame, the inner cone is shorter and more pointed with an almost purple color rather than a brilliant white. This is called an *oxidizing flame*. A slightly oxidizing flame is used in braze-welding and bronze surfacing while a strongly oxidizing

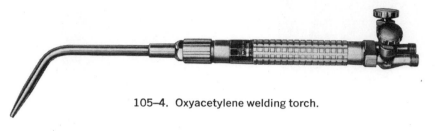

105–4. Oxyacetylene welding torch.

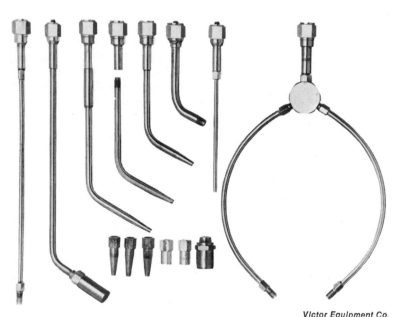

Victor Equipment Co.

105–5. Welding tips and nozzles.

105–6. Schematic illustration of oxyacetylene torch and gas supply.

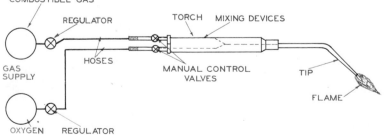

flame is used in fusion welding certain brasses and bronzes.

A *carbonizing flame* is the result of an excess of acetylene over the ratio required for a neutral flame. The excess acetylene flame has a third zone between the inner cone and the outer envelope, known as the excess acetylene feather. This feather contains white hot carbon particles, some of which, during welding are dissolved by the molten metal.

Union Carbide, Linde Div.

105–7(A). Regulator for an oxygen tank.

105–7(B). Regulator for an acetylene tank.

Union Carbide, Linde Div.

AIR-ACETYLENE WELDING

This process uses a torch similar to a Bunsen burner. The air is drawn into the torch as required for proper combustion. This type of welding has limited use since the temperature is lower than that attained by other gas processes. It can be used successfully in lead welding and low-temperature brazing or soldering processes.

PRESSURE GAS WELDING

This is used in applications where butt joints are required, as in welding railroad rails or pipe. In this process the ends of the material are heated with a gas flame to a temperature below the melting point. Then pressure is applied to the parts, forcing the two ends together to form a weld.

OXYHYDROGEN WELDING

Used to weld thin sheets, this process can also be used in some brazing work.

Oxyhydrogen burns at a temperature of approximately 3600° F. The same equipment can be used in this process as in oxyacetylene welding. Flame adjustments are rather difficult, however, as there is an absence of color to judge the correct gas proportions. No oxides are formed on the surface of the material in oxyhydrogen welding. The qual-

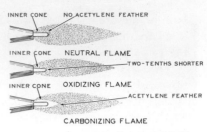

INNER CONE NO ACETYLENE FEATHER

INNER CONE NEUTRAL FLAME

TWO-TENTHS SHORTER

INNER CONE OXIDIZING FLAME

ACETYLENE FEATHER

CARBONIZING FLAME

Union Carbide, Linde Div.

105–8. Three types of oxyacetylene welding flames.

ity of the welds is the same as by other gas welding processes.

FLAME CUTTING

The flame cutting process of cutting ferrous metals has become an important industrial production process.

Flame cutting consists of heating metal with a flame cutting torch and then directing a stream of oxygen on the spot. This causes rapid oxidation that reduces the metal to iron oxide.

Oxyacetylene cutting torches are designed to provide both a stream of pure oxygen that does the actual cutting and small acetylene flames that are used to accomplish the original heating of the material and supply additional heat so that the cutting will be a continuous operation. 105–9.

The cutting tip has an orifice in the center surrounded by several smaller holes. These are for preheating the material. Three valves are provided with the

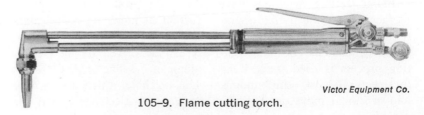

Victor Equipment Co.

105–9. Flame cutting torch.

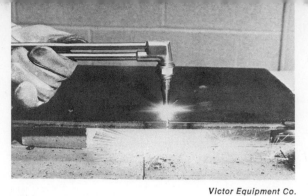

Victor Equipment Co.

105–10. Operation of flame cutting torch.

Chemtron Corp.

105–11. Oxyacetylene cutting machine.

cutting torch. Two of these valves are used to regulate the mixture of oxygen and acetylene which produces the preheating flames. The third valve regulates the flow of pure oxygen needed for cutting. 105–10.

Cutting torches can be manipulated manually or controlled by mechanical means. Cutting machines of various types have been developed. One such type has the tool mounted on a small electrically driven carriage which moves on a track, controlling the movement of the torch.

For production processes, cutting machines have been developed which automatically cut several parts simultaneously. 105–11. These machines are equipped with several torches and have tracer mechanisms which follow a template similar to devices used on machine tools.

Recently, tape controlled cutting torch machines have been developed. This equipment increases production and provides greater accuracy than other flame cutting machines.

Flame cutting machines have replaced many machining operations, particularly where accuracy is not demanded. The flame cutting process is used successfully in structural work, shipbuilding, and in similar industries.

528

Unit 106. Arc Welding

Arc welding is the process of joining metal by means of heat created by an electric arc. Additional metal melted in with the base metal fills the bond. By bringing the material to be welded and the electrode together, an electric circuit is created, and by separating the conductors, an electric arc is formed. The electrical energy produced is converted into intense heat (approximately 10,000° F. in the arc).

ARC WELDING EQUIPMENT

Welding machines in common use are of two basic types: (1) DC welders using direct current and (2) AC welders using alternating current. 106–1 & 106–2. Some machines are made to provide both types of current.

The DC welder has a generator to produce the required current in much the same manner as an automobile generator. It can be driven by an electric motor or gasoline engine. 106–3. This machine, which uses a wide variety of electrodes, can do

certain types of jobs that AC welders cannot do. Output can be controlled to a better advantage because the polarity in the circuit can be changed, which permits the use of a wider selection of electrodes.

The AC welder uses a built-in transformer. The polarity in this machine is constantly reversing itself, minimizing its importance.

106–1. DC welder.

Hobart Brothers

One advantage of the AC welder is the freedom from magnetic arc blow which can occur with DC machines. Other advantages are its low operating cost and its high electrical efficiency.

CARBON-ELECTRODE WELDING

Early arc welding was done with a carbon electrode. Most arc welding today is done with metallic electrodes. Carbon-electrode welding uses the arc solely as a source of heat, and the torch is used in a manner similar to the oxyacetylene torch. However, the temperature runs considerably higher and filler rods supply weld metal if additional metal is required. Early methods used a twin-carbon-arc process where the arc was produced between two electrodes. This type of welding is confined to brazing and soldering.

106–2. AC welder.

In a later process a single carbon electrode was used and an arc created between the electrode and the workpiece. Additional metal could be supplied by a separate rod.

METAL-ELECTRODE WELDING

In the metal-electrode welding process, the heat of the arc melts the electrode and the workpiece simultaneously, and this supplies the filler metal to the weld. 106–4. The electrode is in the form of wire of the desired size and metal. The process can be done either by hand or performed on an automatic machine.

The welding operation is started by adjusting the machine to the correct amperage which is determined by the size of the rod to be used. 106–5.

Two methods are used in striking the arc: (1) the scratch method and (2) the down-up tapping method. 106–6. In the tapping method the electrode is lowered and lightly touched to the workpiece. The electrode is then raised quickly away from the work and lowered again until the proper arc length is obtained.

The scratch method resembles the action of striking a match. The electrode is dragged across

Miller Electric Mfg. Co.
106–3. DC generator driven by gasoline engine.

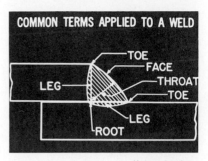

Hobart Brothers
106–4. Common terms applied to a weld.

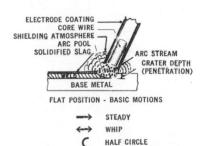

Hobart Brothers
106–5. Electrodes are metal rods covered with a hard-baked enamel.

106–6. Left: the scratch method for starting a weld; right: tapping or down-up method for starting a weld.

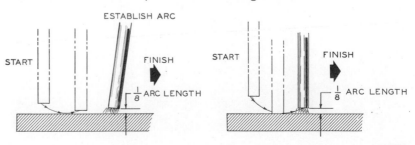

WELD STRESSES

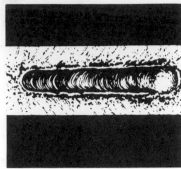

WHY

1. Faulty welds
2. Faulty sequence
3. Rigid joints

WHAT TO DO

1. Allow parts to move freely as long as practical
2. Make as few passes as practical
3. Peen deposits
4. Anneal according to thickness of weld
5. Move parts slightly in welding to reduce stresses

Hobart Brothers

106–7. Weld stresses.

the metal and then raised until the proper arc has been obtained. As the end of the electrode is melted, most of it is transferred across the arc in the form of droplets to a molten pool. The arc is moved at a steady uniform rate. As the electrode shortens in length, it is moved down to maintain the same arc length.

The correct welding speed is important. 106–7. Various currents can have a decided effect on the forming of proper beads. The illustration shows bead characteristics under different conditions: (A) welding current too low; excessive piling up of metal; (B) welding current too high, causing excessive splatter; (C) voltage too high; bead irregular with poor penetration; (D) welding speed too fast and bead too small; (E) welding speed too slow, causing excessive piling up of weld metal; and (F) proper current and timing create a smooth, regular, well-formed bead.

An excessively high current will cause the electrode to melt too fast and create a pool that is too large and irregular. 106–8. Undercutting is also a result of too much current. Not enough current results in overlapping and a lack of fusion with the metal.

Electrodes for Metal-Electrode Welding

Metal electrodes can be classified as bare, fluxed, and heavy-coated.

Electrodes are made for both AC and DC machines to weld specific metals. The American Welding Society has established classifications for identifying and standardizing electrodes. There is also a uniform color code for electrodes.

Symbols such as E–6011 and E–6012 are used to designate specifications of electrodes.

Electrodes are metal rods covered with a hard-baked chemical coating. The size of the electrode, in fractions of an inch, is determined by the diameter of the core rod or wire. The purposes of the chemical-flux coating are as follows:

1. As part of the coating burns, it forms a blanket of gas that acts as a shield around the arc.

2. Part of the flux melts and mixes with the weld metal and floats impurities to the surface to form a slag.

3. It shields the molten metal from the air to prevent nitrogen

106–8. Characteristics of beads under various conditions.

Hobart Brothers

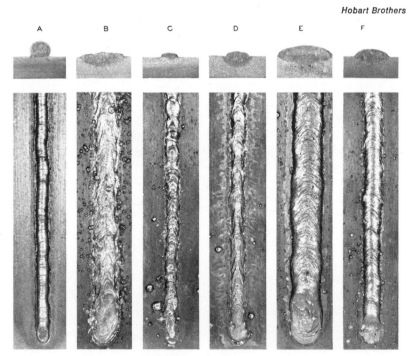

and oxygen from forming impurities in the weld.

4. It slows the hardening rate of the metal.

The coatings on light-coated electrodes seem to increase the arc stability. The illustration shows the action of an arc obtained with both light- and heavy-coated electrodes. 106–9.

Heavy-coated electrodes are made in two forms with cellulose and mineral coatings. Cellulose-coated electrodes depend upon a gaseous shielding as well as a slag covering over the weld deposit for protection around the arc stream. The mineral type depends entirely upon the slag as a shield.

The use of iron powder in the electrode coatings seems to double the speed of the welding process. In contact welding iron powder is used in rather large amounts in the coating of the electrode.

Most metals can be arc welded if an electrode suited to the metal to be welded is used.

In contact arc welding, the coating at the end of the electrode is kept in contact with the workpiece with a drag or contact technique of welding used. Here, welding speeds are high, penetration is deep at the center, and the welds can be made in all positions.

Gas Tungsten-Arc Welding— Inert Shielding (TIG)

Gas tungsten-arc welding is a gas shielded arc welding process which uses the intense heat of an electric arc between a nonconsumable tungsten electrode and the material to be welded. 106–10. Shielding is obtained from

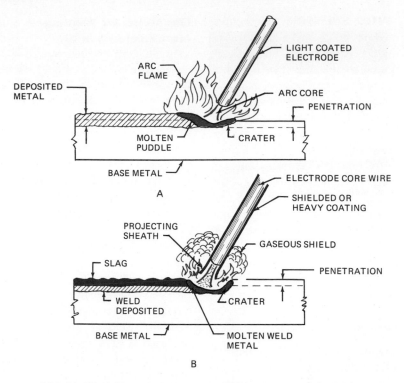

106–9. (A) Light-coated electrode; (B) Heavy-coated electrode.

an inert gas or from a mixture of inert gases. Filler metal may or may not be used. However, it is usually employed, except when welding thin material. When a filler metal rod is used, it is usually fed manually into the weld pool.

The shielding gas displaces the air surrounding the arc and the weld pool. This prevents the contamination of the weld metal by the oxygen and nitrogen in the air. Either argon or helium gas or a mixture of both is used in the inert shielding gas. Argon is more widely used than helium because it is a heavier gas, providing better shielding at a lower flow rate. A gas flow of 15 to 30 cfh is normally used. A somewhat higher rate is used for overhead position welding.

Electrodes used in this process are made of tungsten and tungsten alloys. The melting rate of these electrodes is very high. The electrodes are practically nonconsumable and do not come in contact with the molten weld puddle. The electrode is positioned over the work, and the intense heat from the arc keeps the puddle fluid.

106–10. Schematic illustration of gas tungsten-arc welding (TIG).

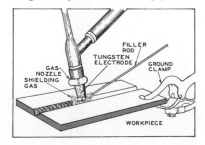

The torch used in this welding method holds the electrode and directs shielding gas and welding power to the arc. Two types of torches are used, either water, which is most widely used, or air cooled. 106–11. A fixture torch is used in the automatic method of welding.

AC or DC current may be used. The selection of current and polarity and the use of high frequency depends upon the material being welded. A specially designed machine is used with the TIG process. This machine may be an AC/DC rectifier or DC generator.

Advantages

Some of the advantages of TIG welding are: (1) it produces high-quality welds in nonferrous metals, (2) practically no weld cleaning is necessary, and (3) the arc and weld pool are clearly visible to the welder.

106–11. Gas tungsten-arc welding (TIG) water-cooled gun.

Hobart Brothers

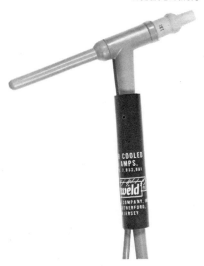

Gas Metal-Arc Welding—Inert Shielding (MIG)

Gas metal-arc welding is a gas shielded, metal-arc welding process which uses the high heat of an electric arc between a continuously fed, consumable electrode wire and the material to be welded. Metal is transferred through the gas protected arc column to the work. 106–12. Inert gas is used for shielding.

In this process, a wire is fed continuously from a reel through a gun to a contact surface which imparts a current upon the wire. A fixed relationship exists between the rate of wire burn-off and the welding current. This means that at a given wire feed speed rate, the welding machine will produce the current necessary to maintain the arc.

The welding current, which is indicated on the machine's ammeter (only while welding) ranges from 100 to 400 amperes, depending upon the diameter of the wire.

Solid, bare wire in sizes from 0.035″ to ⅛″ in diameter is used and should have similar mechanical properties to the base metal being welded.

The welding gun can be either air- or water-cooled depending upon the amperage being used. With the higher amperages, a water-cooled gun is used.

Argon, helium, or an argon-helium mixture is used for shielding in this process. These gases displace the air around the weld pool and thereby eliminate contamination of the weld metal. The MIG process is used to a great extent for welding aluminum, magnesium, copper and alloys, nickel, stainless steel, and titanium.

The advantages of this process include economy, ability to weld metals that are hard to weld by other means, possible to weld in all positions, good visibility of the arc, and a minimum amount of spatter clean-up.

Submerged-Arc Welding

Submerged-arc welding is a process which uses the intense heat of an electric arc between a continuously fed consumable electrode wire and the material to be welded. 106–13. A blanket of granular fusible material serves as shielding. This material is deposited directly on the work and is known as flux. The process is quite similar to other automatic arc welding processes.

The bare electrode is fed from a reel through the welding head into the granular substance, and the flux protects the metal from contamination. The welding action takes place under the granular blanket, preventing sparks and spatter.

In the operation the arc is started by striking the metal beneath the flux or by placing a

106–12. Schematic illustration of gas metal-arc welding process (MIG).

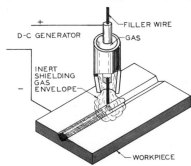

conductive material beneath the electrode. The intense heat of the arc forms a molten pool of metal in the joint underneath the flux. A portion of the flux is melted at the same time and floats to the top of the molten metal. The visible portion of the flux material does not become molten and does not change during welding. It can be recovered and re-used. Grades of flux are selected for the type of material to be welded.

Submerged-arc welding is used to weld low- and medium-carbon steels, low-alloy, high-strength steels, quenched and tempered steels, and many stainless steels. Some of its advantages are: (1) high metal deposition rates, (2) smooth welds, (3) high welding speed, (4) easy removal of slag, and (5) wide range of thickness and materials.

Open-Arc Welding Process

The open-arc welding process is accomplished by using a tubular electrode wire containing a core of gas-forming and deoxidizing fluxes which provide self shielding properties.

The high heat of the arc between the continuously fed electrode wire and the work causes the metal to melt and the fluxes to vaporize, forming a shielding gas. The core contains slagging elements as well as metal alloys, giving the deposited metals special properties. The process is used primarily in hard surfacing applications.

Gas Metal-Arc CO_2 Shielding

The gas metal-arc CO_2 shielding welding process is a method of welding whereby metal is

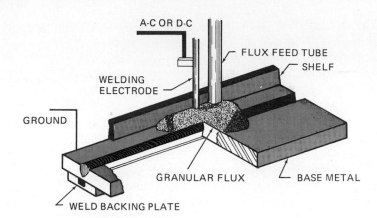

106–13. Schematic diagram of submerged-arc welding.

transferred through the gas-protected arc column to the work. 106–14. Shielding is obtained from carbon dioxide (CO_2) gas, or a CO_2 gas mixture (which may contain an inert gas).

A specially designed welding machine is used for this process. It is a constant voltage type of power source.

The heart of this process is in a special wire feeder and the constant voltage machine. The electrode wire feed rate determines the welding current. There is a fixed relationship between the electrode wire burn-off and the welding current.

The shielding gas in this process replaces the air surrounding the weld pool, preventing contamination of the weld metal by oxygen and nitrogen in the air.

The process is used for welding low- and medium-carbon steels in a thickness range of 10 gage to ¾" without edge preparation.

This process can be either semi-automatic or automatic. A fixtured welding torch or manually controlled welding gun can be used.

Micro-Wire Welding

Micro-wire welding uses a small-diameter, consumable electrode wire, fed continuously into the arc. 106–15 (Page 534). Metal is transferred through the gas-protected arc column to the material.

A welding grade of CO_2 gas with a dew point temperature of −40° F. is recommended. Sometimes mixtures of CO_2 and argon gases are used. A pressure reducing regulator and flowmeter are required on the gas cylinder, as the gas flow rate is very important.

The welding gun and cable assembly are used to carry the

106–14. CO_2 gas shielded metal-arc welding.

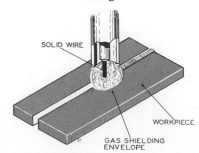

533

electrode wire, current, and shielding gas from the wire feeder to the workpiece.

The advantages of this process include its economy and versatility. There is no slag to remove, and welding is possible in all positions. Welding can be done on thin materials as small as 20 gage and is useful in welding operations on such products as household appliances, metal furniture, pressure vessels, electrical equipment, and industrial machinery.

Stud Welding

Stud welding is used to end-weld metal studs to flat surfaces. 106–16. The process is accomplished by the use of a stud gun which holds the stud in contact with the workpiece. The welder depresses a trigger on the gun causing the current (DC) to flow from the power source through the stud to the work surface, with the stud acting like an electrode. The current activates a solenoid within the gun, lifting the stud away from the workpiece and establishing an arc. Partial shielding is obtained from a protective ceramic ferrule which also serves to confine the metal to the weld area.

The intense heat of the arc melts the end of the stud and work surface at the same instant. A timing-device built into the control unit controls the arc duration. When the current is shut off, the pull is released on the stud and the stud is pushed down into the molten pool of the workpiece. As the molten stud end and molten workpiece come into contact, the metals on both solidify and the weld is complete.

Electroslag Welding

This is a welding process which produces coalescence through electrically melted flux which melts both the filler metal and the surfaces of the workpiece to be melted. 106–17. A heavy slag shields the weld pool and moves along the full cross section of the weld as the welding operation progresses. The resistance to the flow of electric current passing between the electrode and workpiece serves to keep the conductive slag in a molten condition. The cavity formed by the parts to be welded and the molding shoes contains the molten flux pool, the molten weld metal, and the solidified weld metal. The molten weld metal is formed by a combination of the melted base metal, electrode, and guide tube which collect at the bottom of the flux pool. The workpiece is joined together as the weld solidifies.

Welding is usually accomplished in a vertical position using water cooled retaining shoes contacting the joint sides to contain the molten flux and molten weld metal.

This process can be used for welding joints as short as 4″ to as high as 10′.

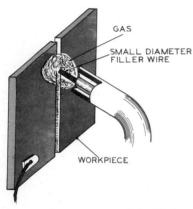

GAS

SMALL DIAMETER FILLER WIRE

WORKPIECE

Hobart Brothers

106–15. Micro-wire gas shielded metal-arc welding.

106–16. Stud welding.

Hobart Brothers

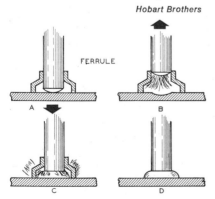

FERRULE

A

B

C

D

106–17. Section through workpieces and weld showing electroslag welding process.

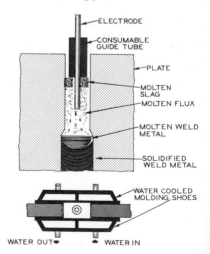

ELECTRODE

CONSUMABLE GUIDE TUBE

PLATE

MOLTEN SLAG

MOLTEN FLUX

MOLTEN WELD METAL

SOLIDIFIED WELD METAL

WATER COOLED MOLDING SHOES

WATER OUT   WATER IN

Unit 107.

Other Welding Processes

RESISTANCE WELDING

Resistance welding includes the following: (1) *spot welding,* (2) *seam welding,* (3) *flash-butt welding,* (4) *projection welding,* and (5) *percussion welding.*

A welding machine which contains a transformer is used in resistance welding. The transformer reduces the alternating current voltage from either 120 or 240 volts down to 4 to 12 volts. The amperage is raised to produce a good heating point.

The electric current passes through the metal at the point of greatest resistance. Heating takes place at the joint and pressure is applied to complete the weld. The pressure necessary to effect a good weld is around 4,000 to 8,000 psi. Electrical current requirements amount to approximately 30 to 40 kva per square inch of the area to be welded.

With the exception of lead, tin, and zinc, all metals may be welded by this process.

Resistance welding is used for production purposes and is the only welding process that uses a pressure application at the weld during the application of heat. The control of pressure in resistance welding is of the greatest importance because it: (1) permits welds to be accomplished at lower temperatures, (2) affects contact resistance, and (3) produces a forging action.

It is important that controlled pressure and timing be used. To obtain a satisfactory weld, a moderate pressure should be applied before and during the passage of the electrical current. Better results will also be had by increasing the pressure greatly as the proper welding heat is obtained, bringing the material to a red heat which forges the weld. Weld pressure can be obtained manually, by air pressure, mechanical means, springs, or by hydraulic pressure.

Spot Welding

This form of resistance welding is done on machines called spot welders. 107–1. Spot welding is used principally in sheet metal work. It consists of applying pressure to two or more sheets by means of conducting electrodes and then passing a high current at low voltage through the sheets from one electrode to the other. 107–2. The electrical resistance of the materials causes the metal to become heated at the juncture of the two parts and to take on a plastic state. This action, combined with the correct amount of pressure, causes fusion.

The welding time is controlled by a timer built into the machine. It controls the squeeze, weld, hold, and off periods. Calculations on the exact time of each stage for different types and thicknesses can be obtained from tables furnished by the manufacturers of the machines. All times are measured in current cycles

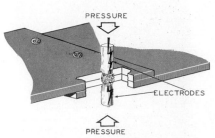

107–2. Fusion is achieved in spot welding by heat resulting from resistance of electrical current through workpieces held under pressure by electrodes.

107–1. Periods of spot welding.

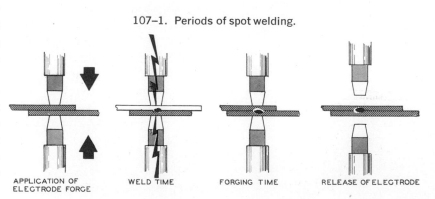

APPLICATION OF ELECTRODE FORCE   WELD TIME   FORGING TIME   RELEASE OF ELECTRODE

and generally range from 3 to 60 where 1 cycle is equal to $\frac{1}{60}$ second.

To obtain good welds, the sheet metal should be free of foreign matter and scale. Films of any type have a tendency to cause variations in surface resistance and also increase the heating effect of the metal in contact with the electrodes.

In spot welding, heat is generated at several different zones: (1) between the upper and lower pieces, (2) at the upper and lower contact surfaces of the

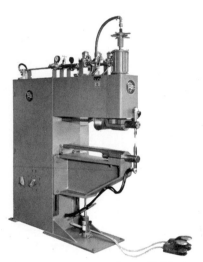

Banner Welder, Inc.

107–3. Spot welder.

107–4. Portable spot welding gun.

Falstrom Co.

sheets, and (3) within both the upper and lower sheets. The contact point between the upper and lower pieces of metal should be the highest point of resistance and is where the weld formation takes place.

Machines for Spot Welding

Spot welding machines are as follows: (1) *stationary single spot,* including *rocker-arm* and *direct-pressure,* (2) *portable single-spot,* and (3) *multiple-spot.*

The rocker-arm type has a stationary lower electrode. Movement of the upper electrode is obtained by means of an arm which moves about a pivot point. 107–3. Movement of this arm can be by a foot-pedal, air cylinder, or electric motor. Rocker-arm machines have throat capacities of 12 to 48".

Direct-pressure spot welders are used for heavy, high-production work with throat openings up to 60". Some of these machines are capable of completing 200 spot welds in 6 seconds and are used to make welds on automobile underbodies.

Portable spot welders are used where work is too large to be brought to the machine. 107–4. Portable spot welding guns can be moved to the part to be welded and are connected to the transformer by long cables. These welding guns are used in mass-production operations on aircraft, automobiles, railroad cars, and any product requiring the fastening together of large sheets of metal.

Multiple spot welders have a series of hydraulically or air operated welding guns mounted in a

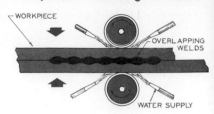

107–5. Schematic diagram of seam welding.

header but using a common mandrel for the bottom electrode. Flexible bands connect the guns to individual transformers or to a common buss bar attached to a transformer.

All guns make contact with the workpiece simultaneously. The guns are synchronized to fire in a predetermined sequence. The welding current can be fed to one gun at a time or to several guns. This type of spot welding machine is used to a great extent by automotive manufacturers.

Seam Welding

Seam welding or line welding is an adaptation of spot welding, employing continuously rotating rollers for electrodes. 107–5.

107–6. Flash and butt welder.

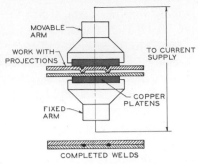

107–7. Projection welding.

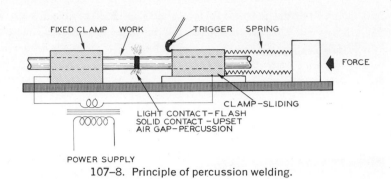

107–8. Principle of percussion welding.

Successive impulses of electrical current produce, in effect, a series of overlapping spots. The current is automatically turned on and off as the electrodes revolve, corresponding to the speed at which the work is set to move. External cooling of the work is sometimes employed to avoid overheating. Specially shaped electrodes are sometimes used in this process.

Seam welding is used in manufacturing containers, refrigerator cabinets, gasoline tanks, mufflers, and fenders. Material savings, and neat and tight joints are two of the advantages of this welding process.

Flash-Butt Welding

Flash-butt welding is a resistance welding process used to join the ends of rods, bars, strips, rings, tubes, forgings, and fittings. 107–6. The size and shape of the two ends to be joined should be similar in order to obtain the best results.

The two pieces to be welded are clamped in fixtures which position them facing each other. During flashing, these parts touch lightly and are burned away by the welding current, thus heating the ends of the workpieces.

As the metal is burned away, the pieces are moved together at a controlled rate of speed. The control of this movement must be exact in order to provide the best quality weld.

When the ends of the work attain the proper temperature, the pieces are suddenly pushed together. This upsetting action happens very fast, and a great amount of force is usually applied at this instant.

The upsetting action forces out the impurities caused by the flashing. The forced-out metal is called the flash. The inner weld metal is then sound and free of oxides and cast metal. A flash-butt welded joint is usually as strong as the parent metal. Welding rods, gas, flux, or other materials are unnecessary in this welding. The weld is made from the parent material itself.

There are several high forces applied in a flash welder. The clamping forces hold the workpieces firmly in alignment so that they will not slip during flashing or upsetting. The flashing action is a controlled motion sequence, finally ending with the upsetting action which applies a high force, forging together the two workpieces.

Power is supplied by air, hydraulic, motor, or manual action. One or more of these methods may be used on any machine for the different required actions.

Flash-butt welding is employed in welding such products as automobile trim, exhaust tubular assemblies, automobile headlamp rings, bumpers, transmission bands, window sashes, bicycle frames, tubular aircraft frames, and many similar products.

Projection Welding

Projection welding closely resembles spot welding. 107–7. The metal to be welded has projections located on its surface. On sheet metal these projections where the welds are to be made can be formed on a punch press.

In this process the workpiece, with its projections, is placed between plain large area electrodes in the welding machine. As current and pressure are applied, the projections are melted and flattened, causing the material surfaces to come together. The projections melt forming the weld.

Advantages of this welding process are:

1. A number of welds can be made simultaneously.

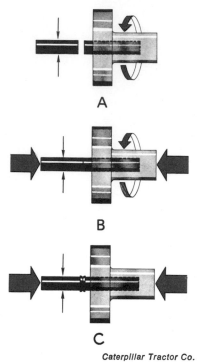

A

B

C

Caterpillar Tractor Co.

107–9. (A) The flywheel, chuck, and part are accelerated to preset speed; (B) Rotating part is forced against fixed part. As flywheel slows down, it discharges all of its energy into the interface; (C) The weld is completed as rotation stops. Time—1 to 10 seconds.

2. The life of electrodes is much longer as compared to spot welding.

3. Electrodes may serve as an assembly fixture, making assembly easier.

4. Welds can be spaced closer together.

Percussion Welding

For heating percussion welding depends upon an arc effect rather than the resistance within the metal. 107–8 (Page 537). The operation is performed with one part held in a stationary holder and the other in a clamp mounted on a slide which is backed up against pressure from a heavy spring, as shown in the illustration. In the welding operation the movable clamp is released rapidly, carrying the part forward. When the two parts are approximately $\frac{1}{16}''$ apart, a sudden discharge of electrical energy is released, causing an intense arc between the two surfaces. The percussion blow of the two parts

coming together extinguishes the arc and creates a weld.

The electrical energy for the discharge can be produced by two methods: (1) electrostatic, and (2) electromagnetic. In the former method, energy is stored in a capacitor and the parts are heated by the sudden discharge of the current from the capacitor. In the electromagnetic method, the energy is created by collapsing of the magnetic field of the two windings of a transformer. In both methods an intense arc is created and the sudden blow effects a weld.

The heat is concentrated only on the two surfaces and heat-treated parts may be joined without being annealed. To complete a weld takes about 0.1 second. No upset or flash occurs at the weld. This method of welding is limited to small areas of $\frac{1}{2}''$ square maximum.

INERTIA WELDING

The inertia welding process was developed in the United States in the early 1960's and overcame most of the early limitations that were associated with friction welding. Inertia welding is a forge welding process that releases stored kinetic energy as

107–10. Photomicrograph illustrates the result of the inertia welding process. Note the clean sound weld in welding titanium to titanium.

Caterpillar Tractor Co.

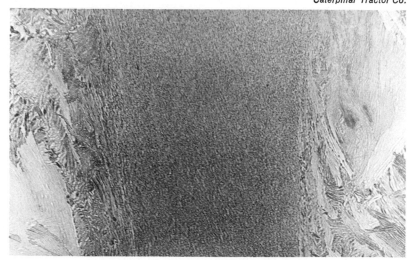

107–11. Stainless steel studs inertia welded to terne plate.

Caterpillar Tractor Co.

a frictional heat when two parts are rubbed together under proper conditions.

Inertia welding, a relatively simple process, produces a superior weld. In the process, one of the members to be welded (bar, plate, casting, tube, formed piece) is placed in a stationary chuck, or fixture. The other member—which must be round, or nearly so—is securely clamped in a rotating spindle. Attached to this spindle is a flywheel of a specified moment of inertia.

Next, the clamp part, spindle, and flywheel are rotated by an external energy source. 107–9. Members to be welded are not yet in contact. When a predetermined rpm has been reached, the drive source is disconnected. This freely rotating mass contains a specific amount of kinetic energy.

The members are now brought into contact under a precomputed constant thrust load. The kinetic energy contained in the rotating mass converts to frictional heat. The proper heating rate for a particular application is always the most favorable, since inertia can be controlled to supply whatever energy is needed.

Welding occurs as rotation ceases. The process produces plastic deformation in the weld zone, resulting in grain refinement, favorable flow line orientation, and flash expulsion. The heat affected zone is narrow. 107–10.

Converting kinetic energy to heat at such a rapid rate efficiently utilizes a small amount of energy to produce a high-quality weld. 107–11. Power consumption is held at a minimum. Time

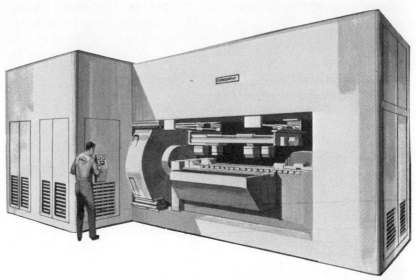

Caterpillar Tractor Co.

107–12. Horizontal inertia welder.

necessary for heat conduction is minimal and controllable.*

Though new to industry, one company's inertia welding process utilizes a machine which has been in research and development for years. 107–12. The process, which produces a superior quality, complete interface weld, is actually a computed weld from which the human judgment factor has been eliminated. 107–13. The technique has been successfully applied to super-alloys as well as standard metals. Different metals can be welded together by this process. 107–14 (Page 540).

Applications of the inertia welding process which involves the welding of dry bearing materials such as oxides, leaded bronzes, and molydisulfide surfaces should be avoided. This would also include metals which will not hot forge. Thrust load is an important part of the process and, therefore, structures which are difficult to support should be carefully checked.

———

*Caterpillar Tractor Company.

107–13. Steel welded to steel. A complete interface weld.

Caterpillar Tractor Co.

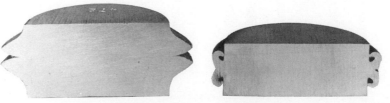

Advantages of the Process

The advantages of the inertia welding process are many. Some are listed here:

1. Superior weld.

2. A very narrow "heat affected zone" adjacent to the weld.

3. Uniform production quality welds.

4. Fast production welds.

5. Clean operation.

6. Low cost of energy.

7. Minimum skill required to operate inertia welder.

8. Amount of upset of welded parts can be controlled to close tolerances.

9. A complete interface weld can be obtained.

10. Process is safer than others.

ULTRASONIC WELDING

Joining metals by ultrasonic welding has gained production status in a variety of applications where joining cannot be accomplished in a satisfactory manner by other processes. 107–15.

Ultrasonic welding will join similar or dissimilar metals by the introduction of high-frequency vibratory energy into overlapping metals in the area to be joined. No fluxes or filler metals are used, no electrical current passes through the weld metal, and usually no heat is applied.*

The parts to be joined are clamped together between a welding tip and a supporting member under low-static pressure. High-frequency virbratory energy is then transmitted into the weld area through the tip for a brief interval. This process produces a sound metallurgical bond without an arc or melting weld metal and with an absence of filler metal or fluxes.

The ultrasonic welding process can be utilized in *spot welding, line welding, ring welding,* and *continuous-seam welding.*

Spot welds (elliptical in form) may be overlapped to form a continuous bonded area. Line welds have a bond that is a narrow line 6″ to 8″ in length made with a single power pulse. Ring welds are made with a single weld pulse, and the bond consists of a 360° peripheral weld which may be circular, square, rectangular, elliptical, or irregular in shape. The welds may be overlapped to produce a seam. Continuous-seam welds are produced with a rotating disc. The disc is in a rolling contact with the joint materials. Linear speeds up to several hundred feet per minute are attained.

Many different materials may be effectively joined with ultrasonic welding. 107–16. Metals can be joined to other metals or to nonmetals such as glass and alumina.

The joining capability is limited only by the power capacity of the equipment. The maximum thickness for high-strength spot welds done ultrasonically may vary from 0.015 to 0.10″, depending upon the hardness of the material and factors which might affect weldability. The above limitation applies to only one member of the parts to be welded. The other part may even be heavy sheet or plate. Thin materials such as fine wires less than 0.0005″ in diameter, and foils 0.00017″ thick have been successfully welded.

THERMIT WELDING

Thermit welding is used primarily when heavy welding applications are necessary. 107–17.

---

* Arthur L. Phillips, American Welding Society, United Engineering Center, New York, N.Y.

107–14. Various metals can be welded together by the inertia welding process.

Caterpillar Tractor Co.

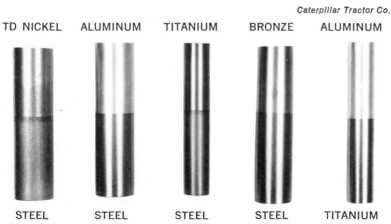

TD NICKEL	ALUMINUM	TITANIUM	BRONZE	ALUMINUM
STEEL	STEEL	STEEL	STEEL	TITANIUM

The process is accomplished by filling a joint with molten metal. This metal is obtained by reducing its oxide with aluminum. The Thermit compound usually is made of finely divided aluminum and iron which are mixed at a rate of about 1 to 3 by weight. This mixture is ignited and the resulting chemical reaction is as follows:

$$8A1 + 3Fe_3O_4 = 9Fe + 4Al_2O_3.$$

The chemical reaction is rapid, requiring only about 30 seconds to reach a temperature around 4500° F.

The Thermit weld is produced by preparing a mold of the metal. The pieces to be welded are first aligned properly, and the ends to be welded are cut to provide a parallel-sided space. Around the space or gap a wax pattern is built up. Around the

zone to be welded a refractory sand is packed. A riser and gates are provided in the mold as shown in the illustration. A torch is inserted in the mold which serves to melt the wax, dry the mold, and heat the workpieces to a red heat.

The Thermit mixture in the crucible is then ignited. When the reaction is complete, the metal is drawn off and flows into the mold and around the pieces to be welded. The high temperature of the weld metal causes it to fuse to the joint, creating a strong bond. After cooling, the mold is torn apart and the weld cleaned and chipped.

Thermit welding is usually used on large parts. Welding rails, broken machinery frames, shafts, and gears are some examples. For welding large sections, this method is fast, economical,

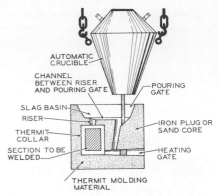

107–17. Thermit welding.

and will produce better welds than most other processes.

ELECTRON BEAM WELDING

Electron beam (EB) welding utilizes the energy from a fast-moving beam of electrons focused on the base material. 107–18 (Page 542). The electrons strike the metal surface, which

107–15. Schematic illustration of ultrasonic welding.

Sciaky Brothers, Inc.

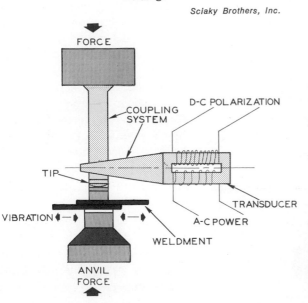

107–16. Aluminum ribbons spot-welded to glass ultrasonically.

Sciaky Brothers, Inc.

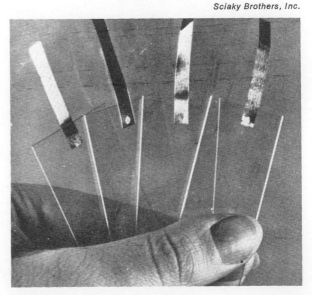

gives up kinetic energy almost completely in the form of heat. Welds are made in a vacuum (10^{-3} to 10^{-5} mm Hg). This practically eliminates contamination of the weld material by the remaining gases in the vacuum chamber. 107–19. The high vacuum is necessary to produce and focus a stable, uniform electron beam. Welds produced by this process are coalesced from vac-

uum-melted material, which eliminates such usual fusion-weld contaminants as water and vapor, oxygen, nitrogen, and slag.

In all types of electron beam machines, the beam is formed by bypassing current through a tungsten filament. The heat generated is about 2500° C. In the process the filament "backs off" electrons that are formed into a rudimentary beam by a bias grid cup.

The speed of the beam is stepped up to half the speed of light by passing it through a high-voltage electrostatic field. 107–20. An electromagnetic lens is employed to obtain correct focusing of the beam. The beam follows a seam in much the same manner as a conventional welding torch by the use of an electromagnetic deflection coil.

Near zero pressure is necessary for the formation of the beam. In EB welding the workpiece is loaded into the vacuum chamber. The chamber is then evacuated to pressures of 10 mm Hg. Welding begins at this point.

A similar process, known as *nonvacuum electron beam welding* is rapidly coming into use today. Bringing the electron beam out of its vacuum into the atmosphere has been a major advance in welding technology. This means that many welds can now be made without the elaborate tooling required for vacuum electron beam welding and with fewer pump-down requirements.

Nonvacuum electron beam welding is quite similar to conventional EB welding. However, with nonvacuum electron beam welding, the vacuum chamber in which the beam is created is evacuated to a lower pressure. The beam is first passed through the chamber, then through a specially designed orifice system. It then passes through atmospheric pressure moving around the workpiece.

In situations where contamination of the workpiece must be held to a minimum, the beam should be passed through argon or helium.

107–18. Schematic illustration of electron beam welding machine.

Hamilton-Standard

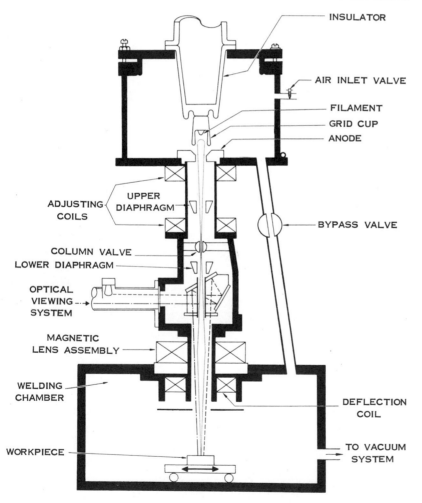

INSULATOR

AIR INLET VALVE

FILAMENT
GRID CUP
ANODE

ADJUSTING COILS

UPPER DIAPHRAGM

BYPASS VALVE

COLUMN VALVE
LOWER DIAPHRAGM

OPTICAL VIEWING SYSTEM

MAGNETIC LENS ASSEMBLY

WELDING CHAMBER

DEFLECTION COIL

WORKPIECE

TO VACUUM SYSTEM

Sciaky Brothers, Inc.

107–19. A large electron beam welder with vacuum chamber measuring 116″ x 50″ x 62″. Sliding door with viewing ports is open.

Sciaky Brothers, Inc.

107–21. A 4″ cube of aluminum EB welded through the center.

Nonvacuum welding is a supplement and not a replacement for conventional EB welding. Working distances up to 0.5″ are practical. The principal advantage of this process is that it does not require evacuation of the area surrounding the workpiece.

107–20. Close-up of electron beam gun and beam welding a gear cluster.

Sciaky Brothers, Inc.

Unit 108. Soldering and Brazing

Soldering is a process that consists of joining two or more metal surfaces by means of a molten, fusible metal or alloy. The joining of the two surfaces is accomplished by the adhesion between the solder and the metal surfaces. The solder has a melting temperature below 800° F.

Most solders are composed of a mixture of tin and lead and usually contains about 0.5% antimony. The melting point is largely determined by the proportions of tin and lead.

Solder consisting of half tin and half lead is called "half and half" or "50–50" solder and melts at 415° F.

If the proportion of lead and tin is changed to 60% tin and 40% lead, the melting point is 370° F.

Pure tin melts at 450° F. but, surprisingly, if another metal like lead, which liquifies at 620° F., is mixed with tin in a proportion of 63 parts of tin by weight to 37 parts of lead by weight, a fusible alloy results which melts at an even lower temperature of 361° F.

Tin mixes with lead in all proportions. The most common compositions are 40/60, 50/50, and 60/40. Tin, contrary to popular belief, is an expensive metal imported from Asia, Africa, and South America. Lead on the other hand, is less expensive, so that the more tin in the solder, the more expensive it is.

A good solder is 40/60. The first number is always tin. This type of solder starts to soften at 361° F. It then goes through a

543

mushy or plastic stage and becomes completely liquid at 460° F. Solders in the form of wire are of this type. Wire solders come plain or with acid or rosin core centers.

FLUXES

To secure good adherence, the surface of the metal and solder must be free of oxide and foreign materials.

To prepare for the wetting or alloying of metal with molten solder, a chemical material is used—a soldering flux. The flux accomplishes three things: (1) removes tarnish or metallic oxide, (2) prevents further oxide from forming while the metal is being heated to soldering temperature, and (3) lowers the surface tension of the molten solder, enabling it to spread about the area and penetrate.

Fluxes are classified as corrosive and noncorrosive. The common fault of most corrosive fluxes is that, after the soldering operation, the flux residues attract moisture unless they are removed.

The most common noncorrosive flux is rosin in alcohol. This can be used on copper, brass, tin, cadmium, or silverplated surfaces.

The most commonly used corrosive fluxes are muriatic acid or a mixture of zinc and ammonium chlorides.

SOLDERING DEVICES

There are many heating devices that can be used in soldering. The most common are: *soldering copper and furnace, blowtorch, electric soldering iron, soldering gun,* or *bottled-gas soldering torch.*

Successful soldering requires heat enough to raise the temperature of metals to be joined to a melting point in the area concerned.

Electric soldering irons are convenient for many types of soldering operations. These soldering tools are made in many different types and in sizes from 25 watts to 550 watts.

Soldering pencils are used a great deal in electric and electronic work. 108–1. Soldering guns provide instant heat at the tip when the trigger is pulled. 108–2. On most guns the trigger also turns on a light which focuses at the point. The soldering gun is very popular for electronic work.

RESISTANCE SOLDERING

Resistance soldering does what all other soldering systems do—furnishes heat to activate flux and melt solder on the metal parts to be joined together. But resistance soldering is unique in one respect. The electrodes actually conduct low-voltage, high-

108–1. Electric soldering pencil.

Weller Electric Corp.

108–3. Step-controlled, resistance-type soldering unit.

American Electrical Heater Co.

108–2. Electric soldering gun.

Weller Electric Corp.

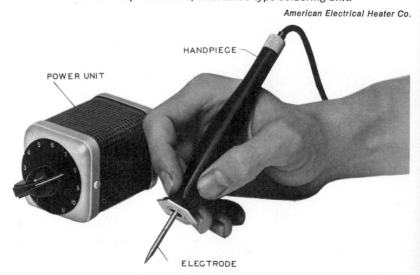

HANDPIECE

POWER UNIT

ELECTRODE

amperage current. The current is conducted through the parts to be soldered. Heat is generated by the resistance to this current.

Three pieces of equipment are necessary for the basic system: (1) a step-down transformer, called the power unit, (2) the tool to hold the electrodes and place them in contact with the work being soldered, and (3) the electrodes themselves.

Resistance-soldering power units are generally divided into four classes: (1) miniature power unit—up to 100 watts, (2) medium power unit—between 100 and 250 watts, (3) standard power unit—between 250 and 500 watts, and (4) heavy-duty power unit—over 500 watts. 108–3.

Resistance-soldering handpieces are of two main types: (1) dual electrode and (2) single-electrode. When the dual-electrode is used, the two electrodes form both the current supply and return terminals.

When the single-electrode handpiece is used, ground is made by means of an additional clamp which is attached to the work itself.

Handpiece sizes range from the tiny tweezer type, for extremely fine work, to the large fork and plier types, for the heaviest soldering jobs. 108–4, 108–5 & 108–6.

Resistance-soldering electrodes are: (1) carbon and (2) metal-alloy. Carbon electrodes are generally used in single-electrode handpieces, while metal-alloy electrodes are used in dual-electrode handpieces.

While carbon electrodes have a higher working temperature limit, electrodes of metal-alloy have a higher tensile strength and can be bent or formed (by grinding) in order to work on fine, hard-to-reach setups.

The circuiting in resistance soldering is the same as in arc welding. However, the resistance soldering electrode is always in contact with the workpiece. 108–7 (Page 546). There is no arcing first because of the contact principle, and, second, because low voltages are used in resistance soldering.

BRAZING

Brazing joins two pieces of metal and is defined by the American Welding Society as a group of welding processes where coalescence is produced by heating to suitable temperatures above 800° F. and by using a nonferrous filler metal having a melting point below that of the base metals. The metal is distributed between the closely fitted surfaces of the joint by capillary action. Most types of

108–4. Tweezer-type handpiece.

American Electrical Heater Co.

American Electrical Heater Co.

108–5. Heavy-duty, plier-type handpiece.

108–6. Heavy-duty, fork-type handpiece.

American Electrical Heater Co.

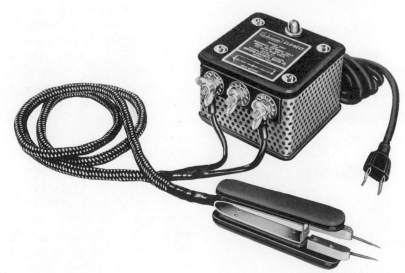

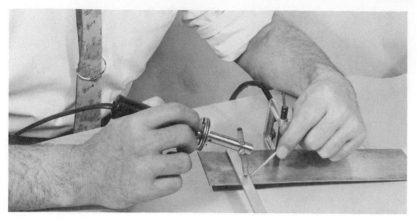

108–7. Electrode placed in contact with work while solder is fed to the joint.

commercial metals can be brazed. Filler metals are generally of two types: (1) copper alloys and (2) silver alloys.

Prior to brazing, the surfaces require cleaning to remove oxides and grease or foreign particles. After cleaning, a flux is applied to all surfaces to be brazed. Fluxes serve to: (1) dissolve oxides prior to heating the metal and (2) prevent the formation of oxides during the heating process. The common commercial fluxes are in paste, liquid, or powder form. Fluxes have as their main ingredients fused borax, boric acid, fluorides, fluborates, borates, and chlorides. Flux residues must be removed after brazing to prevent corrosion.

After the flux is applied to the joint, the joint is heated to the proper brazing temperature. The heat may be applied by oxyacetylene, oxyhydrogen, or other gas-flame welding torch.

In furnace brazing, a controlled-atmosphere furnace is used to heat the work to the proper temperature. This method of heating is used sometimes by dipping parts in a bath of molten salt. The molten salt is heated to a temperature slightly above the melting temperature of the brazing metal.

With dip brazing, assemblies can also be dipped in a bath of the molten brazing metal.

High-frequency induction currents can be used in brazing. This is known as induction brazing. In this process the joint is held surrounded by a copper inductor coil for a short period of time. Heating is very rapid. This method lends itself to a high production of parts with uniform results. Heating can be confined to a localized section of the joint.

TYPES OF JOINTS FOR BRAZING

The lap and butt joint are the two basic joints used in brazing operations. 108–8. The lap joint is considered a strong type of joint. The overlap should be at least three times the thickness of the thinnest section to obtain a strong joint. Maximum efficiency cannot be obtained with the butt joint. However, the weakness of a butt joint can be minimized by using a scarf joint.

Brazing methods offer many advantages: economy, speed, and a method for fastening joints that might be difficult to accomplish by other methods.

108–8. Types of joints used in brazing operations.

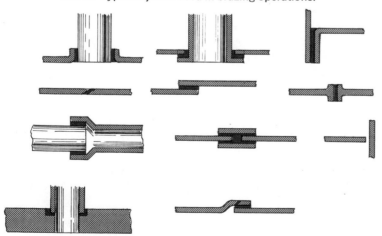

Check Your Knowledge

1. What is welding?

2. Why is no pressure needed in oxyacetylene welding?

3. Name the basic equipment used in oxacetylene welding.

4. Explain by means of chemical equations the combustion of the acetylene in the oxyacetylene flame.

5. Why is a neutral flame used in most gas welding?

6. Explain the process by which steel is cut through the use of an acetylene torch.

7. What fuel gases are commonly used for torch cutting of metals?

8. Name the two basic arc welding machines.

9. What are the advantages of metal electrodes as compared with carbon electrodes in arc welding?

10. Explain the effect welding currents can have on forming proper beads.

11. What are the functions of the coating on welding electrodes?

12. How are metal electrodes classified?

13. Name three basic welds.

14. Name five basic joints that are common to both arc and gas welding.

15. What are the advantages of contact electrodes?

16. Explain the advantages of the gas tungsten-arc welding (TIG) process as compared with conventional metal-arc welding.

17. What is the purpose of the shielding gas in TIG welding?

18. What gases are used in inert shielding gases?

19. Name three advantages of this type of welding.

20. Explain the gas metal-arc welding process.

21. Why is it easier to obtain high weld quality by the submerged-arc welding process than by ordinary metal-arc welding?

22. What is the purpose of the gas metal-arc CO_2 shielding welding process?

23. Name some advantages of micro-wire welding.

24. What is stud welding?

25. Explain the Thermit welding process.

26. What products are welded by this method?

27. Explain the theory of electron beam welding.

28. What is the source of heat in resistance welding?

29. Why is the control of pressure important in resistance welding?

30. In spot welding, heat is generated at several different zones. Name these zones.

31. Name the nature of a seam weld.

32. What products are welded by the flash-butt welding process?

33. What are the principal advantages of projection welding as compared to spot welding?

34. How does inertia welding differ from flash-butt welding?

35. What type of energy is used in the ultrasonic welding process?

36. What materials are commonly used as soldering fluxes?

37. Explain the resistance soldering process.

38. What methods are commonly used to supply brazing metals to the joints?

References

American Society of Tool and Manufacturing Engineers, *Tool Engineers Handbook,* 2nd ed., New York, McGraw-Hill Book Co., 1959.

American Welding Society, *Ultrasonic Welding,* 1965.

American Welding Society, *Welding Handbook,* 5th ed., Vol. 1–4, 1966.

Hobart Brothers Company, *Welding Processes.*

Irving, R. R., "Ultrasonic Energy Extends Uses for Soldering and Tinning," *Iron Age,* March 22, 1962.

Jefferson, T. B., and Woods, G., *Metals and How to Weld Them,* James F. Lincoln Arc Welding Foundation, 1962.

Kwalle, Jozef, "Designing for Inertia Welding," *Machine Design,* November 7, 1968.

Oberle, T. L.; Loyd, C. D.; and Catton, M. R., *Caterpillar's Inertia Welding Process,* The Caterpillar Company.

The shielded-ark welding process.

Section Twenty-Five

Plastics

IN general, the term "plastic" is applied to all materials capable of being modeled or molded. However, the meaning of the word today has changed or been limited to a group of materials which, when heated, can be formed into a variety of

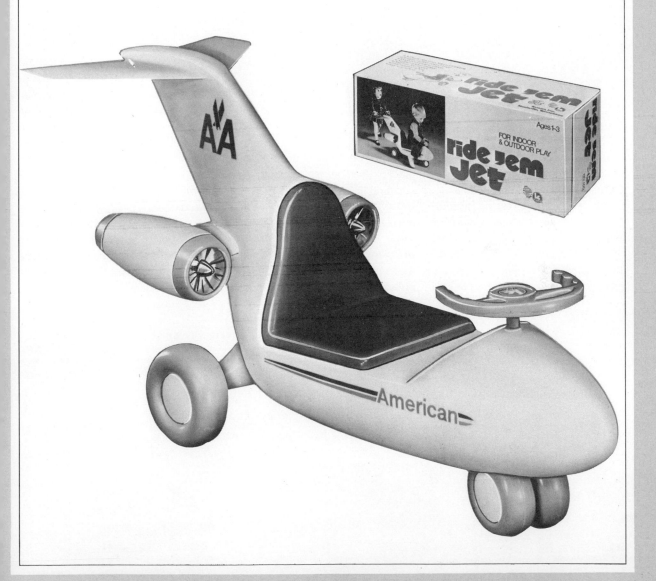

shapes by molding, casting, or extrusion. The great majority of plastics are organic substances or resins, usually containing oxygen, carbon, hydrogen, nitrogen, and sometimes other elements. Technically, these organic compounds are called polymers.*

The raw materials from which plastic compounds are produced include: gas, coal, petroleum, sulfur, limestone, and silica. 109–1. Other materials, such as solvents, lubricants, color powders, filler materials, and plasticizers, are ingredients added in the manufacturing processes. Fillers, usually flour, cotton, wood powder, rag fibers, asbestos, glass, clays, or metal powders provide heat resistance, increase strength, and reduce shrinkage of plastic products.

The manufacture of plastic products on a large scale is a recent development. Charles Goodyear discovered ebonite or hard rubber in 1839. Celluloid, developed about 1869 by J. W. Hyatt, was a forerunner of today's plastic materials. About the year 1909, phenol formaldehyde resin was developed by Dr. L. H. Baekeland and other individuals working with him. Since then a great variety of synthetic materials have been created to make this industry one of the largest in the world.

---

* When simple chemical units are duplicated in chainlike fashion, a large molecule, called a *polymer,* is formed. With hundreds of repeat units on the chain, a *high-polymer molecule* results. The starting material which forms a polymer is called a *monomer.*

Unit 109. Types of Plastics

There are two broad classifications of plastics: (1) *thermosetting* and (2) *thermoplastic.* Heat is used to form thermosetting plastics to shape, with or without pressure. The heat first softens the material and as additional heat is applied, or special chemicals are added, a chemical change (polymerization) takes place, hardening the material *permanently.* (Through polymerization, a compound is changed into another compound with the same elements in the same proportions but with a higher molecular weight and different physical properties.)

With thermoplastic materials, however, no chemical change takes place in molding. This material does not harden permanently when heat or pressure is applied, but remains soft at elevated temperatures until hardened by cooling. The material may be remelted as often as desired by application of heat. Parts can be made from this material by such processes as injection, extrusion, thermoforming, and calendering (formation of thin sheets).

109–1. Raw materials from which plastic compounds are made.

Polymer Corp.

<table>
<tr><td>

Unit 110.

</td><td>

Thermosetting Compounds

</td></tr>
</table>

These compounds include epoxides, phenolics, furane resins, silicones, and amino resins.

EPOXIDES

The manufacture of surface coatings was one of the first, and continues as one of the largest uses of epoxy resins. Coatings made from these resins combine the properties of toughness, flexibility, adhesion, and chemical resistance to a degree not found in other coating materials.

Epoxy surface coatings can be divided into the following broad categories:

1. Esters of drying and non-drying oil fatty acids.
   A. Air dried.
   B. Baked.
2. Straight epoxies cured with various cross-linkers.
   A. Heat-cured epoxy-phenolic or urea combinations.
   B. Room-temperature-cured epoxy poly-amine, polyamide, etc.

110–1. Shell mold made from powdered resin.

Shell-O-Matic, Inc.

Epoxy resins are used in both low-pressure and high-pressure laminates.

Beginning with the first significant commercial use in the fabrication of jet fighter landing flaps, epoxy adhesives are now finding applications in aircraft, automobiles, and in the home. Cured resins have low shrinkage, good chemical resistance, excellent nonconducting electrical characteristics, and will adhere to both metal and glass.

PHENOLICS

With the exception of cellulose nitrate, phenolics have been in use for a longer period of time than any other synthetic plastic. When phenolics are properly made and applied, they result in strong, rigid, stable products which are resistant to heat and most corrosion agents. Moreover, they are electrical nonconductors.

Phenol and formaldehyde combine in the presence of a catalyst to produce phenolic resins. These resins may exist in either solid or liquid forms of viscosity varying from watery to extremely viscous. Alcohol solutions of these resins are used as varnishes.

Very finely ground (powdered) phenolic resins are generally used for the manufacture of molding compounds, and in the foundry trade for shell molding. 110–1.

For brake lining production, powdered phenolic resin is mixed with asbestos fiber, pressed into flat sheets, and subjected to heat. 110–2. Before curing is complete, the sheets are cooled, and the brake lining segments are die-cut.

Phenolic resins, in molded and low-pressure laminated shapes, are playing an important role in the structure of new missiles and missile hardware. They can stand short-term exposures to extremely high temperatures (15,000° F. plus). Under these conditions, metals vaporize and ceramic materials melt, but phenolic resins coke, thereby maintaining the thermal barrier needed for a missile nose cone. Many useful items, such as appliance plugs, bottle caps, dials, knife handles, radio cabinets, and many electrical parts, can be made from this material. 110–3 (Page 552). Phenolic compounds are molded by compression or transfer molding.

FURANE RESINS

These resins are made by processing with certain acids and such farm waste products as cotton seeds and rice hulls. Unlike some of the other thermosetting

110–2. Powdered phenolic resin is mixed with asbestos fiber to make brake lining.

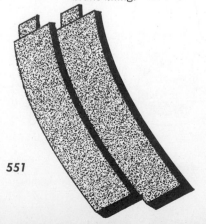

polymers, furane resins remain as liquids until cured.

Whether impregnating plaster of paris castings or sand foundry patterns, the rapid and effective penetration of furane resins is noteworthy. They also assist in the manufacture of grinding wheels because of their effective wetting action. Furane resins are also used for core and sand binders and as hardening agents for gypsum plaster.

SILICONES

In addition to stability at extremely high and low tempera-ture, silicones as a class, offer the following outstanding properties: (1) resistance to oxidation and effects of weather, (2) excellent electrical properties (heat resistant), (3) water repellency, and (4) incompatability with most organic polymers (release agents). Silicone-base polymers possess a combination of properties that make them valuable for a large group of industrial products including greases, oils, adhesives, resins, and rubber compounds. Silicone greases are applied to threads of studs and head bolts of continuous extruders and to nozzles and inserts of injection machines.

Special silicone fluids are fast becoming an ingredient in cosmetics since they are crystal-clear, odorless, and harmless. They repel water and prevent a sticky oily feeling in cosmetics.

The silicones are also useful in furniture, auto, shoe, glass, and silver polishes. Silicone rubbers are used in extrusions, moldings, gaskets, glass cloth, and electrical connectors. Silicone resins can be processed by extrusion, transfer molding, casting, and compression.

AMINO RESINS

The two important groups of amino resins are the *urea-* and *melamine-formaldehyde* resins.

These resins have been accepted because of their properties of heat resistance, solvent and chemical resistance, extreme surface hardness combined with initial absence of color, and resistance to discoloration. No other class of synthetic resin shows a similar favorable combination of properties. Moreover, the amino resins, particularly the melamine types, are very versatile, finding important uses in many industrial fields.

Urea-formaldehyde resins have been produced commercially for a great many years. They were first used in molding compounds; their largest use now is as adhesive in plywood production and in particle board bonding. Large amounts are used in various textile treatments in marproof finishes for indoor applications.

Melamine resins are similar in behavior in many respects to urea resins. Melamine resins in cured form are highly resistant to heat. High-grade dinnerware is an important application of melamine resins today. Other products include ignition parts, knobs, and electric-shaver housings.

LAUNCH
ESCAPE SYSTEM

BOOST
PROTECTIVE COVER

COMMAND MODULE

SERVICE MODULE

82 FT

363 FT

ADAPTER

LUNAR MODULE

Apollo spacecraft

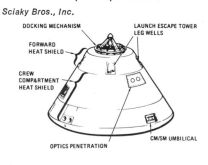

110–3. Phenolic resins are playing an important part in the structures of the Apollo spacecraft.

Sciaky Bros., Inc.

DOCKING MECHANISM

LAUNCH ESCAPE TOWER
LEG WELLS

FORWARD
HEAT SHIELD

CREW
COMPARTMENT
HEAT SHIELD

OPTICS PENETRATION

CM/SM UMBILICAL

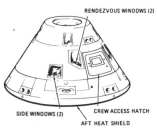

RENDEZVOUS WINDOWS (2)

SIDE WINDOWS (2)

CREW ACCESS HATCH

AFT HEAT SHIELD

Command module

Unit 111.

Thermoplastic Compounds

NYLONS (POLYMIDES)

This thermoplastic compound, developed by W. H. Carothers, for DuPont, was introduced on the market in 1938 in the form of bristles and hosiery fabrics. It became quickly apparent that the inherent properties of the material, such as strength, toughness, and chemical resistance made it a potential as an industrial molding powder. Extruded and molded products include glass, valves, tubing, bearings, luggage, and kitchen accessories. Hosiery, brush bristles, glider tow ropes, shroud lines for parachutes, and luggage are made from nylon monofilaments. 111–1(A).

POLYETHYLENE RESINS

More polyethylene is produced than any other plastic material. 111–1(B). Polyethylene resins

111–1(A). Nylon pressure hose.

Polymer Corp.

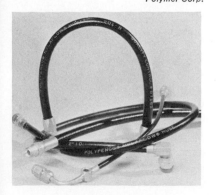

may be classified as: (1) low density, (2) medium density, (3) high density, and (4) copolymers (polymers combined to form new product with different properties). All of these can be molded or extruded into a very wide range of products.

Use of this material has grown in the molding field due to the ease of processing and coloring and its flexibility and chemical resistance.

Over one half of the *low-density* material used for molding goes into the construction of such products as buckets, waste baskets, bowls, garbage cans, and containers of various types.

Medium-density materials are used in a wide variety of consumer products such as housewares.

High-density materials are injection molded and the resulting products are used for industrial parts and housewares.

The copolymer materials are also used in the houseware field where a rigid material is required, as in dishpans and garbage cans.

More polyethylene has gone into film than into any other form. Over 75% of the film produced is used in packaging food, soft goods, toys, and chemicals.

POLYSTYRENE

This material was first introduced in 1935. 111–2(A) (Page

554). Styrene monomer, the basic raw material, was originally polymerized only with itself. Now it is being polymerized with other monomers and polymers to produce a versatile group of plastics. This material, which has a low specific gravity, can be made in colors from clear to opaque, has insulating ability, and is resistant to most chemicals.

Styrene polymers are rigid thermoplastic materials. They can easily be molded or extruded on conventional equipment.

POLYPROPYLENE

Polypropylene is the lightest of plastics, with a specific gravity of 0.905. Two advantages accrued from this low density are: (1) extra unit yield per pound of material, providing cost savings over other plastics in the same price and property range and

111–1(B). Plastic bag made from low-density polyethylene.

Enjay Chemical Co.

Marbon Div., Borg Warner

111–2(A). This boat is made of a high impact grade of plastic composed of plastic compound of acrylontrile, butadiene and styrene. These monomers form a polymer.

Enjay Chemical Co.

111–4. This bread rack was made from polypropylene.

111–2(B). Medical supplies made from polypropylene.

Enjay Chemical Co.

111–3. Rear deck of automobile made from polypropylene.

Enjay Chemical Co.

(2) weight saving to the consumer. 111–2(B).

A great variety of products can be made from this versatile material. 111–3. Products such as medical supplies, automobile rear decks, bread racks, washing machine parts, steering wheels, and waste baskets are good examples of products in this category. 111–4, 111–5, 111–6 & 111–7.

Polypropylene is resistant to heat and, due to this fact, such products as vaporizers, coffee makers, automotive parts, and monofilaments for rope and fabrics can be made from this material. Where strength and weight saving is important, the material has proven useful in many applications to the manufacturer of plastic products.

POLYCARBONATE

The high impact strength of polycarbonate resin lends itself for use in applications where toughness is of prime importance. Housings for business machines, communication equipment, and electrical apparatus fill this category.

Its ability to be colored, transparency, and extinguishing rating make it suitable for products which require these qualities. Parts may be decorated by dyeing, painting, or vacuum metallizing. The material has a higher impact strength from very low temperatures up to their heat distortion point. For this reason, it is useful in many military applications where a part must be serviceable over a temperature range of —6° to 180° F.

ACRYLIC RESIN

This resin has excellent light transmitting power, is easily fabricated, and has high resistance to moisture. The acrylic resin most commonly used is methyl methacrylate and is marketed under commercial names, Plexiglas

Enjay Chemical Co.

111–5. Washing machine agitators made from plastic material.

Enjay Chemical Co.

111–6. Polypropylene is used in steering wheels like this one.

Enjay Chemical Co.

111–7. Waste paper basket produced from polypropylene.

(Rohn & Haas) and Lucite (Du Pont), for example. This material has many applications. Among them are: transparent material for canopies, windows, instrument panels, landing light covers on aircraft, and tool handles. 111–8 & 111–9.

In the general field of merchandising, acrylics are used for sign material—for faces and lettering. In addition, acrylics are used for counter dividers, display fixtures and cases, and vending machines. In molding powder form, it is used for the manufacture of automotive parts. The beauty of this material has made it useful for many products.

CELLULOSE ACETATE

Cellulose acetate is one of the cellulosics, any plastic made of cellulose. The cellulosics are prepared from various treatments of wood fibers and cotton.

Cellulose acetate molding compositions are made from cellulose acetate flake, plasticizers, pigments, and dyes. Mixing is carried out on heated compounding rolls in an extruder or a Banbury-type mixer. Processing temperatures are in the 350° to 500° F. range.

Acetate plastics have outstanding toughness and high impact strength. Materials can be produced in a wide range of colors. Cellulose acetate is a good electrical insulator. Toys, beads, cutlery handles, electrical parts, and knobs are made from this material. In sheet form it is widely used as a packaging material, electric insulation, and photographic film.

CELLULOSE NITRATE

Several grades of cellulose nitrate are available, differing in nitrogen content as well as in degree of viscosity. It is the toughest of all thermoplastics, having dimensional stability, resilience, and low water absorption.

Cellulose nitrate is not adaptable for compression or injection molding because of its flammability. It can be formed into hollow articles by application of air or a liquid pressure between heated sheets.

CELLULOSE ACETATE BUTYRATE

This material is a molding compound usually processed by injection molding or extrusion. It has also been processed by blow molding techniques.

The material ranges from crystal clear to opaque, and is available in almost any color and

111–8. Tool handle made from Plexiglas.

111–9. Phillips screwdriver made from acrylic resin.

Duro-Metal Products Co.

shade. Dielectric strength is high with a low heat conductivity. Among the products made from this material are: tool handles, steering wheels, football helmets, trays, belts, goggle frames, pistol grips, fishing lures, and many other items.

CELLULOSE PROPIONATE

These compounds have considerable toughness and shock resistance. Extrusion and molding processes lend themselves to the production of articles of this material. Automotive parts, pens and pencils, telephone housings, toys, transistor radios, and television parts are some of the applications.

SYNTHETIC RUBBER

Because they had no source of raw rubber, highly industrialized nations developed synthetic rubber. This led to the development of many types of synthetics— GR-S, neoprene, Thiokol, nitrile, butyl, and silicone rubber.

GR-S is particularly adaptable to the production of tires and, for this reason, is produced in the largest quantity. GR-S, a copolymer of butadiene and styrene, is often compounded with natural rubber.

Produced from coal, limestone, salt, and water, *neoprene* is used for making insulation, hose, tires, tubes, protective clothing, and printing rolls.

Thiokols are organic polysulphides and are very resistant to oils, paints, and gasoline. Some of their applications are: hose, shoe heels, insulation coatings, and coated fabrics.

Nitrile rubber, because of its resistance to oils, is used in such products as gaskets, oil hose, and diaphragms.

An all petroleum product *Butyl* is an isobutylene copolymer. It has many of the properties of natural rubber. The material has outstanding shock-absorbing properties. It is used mostly in the manufacture of inner tubes.

Silicon rubber is a plastic material produced from silicon, oxygen, hydrogen, and carbon. It is resistant to temperature changes as well as to oils, sunlight, and dilute acids. Silicone rubber is used for seals in engines, gaskets, and in applications where heat resistant material is essential.

Unit 112.   Production Processes

Not many plastics are processed without additives of some type. A great many industrial processes require the mixing of certain ingredients before they can be molded. Most thermoplastic materials come in granular form and are dry in nature. Thermosetting materials are purchased in liquid form or as partially polymerized compounds.

A mixer is usually used to compound the several ingredients that make the mix. 112–1. The ingredients may be made of resins, color pigments, stabilizers, plasticizers, and fillers. These mixtures can then be fed into the hoppers of extrusion, injection, or calendering machines. Sometimes a preforming operation is used to form the material into small pellets of the proper size.

Thermosetting powder is normally cold-molded with no curing of the material necessary. Preformed material is used only in compression and transfer molding methods. Some materials are preformed into disc pellets on a rotary preforming press.

Common production processes used in molding plastics are: compression molding, transfer molding, injection molding, extrusion, blow molding, rotational molding, forming sheet and film, thermoforming, laminating, reinforced plastic molding, and casting.

COMPRESSION MOLDING

In compression molding, the compound, in powder or preform shape, is loaded directly into a hot cavity at an average temperature of 340° F. 112–2. Hydraulic pressure of 2,000 to 10,000 psi is applied, causing the material to flow and fill the entire cavity.

The required compression molding pressure depends upon: (1) the type of material, (2) the conditioning and preheating of the material before molding, (3) temperature of the mold, (4) part design, and (5) mold design. Most thermoplastic materials are not suited for this process, so compression molding

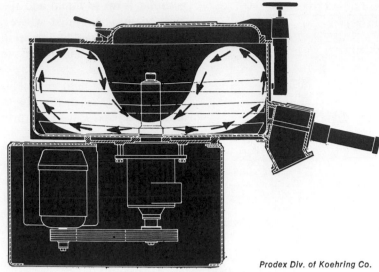

Prodex Div. of Koehring Co.

112–1. Cooling mixer.

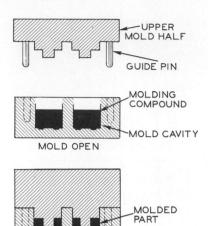

Hydraulic Press Mfg. Co.

112–3. Schematic diagram of compression molding press.

is used for molding thermosetting resins.

There are four methods of molding by the compression (and transfer) processes. These are: (1) hand, (2) semi-hand, (3) semi-automatic, and (4) automatic. Many different types of presses are made for compression molding.

112–2. A 75-ton automatic compression molding press.

Pennwalt Corp., Stokes Div.

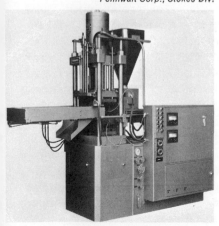

The requirement of a press is to apply the needed pressure and provide sufficient heat to plasticize and cure (make infusible) the plastic materials. Heat is applied by transferring heat from heated platens, or it can be applied directly to the mold.

Heat can be supplied in several manners: (1) steam, (2) electrical resistance, (3) heated liquids, or (4) ultra-high frequency current.

The basic procedure for compression molding consists of placing the molding compound (generally preheated) into the open mold cavity, closing the mold, and then applying heat and pressure through a downward-moving force-plug to the material until it softens and is forced to fill the mold cavity. 112–3. In the closed mold, a chemical reaction that cross-links the polymer chains takes place and the material hardens into the required shape.

TRANSFER MOLDING

This type of molding consists of combining high-frequency preheating with plunger molding techniques. In some instances, this method is almost as fast as injection molding the thermoplastics that are of similar part size. Dimensional and warpage problems are greater in transfer molding than in compression molding.

As shown in the illustration, the material is loaded into a chamber, and pressure (hydraulic) of several thousand psi is applied in the chamber area. 112–4 (Page 558). As the material reaches a semi-fluid condition, it flows from the chamber through a sprue into the die cavities.

INJECTION MOLDING

Injection molding is an ideal method for processing thermoplastic material because the material can be repeatedly changed

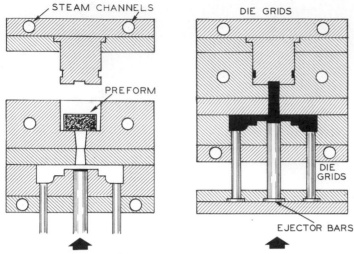

112–4. Basics of the transfer molding operation showing the material being loaded (left) and as it flows from the chamber into the mold cavities (right).

from a solid to a liquid without any chemical change. 112–5(A).

Plastic materials are measured and fed into injection molding machines in a variety of ways. These methods fall into two main classifications: (1) measurement by volume and (2) measurement by weight. Accurate feed measurement depends largely upon the part being molded and the material.

The basic requirement of a feed system is to measure out the amount of plastic needed to fill the mold, sprue, and runner. A precision feeding system is important because rejects are greatly reduced through accurate control. In addition, less material is wasted, which saves on manufacturing costs. Also, production is increased because the exact amount of material will not produce flash, regardless of injection pressure.

In operation, the thermoplastic material is changed from a granular form to liquid and then injected into the mold where it solidifies. The molding machine resembles a machine used for die-casting metal.

The machines used in injection molding are rated as to: (1) the tonnage it takes to clamp the dies and (2) the amount of material that can be injected into the mold. 112–5(B) & 112–6. Ratings of these machines may range from a 50 to 2,500 lb. clamping force. Some machines have a shot capacity of plastic up to 19 lb. per cycle.

Injection molding is accomplished by feeding the material by gravity from a hopper into a pressure chamber ahead of a plunger. 112–7. The plunger forces the material into a heating chamber where preheating takes place. It is then forced through the torpedo section where it is transformed to a liquid and the flow is carefully regulated. The liquid plastic then passes through a nozzle and allows the molten plastic to enter the mold through gates and runners.

The cool die solidifies the plastic almost immediately after the mold is filled. Only a few seconds are required to complete a cycle. The mold opens and ejects the formed part and another cycle is then in operation.

Thermoplastics are also being molded into parts by the use of an in-line reciprocating screw machine.

Injection molding has certain advantages over compression molding. These are: (1) injection molding is much faster, (2) constant temperature can be maintained by circulating water at 165° to 200° F., (3) mold

112–5(A). Fishing tackle box made from CyoLac brand (ABS). Seven parts are injection molded.

Marbon Div., Borg Warner

Pennwalt Corp., Stokes Div.

112–5(B). Horizontal injection molding press.

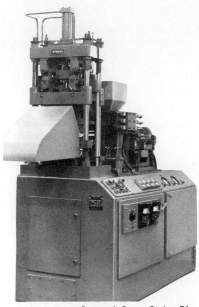

Pennwalt Corp., Stokes Div.

112–6. Automatic vertical injection molding press.

costs are lower, (4) parts with difficult shapes and thin walls can be produced, and (5) parts to 8 lb. can be produced with low material loss.

Injection molding products are garbage cans, laundry baskets, furniture, automobile dashes, and refrigerator parts.

Thermosetting plastics can be molded by the injection process. 112–8. A modified version of the injection molding machine is used and the process is known as *jet molding*. By this process the plastic is preheated to about 200° F. in the cylinder surrounding the nozzle. It is then further heated as the plunger forces the resin through the nozzle. After the mold has been filled, the nozzle is cooled by running water to prevent polymerization of the remaining material.

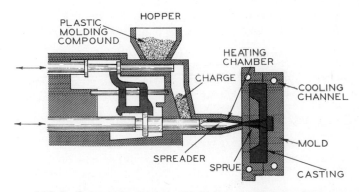

112–7. Schematic diagram of injection molding machine.

112–8. Jet molding process for injection molding thermosetting plastics.

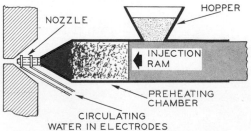

559

The reciprocating screw injection machine has largely replaced the jet molding machine. 112–9. A gravity feed is used to bring the material down to a rotating feed screw. The barrel is heated and additional frictional heat is also developed by the feed screw. Plasticized material is built up ahead of the revolving screw. The material is kept from entering the transfer chamber by the up position of the ram. The ram is lowered and the revolving screw forces the material into the mold cavities.

EXTRUSION

In this process, thermoplastic molding powders are fed through a hopper to a heated plasticizing cylinder, then driven through a die of the desired cross section by a rotating screw. 112–10. Granulated powder made of such materials as vinyl resins, cellulose derivatives, nylon, polyethylene and polypropylene make up the materials used in the process.

After heating, the material is a thick viscous mass. As it leaves the die, it is gradually cooled while resting on a conveyor.

Rods, sheets, tubes, and bars are typical applications. Profiled parts such as trim, edgings, joint and panel moldings, light shields, gaskets, and many similar products can be processed by this method.

There are advantages to the extrusion process. The tooling is low-cost compared with injection molding. Material thickness can be accurately controlled. In addition, production rates are high, and intricate profiles can be produced.

Extrusion coating with polyethylene is used to a considerable extent in the packaging field. 112–11. This material can be extruded onto paper, foil, cellophane, paperboard, films, and in combinations. The usefulness of polyethylene in packaging comes from its excellent moisture barrier properties, resistance to most chemicals, sealability, toughness, strength, and economy.

The high-density compounds used today can be processed at rates higher than 250 ft./min.,

and at coating weights as low as 6 lb./ream.

In operation the substrate is passed between the nip of two rolls. Here it comes in contact with the hot web from an extruder. The rolls apply the necesary pressure to achieve lamination. A water-cooled chill roll solidifies the polyethylene. The chill roll is driven and draws the extruded film to the required thickness. The other roll is a rubber surfaced pressure or "back up" roll. After trimming, the finished product is wound into rolls and is usually cut to the desired widths in another step.

BLOW MOLDING

Thermoplastic material can be molded on an injection molding machine fitted with a special mold with removable core, ending in a hand grip, to allow a closed-end parison somewhat like a test tube, which is a cylinder of plastic material and is extruded as rapidly as possible and positioned between the jaws of a split mold. On a separate frame situated alongside the machine, a second mold, consisting of a blowing cavity and a locking device, is carried.

112–9. Screw injection molding cycle: (A) The screw forces material into vertical plunger chamber; (B) Hydraulic plunger forces plasticized material into mold to form part.

F. J. Stokes Co.

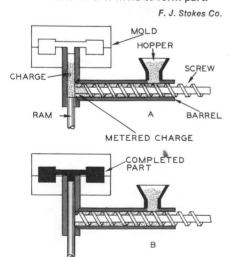

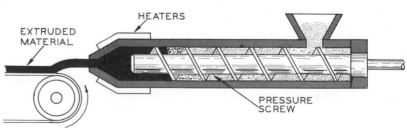

112–10. Schematic illustration of typical extrusion process.

In operation, the parison is molded around the core through a hot-runner pin gate. 112–12(A). The mold is opened before the material is set up, and the core with the parison is moved manually to the blow mold. As the mold is closed, male and female parts lock the core and parison in position. An air nozzle enters into the seat in the core at the same time, and air pressure is introduced to inflate the parison. The mold is then opened and the completed part is removed.

Production methods range from simple manual operations to relatively complicated automatic ones. Blow molded products include bottles, floats, automobile heater ducts, liquid detergent containers, and packaging bottles. 112–12(B) (Page 562).

ROTATIONAL MOLDING

Rotational molding equipment is classified as: (1) continuous type and (2) batch type. Molds for this type of operation are either electroformed copper or cast aluminum.

The batch-type equipment consists of a platform which rotates simultaneously in two dimensions and is enclosed in an oven for heating the rotating molds. The molds are filled before they are placed in the oven. Then they are clamped on a plate and locked on the rotating platform. A material called plastisol is used and is fused while in the rotator.

The continuous type of equipment consists of a conveyorized setup with individual rotational stations which travel on a conveyor. During one cycle the molds are filled and closed automatically, the plastisol fuses while rotating, the mold is cooled by water spray or oil, and the mold opens automatically for removal of the finished product. Products made by this process include beach balls, piggy banks, artificial fruit, toilet float balls, industrial casings and squeeze bulbs.

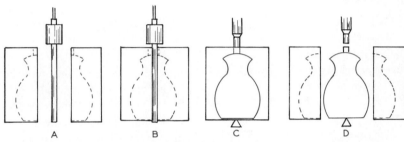

112–12(A). Steps in blow molding parts: (A) A tube of heated plastic is placed in open mold; (B) The mold closes over extrusion tube; (C) Air forces tube against mold sides; and (D) The mold opens to release finished product.

112–11. A typical view of the commercial extrusion coating process.

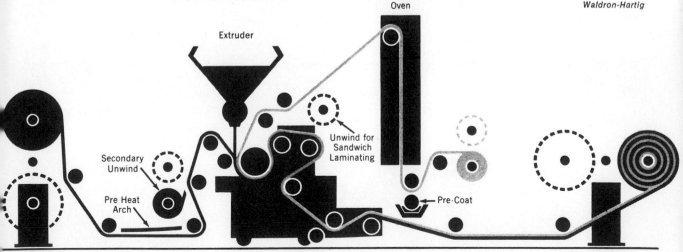

Waldron-Hartig

Oven

Extruder

Unwind for Sandwich Laminating

Secondary Unwind

Pre Heat Arch

Pre-Coat

Turnareel Unwind

Laminator

Turnareel Winder

can be made in sizes from 0.001″ to 0.125″.

In calendering, thermoplastic resin (composed of resin, filler, plasticizer, and color pigment) is formed into thin sheet between rolls. 112–14. The compounded material is heated before being fed into the machine. Thickness is controlled by a combination of squeezing and altering the speed of the finishing rolls. The finished product is cooled by passing through water-cooled rolls. Vinyl floor tile, cellulose acetate sheeting, and films are some of the applications.

Blowing consists of forming tubing by extruding a tube vertically through a die ring. Air is then blown into a large diameter cylinder. The air is cooled as it rises and is flattened by forcing through driven rolls before reaching the winder. Film used by the packaging industry is formed in this manner.

Casting is a process used to form sheet by dissolving plastic resins in a solvent and spreading the resultant material on a polished drum or a continuous belt arrangement. This process is known as *film casting*. Another process called *cell casting* is done by using a cell consisting of two sheets of polished glass. The glass is spaced to obtain the proper sheet thickness. The cell is gasketed about the edges and contains a water white liquid monomer.

Sinclair-Koppers Co.

112–12(B). Bottles molded from polyethylene resins.

FORMING SHEET AND FILM

Thin sheets and film can be formed by various processes which include: (1) extruding, (2) calendering, (3) blowing, and (4) casting. The plastic determines the method to be used.

The extrusion process is used when making sheets of polystyrene, polyethylene, or polypropylene. 112–13. After the material has been prepared, it is placed in the feed hopper. The material is then heated to approximately 600° F. and forced into the die cavity. The screw conveyor provides pressures ranging from 2,000 to 4,000 psi. The sheet thickness is controlled by a choker bar and die opening. After being formed, the sheet passes through a set of chromium-plated rolls which control the thickness of the sheet. It is then cut to size. Sheet thickness

THERMOFORMING

There are several basic techniques for the forming of thermoplastic sheet material. All involve the heating of the material until it becomes limp, causing the

112–13. Sheets and films are made by the extrusion process.

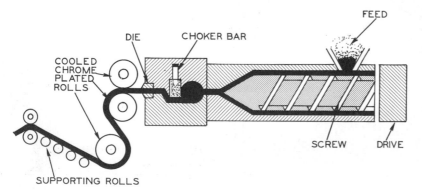

sheet or film to slump over the mold or form a profile. Vacuum, air, or mechanical pressure is used to create close profile conformity. Free forming employs pressure or vacuum without a mold to produce simple "bubbles."

Thermoforming is adaptable to any thermoplastic and can be used to produce moderately complex shapes. Among the items made by this process are automobile dashes, door panels, tail lights, aircraft canopies and windshields, signs, displays, light fixtures, packaging units, housewares, toys, television, funiture drawers, trays, refrigerator parts, luggage, and instrument panels.

Thermoforming offers several advantages. It can provide inexpensive parts with large surface areas at rapid production rates. Draws can be comparatively deep. Tooling costs are usually low. With minimum expense, prototypes can be made, and finally, good dimensional accuracy can be obtained.

There are, however, certain limitations. Undercuts are impossible. Excessive thinning of material may result in some weaknesses depending on part configuration. Also, chill marks may mar surfaces.

Thermoforming Processes

In *vacuum free forming,* heat-softened sheet or film is placed over a female mold and clamped at the edges. 112–15. The vacuum removes the air, drawing the material into intimate contact with the mold face. Due to the fact that thinning occurs along sidewalls, the process is confined to shallow draws. The depth of a round part should be approximately one half the diameter.

A male mold is used in *drape vacuum forming.* The heat-softened sheet is placed in a chase above the mold, then drawn down over it and sealed. A vacuum is created and the material is drawn into contact with the mold. Deep parts and also round parts with depth equal to the part diameter can be formed.

With *plug molding,* the plastic sheet is heated and a metal or wooden plug is forced into the

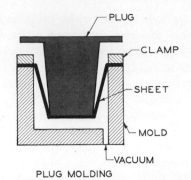

PLUG MOLDING

112–16. One of the thermoforming methods for producing plastic parts.

sheet. The material forms on the bottom and sidewalls. 112–16.

The *vacuum plug mold* method resembles plug molding in that the bottom of the plug is a male mold. The mold is forced into the sheet, and a vacuum draws the material around the mold.

In the *vacuum snap back* process, a vacuum is produced in the chamber, and the sheet is drawn down into the cavity. The male plug descends and clamps against the chase which holds the sheet. Vacuum is then

112–14. Calendering process of forming sheet plastic.

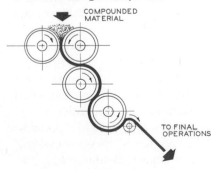

112–15. Typical methods of forming plastic sheet.

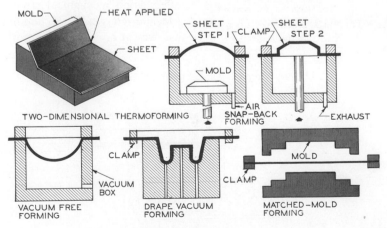

applied to the male plug and the material is drawn to the mold. Deep drawn parts with generous tapers and corners with large radii are possible with this technique.

Two-dimensional thermoforming is accomplished simply by heating a strip of thermoplastic material and bending the material to a mold. This method is usually limited to small (short) parts such as L-brackets. Another characteristic of this method is that it is used to form parts from thicker sheets than can be handled by other thermoforming methods.

Matched-mold forming produces parts with better surface detail and closer tolerances than any other thermoforming technique. In this process, the heated sheet is pressed between two matched molds; entrapped air is

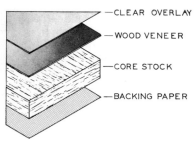

- CLEAR OVERLAY
- WOOD VENEER
- CORE STOCK
- BACKING PAPER

Food Machinery & Chemical Corp.

112–17. Parts that make up a laminate.

released through vents in the mold. After the mold is closed, forming of the part takes place, allowing clearance for material thickness between mold parts. Heat is rapidly dissipated in the thicker sections through direct contact with the two metal surfaces. This technique is limited to relatively shallow draws.

LAMINATES AND LAMINATING

Laminates include combinations of materials ranging from vinyl sheets bonded together to sheets with decorative filler between reinforced plastic molding. 112–17.

A plastic laminate generally consists of two or more sheets or films of plastic bonded together by heat and pressure to form a single piece.

Most laminated plastics consist of sheets of wood, asbestos, fabric, and other special materials. These materials are impregnated or coated wth resin and then processed by applying heat and pressure to form the product.

Laminates based on paper reinforcement are used in electrical applications. Kraft paper from wood pulp is low in cost and offers good mechanical strength. Mechanized grades of laminates use woven or unwoven cotton or other fabrics as a base material. When heat resistance, high insulation, and dielectric strength is desired, asbestos, glass, and some synthetic fibers are used as reinforcement.

The Process

The resins are first dissolved in a solvent to form the impregnation material. 112–18. The untreated reinforcing material is first passed through a trough containing the solution. This is accomplished by feeding the web of the material through rollers into the trough over guide rollers. Squeeze rolls or doctor blades are used to remove excess solution and to control the amount of resin remaining on the web.

Upon leaving the saturating bath, the web passes through an oven where the proper degree of "dryness" is obtained by evaporating the volatiles. When removed from the coating and drying machine, the webs are cut to the desired sheet size by rotary cutters or vertical blades.

Many products including gears, safety helmets, boats, and automobile bodies use laminated plastics.

REINFORCED PLASTIC MOLDING

This is a process for combining glass fibers in the form of filaments, strands, cloth, roving, or other fillers or extruders with a thermosetting resin such as epoxy, polyester, or phenolic to produce a finished part. Sometimes organic fibers are used, sometimes thermoplastic.

There are six basic processes for reinforced plastic molding: (1) contact molding, (2) vac-

112–18. Preparing sheet material for lamination.

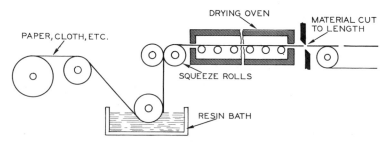

PAPER, CLOTH, ETC.

DRYING OVEN

MATERIAL CUT TO LENGTH

SQUEEZE ROLLS

RESIN BATH

uum bag, (3) pressure bag, (4) spray molding, (5) match-die molding, and (6) filament winding.

Contact molding is also known as hand layup. Glass cloth or woven roving is draped over the mold. A mixture of resin and catalytic agent is poured over the cloth, and the mixture is manipulated by hand to close the mold. Hardening then takes place. Contact molding is used in model making and prototypes.

The *vacuum bag* process is accomplished by adding resin to matted fiber batting. A flexible polyvinyl alcohol film is placed over the layup, and a vacuum of about 12 psi is drawn between the mold and film.

In the *pressure bag* process, a rubber bag or blanket is placed against an impregnated mixture and inflated to 5 psi. A higher glass content and a more dense product is produced than by the vacuum bag method.

Two spray nozzles are used in *spray molding*. One nozzle sprays chopped glass or asbestos fibers and the other sprays resin. This mixture is then compacted by hand and the part is allowed to cure at slightly elevated or ambient temperatures.

Match-die molding resembles metal stamping. Close fitting male and female molds are used. The molds have a telescoping circumferential area to seal in resin and trim reinforcement. Fiber batting is placed in the mold. Resin of the proper proportions is poured in and the mold closed. Heat is then applied under pressures of 150 to 400 psi.

With *filament winding,* glass filaments in the form of yarns or monofilaments are coated with resin and wound by machine onto collapsible mandrels which are the shape of the desired part. Curing can be done either at room temperature or in an oven depending upon the part size and the resin used.

CASTING

Phenolics, epoxies, allyl resins, and polyester are thermosetting materials used in casting processes.

When there is not sufficient justification for making expensive dies, the casting process is generally used. Open molds can be made of lead by dipping a steel mandrel of the desired shape into molten lead and then stripping the formed shell from the sides of the mandrel after it has solidified. The slush-casting method can be used where hollow castings are required. Molds made from wood, plaster, metal, or glass are frequently used when solid parts are produced.

Slush molding consists of filling a preheated hollow mold with plastisol, (liquid compound containing plasticizers, stabilizers, fillers and color pigments) allowing the material to the adjacent mold walls to gel, and returning the remainder to the reservoir.

When the part is to be carved or machined, the casting process can be used to produce tubes, rods, and other shapes prior to machining.

Some of the applications of the casting process are: toys, optical lenses, costume jewelry, knobs, clock cases, handles, drill jigs, and reinforced plastics.

Unit 113. Machining and Finishing Plastics

MACHINING

Plastics can be machined satisfactorily with conventional machine tools. Care has to be taken when machining the material since plastics have a greater heat sensitivity than metals. Furthermore, plastics have a greater thermal expansion rate and can soften and distort at temperatures well below those of metal.

The following techniques should be employed when machining this material: (1) use proper coolants; (2) use tools with proper clearance angles; and (3) use a light cut at relatively high speeds combined with slow feeds.

Coolants with a 10% solution of water soluble oil are best. Coolants that contain certain chemicals could attack some plastics.

Tools should be set with zero or slight negative rake and should have a scraping instead of a cutting action. Tools should also be sharp to reduce frictional heat.

Sawing can be done with conventional woodworking blades.

Curved sections can be machined with routers using a straight two-flute cutter running at 15,000 to 20,000 rpm under no load with a slow feed.

FINISHING

After a part has been fabricated, some form of finishing is necessary to remove tool marks and to bring out the natural beauty and luster of the material.

The part can be buffed, sanded, or polished. In these operations, care must be taken that too much pressure for too long a time is not applied. Burning or softening of the material can result if proper care is not taken during this operation.

On large production runs, tumble finishing can be used satisfactorily. Materials such as felt blocks, maple wood pegs, sawdust with oil and also abrasive particles can be used in the tumbling barrel.

COLORING

The part may be colored by incorporating color in the base resin. From the standpoint of color, two general types of plastics must be considered, transparent and opaque. Transparent plastics have more color possibilities because they can be decorated on the first or second surface.

Some molded thermoplastics such as polyethylene and styrene can be colored during the molding operation. Clear or "natural" resins can be molded into a diversity of colored objects. This dry coloring process is commonly used in toys, housewares, and similar articles. Color control is rather difficult to maintain and has many ramifications.

Check Your Knowledge

1. Name the two broad classifications of plastics. Distinguish between them.

2. Explain polymerization.

3. What raw materials are used to produce plastic compounds?

4. What is the purpose of using fillers in plastic materials?

5. Name five different fillers.

6. Name five thermosetting compounds.

7. What properties account for the wide use of epoxies?

8. How are phenolic resins produced?

9. Why are phenolic resins so important in the construction of new missiles and missile hardware?

10. Name four uses of furane resins.

11. What important properties do silicone base polymers possess?

12. Name five uses of silicones.

13. Name two important groups of amino resins.

14. In what unique way do silicones differ from most other plastics?

15. Why are more polyethylene resins produced than any other plastic material?

16. What is the basic raw material of polystyrene?

17. What are the two advantages that accrue from the low density of polypropylene?

18. What property does polycarbonate have that is useful in some applications?

19. What acrylic resin is the most commonly used in many applications?

20. What are cellulosics?

21. Name seven production methods for producing plastic parts.

22. Upon what does the pressure depend in compression molding?

23. Name four methods of molding by the compression molding process.

24. Describe the compression molding process.

25. How is heat supplied in compression molding?

26. Why is injection molding the ideal method for processing thermoplastic materials?

27. How are injection molding machines rated?

28. Describe the injection molding process.

29. Explain why injection molding has certain advantages over compression molding.

30. What is jet molding?

31. What type of plastic material is normally used in injection molding? Explain why.

32. Name two types of rotational molding equipment.

33. What are the purposes of forming sheet and film?

34. What is calendering?

35. What is a plastic laminate?

36. How are plastic bottles made?

References

Bernhardt, Ernest C., *Processing of Thermoplastic Materials,* New York, Reinhold Publishing Corp., 1964.

Brown, G. S., "The Mechanical Process of Blow Molding," *Plastic World,* May, 1959.

Harwood, R. W., "Vacuum Forming and Its Applications," *Plastics,* July, 1958.

Modern Plastics Encyclopedia, New York, McGraw-Hill Book Co., 1967.

Rohn & Haas Co., *Plexiglas,* December, 1960.

The Society of the Plastics Industry, *Plastics Engineering Handbook,* 3rd. ed., New York, Reinhold Publishing Corp., 1960.

Plastic target bullets for indoor shooting fun.

Marbon Div., Borg-Warner

INDEX

A

Abrasive cleaning, 466
Abrasive machining, 410
Abrasives
  aluminum oxide, 391
  coated, 397–399
  description of, 390
  grain sizes and structure, 392
  grinding wheel, 393–397
  manufactured, 390
  silicon carbide, 391
Acrylic resin, 554
Adapters, for milling cutters, 347
Adjustable reamers, 306
Air gages, 226–229
Alkaline cleaning of metals, 474
Allotropy, 55
Allowance between parts, 234
Alloys, 28–30, 39, 40, 48, 128, 129, 162
Alpha iron, 55, 62
Aluminum
  a product of bauxite, 45–47
  base alloy, 128, 129
  oxide abrasive, 391
  powder, 455
  rubber forming, 198, 199
American Gear Manufacturers Association (AGMA), 433
American Iron and Steel Institute (AISI), 39, 43, 256
American Society of Mechanical Engineers, 256
American Standard Gage Design, 225
American Welding Society, 521, 545
Amino resins, 552
Angle, lip, on drills, 291
Angular measuring instruments, 208–210
Angular milling cutters, 343
Annealing steel, 68, 69
Apollo spacecraft, 552
Arbor cutters, 343
Arbors, collets, and adapters, 347
Arc welding, 20, 528–534
Austempering steel, 68
Austenite, defined, 54, 55
Automatic cycle lathes, 279–287
Auto-scan milling machine, 339

B

Baekeland, Dr. L. H., 550
Band filing machines, 371
Band sawing machines, 365–369
Bar and chucking machines, 274
Barrel rolling, a cleaning process, 468
Bauxite, 391
Bayer, Karl Josef, 45
Bellows, used in mold making, 101
Bench molding, 105
Bending, a forging operation, 157
Bending and forming metal, 197, 198
Bessemer process of producing steel, 35, 38
Bevel gears, 435, 445
Billet or structural shear, for cutting metal, 194
Binders, core, 93
Black-heart, malleable iron, 119, 120
Blanking, metal, 197
Blast furnace, 34
Blending, metal powder with lubricants, 456
Blind risers, 104
Blow molding, 560, 562
Bolster, used in die making, 200
Boring
  machines, 314–316
  mill, vertical, 284
  on the lathe, 273
  tools, 295–297
Bottom gate, controls metal flow in molding, 104
Brazing, 545, 546
Brinell hardness test, 78
Brittleness of metals, 30
Broaching, 247, 373–387
Bronze yard measurement, 205
Buffing, metal, 468–470
Burns, Dr. Fred P., 488

C

Calendering, 562
Calipers, 206–208, 210–212
Cams and toggle mechanisms on presses, 195
Carbide tools, cemented, 251

Carboloy, cemented carbide tools, 251, 296
Carbon
  effects on steel, 40, 41, 43, 59
  plain and alloy steels, 39–42
  steels, tools, 250
Carbon electrode and metal electrode welding, 529
Carbonitriding steel, 71, 72
Carburizing steel, 69
Careers in metalworking, 14–20
Carothers, W. H., 553
Cast alloy tools, 251
Casting
  centrifugal, true, semicentrifugal, and centrifuge, 132, 133
  cleaning, 20, 115, 116
  metals, 112–121
  processes, special, 123–144
  thermosetting materials, 562, 565
Cast iron, 35, 116–120
Caterpillar Tractor Co., 241
Cellulose acetate, 555
Cellulose acetate butyrate, 555
Cellulose nitrate, 555
Cellulose propionate, 556
Cementite, 40
Centerless grinding, 404
Chaplets, 98
Charpy test of metal, 82
Check Your Knowledge:
  Section One: Human Needs, 26
  Section Two: Producing and Processing Ferrous and Nonferrous Metals, 49
  Section Three: Metallurgy and Heat Treatment of Steel, 83
  Section Four: Foundry Processes, 121
  Section Five: Special Casting Processes, 143
  Section Six: Hot-Working Metal, 163
  Section Seven: Cold-Working Metal, 186
  Section Eight: Forming Metal on Presses, 203
  Section Nine: Measurement and Inspection, 243
  Section Ten: Changing the Shape of Metals with Machine Tools, 257

Check Your Knowledge—*Cont.*
  Section Eleven: Machining Metal with Turning Machines, 287
  Section Twelve: Producing Cylindrical Holes, 316
  Section Thirteen: Machining Metal with Shapers and Planers, 330
  Section Fourteen: Machining Metal with Milling Machines, 357
  Section Fifteen: Sawing and Filing, 371
  Section Sixteen: Broaching, 387
  Section Seventeen: Grinding and Grinding Machines, 414
  Section Eighteen: Screw Threads, 429
  Section Nineteen: Gearing, 450
  Section Twenty: Powder Metallurgy, 463
  Section Twenty-One: Polishing and Finishing Metals, 479
  Section Twenty-Two: Recent Techniques in Metalworking, 499
  Section Twenty-Three: Numerical Control Machining, 520
  Section Twenty-Four: Welding Processes, 547
  Section Twenty-Five: Plastics, 566

"Cheek" in mold making, 100
Chemical
  cleaning of metal, 474
  machining, 497–499
  milling, 482–485
  properties of metals, 30
Cherry snap flask in making molds, 100
Chill (core) defined, 98
Chills, external and internal, 104
Chip breakers, 250, 251
Chip formation
  and cutting action, 247, 248
  in drilling, 299, 300
Chrome plating to protect metals, 476
Chromium, 41, 43
Chucking
  machines, 274, 275
  reamers, 305
Circular sawing machines, 363
Classification of metals, 28–30
Cleaning, abrasive, 466
Cleaning metals, 20, 466–468, 474
Clearance, lip, on drills, 291

Coal, used in extracting iron from ore, 33
Coated abrasives, 397–399
Cobalt, 42
Coining of compacting powder metals, 461, 462
Coke, a coal extraction, 33
Cold-drawing, 166–168
Cold extrusion, methods of, 183
Cold-heading, an operation in wire forming, 168–170
Cold-working metal, 165–186
Collet chucks, of lathes, 263
Collets, for milling cutters, 347
Color anodizing of metals, 476, 477
Combination set, a measuring rule with attachments, 206, 207
Compacting powder
  machining of metals, 462
  metallurgy parts, 456, 457
  multi-motion and single action presses, 460
Compacting presses, 460–463
Compression molding, 556
Contact gaging, 228
Control chart method of quality control, 233
Conversion scales, using metric system, 242
Coolant, used in electrical discharge machining, 494
"Cope" in mold making, 100
Copper-base alloys, 48, 129
Copper plating to protect metals, 475, 476
Core binders, sand for molding, paste, 93
Coremakers, 19
Cores and core making, 96–98
Counterboring, 297
Countersinking, 298
Craneman, 16
Crank shapers, 318
Crucibles, 112–115
Cupola furnace, 111
Cut, depth of, on turning machines, 268
Cutter-gear generating with a reciprocating tool, 442–445
Cutters, milling, 343–350
Cutting fluids, 255, 256, 304, 426
Cutting speeds
  and feeds, 254
  on shaper, 326, 327
  turning machines, 268
Cutting tools and cutting fluids, metal, 247

Cyaniding steel, 71
Cylindrical holes, producing, 289, 316

D

Dendrites, 56
Dial indicator, 225
Dial station feeding mechanism, 196
Die casting, 18, 125–128
Die-disc filing machines, 371
Die machines, cylindrical, for thread rolling, 179
Die, single and multiple, cavity, 127
Dies
  air-bend, 194, 197
  and die sets, 200–203
  forging, 153
  progressive, 201
  solid and open, 168
Dividers (measuring tool), 208
Double-action presses used in compacting powder metals, 460
Double-housing planer, 328
Down milling, 352–354
Draftsmen, 14
"Drag" in mold making, 100
Draw-cut shaper, 319–321
Drawing metal, 198
Draw pin, spike, and screw, 101
Drilling machines, 308–316
Drilling on the lathe, 273
Drills, 290–305, 308
Drive mechanisms on presses, 195
Drop hammer, board or gravity, 151, 152
Dry sand core, 96, 97
Dual dimensioning, 236
Ductility of metal, 30
Dynapak forming, 184

E

Eccentric drives on presses, 195
Egyptians and the Royal Cubit measurement, 205
Electrical discharge machining terms, rate, and frequency, process, 492–495
Electric furnace process of producing steel, 36, 37
Electrochemical
  grinding, 407–409
  machining, 495–497
Electrode material, 494

Electro-hydraulic forming, 184
Electron beam
    machining, 491, 492
    welding, 541–543
Electronic gages, 228, 229
Electroplating, a protective coating
    of metals, 474–476
Electroslag welding, 534
Elongation, metal, 32
Enamels, metal, 477
Encyclopedia Americana, 33
End milling cutters, 343
Engine lathe, 260–265
Epoxides, 551
Expansion hand reamers, 306
Experimental machinists, 15
Explosive forming, 184, 185
Extrusion, 183, 560, 562

F

Face grinders, 401
Faceplate, live center, and dog, of
    lathes, 262
Facing, on turning machine, 268
Facing sand, for molding, 93
Fatigue of metal, 32, 82
Feed
    as applied to milling, 349
    mechanisms on presses, 195
    of cutting tools, 255
    on turning machines, 268
    (Also see *Speeds and feeds*)
Ferrite, 29, 40, 54
Ferrous and nonferrous metals, pro-
    ducing and processing, 27–50
File classification, 370
Filing, 370, 371
Fillers, metal, 477
Fillets on castings, 87, 88
Film, forming, 562
Fineness test of sand, 96
Finishes, selecting, decorative and
    protective, 221, 474–479
Firthite, trade name for cemented
    carbide tools, 251
Fixed-bed milling machine, 335
Flame
    and thermal cutters, 20
    hardening steel, methods, 72, 73
    spraying, 486–488
Flash-butt welding, 537
Flasks in making molds, 100
Floor molding, 105
Flo-peeling, of metal, 185, 186

Floturn process of spinning metal,
    175–177
Fluorescent penetrant testing, 230,
    231
Fluxes, 544
Fly cutters, 347
Flying shears, used to cut steel
    sheets, 150
Forge shop, 16
Forge welding, 522–524
Forging, 151–159
Form cutting method of producing
    gears, 439
Forming, high-energy-rate, 184,
    185
Forming metal, on presses, 187–204
Form milling, 357
Form-relieved cutters, 343
Foundry
    inspectors, 20
    occupations, 17–20
    processes, 85
    sands, 91–93
    tools and equipment, 98–104
Fracture test of high carbon steel,
    57
France, developer of the meter, 206
Friction sawing with steel discs, 364
Furane resins, 551
Furnaces
    and temperature control, 52
    Cupola, 111
    for nonferrous melting, 44
    stationary and tilting, 112
Fusibility of metal, 32

G

Gage blocks and gages, 215, 216
Gages, 208, 223, 224, 228, 229
Galvanizing of metal, 478, 479
Gamma iron, 55
Gang drilling machine, 309, 310
Gang milling, 357
Gap press, 189, 190, 193
Gas carburizing steel, 70
Gas welding
    general discussion, 524–527
    metal-arc, 532, 533
    tungsten-arc, 531
Gates, types of, used in molding
    operations, 102, 103
Gearing, 431–450
Gear terminology, 433
Go gages, 223–225
Goodyear, Charles, 550

Grain structure of steel, 54–59
Graphite crucible, 113
Grinders, 401, 407
Grinding and grinding machines,
    247, 389–413
Grinding Wheel Institute, 393
Grinding wheels, 392–397
Guerin process (rubber forming) of
    aluminum, 198, 199
Gullet type chip breaker, 250
Gun drill, 293
Gun drilling machine, 311–313

H

Hacksaws, 360, 361
Hammer driver, 16
Hammers, used in forging, 151
Hammersmiths, 16
Hand reamer, 305
Hardening steel, 62–65
Hardness of metals, 30
Hardness testing, 76–80
Headstock of lathe, 260
Heater (one who heats metal), 16
Heat treatment, 52–54, 59
Helical gears, 434
Helicon gears, 437
Herringbone gears, 437
Heterogeneous alloys, 28
High-speed steel tools, 251
Hob, how machined, 181
Homogeneous alloys, 28
Honing and lapping, 411–413
Horizontal boring machine, 314
Horizontal surface broaching
    machines, 384
Horning press, 190
Hot extrusion and spinning of
    metals and alloys, 162, 163
Hot forgings, trimming and punch-
    ing, 158, 159
Hot-working metal, 145–164
Hyatt, J. W., 550
Hydraulic drives on presses, 195
Hydraulic shaper, 319
Hydrodynamic process, 199
Hydroforming, 199
Hydrospinning, 173
Hyper-eutectoid steel, 62
Hypoid gears, 436

I

Impact testing, 81, 82
Induction hardening of steel, 73–76

Index

Inertia welding, 538–540
Infiltration of compacting powder metals, 462
Injection molding, 557–560
Inspection, nondestructive, of parts, 230–234
Inspectors, 20
Interferometers, 218
Internal gears, 437
International Bureau of Weights and Measures, 206
Investment casting, for molding metals, 134–140
Iron
carbide phase diagram, in heat treatment of steel, 60
ore, 33, 34
production and uses, 33–35
Isostatic pressing of powder during compacting process, 463
Isothermal transformation diagram, 65, 66
Izod test of metal, 81, 82

J

Jacobs, Charles B., 391
Jig
boring machines, 314–316
grinders, 407
Jigs, vises, 301
Jolt-rollover molding machine, 109
Jolt-squeeze molding machine, 109

K

Kennametal, trade name for cemented carbide tools, 251
Knoop hardness scale, 79, 80
Knuckle-joint press, 190

L

Lacquers for metal finishing, 477
Ladles, 113
Laminates, 564
Lapping, 412
Laser machining, 489
Lathes, 261–266, 279–287
Layout men, 15
Length of cut in broach design, 378
Lifters, used in molding, 102

Limestone, as used in extracting iron from ore, 33, 34
Lip angle, clearance, and length of drill, 291
Liquid carburizing steel, 70
Lodge and Shipley Co., developers of cold-working process, 185

M

"Machinability," a widely used term in the machining industry, 252
Machinists
all-around, 14
experimental, 15
Machine tool(s)
operators, 16
standard types, 246, 247
Magnaflux and Magnaflo, methods of non-destructive testing, 230
Magnesium, 47, 48
Magnesium-base alloys, 129
(Also see Alloys)
Magnetic forming, 184
Magnetic particle testing, 230
Malleability of metal, 31
Mandrel, 163
Manganese, 41
Manufactured abrasives, 390
Marform process in rubber forming, 199
Martempering steel, 68
Martensite, 62
Maskant, a rubber coating material, 482–484
Match plate, 90, 91
Measuring tools and instruments, 206–229
(See specific tool names)
Mechanical properties of metals, 30
Medium-alloy steel tools, 251
Melters, 19
Melting and casting metals, 111–121
Mendenhall Act, 1893, 206
Metal(s)
alkaline cleaning of, 474
and alloys, heating and placing in extruding press, 162
bending and forming, blanking, 197, 198
brittleness, 30
buffing, 468–470
changing the shape with machine tools, 245–258

Metal(s)—Cont.
Charpy test, 82
chemical cleaning, 474
chemical properties, 30
classification of, 28–30
cleaning, 474
cold-working, 165–186
color anodizing, 476, 477
cutting tools and fluids, 247
drawing-single, double, and triple action, 198
ductility, 30, 31
elongation, 32
enamels, 477
fatigue, 32
ferrous and nonferrous, 28
fillers, 477
finishes, selecting, decorative and protective, 221, 474–479
Flo-peeling, 185, 186
Floturn process of spinning metal, 175–177
forming on presses, 187–204
fusibility, 32
galvanizing, 478
hardness, 30
hot-working, 145–164
Izod test, 81, 82
malleability, 31
mechanical properties, 30
melting and casting, 111–121
molding, 134–140
nonferrous, 44–49, 112
parts, 181
pickling, a cleaning process, 474
plasticity, 30
polishing and finishing, 465–479
powders, production methods of, 454, 455
properties of, 30–33
protection, 475, 476
rolling, 146–150
shaving and slitting, 197
shearing, 196
slitting saws, 343
spinning, 163, 171–177
strain, 32
strength—tensile, shear, torsion, and compression, 31
stress, 32
toughness, 31
working, recent techniques, 481–499
yield point, 32
Metal machining
milling machines, 331–357

Metal machining—*Cont.*
  shapers and planers, 317–329
  turning machines, 259–288
Meter, developed by the French, 206
Metric system of measurement, 206, 235–243
Microhardness tester, 79
Micro-height gage, 213
Micrometer caliper, 210–212
Micrometer depth gage, 212
Micrometer, taper, 210
Microscope, toolmaker's, 214
Micro-wire welding, 533
Mill, cold reduction, for making thin steel sheets, 150
Milling
  cutters, 343–350
  machines, 246, 332–336, 339–342
  methods of, 351
  operations, 350–357
  plain or slab, 353
Moisture content test of sand, 95
Mold
  casting, permanent, 124
  making a one-piece pattern on the bench, 105–107
Molders, 18, 98–100, 102
Molding
  blow, 560
  compression, 556
  injection, 557–560
  lifters, 102
  line, design of, 98, 99
  machine operations, 109, 110
  metals, 134–140
  mono-shell, 137, 139
  parting compounds, 93
  parting gate, 103
  plastic, reinforced, 564
  processes, fundamental, 105–108
  rotational, 561
  sand, Albany No. 1, 92, 93
  shell, 140, 141
  transfer, 557
Molybdenum, 42, 43
Monel metal, 29, 30
Monomer, 550
Mono-shell molding, 137, 139
Moore, R. R., fatigue test, 82
Multiple-motion presses, 460
Multiple-spindle
  automatic lathe, 283, 284
  drill heads, 303, 304
  drilling machine, 311

N

National Bureau of Standards, 96
Nibbler, for cutting metal, 194
Nickel, 41, 43
Nickel-base alloys, 48
Nitriding steel, 71
No-go gages, 223–225
Nonferrous metals, 44–50, 112
Normalizing steel, 69
Numerical control
  advantages and disadvantages, 516
  basic components of a numerical control system, 503–505
  definition of, 502
  machines, 501–519
  measuring basis for numerical control systems, 507
  process sheet (sample), 515
  programming and tape preparation, 508–512
  tape controlled continuous path milling, 514
  "Turning Center," 284
  types of, 506
Nylons (polymides), 553

O

O.B.I. (open-back inclinable) press, 189
Occupations in metalworking industry, 14–20
Oil binder, molding sand, 92
Oil hole or coolant feeding drills, 293
Omnilathe N/C Turning Center, 516
Open-arc welding process, 533
Open-hearth process of producing steel, 35, 36
Open-side planer, 329
Optical comparator, 214, 215
Optical flat, 217–220
Oxygen and arc cutters, 20
Oxygen process used in steel refining, 37, 38

P

Pack carburizing steel, 70
Painting systems as applied by industry, 477, 478
Pantograph engraving machine, 338

Parkerizing, a primer used on metal, 479
Parting compounds, 93
Parting gate, 103
Paste, core, 93
Patternmakers, 17, 18
Patternmaking
  construction, 87
  common types, 88–91
Pearlite, 28, 29
Percussion and inertia welding, 538, 539
Permeameter, electric, 94
Phenolics, 551
Pickling of metals, a cleaning process, 474
Piercing, a forging operation, 157
Pig iron, production, characteristics, and uses, 34, 35
Pilots, used to guide broach in cutting, 380
Pipe and tube manufacture, 159–162
Piston-lift hammer, 152, 153
Pit molding, 105
Pit-type planer, 329
Pla-check height gage, 213, 214
Plain or slab milling, 353
Planers, 246, 327–329
Planer-type milling machine, 336
Plaster mold casting, 141, 142
Plasticity and ductility, 30, 31
Plastics, 549–566
Plate bending, 182, 183
Plates, rolled from metal slabs, 149
Plating metals, 474–476
Plug gages, 224
Pneumatic gaging, 226–229
Point angle while drilling, 298
Polishing and finishing metals, 465–479
Polycarbonate, 554
Polyethylene resins, 553
Polymer, 550
Polypropylene, 553
Polystyrene, 553
Portable drills, 308
Pot type broaching machines, 386
Powder metallurgy, 451–463
Power brush finishing, 472, 473
Power saw blades, 360
Power spinning, 173
Precision measuring instruments, 210
Press(es)
  brake, 193
  compacting, 460–463

Press(es)—*Cont.*
 drives and feed mechanisms, 194
 forging, 155
 hydraulic, 191, 192
 operations, 196
 operators, 16
 types for metal forming, 188–194
Primers used in metal finishing, 477
Production methods of metal
  powders, 454, 455
Production processes, 556–565
Profilometer, 221, 223
Profiling machine, 336
Programming, 508–512
Progressive dies, 201
Projection welding, 537
Properties of metals, 30–33
Protection of metal finishes, 475–
  477
Protractors, 208, 209
Pulse ultrasonics, 232
Pyrometers, 53, 115

Q

Quality control, 232–234
Queen Elizabeth, established Bronze
  yard measurement, 205
Quenching in steel hardening, 63,
  64
Quick change gear box of a lathe,
  263, 264

R

Radial drilling machine, 311
Ram type chucking machines, 275
Rammers, used in molding, 102
Ram-type milling machine, 333
Reamers, 305, 306
Reaming, 273, 305, 308
Reciprocating machines (flat die)
  for thread rolling, 179
Refractoriness in sand, 93, 94
Repressing operation of compacting
  presses, 461
Resins, 551–555
Resistance welding, 535
Resistance soldering, 544
Reversing mills, two-high and four-
  high design, 147, 148
Riddles, used for sifting sand, 101
Ring gages, 223, 224
Ring rolling, a forging process, 157

Riser pins, 103
Risers, 104
Rockwell hardness test, 76–78
Rolled threads, physical character-
  istics, 178, 179
Roll forging, 156
Roll-forming, cold, 181, 182
Rolling, barrel, 468
Rolling metal, 146–150
Rose chucking reamers, 305
Rotary attachments, on milling
  machines, 342
Rotary presses, 460
Rotary table milling machine, 336
Rotating beam test of metal, 82
Rotational molding, 561
Rotoforming, 173
Royal Cubit, a standard of mea-
  surement, 205
Rubber
 forming, 198, 199
 synthetic, 556
Rules, common measuring tool,
  206, 207

S

Saddle-type chucking machines, 275
Safety, 21–26, 114, 298
Sand
 molding, 105
 rammer, 94
 slinger, 109
 synthetic, 92
 testing, 93–96
 types for molding, 92, 93
Saugus Iron Works, 86
Sawing and broaching machines,
  247
Sawing and filing, 359–371
Saws, metal-slitting, 343
Schellschmidt, Victor, 241
Screwed on or clamp-type chip
  breaker, 250
Screw machines, automatic, 280–
  282
Screw threads, 415–428
Seam welding, 536
Setup men, machine tools, 16
Shake bag, used in molding, 102
Shank cutters, 343
Shanks, for use when pouring hot
  metal, 114
Shapers
 horizontal, crank, 318
 hydraulic and vertical, 319
 operations, 324–326

Shapers—*Cont.*
 speeds and feeds, 326
 tools and toolholders, 246, 321–
  324
Shaving metal, 197
Shear cutting of gears, 446
Shearing metal, 196
Shears for metal cutting, 194
Shear spinning, 173
Sheet and film, forming, 562
Sheets, made of hot-rolled steel, 150
Shell end mills, 346
Shell molding, 140, 141
Shell Oil Company, Inc., 249
Shell reamers, 306
Shore scleroscope hardness test, 79
Shot peening, 183
Side milling, 354, 355
Side milling cutters, 343
Silicon, 41, 43, 116, 391, 552
Silver plating to protect metals, 476
Sine bar and plate, 209
Single-action presses used in com-
  pacting powder metals, 460
Single crank on mechanical presses,
  195
Sintering in powder metal fabrica-
  tion, 457–459
Sizing of compacting powder
  metals, 461
Slab milling, 353
Slicks used in molding, 102
Slip casting complex shapes from
  powdered metals, 463
Slitting metal, 197
Slitting saws, 343
Slotting and cutting off in milling
  operation, 357
Slurry, a heat-resisting wet
  mixture, 124
Smoothing methods, 466–468
Snap flask, used in making molds,
  100
Snap gages, 223
Society of Automotive Engineers
  (SAE), 42, 43
Soldering and brazing, 544–546
Solute, definition of, 29
Solutions in alloys, solid and
  gaseous, 29
Solvent, definition of, 29
Space lattice, definition of, 54
Spark sintering in powder metal
  fabrication, 459
Spark testing of types of steel, 82, 83
Speeds and feeds
 and depth of cut in gear manu-
  facture, 440

Speeds and feeds—*Cont.*
  as applied to milling, 349
  for drills, 301
Speeds for cutting tools, 254
Spheroidizing steel, 69
Spike, or draw pin, used in mold
    making, 101
Spindle of a lathe, 262
Spinforging, 173
Spinning, metal, 163, 171–177
Spiral-point drills, 294
Spiroid gears, 437
Split pattern, molding, 107
Split-point drills, 295
Spoons used in molding, 102
Spotfacing, 297
Spot welding, 535, 536
Sprue pin and cutter, 103
Spur gears, 434, 439, 440
Staggered tooth milling cutter, 343
Steady rest and follow rest of lathes,
    264
Steam hammer, 151
Steel
  alloy, 39, 40
  annealing, 68, 69
  austempering, 68
  austenitic, grain structure, 60, 62
  Bessemer process, 35, 38
  carbon, function of, 40, 41, 43
  carburizing, 69, 70
  classification and identification,
    42–44
  grain structure, 54–59
  hardening, 62–65
  heat treatment, 59
  hyper-eutectoid, 62
  induction hardening, 73–76
  liquid carburizing, 70
  low, medium, and high carbon,
    39
  manufacture of, 35–38
  metallurgy and heat treatment,
    51–84
  normalizing, 69
  spheroidizing, 69
  surface hardening, 69–75
  tempering, 67, 68
  tubing or pipes, welding, 161
Stellites, a nonferrous alloy used in
    making cutting tools, 251
Step drills, 294
Step type chip breaker, 250
Stock removal allowance for
    reaming, 308
Straddle milling, 354, 355
Straight-side mechanical press. 190
Strain, metal, 32

Strength of metals, 31
Stress of metals—tension,
    compression, shear, and bolt,
    32
Stretch forming of metal, 179, 180
Strike-off bar, 103
Stud welding, 534
Subland drills, 294
Superfinishing, 412, 413
Surface finish
  grinding, 399–401
  how to obtain, 248
  measurements, 216–226
Surface gage, 217
Surface hardening of steel, 69–75
Surface plate, 216
Swaging machines, rotary, 158
Swiss type automatic lathe, 282
Symbols for gear terminology, 433
Synthetic rubber, 556

T

Tables and charts, 576
Tailstock of lathes, 263
Tape preparation, 508–512
Taper attachment on lathes, 264
Taper micrometer, 210
Taper pin and socket reamers, 308
Tapping
  hand, 421, 422
  machines, 424–428
Telescoping gage, 208
Temperature control equipment,
    53, 54
Temperature failure, 254
Temperatures, transformation, 56,
    60, 62
Tempering steel, 67, 68
Tensile testing, 80, 81
Testing
  metals, 76–83
  parts, 230–234
  sand, 93–96
  steel, 57
Texture, surface, 220, 221
Thermal cutters, 20
Thermit welding, 540, 541
Thermoforming, 562–564
Thermoplastic compounds,
    553–556
Thermosetting compounds, 551,
    552
Thread
  and form rolling, 178, 179
  chasing on turning machines,
    271–273

Thread—*Cont.*
  cutting dies, 422, 423
  cutting on a lathe, 271
  grinding, measurement, and
    milling, 425, 427, 428
  ring and plug gages, 225
  rolling, 179
  snap gages, 225
Three- and four-fluted core drills,
    292, 293
Tin-base alloys, 48
Tin coating of metal, 479
Toggle mechanisms on presses, 195
Tolerance, 234
Tongs, for handling molten metal,
    113
Tool and die makers, 15
Toolmaker's microscope, 214
Tools (See specific names)
Top gate, a strainer used in
    molding, 103
Toughness of metal, 31
Tracer control lathe, 285
Transfer molding, 557
Transfer press, high-production,
    192, 193
Transfer-type drilling machine, 313,
    314
Trowels, used in molding, 102
T-slot cutters, 346
Toughness of metals, 31
Tube drawing, 166
Tumbling, a cleaning process, 466,
    467
Tungsten, 42, 43
Turning machines, 246, 259, 260,
    268–273
Turret lathes, 274–279
Turret press, 192
Tuyeres, definition of, 34
Two-dimensional cutting, 247

U

Ultrasonic welding, 540
Ultrasonic machining
  rates and capacity, finish,
    and accuracy, 491
  tools for, 490
Ultrasonic testing, 231
United States Department of
    Commerce, 393
Universal bevel protractor, 209
Up milling, 351, 352, 354
Upright drilling machine, 309
Upset forging, 155
Upsetter operators, 17

Index

Urea-melamine-formaldehyde
resins, 552
Urethane (Adiprene) die pads,
202, 203

V

Vanadium, 42, 43
Vapor degreasing to clean metals,
474
Variable speed drives and presses,
195
Vascoloy-Ramet, trade name for
cemented carbide tools, 251
Vent wire, or rod, in mold making,
102
Vernier caliper and depth gage, 212
Vernier height gage, 213

Vertical boring mill, 284
Vickers scale hardness test, 78
Vises, 339

W

Waterbrush used in molding, 102
Water-soluble oils for cutting tools,
255, 256
Web thinning while drilling, 298,
299
Welders, arc and gas, 20
Welding processes, 521–546
Weld stresses, 530
White-heart malleable iron, 120
Wire, cold-drawing from rod, 167,
168
Woodruff key seat cutters, 346

Working metal, recent techniques,
481–499
Worm gears, 437
Wrought iron, 120, 121

X

X-ray and gamma ray testing, 232

Y

Yield point of metals, 32

Z

Zinc-base alloys, 48, 128

TABLES AND CHARTS

Table 4. Properties of Principal Metals, 31

Table 7. Range of Plain and Carbon Steels, 39

Table 8-A. AISI and SAE Numerical Designations of Alloy Steels, 43

Table 8-B. Classification of Carbon and Alloy Steels, 44

Table 9. Copper-Zinc-Tin Casting Alloys, 49

Table 11. Grain Size Chart, 57

Table 13. Recommended Induction Hardening Temperatures and Minimum Surface Hardness for Various Materials Successfully Induction Hardened, 74

Table 14-A. Estimating Hardness With a File, 76

Table 14-B. Rockwell Hardness Scales, 77

Table 15. Metal Shrinkage in Fractions of an Inch per Foot, 86

Table 16. Analysis of Albany No. 1 Sand, 92

Table 17. Permeability Numbers, 94

Table 22-A. Furnaces Used for Melting Metals, 111

Table 22-B. Chemical Composition of Malleable Iron Percentage, 119

Table 22-C. Average Properties of Malleable Iron, 119

Table 24-A. Properties of Die-Casting Metals, 129

Table 24-B. Fabricating Characteristics, Die-Casting Alloys, 130, 131

Table 34. Temperatures for Hot Extrusion, 162

Table 38. Comparison of Common Thread Finishes, 179

Table 52. Surface Roughness Produced by Common Production Methods, 222

Table 55-A. Metric Units, 236

Table 55-B. Metric Conversion Table, 237

Table 55-C. Conversion Chart Inch/mm, 238, 239

Table 56-A. Comparison of Cutting Speeds of High-Speed Steel and Carbide Tools, 252

Table 56-B. Machinability Ratings of Steels, 253

Table 56-C. Type of Machining Operations According to Severity, 257

Table 58. American Standard Taper (Morse), 267

Table 61-A. Suggested Lip Clearance Measured Across Margins, 290

Table 61-B. Common Drill Troubles and Causes, 300

Table 61-C. Drill Speeds, 301

Table 61-D. Drill Feeds, 301

Table 61-E. Lubricants Used in Drilling Operations, 304

Table 62-A. Reamer Expansion Limits, 306

Table 62-B. Speeds, Feeds and Stock Removal Allowances for High-Speed Steel and Carbide Tipped Machine Reamers, 307

Table 70. (Speeds and Feeds). Basic Recommendations for Milling Cutter Surface Footage, 349, 350

Table 72-A. Recommended Pitch Cutting Speeds and Feeds for Power Hacksawing, 362

Table 72-B. Recommended Speeds for Band Machining Common Metals, 367

Table 74-A. Empirical Values for Lbs. of Force, 379

Table 74-B. Typical Face Angles of Broaches, 379

Table 76-B. Letters Which Represent the Method of Designating Various Dimensions of Standard Wheel Shapes, 393

Table 76-C. Table of Comparative Grit Sizes— Approximate Comparison of Numbers, 398

Table 84. AGMA Standard for Involute Gearing, 433

Table 86. Involute Cutters, 439

Table 91. Finish Appearances from Bright to Dull, 469

Table 99-A. Typical Penetration Rates, 496

Table 99-B. Current Density of Metals, 497